Paul Horowitz

W9-AGV-450

NUMERICAL METHODS

NUMERICAL METHODS

BY

R. A. BUCKINGHAM, Ph.D. (Camb.)

Director, University of London Computer Unit

LONDON
SIR ISAAC PITMAN & SONS LTD.

First published 1957
Revised and reprinted 1962

SIR ISAAC PITMAN & SONS Ltd.
PITMAN HOUSE, PARKER STREET, KINGSWAY, LONDON, W.C.2
THE PITMAN PRESS, BATH
PITMAN HOUSE, BOUVERIE STREET, CARLTON, MELBOURNE
22–25 BECKETT'S BUILDINGS, PRESIDENT STREET, JOHANNESBURG

ASSOCIATED COMPANIES
PITMAN MEDICAL PUBLISHING COMPANY Ltd.
46 CHARLOTTE STREET, LONDON, W.1

PITMAN PUBLISHING CORPORATION
2 WEST 45TH STREET, NEW YORK

SIR ISAAC PITMAN & SONS (CANADA) Ltd.
(INCORPORATING THE COMMERCIAL TEXT BOOK COMPANY)
PITMAN HOUSE, 381–383 CHURCH STREET, TORONTO

©

R. A. Buckingham
1962

MADE IN GREAT BRITAIN AT THE PITMAN PRESS, BATH
F2—(T.642)

CARLSON

QA
297.5
.B92n
1962

PREFACE

IT will be evident from the contents of this book that its main concern is with the needs of those engaged in scientific computing problems using desk calculators. Nevertheless, one hopes that it will also serve some of those fortunate enough to have access to electronic computers, the advent of which has certainly multiplied many times the quantity of computing being done, but has not made unnecessary a study of methods suitable for hand calculations. The danger is rather that too many may come to use fast machines without adequate knowledge and experience of such methods and the pitfalls of numerical work generally. No doubt the day will come when a handbook of techniques appropriate to electronic computers can be written, but experience is still growing too rapidly to make this other than a hazardous adventure at present.

An attempt has been made to cover a fairly wide range of computing problems, and to blend the old with the new. Many familiar and well-tried methods are therefore to be found here as well as more recent developments. The importance of matrix methods in computing is such that they have been introduced gradually towards the middle of the book, and subsequently stressed; the same applies to processes involving iteration. However there are some notable omissions, such as quadrature formulas of the Gaussian type, and Runge-Kutta methods of integration. If any excuse need be made for this, it is that they are well described elsewhere, and that their value for hand computing is limited. A more serious fault perhaps lies in the emphasis given to methods based on polynomial approximation and comparative neglect of trigonometrical functions; this should some day be remedied.

The fact that the book runs to nearly 600 pages is largely due to the inclusion of many worked examples. It is hoped that these will give readers a reliable impression of the value of the methods described. Apart from this no attempt has been made to provide exercises of a purely numerical kind. These are extremely easy to construct, and those engaged in computing will mostly prefer to get on with their own problems. When practice is wanted it is more profitable to repeat step by step the example given in the text, and to consider whether it has in fact been done in the best way. The exercises following some chapters are often exercises in name only, being rather extensions of the text with possibly significant applications.

In writing the book I have been aided greatly by the published work of British mathematicians, past and present, whose contributions to numerical analysis have indeed been considerable. A similar debt is owed to America, especially to the work of W. E. Milne. To Prof. A. C. Aitken I am grateful among other things for allowing me to include some early numerical examples of his on the solution of polynomial equations. Finally, it is very pleasant to acknowledge that my interest in computation was greatly stimulated by the enthusiasm of the late Dr. Comrie, and sustained by Prof. H. S. W. Massey, whose insistence on the importance of numerical techniques for scientists in general and physicists in particular gave to this volume its origin and purpose.

R. A. BUCKINGHAM

UNIVERSITY COLLEGE
    LONDON

AUTHOR'S NOTE

SINCE the first appearance of this book in 1957 there have been considerable developments in the field of numerical analysis, stimulated by the amazing growth of automatic computers. However, the greater part of the subject-matter probably remains useful and I have not judged it expedient to make a thorough revision at the present time. The fact that *Modern Computing Methods*, prepared by the staff of the Mathematics Division, National Physical Laboratory, is now available, means that students have a valuable and up-to-date supplement to this text.

The main changes have occurred in Chapters 8 and 9, and an appendix on Gaussian quadrature has been added. Some obvious gaps have been filled, including the integration methods of Runge-Kutta and de Vogelaere. Several examples have been revised, many references to recent work included, and a number of misprints removed. For the latter I am most indebted to the help of Dr. J. C. E. Jennings, Mr. S. Michaelson, and Mrs. J. G. B. Wallace, and I am grateful also to Professor Aitken for several valuable comments and suggestions.

UNIVERSITY OF LONDON COMPUTER UNIT

CONTENTS

BOOKS AND TABLES REFERRED TO IN THE TEXT

The abbreviated titles on the left are used in the text.

Books

Collatz, *N.T.D.E.*
 Collatz, L. (trans. P. G. Williams), *Numerical Treatment of Differential Equations*, 3rd ed. (Springer, 1960).

Bodewig, *M. C.*
 Bodewig, E., *Matrix Calculus*, 2nd ed. (North Holland, 1959).

Dwyer, *L.C.*
 Dwyer, P. S., *Linear Computations* (Wiley, 1951).

Fox
 Fox, L., *Numerical Solution of Two-Point Boundary Problems in Ordinary Differential Equations* (Oxford, 1957).

Frazer, Duncan and Collar
 Frazer, R. A., Duncan, W. F., and Collar, A. R., *Elementary Matrices* (Cambridge, 1938).

Hartree, *N.A.*
 Hartree, D. R., *Numerical Analysis*, 2nd ed. (Cambridge, 1958).

Jeffreys, *M.M.P.*
 Jeffreys, H. and Jeffreys, B. S., *Methods of Mathematical Physics*, 3rd ed. (Cambridge, 1956).

Lanczos, *A.A.*
 Lanczos, C., *Applied Analysis* (Pitman, 1956).

Modern Computing Methods
 National Physical Laboratory, *Notes on Applied Science No. 16.*, 2nd ed. (H.M.S.O., 1961).

Milne, *N.C.*
 Milne, W. E., *Numerical Calculus* (Princeton, 1949).

Milne, *N.S.D.E.*
 Milne, W. E., *Numerical Solution of Differential Equations* (Wiley, 1953).

Steffensen
 Steffensen, *Interpolation* (1925, Dover rep. 1950).

Whittaker and Robinson
 Whittaker, E. T. and Robinson, C., *Calculus of Observations*, 4th ed. (Blackie, 1944).

Tables, etc.

Barlow
 Barlow's Tables of Squares, Cubes, etc., ed. Comrie, 4th ed. (Spon, 1941).

Chambers [4]
 Chamber's Four-figure Mathematical Tables, ed. Comrie (1947).

Chambers [6]   *Chamber's Six-figure Mathematical Tables*, Vol. 2,
                      "Natural Values," ed. Comrie (1949). *Note:* Vol. 1
                      contains logarithmic values.

Dale [5]   Dale, J. B., *Five-figure Tables of Mathematical
                      Functions*, 2nd ed. (Arnold, 1949).

I.A.T.   *Interpolation and Allied Tables* (H.M. Stationery
                      Office, 1956).

Jahnke-Emde   Jahnke, P. R. E. and Emde, F., *Funktiontafeln*,
                      3rd ed. (Dover rep., 1943); also 6th ed. revised
                      by F. Lösch (Teubner and McGraw-Hill, 1960).

M.T.C. [4]   Milne-Thomson and Comrie, *Standard Four-figure
                      Mathematical Tables* (Macmillan, 1931).

Index   Fletcher, A., Miller, J. C. P., and Rosenhead, L.,
                      Index of Mathematical Tables (Scientific Com-
                      puting Service, 1946; 2nd ed. in preparation).

Math. Tab., Wash.   *Mathematical Tables and Other Aids to Computation*
                      (sometimes referred to as *M.T.A.C.* but renamed
                      in 1960, *Mathematics of Computation*; a valu-
                      able quarterly journal).

In addition to the above general books of tables, there are some
valuable series of more specialized tables; in particular, those spon-
sored by the British Association (and subsequently by the Royal
Society), and by the U.S. National Bureau of Standards (Applied
Mathematics Series).

CHAPTER 1

AN INTRODUCTION TO COMPUTATION

WHAT is the art of computation? This question may for the moment be answered as follows. Most calculations are carried out with numbers which are to some extent approximate, by methods which are often inexact, and their results, expressed in numerical form, are also approximate; yet there is normally only one answer which is correct to a specified degree of accuracy. The art of computation therefore lies in obtaining this correct answer with reasonable certainty, and with the least unnecessary labour.

Like most short definitions, this statement implies a great deal more than is immediately obvious. The emphasis, however, is not merely on attaining the right result, but also on knowing that it is right, and the extent to which it can be relied upon, even though in the process rather more work has been done than seemed essential. A satisfactory end to a computation depends largely on using well-tried methods in solving particular types of problem, chosen both for ease of checking and economy of effort. The development of such methods is the main preoccupation of later chapters; for the present we shall be concerned more with the question of accuracy, which is now seen to have two aspects. First, there is the assessment of errors which are legitimate and unavoidable; secondly, the avoidance of those which are illegitimate, or what is so often necessary, the speedy discovery and removal of mistakes which should never come into being. It is therefore not inappropriate that the first section of this chapter dealing in general terms with the art of computation should be mainly concerned with errors, both genuine and accidental. In it, we hope to discuss satisfactorily what errors are and how they are propagated in simple calculations, and the principles, rules and precautions which all help to eliminate blunders.

In asking for a minimum of effort the definition implies further that the best possible use should be made of auxiliary information, provided for instance by tables, and of such machines as may be available.

We envisage the computer as presiding over (*a*) one or more

1

calculating machines on which the majority of arithmetical operations are performed and numbers are temporarily stored, (*b*) all the necessary tables, representing a storehouse of numerical knowledge on which the computer can call at will, (*c*) a sheet of paper containing the preliminary data of the problem, to which are added the essential parts of the calculation as it proceeds, and the final result. The computer's task is then so to organize the transference of numbers between the three sets of equipment under his control that the solution of the problem is achieved as rapidly and as surely as possible.

With a view to filling in some of the details of this general picture, the second and third sections of this chapter discuss some of the questions raised by the use of tables, and the role of calculating machines, particularly desk calculators.

Errors

A few elementary definitions are necessary. If y' is the approximate value of a quantity whose exact value is denoted by y, practice differs as to whether the error of y' should be defined by $y' - y$ or $y - y'$. The distinction is often irrelevant, and we shall often use the term error in the broad sense when sign does not matter. When it does matter, we shall try to adhere to the following definitions—

$$\text{Absolute error} \qquad e = y' - y$$
$$\text{Absolute correction or remainder } r = y - y'$$

Thus to obtain the correct value, the error should be subtracted or the correction added to the approximate value. The term *deviation* may sometimes be used instead of absolute error, particularly when this represents, not the difference between y' and y itself, but between y' and the best estimate of y that happens to be available.

Although errors are often expressed in absolute measure, which will involve the dimensions, if any, of the quantity concerned, a better guide to the merit of an approximation is often given by its relative error

$$\delta = \left| \frac{y' - y}{y} \right| \simeq \left| \frac{y' - y}{y'} \right|$$

or by the *percentage error*, which is 100δ. Here it is usually only magnitude which matters, and relative errors are obviously dimensionless. In particular the measurement of a physical quantity, e.g. length, mass, time, is regarded as more accurate the smaller the relative error. The term tends to lose any significance, however, if δ exceeds, say, 0·5, and it may then be preferable to define the error logarithmically, e.g.

$$\text{logarithmic error} = \log_{10} |y'/y|$$

A logarithmic error of ± 1, i.e. a factor of 10, is loosely described as "an order of magnitude." We shall be concerned mainly with relative errors.

So much for definitions which do not involve any consideration of the nature or origin of the errors concerned. When we consider the numbers which provide the starting-point for calculation, however, it is important to distinguish two types of error which they may contain. These are

(a) rounding errors,
(b) experimental or statistical errors.

We shall discuss rounding errors first.

1.1. Rounding Errors

The usual method of rounding off a number to a desired number of decimals is illustrated by successive reductions of π—

3·1415926535...
3·141593
3·14159
3·1416
3·142
3·14

The rule for rounding k decimals may be summarized as follows—

Rule A

$(k + 1)$th decimal	kth decimal
0, 1, 2, 3, 4	unchanged
6, 7, 8, 9	increased by 1

If this rule is correctly applied, the absolute rounding error will not exceed $\pm 0·5 \times 10^{-k}$.

The example above does not involve the critical case represented by the number

1234·5000...

which might be rounded up to 1235 or down to 1234 without violating the limits $\pm$ 0·5 for the rounding error. To dismiss the critical case thus, however, is to be a trifle unrealistic. The computer rarely knows a large number of digits beyond the one which is being rounded; often he knows only two or three, or perhaps only one, and the last known digit may itself be uncertain to 1 or 2 units, because of previous rounding and other causes.

A typical instance is the rounding of a $(k + 1)$-decimal table to k decimals. Of the final digits to be dropped, roughly one-tenth will be 5's, and of these about one-half would involve rounding up and one-half rounding down if further decimals were available. Since the computer does not know which to round up and which to round down, a convention is necessary which preserves the random distribution of rounding errors between positive and negative values. The usual convention may be expressed as a rule supplementary to rule A already given—

Rule B

When the $(k + 1)$th decimal is 5, the kth decimal is increased by 1 when odd, and unchanged when even.

This involves an increase in the maximum possible rounding error. Thus if 1234·5 can in fact represent any number between 1234·40... and 1234·60..., the effect of rounding to 1234 may introduce a rounding error of magnitude 0·6.

When numbers are rounded off to k decimals from $(k + 2)$ decimals, the last of which is uncertain to 1 unit, a rounding error of $\pm$ 0·51 of the kth decimal should not be exceeded in the critical case, which is now ten times less frequent.

In the light of this it is interesting to examine a device commonly used in printing tables*; this is the addition of 5 in the place following the last to be retained, as in the following table of sin x (to be rounded to 4 decimals)—

x	sin x		
0·10	0·0998 33		0·0998 **83**
0·11	0·1097 78	modified	0·1098 **28**
0·12	0·1197 12	to	0·1197 **62**
0·13	0·1296 34		0·1296 **84**

* It is also used in automatic digital machines.

In the modified table the figures to the right of the gap can merely be removed, and the result is a table correctly rounded according to rule A. All critical cases, however, are rounded *up*, thus violating rule B. When two or more decimals are dropped this rarely matters, because it is so infrequent, but when dropping one decimal only, about 5 per cent of values would be improperly rounded and so give an appreciable excess of positive rounding errors. If these were extensively combined by, say, addition, the result might be an unwelcome accumulation of errors.

It is sometimes an advantage to limit rounding errors more closely than is possible by the standard method of rounding. We mention two notations which achieve this to some extent.

(a) SINGLE-DOT NOTATION

In this, the last digit to be kept is rounded up only if the figures neglected lie between 0·750... and 0·999..., in units of the last decimal; if these figures lie between 0·250... and 0·750..., the last digit is followed by a dot or some other symbol. Thus 1·23456 might be denoted by—

$$1·234^{\cdot} \quad \text{or} \quad 1·234^{+} \quad \text{or} \quad 1·234_{5}$$

Further examples are given by successive approximations to π—

3·1415926˙	3·1416
3·141592˙	3·141˙
3·14159˙	3·14

Addition and subtraction of numbers thus rounded proceed on the assumption that ˙ is equivalent to 1/2.

(b) HIGH- AND LOW-DOT NOTATION

Rounding is carried out by the standard method, but *in addition*, a high dot is added if the neglected figures lie between 1/6 and 1/2 (in units of the last decimal), or a low dot if these figures lie between 1/2 and 5/6.

Thus, using π again as an example, we have—

3·14159265˙	3·1416
3·1415927.	3·142.
3·141593.	3·14
3·14159˙	

Addition and subtraction are carried out as if a high dot were equivalent to $+$ 1/3, and a low dot to $-$ 1/3; thus

$$2^{\cdot} + 2. = 4 \qquad 2^{\cdot} + 2^{\cdot} = 5. \qquad 3 \times 2^{\cdot} = 7$$

Obviously method (a) limits the rounding error to $\pm 1/4$ and (b) limits it to $\pm 1/6$, excluding critical cases. An advantage of (b), when used in printed tables (e.g. *M.T.C.*), is that the dots can be ignored if the table is accurate enough without using the extra information which they provide.

Let us return for a moment to the definitions of absolute and relative error. When the errors of numbers arise mainly from rounding, as in tables of mathematical functions, a good measure of their absolute accuracy is provided by the number of correct decimal places. A much cruder measure of relative accuracy is given by the number of significant figures. Thus the numbers 0·000101 and 0·000999, both of which have the same absolute accuracy afforded by 6 decimals, and 3 significant figures, may yet have relative errors differing by an order of magnitude. It is common practice to use nD or nS to denote that a number is specified with n correct decimal or significant figures respectively.

1.2. Experimental Errors

The numerical description of experimental errors is usually less simple than that of rounding errors. One of the properties commonly associated with rounding errors, say in a standard mathematical table containing k decimals, is that they are uniformly distributed between extreme values $\pm 0·5 \times 10^{-k}$.

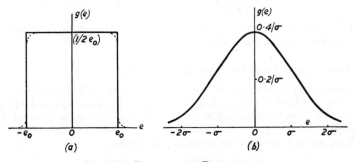

FIG. 1.1. PROBABILITY DISTRIBUTIONS

(a) Rectangular distribution of rounding errors.
(b) Distribution of experimental errors. The probability of an error between e and $e + de$ is $g(e)\, de$.

This implies a probability distribution which is rectangular in shape (see Fig. 1.1 (a)) or very slightly rounded if critical cases are significant. It is true that some distributions of rounding errors may be far from uniform, e.g. in a 2- or 3-decimal table of

$n/16$ or $n/3$, where n is an integer; so one must be on the watch for exceptional cases. However, if a quantity is stated to have the value

$$y' \pm e_0$$

and the error arises from rounding, it is generally assumed that the same probability is attached to any error between the limits $\pm e_0$.

When the error is experimental in origin, however, and the same form is used, the significance of e_0 is usually quite different. This is because experimental errors (systematic errors apart) tend to be distributed in a way more resembling the curve in Fig. 1.1 (b), representing the *normal error distribution*, in which

$$g(e) = \frac{1}{\sigma\sqrt{(2\pi)}} \exp\left(- e^2/2\sigma^2\right)$$

This contains a parameter σ, usually called the *standard deviation*, such that about 5 per cent of errors exceed 2σ in magnitude and slightly less than 0·3 per cent exceed 3σ. On the supposition that errors are distributed according to the normal law, it is possible to state the approximate value of a physical quantity as $y' \pm \sigma$, where σ is estimated in a prescribed way from a set of measurements of the quantity. One warning is necessary: the *probable error*, approximately 0·6745σ, is sometimes used in place of σ; so, if confronted with, say, a measured length 23·45 $\pm$ 0·21 cm, one must make sure whether 0·21 represents the standard deviation or probable error of the measurements.

1.3. Effects of Simple Calculations on Errors

The result of any computation is affected by

(a) errors in the data, which we have seen may be due either to rounding or to experiment or possibly both;

(b) approximations made during the computation, leading to what may be termed *computational errors* or *truncation errors*. The latter term is used because the kind of approximation which is made involves the use of a finite number of terms of an infinite series, or a finite number of repetitions of an iterative process which should strictly be carried out *ad infinitum*. Rounding errors, too, made during the computation, are essentially computational, and are often such that their cumulative effect is very difficult to assess. On the other hand, a calculation which involves only arithmetical processes, such as addition, subtraction, multi-plication, etc., and which can be carried out with virtually complete accuracy, does not contribute to computational errors, but only modifies errors already present in the data. It is the effect of such calculations that we are concerned with at the moment, though some simple computational errors, arising in linear interpolation, will be considered in § 1.6.

ADDITION AND SUBTRACTION

Let $$Y = a_1 y_1 + a_2 y_2 + \ldots + a_n y_n$$

where the coefficients a_k may be positive or negative. If Y' is an estimate of Y obtained by using approximate values for the y's, e.g. y_1' for y_1, with an error $e_1 = y_1' - y_1$, etc., then the resulting error in Y' is E, where

$$E = a_1 e_1 + a_2 e_2 + \ldots + a_n e_n$$

and hence

$$|E| \leqslant |a_1| \cdot |e_1| + |a_2| \cdot |e_2| + \ldots + |a_n| \cdot |e_n| \qquad (1.1)$$

When the magnitudes of the individual errors are limited, (1.1) provides an upper limit to the error involved in Y'. It is easy to see how $|E|$ may be dominated by a single large absolute error, as in the sum of 4-digit numbers shown below. If each number is assumed to have been rounded in the 4th digit, the error of the sum comes almost entirely from 1001; digits to the right of the dotted line have little significance.

$$
\begin{array}{r}
23 \cdot 8 | 2 \\
12 \cdot 9 | 1 \\
0 \cdot 3 | 281 \\
1001 \cdot | \\
821 \cdot 4 | \\
\hline
1859 \cdot 4
\end{array}
$$

MULTIPLICATION AND DIVISION

Let $$Y = y_1{}^{p_1} y_2{}^{p_2} \ldots y_n{}^{p_n}$$

where the p's may be positive or negative integers, and let an estimate of Y again be made, using y_1' for y_1 and so on. With the assumption that the relative errors of y_1', etc., are small, so that, for instance,

$$(y_1 + e_1)^{p_1} \simeq y_1{}^{p_1}(1 + p_1 e_1/y_1)$$

it follows that

$$Y' \simeq Y(1 + p_1 e_1/y_1 + p_2 e_2/y_2 + \ldots + p_n e_n/y_n)$$

and $\quad (Y' - Y)/Y \simeq p_1 e_1/y_1 + p_2 e_2/y_2 + \ldots + p_n e_n/y_n$

Corresponding to (1.1), we now have

$$\Delta = |(Y' - Y)/Y| \leqslant |p_1|\delta_1 + |p_2|\delta_2 + \ldots + |p_n|\delta_n \quad (1.2)$$

where $\delta_1 = |e_1/y_1|$, etc. Thus in forming products or quotients it is the weighted sum of the largest possible *relative* errors of the y's which gives an upper limit to the *relative* error of Y'. The accuracy of a product is therefore determined by the factor or factors having fewest significant figures, e.g. in the calculation

$$\frac{1001 \cdot 2345 \times 821 \cdot 4153 \times 0 \cdot 3281}{12 \cdot 9082 \times 23 \cdot 8234} = 877 \cdot 47 \pm 0 \cdot 13$$

in which all numbers are rounded to 4 decimals, the factor controlling the error is $0 \cdot 3281$, and digits in italics are not significant. The final answer cannot have more than 4-figure accuracy—a fact too often overlooked—although, if this forms part of a larger calculation, there may be good reasons for retaining more digits than have immediate significance. It would then be appropriate, and indeed this is the common practice, to regard the approximate number $0 \cdot 3281$ as being, to 7D, $0 \cdot 3281000$.

The significance of (1.1) and (1.2) has been stressed because of their fundamental importance. The error which may arise in calculating more complicated functions of the y's, not so readily derived by simple arithmetical processes, can be expressed in a similar way. Thus, let Y' be the estimated value of the function

$$Y = f(y_1, y_2, \ldots, y_n)$$

obtained by substituting y_1' for y_1, etc. Then by a suitable extension of the mean-value theorem to several variables it can be shown that

$$Y' = Y + (\partial f/\partial y_1)_{q_1} e_1 + (\partial f/\partial y_2)_{q_2} e_2 + \ldots + (\partial f/\partial y_n)_{q_n} e_n$$

where each partial derivative, assumed to be a continuous function of the variables, has the value appropriate to *some* value of y_1 in the interval y_1 to $y_1 + e_1$, of y_2 in the interval y_2 to $y_2 + e_2$ and so on. It follows that

$$|E| \leqslant |\partial f/\partial y_1| \cdot |e_1| + |\partial f/\partial y_2| \cdot |e_2| + \ldots + |\partial f/\partial y_n| \cdot |e_n| \quad (1.3)$$

Although it might be possible to put this formula into practice by giving each derivative its maximum value in the range of the variables mentioned above, for most purposes it is sufficient to substitute values corresponding to y_1', y_2', . . ., y_n'. This in effect ignores terms of order e_1^2, etc. It is easily seen that (1.1) and (1.2) are special cases of (1.3).

It may happen that one is interested in the inverse problem, that is, given a desired limit on $|E|$, to derive suitable limits to be placed on $|e_1|$, etc. This is of course not open to any unique solution, but one can adopt a "principle of equal errors," deciding that each term should contribute equally to (1.3). This means that

$$|e_k| \leqslant \frac{|E|}{n|\partial f/\partial y_k|} \tag{1.4}$$

Circumstances may dictate an unequal distribution of errors, but when the results are otherwise sensible, there are good arguments for at least being guided by (1.4).

The following numerical example illustrates the use of (1.3) and (1.4).

EXAMPLE 1.1. The acceleration of a body, moving according to the formula $s = ut + \frac{1}{2}ft^2$, is estimated from the relation—

$$\tfrac{1}{2}f = \frac{s_2/t_2 - s_1/t_1}{t_2 - t_1}$$

where t_1, t_2 are the times at which the body is observed to pass points at distances of s_1, s_2 from the starting-point. Find how accurately s and t must be measured if the estimate of f is to be correct to 5 per cent, given typical values as follows—

$$s_1 = 100 \text{ cm}, \ t_1 = 5 \text{ sec}; \ s_2 = 300 \text{ cm}, \ t_2 = 10 \text{ sec}.$$

For the values given, $f = 4$ cm/sec^2, and the error should not exceed ± 0.2 cm/sec^2. It follows from (1.3) that

$$\tfrac{1}{2}\Delta f \simeq \frac{1}{t_2 - t_1}\left[\left\{\frac{\Delta s_2}{t_2} - \frac{\Delta s_1}{t_1}\right\} + \Delta t_1\left\{\tfrac{1}{2}f + \frac{s_1}{t_1^2}\right\} - \Delta t_2\left\{\tfrac{1}{2}f + \frac{s_2}{t_2^2}\right\}\right]$$

where Δf denotes the error in f, etc., and therefore

$$\tfrac{1}{2}|\Delta f| \leqslant \frac{1}{t_2 - t_1}\left[|\Delta s|\left\{\frac{1}{t_2} + \frac{1}{t_1}\right\} + |\Delta t|\left\{f + \frac{s_1}{t_1^2} + \frac{s_2}{t_2^2}\right\}\right]$$

where Δs, Δt represent the maximum errors in measuring s, t respectively. Inserting numerical values,

$$(1/2)|\Delta f| \leqslant (3/50)|\Delta s| + (11/5)|\Delta t|$$

Equal partition of the error will ensure that $|\Delta f| < 0.2 \text{ cm/sec}^2$ provided

$$(3/50)|\Delta s| < 0.05 \quad \text{or} \quad |\Delta s| < 0.8 \text{ cm}$$

and $\qquad (11/5)|\Delta t| < 0.05 \quad \text{or} \quad |\Delta t| < 0.023 \text{ sec}$

However, if the uncertainty in s can be reduced, say to 0.4 cm, then $|\Delta t|$ can be increased to about 0.035 sec.

A further example, involving the use of tables, is given later (Example 1.6).

The discussion so far has referred only to the maximum error arising from a calculation in which definite limits can be placed upon the errors in the data. It is to be expected, however, that this maximum will rarely be reached in practice, and that, through cancellation perhaps, the average error will be much smaller. Is it possible to say anything about the *probability* of the result of a calculation being in error by more than a certain amount?

This question is most easily answered when each error in the data is distributed as in the normal law described in § 1.2. Consider first the simple addition sum performed above, in which the resultant error

$$E = a_1 e_1 + a_2 e_2 + \ldots + a_n e_n$$

Provided the individual errors are independent, the standard deviation (Σ) of E, according to a well-known statistical theorem, is given by

$$\Sigma^2 = a_1{}^2 \sigma_1{}^2 + a_2{}^2 \sigma_2{}^2 + \ldots + a_n{}^2 \sigma_n{}^2 \qquad (1.5)$$

where σ_1 is the standard deviation of e_1, etc. This result is obviously simplified when all the σ's are equal; in particular, if n quantities with the same standard deviation are added, the standard deviation of the sum is $\sqrt{n}\sigma$, *not* $n\sigma$. The s.d. of the mean is likewise $\sigma/\sqrt{n}$, and is therefore relatively more precise than any of the constituent quantities; this shows the effect of cancellation among the errors.

When we consider products such as that leading to (1.2), in which individual relative errors are small, the resultant error is again a linear combination of independent errors; (1.5) then takes the form

$$\Sigma^2/Y^2 = (p_1{}^2/y_1{}^2)\sigma_1{}^2 + (p_2{}^2/y_2{}^2)\sigma_2{}^2 + \ldots + (p_n{}^2/y_n{}^2)\sigma_n{}^2 \quad (1.6)$$

The extension to the case considered in (1.3) is obvious.

EXAMPLE 1.2. If, in Example 1.1, it is found by a series of measurements that the standard deviations of s and t are 0·2 cm and 0·03 sec respectively, derive the corresponding s.d. for f.

Using the numerical values given,

$$\Delta f \simeq (1/25)\Delta s_2 - (2/25)\Delta s_1 + (12/5)\Delta t_1 - 2\Delta t_2$$

Hence
$$\sigma_f{}^2 = \{(1/25)^2 + (2/25)^2\}\sigma_s{}^2 + \{(12/5)^2 + 4\}\sigma_t{}^2$$
$$= 0·008\sigma_s{}^2 + 9·76\sigma_t{}^2$$

If $\sigma_s = 0·2$ cm, $\sigma_t = 0·03$ sec, then $\sigma_f = 0·095$ cm/sec^2.

The effect of combining rounding errors is less straightforward, but all that need be stated here is that when many small random errors are combined by calculation, the resultant error, for a number of similar calculations, tends to be distributed according to the normal law. This is, of course, the dominant reason why experimental errors so often follow the normal distribution, as they are composed of smaller random errors. It is therefore to be expected that, whether the data errors are due to rounding or are experimental in origin, the effects of combining them in the course of calculation will not be markedly different, unless the initial rounding errors happen to be distributed in a very peculiar way. In particular the average rounding error in the sum of n quantities is likely to be about $\sqrt{n}$ times the average error in any one of these quantities, a fortunate fact which mitigates the seriousness of accumulating errors.

This discussion of errors from the statistical aspect is necessarily very sketchy, and is only intended to draw attention to some of the points involved. For details, the reader is advised to consult a statistical text-book.

1.4. Avoidance of Mistakes

Little has been said so far of that kind of error which causes much of the unnecessary labour of computation—the mistake. Too many blunders, too late detected, lose all the advantages gained by using good methods and reliable machines. This brings us back to the principles—if they may be so called—which underlie all successful computation, because in essence they aim to prevent mistakes arising, or their consequences becoming serious. It seems worthwhile to state some of these principles briefly, and in fairly general terms.

1. PRELIMINARY MATHEMATICAL ANALYSIS

It is easy to remark that the mathematical development of a problem should bring it to the form which is best suited to computation, but in practice this is often the stage requiring most skill and experience. It happens occasionally that a mathematical transformation of an advanced kind so changes a problem that from an impracticable task it becomes a relatively easy one. More often it is only necessary to break down the problem into elements for which standard techniques are available, e.g. quadrature, solution of algebraic equations, or linear simultaneous equations, or ordinary differential equations, etc. However, it must be emphasized that too much mathematical analysis can also be harmful; for steps which to a mathematician may seem to advance the solution of a problem are often retrograde for the computer, who is better advised to get down to numbers at an earlier stage. Obviously this is a matter for judgment, remembering that, in general, the shorter and easier the computation the less chance of numerical mistakes. Perhaps it is worth mentioning that mistakes occur also in algebra, not infrequently.

2. ESTIMATION OF ACCURACY

Some attention has already been given to the limitations imposed on the accuracy of a calculation by errors in the data, and the possibility of computational errors has also been mentioned. The relative accuracy of the data may influence considerably the type of computation to be undertaken. Thus in many physical problems, where a final answer correct to 1 per cent is all that is worth striving for, a computation to many figures would be misplaced effort; the work may thus be brought within the scope of a slide-rule, and require only crudely approximate methods. At the other extreme there are calculations in which a result significant even to one or two figures requires, because of cancellation at some stage, many more figures to be retained in the working. Then there is the type of computation, usually tabulation of a mathematical function, in which the final accuracy is laid down, and this in turn places limits on the errors which can be accepted in the data. All this points to the desirability of correlating initial and final errors as early as possible.

It is equally important to assess the computational errors. With sufficient effort these could be made quite negligible, but what is usually more appropriate is that, by accepting a certain degree of approximation in the methods used, their effect should be kept to a modest fraction, say one-tenth, of the effect of initial errors. On occasion the effects of initial and computation errors may even be comparable, but the latter should not of course dominate. To preserve this balance the computer must have a fairly good idea of the limitations of any method or formula he may choose to use, for such knowledge may save him from unnecessary labour. The effects of rounding errors in the computation must be carefully watched, though in many processes they can be obviated by keeping one or two guarding figures throughout.

3. ARRANGEMENT OF CALCULATIONS

For most calculations, particularly when the same operations are repeated many times, an orderly scheme is the first safeguard against mistakes. For casual calculations this may be less essential, but neither the computer, nor preferably anyone else, should be in any doubt later as to what the numbers mean or what operations upon them have been carried out. Unfortunately it is often the small calculations which cannot easily be systematized, and in which accuracy is of crucial importance, which go wrong; in these extreme care is necessary.

4. USE OF AIDS

There is no point in doing more work than necessary, so increasing the risk of error, and full use should be made of the work of others, as contained, for instance, in tables. Experience is the best guide to what can and cannot be gained from tables; often they are potentially more valuable than one suspects at first sight (e.g. it is not difficult to read directly from Barlow's tables the following powers of n: 9, 6, 4, $3/2$, $2/3$, $1/4$, $1/6$, $1/9$, $-1/3$, $-1/2$, -2, -3). It is important, however, to be sure that they are really accurate enough for any particular purpose.

The use of calculating machines calls for similar discretion. It should be remembered that a calculator, as well as being a device for doing simple arithmetic accurately and quickly, is a potential store for intermediate results which need not be recorded. Its capabilities in this direction, e.g. the ability to sum a series of products, should be used to the full; for it saves mistakes as well as time and labour if nothing is copied from the machine which is not absolutely necessary for subsequent working. Again, some machines are better adapted to doing a particular job than others, which is convenient when a choice of machine can be made; but, equally, when there is no choice, it may yet be possible to adapt the numerical procedure to the machine available. This may happen, for instance, when the machine is one for adding and printing, rather than a calculator which does multiplication.

5. CHECKING

The good computer has confidence in his results because he has devised adequate checks on his working to ensure that no slips have gone undetected. He takes it for granted that he will some-times make mistakes, and proceeds accordingly. A good system (a) avoids repetition of the work, which is notoriously unreliable, but rather makes use of identities; (b) checks the work stage by stage, to prevent the discovery of mistakes being long delayed; (c) includes if possible a final overall check.

No more need be said about this at the moment, except to stress its importance; it is hoped that later chapters will show sufficient examples of checks actually being applied.

Unfortunately, in spite of careful organization, etc., mistakes still occur. It may help to know *how* they occur, and where caution is most necessary, so we conclude by listing some of the commoner causes.

1. Miscopying, probably the most prolific cause of mistakes. It takes various forms—

(a) Transposition of digits, e.g. reading or writing 1236 as 1326.

(b) Misreading of repeated digits, e.g. reading 13346 as 13446.

(c) Failure to memorize numbers correctly (here a visual image is usually more reliable than an aural one).

(d) Wrong "inking in" of pencil figures, particularly if badly written.

(e) Misreading of tables, e.g. reading in wrong column; missing asterisks which denote digit changes (as in Barlow).

(f) Failure to note signs, particularly where a function changes sign.

2. Mistakes in simple mental operations, e.g. division or multiplication by 2.

3. Mistakes in signs or decimal points.

4. Wrong corrections. There is an unfortunate tendency, having discovered a mistake, to make the "correction" incorrectly.

5. Mistakes in using machines, e.g. clearing at the wrong time or failure to clear.

Underlying many blunders are such general causes as tiredness, or mental aberrations due to interruptions. The failure to develop the habit of using neat figures, or an orderly scheme of calculation, is a perpetual handicap to accuracy. Finally, there are few occupations in which incautious haste carries so many penalties; speed, however desirable, must always give first place to correctness.

The Aid of Tables

We now turn to consider some of the properties of tables, particularly of mathematical functions. The first point to observe is that not all function tables have the same form; in particular we can distinguish (a) *normal tables*, in which the argument has simple equidistant values, and (b) *critical tables*, in which the arguments are irregular, but the function itself has regularly spaced values. It is possible to design other types of table, e.g. having so-called optimum or maximum intervals, with the special objects of saving space and giving a uniform error of interpolation, but with these we shall not be concerned.* Their use is mainly with automatic machines.

1.5. Critical Tables

The purpose of critical tables is to eliminate the need for interpolation. This is possible when the function is varying so slowly that every value that it can assume, to the required number of decimals, can be included in the table. If f_k is such a value of the function $f(x)$, it is shown bracketed between two values of the argument, which may be denoted by $x_{k-1/2}$ and $x_{k+1/2}$, such that if $x_{k-1/2} < x \leqslant x_{k+1/2}$, then f_k is the value of $f(x)$ correctly rounded to the specified number of decimals. As a simple example, we take the critical table, to two decimals, of $B'' = x(x-1)/4$, where $0 < x < 1$; this is the Besselian coefficient used in quadratic interpolation. The critical table itself is shown to the left of the vertical line; we find, for example, that if x has any value between 0·23 and 0·32, or between 0·67

---

* See Herget and Clemence, *Math. Tab.*, *Wash.*, **1** (1943/5), 173; Miller, *Math. Tab.*, *Wash.*, **1**, 334; and Sadler, *Math. Tab.*, *Wash.*, **4** (1950), 129.

which contains a rounding error from source (1) equal to

$$(1 - r)e_0 + re_1$$

If neither e_0 nor e_1 exceeds ε in magnitude, the above combination will also not exceed ε. However, if the interpolate is calculated accurately from (1.7) and then rounded in the same manner as the tabular values, we must allow a total rounding error of 2ε, representing the combined effect of (1) and (4). This means one should normally expect an uncertainty of 1 unit in the last decimal, quite apart from any contributions from (2) and (3).

To estimate (3), let us assume for the moment that $f(x)$ has a constant second derivative, so that

$$f(x_0 + rw) = f_0 + rwf_0^{(1)} + \tfrac{1}{2}r^2w^2f_0^{(2)}$$

and $$(1 - r)f_0 + rf_1 = f_0 + rwf_0^{(1)} + \tfrac{1}{2}rw^2f_0^{(2)}$$

The correction to be made to the linear interpolate is therefore

$$R_2 = \tfrac{1}{2}w^2r(r - 1)f_0^{(2)}$$

and since $r(r - 1)$ has its largest value when $r = \tfrac{1}{2}$,

$$|R_2| \leqslant (1/8)w^2 |f_0^{(2)}|$$

When $f^{(2)}$ is not constant it will be seen later (p. 84) that the proper result is

$$|R_2| \leqslant (1/8)w^2 |f^{(2)}(\xi)|$$

where ξ is *some* value between x_0 and $x_0 + w$. We are therefore interested in the largest value of $f^{(2)}$ within the interval of interpolation.

Finally if the uncertainty in x (or rw) is Δx, the error from cause (2) will not exceed

$$|f^{(1)}| \cdot |\Delta x|$$

where $f^{(1)}$ is also given its largest value between x_0 and $x_0 + w$.

Thus the total error of the linear interpolate

$$|E| < |f^{(1)}| \cdot |\Delta x| + (1/8)w^2|f^{(2)}| + 2\varepsilon \qquad (1.8)$$

We can ignore the first term in (1.8) for the present, as it is outside the control of the table-maker, and consider how the second affects the choice of w. As a general rule this error should be kept small, but its magnitude may be allowed in the least favourable circumstances to approach 2ε. For illustration we consider the tabulation of some simple functions, using the criterion that $|R_2|$ should not exceed 0.5×10^{-N}, where N is the number of decimals.

(a) COMMON LOGARITHMS

Assume that $\log_{10}x$ is to be tabulated at unit intervals in x.

Now $\qquad\qquad R_2 = (w^2/8x^2)\log_{10}e < 0.06/x^2$

which is greatest for the smallest x in the table. If this is 10^p, then the above criterion implies that

$$0.5 \times 10^{-N} \simeq 6 \times 10^{-(2p+2)} \quad \text{or} \quad N \simeq 2p + 1$$

Thus in a table starting at 100, not more than 5 decimals should be included, and so on.

(b) ANTILOGARITHMS

Tables of common antilogs usually cover a range of x between 0 and 1.

When $\qquad\qquad f(x) = 10^x, \; R_2 = (1/8)w^2(\log_e 10)^2 \, . \, 10^x$

and, if $\qquad\qquad |x| < 1, \; |R_2| < 7w^2$

The criterion requires that $0.5 \times 10^{-N} \simeq 7w^2$, and so we obtain corresponding values of w and N, of which the following are typical—

w	0·01	0·001	0·0001	0·00001
N	3	5	7	9

Thus in a table in which $w = 0.0001$, i.e. with 10,000 entries, it is reasonable to include 7 decimals.

(c) EXPONENTIAL FUNCTION

This is a function which is more conveniently tabulated with a specified relative rather than absolute accuracy, since $R_2 = (1/8)w^2e^x$. However, for the section of the table in which $1 < e^x < 4$, the appropriate number of decimals is given by the relation $10^{-N} \simeq w^2$, e.g.

w	0·01	0·001	0·0001	0·00001
N	4	6	8	10

When $e^x > 4$, either w must be decreased, which is not usually justified, or a decimal must be dropped each time that e^x increases by a factor of 10, i.e. at rough intervals of 2·3 in x. Thus *Chambers* [6] contains a table with $w = 0·001$, and 6 decimals up to $x = 2$, 5 decimals to $x = 4$, 4 decimals to $x = 6$. Between 1·4 and 2·0, however, the error of linear interpolation in the 6th decimal may be rather more than we have prescribed. Between 6 and 16, $w = 0·01$ and the number of decimals is gradually reduced to none, though the table always contains 6 or 7 significant figures.

(*d*) TRIGONOMETRICAL FUNCTIONS, WITH RADIAN ARGUMENTS

Consider

$$\sin x \text{ or } \cos x \quad (0 < x < \pi/2), \text{ for which } |R_2| < (1/8)w^2$$

or $\quad \tan x \qquad (0 < x < \pi/4), \text{ for which } |R_2| < (1/2)w^2$

For various values of N, we find that w should not exceed the following limits—

N	4	5	6	7
$w\{$ $\sin x, \cos x$	0·02	0·0063	0·002	0·00063
$\tan x$	0·01	0·0032	0·001	0·00032

The maker of standard tables will of course be influenced by other factors than space in deciding what interval, etc., to adopt; he will for instance ease the mental burden even of linear interpolation for the general user if it is possible. Thus *M.T.C.* [4], like *Chambers* [6], uses an interval of 0·001 rad for trigonometrical functions. Frequently, a subdivision of the table into parts with different intervals is desirable; as the following examples from *Chambers* [6] show—

$\tan^{-1} x \quad x = 0(0·001)2(0·01)10(0·1)35(1)80$

$\sin^{-1} x \quad x = 0(0·001)0·990(0·0001)0·9990(0·00001)1·0$

The reader is advised to examine different tables, and reflect on the logicality or otherwise of the choice of layout.

In many tables, particularly of the less commonly used functions, it is not possible to allow the luxury of linear interpolation. It is then preferable to use either 4 or 6 values from the table, symmetrically placed about the interval containing the interpolate; thus to obtain a value between f_0 and f_1, one uses either

$$f_{-1} \quad f_0 \quad f_1 \quad f_2$$

or $\quad f_{-2} \quad f_{-1} \quad f_0 \quad f_1 \quad f_2 \quad f_3$

where $f_k = f(x_0 + kw)$. These correspond to the use of a cubic and quintic approximation to the function respectively. The corresponding interpolation formulas will be derived in Chapter 3, where it is shown that the errors (1) and (3) are as follows—

	Rounding error (1)	Interpolation error (3)
4 points	$< (5/4)\varepsilon$	$R_4 = (3/128)w^4 f^{(4)}(\xi)$
6 points	$< (89/64)\varepsilon$	$R_6 = (5/1024)w^6 f^{(6)}(\xi)$

The total rounding error does not exceed $2 \cdot 25\varepsilon$ and $2 \cdot 4\varepsilon$ in the two cases; ξ is now some value of x within the range of the 4 or 6 arguments used. The reader can use the expressions for R_4 and R_6 to derive relations between w and N for some simple functions, on the lines of the above discussion of linear interpolation.

We should now briefly consider the effect of error (2) from the user's point of view. This is conveniently done by a numerical example.

EXAMPLE 1.3. Find the uncertainty in $x^{1/3}$, using Barlow's tables, when $x = 1000 \cdot 050 \pm 0 \cdot 001$.

Barlow gives cube roots of integers to six decimals; therefore

$$\varepsilon = 0 \cdot 5 \times 10^{-6}, \quad w = 1, \quad \text{and} \quad |\Delta x| = 0 \cdot 001$$

Hence, by (1.8), the total error in the estimate of $x^{1/3}$,

$$E < (1/3)x^{-2/3}|\Delta x| + (1/8) \cdot (2/9)x^{-5/3} + 10^{-6}$$

$$\simeq 3 \cdot 3 \times 10^{-6} + 0 \cdot 3 \times 10^{-6} + 10^{-6}, \text{ when } x = 1000$$

Thus $E < 4 \cdot 6 \times 10^{-6}$, and the value $10 \cdot 000167$ obtained by linear interpolation may be out by nearly 5 units of the last digit, mainly because of the uncertainty in x.

1.7. Inverse Interpolation

When a table of $f(x)$ is used to find the value of x corresponding to a specified value of $f(x)$, the process is known as inverse interpolation; thus we may use a table of $\sin x$ to find $\sin^{-1} x$, assuming that no table of $\sin^{-1} x$ is available in which direct interpolation can be made. When the interpolation is linear, the formula corresponding to (1.7) is

$$x - x_0 = rw \simeq w(f(x) - f_0)/(f_1 - f_0) \qquad (1.9)$$

The calculation of rw is subject to the same kinds of error as arise in direct interpolation. Thus the use of rounded values for f_0 and f_1 introduces an error

$$w \left[\frac{f(x) - f_0 - e_0}{f_1 - f_0 + e_1 - e_0} - \frac{f(x) - f_0}{f_1 - f_0} \right]$$

which may be written

$$w \left[\frac{f(x) - f_0 - e_0}{f_1 - f_0} \left(1 + \frac{e_1 - e_0}{f_1 - f_0} \right)^{-1} - \frac{f(x) - f_0}{f_1 - f_0} \right]$$

With the assumption that e_0 and e_1 are much smaller than $f_1 - f_0$ or $f(x) - f_0$, this error reduces approximately to

$$\frac{w}{f_1 - f_0} \{ - re_1 - (1 - r)e_0 \} \quad \text{or} \quad \frac{1}{f^{(1)}(\xi)} \{ - re_1 - (1 - r)e_0 \}$$

When $0 < r < 1$, this does not exceed $\varepsilon/|f^{(1)}|$ in magnitude. Similarly one finds that the error of linear interpolation does not exceed $(1/8)w^2|f^{(2)}/f^{(1)}|$. The error (2) of direct interpolation now becomes $\Delta f/f^{(1)}$, arising from an uncertainty Δf in the given value of $f(x)$.

There remains the final rounding error. No maximum to this can be laid down, for it depends on the computer, who can in principle calculate rw to as many figures as he wishes, and will be guided by the use to be made of the result. This matter is perhaps best left open; we can summarize by saying that the total error $\bar{E}$ from other causes will not exceed

$$\{ \varepsilon + |\Delta f| + (1/8)w^2|f^{(2)}| \}/|f^{(1)}| \qquad (1.10)$$

On comparing this with (1.8) it appears that the relative size of errors occurring in direct or inverse interpolation depends mainly on whether $|f^{(1)}|$ is greater or less than unity.

EXAMPLE 1.4. Estimate the error which may be involved in using a 4-figure log table to find the antilog of a number uncertain by 0·0001.

By (1.10), when $w = 1$, $\varepsilon = 0·5 \times 10^{-4}$ and $|\Delta f| = 10^{-4}$,

$$\bar{E} < (x/\log_{10}e)(1·5 \times 10^{-4}) + 1/8x$$

which is greatest for the largest argument of the table, say 1000.

Accordingly $\bar{E} < 0{\cdot}15/0{\cdot}4343 \simeq 0{\cdot}34$

Bearing in mind that the antilog here lies between 100 and 999, this means for an arbitrary mantissa the antilog is uncertain by 3·4 in the 4th digit in the least favourable case. The maximum *relative* error is effectively constant and equal to 0·00034. Note that the error of linear interpolation is negligible.

EXAMPLE 1.5. Compare the advantages of using tables of $\sin x$, $\cos x$, $\tan x$ and $\cot x$ for inverse interpolation.

We have the following expressions for the maximum error of inverse interpolation—

$$\sin x \qquad \bar{E} < \varepsilon' \sec x + (1/8)w^2 \,.\, \tan x$$
$$\tan x \qquad \bar{E} < \varepsilon' \cos^2 x + (1/8)w^2 \,.\, 2\tan x$$
$$\cos x \qquad \bar{E} < \varepsilon' \operatorname{cosec} x + (1/8)w^2 \,.\, \cot x$$
$$\cot x \qquad \bar{E} < \varepsilon' \sin^2 x + (1/8)w^2 \,.\, 2\cot x$$

where $\varepsilon' = \varepsilon + |\Delta f|$. Their relative magnitudes are clearly shown by the following special values—

x	~ 0	$\pi/4$	$\sim \pi/2$
$\sin x$	ε'	$\sqrt{2}\varepsilon' + w^2/8$	Large
$\tan x$	ε'	$\varepsilon'/2 + w^2/4$	Large
$\cos x$	Large	$2\varepsilon' + w^2/8$	ε'
$\cot x$	Large	$\varepsilon'/2 + w^2/4$	ε'

It may be fairly assumed that w^2 is either less than or about equal to ε', e.g. in *Chambers* [6], $w = 0{\cdot}001$ and w^2 is about equal to 2ε. It follows that when x is near $\pi/4$, the possible error in using $\tan x$ or $\cot x$ is only about one-half that in using $\sin x$ or $\cos x$. Near $x = 0$, $\tan x$ is slightly to be preferred to $\sin x$, and, near $\pi/2$, $\cot x$ is slightly preferable to $\cos x$. Elsewhere the advantage is sometimes with $\tan x$ and sometimes with $\cot x$.

EXAMPLE 1.6. Use the formula

$$\cos d = \sin \theta_1 \sin \theta_2 + \cos \theta_1 \cos \theta_2 \cos (\phi_2 - \phi_1)$$

to find the angular distance between two points on the earth's surface having the following latitude (θ) and longitude (ϕ)—

$$\theta_1 = 51° 36' \text{ N} \qquad \theta_2 = 59° 50' \text{ N}$$
$$\phi_1 = 0° \qquad \phi_2 = 30° 24' \text{ E}$$

Hence derive permissible errors in the values of θ_1, θ_2, ϕ_1, ϕ_2 such that the error in d is less than $2'$.

This example illustrates many of the points so far discussed. We find from 6-figure tables that

$$\sin \theta_1 = 0\cdot783693 \qquad \sin \theta_2 = 0\cdot864567 \qquad \cos (\phi_2 - \phi_1) = 0\cdot862514$$
$$\cos \theta_1 = 0\cdot621148 \qquad \cos \theta_2 = 0\cdot502517 \qquad \sin (\phi_2 - \phi_1) = 0\cdot506034$$

Hence

$$\cos d = 0\cdot783693 \times 0\cdot864567 + 0\cdot621148 \times 0\cdot502517 \times 0\cdot862514$$
$$= 0\cdot677555 + 0\cdot269223$$
$$= 0\cdot946778$$
$$d = 18° 46\cdot6' \quad \text{and} \quad \sin d = 0\cdot3218$$

It is important to verify that in the calculation of d computational errors are not likely to be comparable with $2'$. Rounding errors in the sine and cosine tables are the main cause of concern; assuming that all values are interpolated and uncertain by 10^{-6}, the two products in $\cos d$ involve possible errors of magnitude (by (1.2))

$$10^{-6}\{0\cdot68(1/0\cdot78 + 1/0\cdot86) + 0\cdot5\} \simeq 2\cdot2 \times 10^{-6}$$
$$10^{-6}\{0\cdot27(1/0\cdot62 + 1/0\cdot50 + 1/0\cdot86) + 0\cdot5\} \simeq 1\cdot8 \times 10^{-6}$$

The total error, allowing for final rounding in each product, may thus amount to 4×10^{-6}. The cosine table shows that d, obtained by inverse interpolation, is uncertain by $0\cdot04'$. This is quite satisfactory, and suggests that in this instance the result using 5-figure tables might just be acceptable; 4-figure tables, however, are inadequate.

The effect of errors in the data can now be considered. We find that

$$-\sin d. \ \Delta d \simeq \frac{\partial f}{\partial \theta_1} \Delta \theta_1 + \frac{\partial f}{\partial \theta_2} \Delta \theta_2 + \frac{\partial f}{\partial \phi_1} \Delta \phi_1 + \frac{\partial f}{\partial \phi_2} \Delta \phi_2$$

where

$$\partial f/\partial \theta_1 = \cos \theta_1 \sin \theta_2 - \sin \theta_1 \cos \theta_2 \cos (\phi_2 - \phi_1) = 0\cdot1974$$
$$\partial f/\partial \theta_2 = \sin \theta_1 \cos \theta_2 - \cos \theta_1 \sin \theta_2 \cos (\phi_2 - \phi_1) = -0\cdot0694$$
$$\partial f/\partial \phi_1 = -\partial f/\partial \phi_2 = \cos \theta_1 \cos \theta_2 \sin (\phi_2 - \phi_1) = 0\cdot1580$$

Hence

$$-0\cdot3218\Delta d \simeq 0\cdot1974\Delta \theta_1 - 0\cdot0694\Delta \theta_2 + 0\cdot1580(\Delta \phi_1 - \Delta \phi_2)$$

and

$$|\Delta d| \leqslant |\Delta \theta_1|/1\cdot63 + |\Delta \theta_2|/4\cdot64 + (|\Delta \phi_1| + |\Delta \phi_2|)/2\cdot04$$

If $|\Delta d| < 2'$, then equipartition of the error requires that

$$|\Delta \theta_1| < 0\cdot8', \ |\Delta \theta_2| < 2\cdot3', \ |\Delta \phi_1| \quad \text{and} \quad |\Delta \phi_2| < 1\cdot0'$$

1.8. Detecting Errors in Tables by Differencing

Although tables are produced with considerable efforts towards eliminating errors—and modern standards in this respect are very high—mistakes do nevertheless occasionally creep in. It is worth discussing one widely practised method of checking tables, as it is applicable not only to printed tables but also to any computation which leads to a smooth function tabulated at regular intervals.

The method is based on the formation of differences. Thus, for the cubes of the first few integers, the result of differencing the function thrice is to give a column of differences which are constant and equal to 6. This is typical of polynomials, and it is

```
        0
                1
        1               6
                7               6
        8               12
                19              6
        27              18
                37              6
        64              24
                61              6
        125             30
                91
        216
```

easily proved that the nth differences of a polynomial of degree n are always constant, whatever the interval of tabulation (if constant) may be (see p. 53). Even a function which is not a polynomial, provided that it is tabulated at a fine interval, leads to differences which tend to decrease rapidly in magnitude, essentially because it can be represented closely by a polynomial over a limited range of the argument. This is illustrated by the following table of 5-decimal logarithms.

$10x$	$\log_{10}x$			
10	0·00000			
		4139		
11	0·04139		− 360	
		3779		57
12	0·07918		− 303	− 11
		3476		46
13	0·11394		− 257	− 12
		3219		34
14	0·14613		− 223	− 4
		2996		30
15	0·17609		− 193	− 7
		2803		23
16	0·20412		− 170	− 4
		2633		19
17	0·23045		− 151	− 2
		2482		17
18	0·25527		− 134	− 3
		2348		14
19	0·27875		− 120	
		2228		
20	0·30103			

Consider now a table which contains an isolated error, one entry being $f(x) + e$ instead of $f(x)$. The effect of this on the differences is shown below, all numbers being multiplied by e.

						1
					1	− 6
				1	− 5	
0		1		− 4		15
	1		− 3		10	
1		− 2		6		− 20
	− 1		3		− 10	
0		1		− 4		15
			− 1		5	
				1		− 6
					− 1	
						1

In the higher differences the error is considerably enhanced by factors which, for the kth differences, are clearly the coefficients in the expansion of $(1 - p)^k$. It follows that a sequence of this kind occurring in the higher differences of a function known to be well-behaved, with signs alternating on either side of the peak values, is strongly suggestive of an error in one entry of the original column. Its position is indicated by that of the largest differences of even order; and its magnitude and sign can be estimated by dividing one of these by the appropriate binomial coefficient.

In practice this method is complicated by rounding errors which also lead to large differences of high order. How this happens is shown on page 28 by some values of x^3, from which 3 digits have been removed by rounding.

It can be seen that although the *average* value of third differences is zero to this approximation (strictly it is 0·006), the more or less regular pattern . . 01–10 . . builds up to large differences with oscillating signs. With functions which are not polynomials, rounding errors tend to give a less regular pattern of higher differences, but again there are occasional groups of large differences, usually with alternating signs. This can be seen by extending the table of log x given above to $x = 30$ and building up tenth differences.

How does this affect the detection of mistakes? It is clearly not possible to disentangle with certainty the effects of a blunder from those of rounding errors, but blunders above a certain size can still be picked out. Consider a succession of rounding errors in the entries of a table—

$$\ldots e_{-3} \quad e_{-2} \quad e_{-1} \quad e_0 \quad e_1 \quad e_2 \quad e_3 \ldots$$

e_0 being associated with f_0, etc. Their combined effect on the even differences level with f_0 is

$$e_{-1} - 2e_0 + e_1 \qquad \text{in } \delta^2$$

$$e_{-2} - 4e_{-1} + 6e_0 - 4e_1 + e_2 \qquad \text{in } \delta^4$$

$$e_{-3} - 6e_{-2} + 15e_{-1} - 20e_0 + 15e_1 - 6e_2 + e_3 \text{ in } \delta^6$$

If the rounding errors are distributed at random between $\pm\,\varepsilon$, the *mean* value of each of these combinations throughout a long table is zero, but in exceptional circumstances the 2nd, 4th, 6th difference, etc., can attain the values $\pm\,4\varepsilon$, $\pm\,16\varepsilon$, $\pm\,64\varepsilon$, etc.; in fact,

x	x^3		δ^2	δ^4	δ^6	δ^8	δ^{10}
70·0	343000						
		1472					
·1	344472		4				
		1476		1			
·2	345948		5	−2			
		1481		−1	3		
·3	347429		4	1	−4		
		1485		0	−1	5	
·4	348914		4	0	1	−5	
		1489		0	0	0	0
·5	350403		4	0	1	−5	20
		1493		0	1	−5	20
·6	351896		4	1	−4	15	−55
		1497		1	−3	10	−35
·7	353393		5	−2	6	−20	71
		1502		−1	3	−10	36
·8	354895		4	1	−4	16	−64
		1506		0	−1	6	−28
·9	356401		4	0	2	−12	56
		1510		0	1	−6	28
71·0	357911		4	1	−4	16	−63
		1514		1	−3	10	−35
·1	359425		5	−2	6	−19	63
		1519		−1	3	−9	28
·2	360944		4	1	−3	9	−28
		1523		0	0	0	0
·3	362467		4	1	−3	9	−28
		1527		1	−3	9	−28
·4	363994		5	−2	6	−19	63
		1532		−1	3	−10	35
·5	365526		4	1	−4	16	−63
		1536		0	−1	6	−28
·6	367062		4	0	2	−12	
		1540		0	1	−6	
·7	368602		4	1	−4		
		1544		1	−3		
·8	370146		5	−2			
		1549		−1			
·9	371695		4				
		1553					
72·0	373248						

$|\delta^{2p}|$ has a possible maximum L equal to $2^{2p}\varepsilon$. All values between 0 and L occur of course, and for practical purposes it is more useful to pick out the magnitude K which is exceeded, in the random case, by about 1 per cent only of differences of order k. Such values have been estimated, both theoretically and empirically,* and are given in Table 1.1. It can be seen that the ratio K/L slowly decreases.

TABLE 1.1

k	K	Percentage differences exceeding K	L
3	6	4	8
4	12	1·3	16
5	22	1·4	32
6	42	1·3	64
7	82	1·1	128
8	160	1·0	256
9	310	1·0	512
10	600		1024
12	2200		4096
15	16000		32768

What mistakes may escape detection? This depends on the extent of cancellation between the effects of rounding errors and genuine mistakes. We must consider only differences to which the exact values of the function tabulated should contribute negligibly; if these exceed L a blunder is unmistakable and if they exceed K it is very probable. If we assume that there is a mistake E in one of the tabular values, which already contains a rounding error e, this will contribute to the $(2p)$th difference on the same level an amount $(-1)^p\{(2p)!/(p!)^2\}E$. The danger is that this will tend to cancel the contribution from the random background of rounding errors; indeed, in the least favourable case, we must have

$$\{(2p)!/(p!)^2\}|E| > 2L \quad \text{or} \quad 2K \qquad (1.11)$$

according to the criterion adopted, in order that the net difference shall stand out as anomalous. The values of $|E|_{max}$ picked out by

* Empirically by L. J. Comrie, theoretically by A. van Wijngaarden and W. L. Scheen; see Miller, *Math. Tab., Wash.*, **4** (1950), 3.

(1.11), representing the largest errors which might pass undetected, are given in Table 1.2.

TABLE 1.2

$2p$	4	6	8	10	12
$(2p)!/(p!)^2$	6	20	70	252	924
$|E|_{max}$, using L	$5{\cdot}3\varepsilon$	$6{\cdot}4\varepsilon$	$7{\cdot}3\varepsilon$	$8{\cdot}1\varepsilon$	$8{\cdot}9\varepsilon$
$|E|_{max}$, using K	$4{\cdot}0\varepsilon$	$4{\cdot}4\varepsilon$	$4{\cdot}6\varepsilon$	$4{\cdot}8\varepsilon$	$4{\cdot}8\varepsilon$

It is clearly desirable to use K rather than L as a practical limit, and to treat any differences exceeding K with suspicion; mistakes exceeding 2 or 3 units (assuming $\varepsilon = 1/2$) should not then be overlooked. Differences less than K may also sometimes be worth investigating for possible mistakes of 1 or 2 units. Quite apart from the important question of labour there is some gain in using 4th or 6th differences for the investigation, if there is no risk of confusion from genuine differences of the function tabulated.

EXAMPLE 1.7. What conclusions can be drawn from the following values of $f(x)$ and its 6th differences, assuming that the rest of the table shows 6th differences to be small and random?

x	$f(x)$	δ^6
70·6	351896	1
70·7	353393	− 24
70·8	354895	71
70·9	356406	− 98
71·0	357911	71
71·1	359425	− 24
71·2	360944	2
71·3	362467	− 3

There is strong evidence for an error in the value of $f(70{\cdot}9)$. Its magnitude can be estimated from the peak difference, i.e. $- 98$, or from the numerical sum of this and neighbouring large differences. Thus, using the appropriate binomial coefficients,

$$|E| \simeq 98/20$$

or $$(24 + 71 + 98 + 71 + 24)/(6 + 15 + 20 + 15 + 6)$$

i.e. $4{\cdot}9$ or $4{\cdot}6$

The most probable value of E is therefore $+ 5$ (the sign being opposite to that of the peak 6th difference), though $+ 4$ or $+ 6$ are both fairly probable. An actual comparison with the table of x^3 given earlier shows that the error in the rounded value for 70·9 is 5 units.

It is worth noting a simple procedure for checking a tabular value under suspicion, which is equivalent to the one above. If f_0 is the value thought to contain an error, the sixth difference opposite f_0 is given by the identity

$$\delta^6{}_0 = f_{-3} - 6f_{-2} + 15f_{-1} - 20f_0 + 15f_1 - 6f_2 + f_3$$

where f_{-3}, f_{-2}, etc., are successive entries in the table. It follows that

$$f_0 = 0 \cdot 75(f_{-1} + f_1) - 0 \cdot 30(f_{-2} + f_2) + 0 \cdot 05(f_{-3} + f_3) - (1/20)\delta^6{}_0$$

If, as frequently happens, the last term is small when the table is correct, f_0 can be verified (or, if need be, roughly corrected) without the trouble of forming differences. The simple coefficients are a pleasing feature of the formula*; applied to the above example it gives $f(70 \cdot 9) = 356401$.

Isolated errors are of course not the only kind which may occur in tables; collective errors are not infrequent, and their effect is illustrated by the case of two consecutive equal errors, giving the

```
                                        1
                            1
                 1                     -4
     0       1                   -3
         1           -2                5
     1      -1                    2
         0            0                0
     1      -1                    2
        -1            2               -5
     0       1                   -3
        -1            1                4
                                 -1
                                        1
                                       -1
```

difference pattern shown. On comparing with the pattern on p. 27 it is clear that such errors may be less easy to detect than isolated ones. A further point is that the computer must beware of mistakes in the difference table itself; these could lead to spurious results which might or might not be easily discernible.†

The method of differencing is nowadays applied extensively to published tables, and in consequence many past errors have been detected, as they might have been by the authors themselves had they taken the trouble to use this check. However, it must be

---

* That the formula from the sixth difference has this special virtue was pointed out by C. R. Cosens, *Math. Tab., Wash.*, **1** (1943/5), 167.

† These and other points are discussed by J. C. P. Miller, *Math. Tab., Wash.*, **4** (1950), 3.

remembered that, although the idea is fairly obvious, and must have been in the mind of Babbage when he began to construct his "Difference Engine" in 1822, the practical means of applying it on a large scale was not discovered until L. J. Comrie in 1931 showed how it could be done by the multiregister National Accounting Machine, which prints a function with its first five differences easily and rapidly. Since then most standard tables have been thoroughly combed, and anyone using tables extensively should consult the Part 3 of the *Index* (2nd edition), and the lists of errata which appear regularly in *Math. Tab., Wash.* It is equally important, however, that the computer should use the method when he can to locate his own errors.

Mechanical Aids

We shall now consider some of the machines which bring further aid to the computer. It will be generally assumed throughout later chapters that anyone with an appreciable amount of computing to do will have available a general-purpose desk calculator, and need not rely on log tables for performing multiplications. This is of course linked in a fundamental way to the choice of method for solving standard types of problem. There are a few occasions when a choice can be made between a method which relies on addition as the basic operation and one which uses multiplication, e.g. the fitting of data by polynomials using either factorial moments or orthogonal polynomials (Chapter 10). Then the computer with only an adding machine available will make an obvious choice of method. However, this is rather unusual, and nowadays a general purpose calculator should be regarded as an essential tool, displacing the log tables of a past era.

Whilst there is no doubt about the present, and probably lasting, importance of such calculators, it would be unwise to underrate the slide-rule type of instrument for calculations involving relatively few figures. Particularly useful in this respect are cylindrical slide-rules, in which the two log scales are drawn in helix form on coaxial cylinders; one scale is fixed and the other free to move along the common axis and to rotate about it; the two scales are related by a cursor also mounted on a cylinder. Quite a small and inexpensive instrument of this kind, with scales about 60 inches long, yields with care an accuracy of multiplication of 1 in 2000; and with larger instruments the accuracy can be increased tenfold. For many purposes such slide-rules are entirely adequate, but they also serve a subsidiary role in association with a larger calculator when minor calculations, involving few figures and often a constant multiplier, need to be carried out. The results of these may represent a correction to some quantity required in the principal calculation; simple examples arise in direct interpolation, when several interpolates are wanted in the same interval, and in inverse interpolation by successive approximation (see § 5.10). By using the slide-rule much inessential clearing and resetting of numbers on the calculator, and incidental recording, can be avoided.

Having thus stressed the value of simpler instruments we can go on to discuss the main tool of the computer, the desk calculator.

1.9. The Desk Calculator

We shall not be concerned here with the mechanical details of this type of machine, which vary from one make to another, but rather with the features which are common to the majority and the elementary numerical operations to which they are best suited. It is, however, convenient to distinguish—

(*a*) Barrel-type machines, usually operated by a hand-crank, e.g. Ohdner, Brunsviga, Muldivo-Britannic, etc.

(*b*) Electrically-operated machines, controlled by presskeys; division on these is almost invariably an automatic process, needing a single touch to set in motion once both dividend and divisor have been set, e.g. Archimedes, Badenia, Facit (also hand-type), Friden, Madas, Marchant, Mercedes, Monroe. Multiplication is commonly automatic also, but a few electric machines use semi-automatic multiplication, with a separate operation for each digit of the multiplier, and these have more in common with machines of type (*a*).

Type (*a*) machines, though slower, are often more flexible in use, for reasons which will be discussed later.

The feature which is common to the design of both (*a*) and (*b*) machines is the presence of three registers: (1) the *setting register* (S), into which any desired number within its capacity can be set, either by a series of levers, one for each digit (as in barrel-type machines), or by a keyboard; (2) the *accumulator* (Acc.) or product register, to which any number in S can be readily transferred, positively or negatively; (3) the *counting register* (C) or multiplier register, which records the number of transfer operations from S to Acc.

The number of digits in each register naturally varies, but typical capacities are (9, 13, 8), (10, 20, 11) and (12, 20, 12). Negative numbers in Acc. usually appear as complements on a power of 10, e.g.

$$- 123 \text{ appears as } 999 \ldots 99877$$

The same may hold in C, although digits of a different colour, e.g. red instead of white, are sometimes used. The number in each register can be "cleared" separately, and, in some machines, all registers simultaneously.

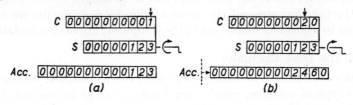

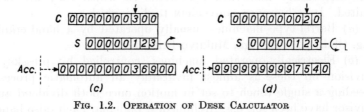

FIG. 1.2. OPERATION OF DESK CALCULATOR

The basic operation of the calculator is the addition or subtraction of the number x set in S to whatever number, say y, is already present in Acc. This is done by one revolution of the crank-handle, in the forward direction for addition, backward for subtraction, or by pressing appropriate keys in an electric machine. Since it is always possible to shift the accumulator register relative to S, this transfer can be made to different positions in Acc., corresponding to the addition (or subtraction) of x, $10x$, $100x$, etc., to y. Simultaneously the number of times x is added to y is recorded in C with the correct power of 10 attached. This is illustrated in Fig. 1.2. By carrying out the three operations indicated in (a), (b), (c) consecutively (in any order), the number finally obtained in Acc. is the product

$$123 \times 321 = 36900 + 2460 + 123 = 39483$$

Thus the machine multiplies two numbers in the same way that this is usually done with pencil and paper. By combining the operations (*a*), (*b*) and (*d*), the product

$$123 \times 281 = 36900 - 2460 + 123 = 34563$$

is obtained. The replacement of the multiplier 280 by the equivalent $300 - 20$ is an example of short cutting, commonly used on hand machines because it lessens the number of turns to be made.

Division may be carried out mechanically in one of two ways—

1. By "breaking down" the dividend. To form a/c, the dividend a is first set on S and transferred to the left end of Acc., the unit count in C being cleared if necessary. The divisor c is then set on S and repeatedly subtracted from Acc. so as to cancel as far as possible the dividend set therein. This is done, as in normal long division, by beginning with the left-most digit and shifting the Acc. carriage to the left when necessary. At any stage the quotient can be read from C and the remainder from Acc. This breakdown method is followed in the automatic division carried out by electric machines.

2. By "building up" the dividend. This is a process which can only be carried out conveniently on a hand machine, or (less easily) on an electric calculator using semi-automatic multiplication. The divisor c is set on S and so multiplied that the dividend a is reproduced, as accurately as desired, in Acc. Obviously the count in C must then represent the quotient a/c. Build-up division is convenient when several quotients are required from the same divisor, since this need be set once only.

The two methods, as used on a hand machine, are summarized in the following table.

	Operation	Contents of		
		S	C	Acc.
1. Division by breaking down	Set Add Clear S, C Set	a a 0 c	 1 0 0	 a a a
Clear Acc. by subtraction		c	a/c (approx.)	remainder
2. Division by building up	Set Build up in Acc.	c c	0 a/c (approx.)	0 a + remainder

Division is of course likely to involve decimals. However, there should be no difficulty in placing the decimal point, either in multiplication or division, if the following universal rule is applied—

No. of decimals in Acc.

    = No. of decimals in S + No. of decimals in C

Finally it should be mentioned that many desk calculators are fitted with a device by which numbers in the accumulator can be transferred mechanically to the setting register, the accumulator being at the same time cleared. It will be seen in the following section that this transfer facility is very valuable.

1.10. Unit Calculations

When a computation is to be performed with the help of a desk calculator, it must first be reduced to a sequence of smaller calculations of a kind suited to the machine, e.g. single multiplications or divisions, etc., or simple combinations of such operations in which no fresh number need be recorded on paper except the final result. A small calculation of this kind, requiring no intermediate recordings, we shall describe as a *unit calculation*. It is one of the essentials of a good working solution to any problem that the computation should be reduced to easy unit calculations. Allied to this is the general aim of recording only those numbers which are essential, or which form part of a checking process.

It is possible to give a short list of unit calculations which occur very frequently, and which the computer must be able to handle with ease. In what follows, the algebraic symbols may represent either positive or negative numbers.

1. SUMS $s = a_1 + a_2 + \ldots + a_n$

The process of forming a sum is straightforward, but it may be necessary to translate a negative sum, appearing in Acc. in complementary form, into the more usual modulus with − sign. The modulus can be read off mentally and recorded, but it is advisable to check the result on the calculator. This can be done easily in two ways, the operations being tabulated below, although the second method requires a transfer device.

(*a*) Check without transfer

Operation	S	C	Acc.
Set Add	0 $\|s\|$ $\|s\|$	0 0 1	$s(<0)$ s 0

Final content of Acc. should be zero if $|s|$ correct.

(*b*) Check using transfer

Operation	S	C	Acc.
Transfer Subtract	0 s s	0 0 -1	$s(<0)$ 0 $\|s\|$

Ignore spurious 9's in Acc.

This check should be applied to any negative result read off the accumulator.

2. PRODUCT SUM $a.b = a_1b_1 + a_2b_2 + \ldots + a_nb_n$

This calculation occurs very frequently. The procedure is fairly obvious, though care must be taken to keep the same number of decimals in each product.

Operation	S	C	Acc.
Set	a_1	0	0
Multiply	a_1	b_1	a_1b_1
Clear S, C	0	0	a_1b_1
Set	a_2	0	a_1b_1
Multiply	a_2	b_2	$a_1b_1 + a_2b_2$ and so on.

Alternatively, $b_1 + b_2 + \ldots$ can be accumulated in C, or (in some machines) $|b_1| + |b_2| + \ldots$.

3. PRODUCT SUM, FOLLOWED BY DIVISION, $r = (a.b)/c$

If breakdown division is used, sufficient decimals should be introduced during the multiplications to ensure that the leading digit of $a.b$ occurs well to the left in Acc., otherwise the quotient may be obtained with too few digits. Alternatively, build-up division can be used if, when $(a \cdot b)$ is in Acc., c is set on S and multiplied so as to reduce the contents of Acc. to zero (as far as possible); then the quotient can be read from C and adjusted for sign.

4. Division by Product Sum, $r = a/(c \cdot d)$

Build-up division is almost essential here if the product sum $c \cdot d$ is not to be recorded. The procedure is to transfer $c \cdot d$ from Acc. to S, changing from complement to modulus if necessary, and then to build up a in the accumulator.

However, if $c \cdot d$ does not occupy more than about half the accumulator the following rather longer procedure can be used.

We distinguish the left and right halves of Acc. by Acc. (L) and Acc. (R), and consider only a simple calculation in which $c \cdot d = cd$.

Operation	S	C	Acc. (L)	Acc. (R)
Set	a	0	0	0
Add	a	10^p	a	0
Clear S, C	0	0	a	0
Set	c	0	a	0
Multiply	c	d	a	cd
Clear S	0	d	a	cd
Set	cd	d	a	cd
Subtract	cd	$d-1$	a	0
Clear C	cd	0	a	0
Divide (breakdown)	cd	a/cd	remainder	

It is assumed above that the transfer of cd to S is done manually, and checked by the next operation. Some calculators with a mechanical transfer also possess a "split-accumulator," in which Acc. (R) can be cleared whilst a number in Acc. (L) is retained. In this case, the number in Acc. (R) could be transferred mechanically to S without affecting that in Acc. (L), which is an advantage.

5. Quotient of Form $r = (a \cdot b)/(c \cdot d)$

If $c \cdot d$ occupies more than half the accumulator $a \cdot b$ must be recorded temporarily whilst $c \cdot d$ is calculated. However, if the numbers are small enough, a procedure similar to that in (4) can be followed, $a \cdot b$ and $c \cdot d$ being formed in Acc. (L) and Acc. (R) respectively. A mechanical transfer and "split-Acc." are again useful.

6. Repeated Product, $r = abcd \ldots$

On calculators of type (a) with a mechanical transfer, this is done easily by forming ab in Acc., transferring to S, multiplying by c, and so on. Otherwise ab must be transferred to S by hand, and it is wise to check this transfer by subtracting the number set from that in Acc. so as to cancel all significant digits.

7. Product of Form $r = p(a \cdot b) + q(c \cdot d)$

Each term can be formed separately, as in (6). In general it is necessary to record one term, say $p(a \cdot b)$, whilst $q(c \cdot d)$ is calculated; then $p(a \cdot b)$ is reset and added. However, with small numbers it may be possible to store one term in Acc. (L) whilst the other is calculated in Acc. (R).

8. Sum of Quotients, $r = a_1/c_1 + a_2/c_2 + \ldots + a_n/c_n$

This calculation can be treated as in (2) by using reciprocals of the divisors read from a table. With 4- or 5-figure numbers this may be quicker and more reliable than recording the results of a series of breakdown divisions. An alternative is to use build-up division as follows—

Operation	S	C	Acc.
Set	c_1		
Build up	c_1	a_1/c_1	a_1
Clear S, Acc.	0	a_1/c_1	0
Set	c_2	a_1/c_1	0
Build up	c_2	$(a_1/c_1) + (a_2/c_2)$	a_2 and so on.

Thus, if the C register is not cleared between each division, the quotients will accumulate in C. Care must be taken to maintain the same number of decimals in each quotient. If some quotients are negative, these can be included if the correct negative number (in complement form) is built up in Acc.; or, in some machines, forward turns on the crank can be counted negatively in C, giving a similar result.

9. Quotient of Form $(abc \ldots)/(pqr \ldots)$

With a transfer device the most straightforward method is to calculate the numerator as in (7), record it; then calculate the denominator, transfer it to S and build up the numerator in Acc. It has the advantage that the operation of division, which is necessarily approximate, is delayed to the end. Without a transfer it may be easier to form the sequence of quantities

$$a/p, \ ab/p, \ ab/pq, \ abc/pq, \ . \ . \ .$$

This can be done without recording, although numbers must be transferred by hand from C to S.

10. SQUARE ROOT

There are various methods of finding square roots by successive approximations. The simplest is perhaps the following. Let x_0 be an approximate value of $a^{1/2}$; set this on S and multiply until a appears in Acc. If the number then appearing in C is $x_0 + \varepsilon$, the next approximation $x_1 = x_0 + \varepsilon/2$, which can be treated similarly.

Since $\qquad (x_1 + \varepsilon/2)(x_1 - \varepsilon/2) = (x_0 + \varepsilon)x_0 = a$

or $\qquad\qquad\qquad x_1{}^2 = a + \varepsilon^2/4$

the error in x_1 is approximately $\varepsilon^2/8a$. Thus, if x_0 is correct to 4S, being taken from Barlow's tables say, then x_1 will probably be correct to 8S. For electric machines, other methods may be more suitable (see § 9.2). At least one machine is available which will compute square roots automatically.

In looking over this selection of unit calculations one is struck by the important contribution which the "build-up" method of division can make towards easing such calculations and avoiding undesirable recording of numbers. This advantage is largely lost on calculators using automatic multiplication, and the greater flexibility which accrues to calculators of class (a) often more than compensates for their slower speed. This is enhanced when such machines are fitted, as they often are, with a mechanical transfer. The advantage of a split accumulator in conjunction with a transfer has also been stressed. Some of the more expensive electric machines now include one or two additional registers which can be used to store intermediate results. This makes them far more versatile for general computation.

1.11. Other Machines

The following remarks about other types of machines are necessarily very brief and intended merely to call attention to the existence and purpose of these further computational aids, some of them very elaborate.*

1. ACCOUNTING MACHINES

These are primarily adding machines with a keyboard for introducing numbers and one or more fixed registers between which numbers can be transferred with addition or subtraction. Multiplying facilities are very restricted. Simple adders, with a single accumulator register, which print numbers added into the accumulator and also totals when required, are occasionally useful in computing. More can be done with a two-register machine, but those with up to ten or so registers and wide transfer and printing facilities, such as are produced by Burroughs and the National Cash Register Company, obviously provide greater scope for ingenious applications.

As mentioned earlier, L. J. Comrie was the pioneer in adapting this type of machine to scientific computing, and he showed their usefulness in forming sum and difference tables, and in performing numerical integration. Some accounting machines also punch results on paper tape which then provides an input medium for other types of computer.

2. PUNCHED CARD MACHINES

These machines, originally developed to process the vast amount of information arising in the actuarial, accounting and statistical fields, can add, multiply and perform other operations on numbers punched in code on cards. They can therefore be adapted to tasks such as tabulation, integration, the solution of linear simultaneous equations and even of simple differential equations. An important scientific application in the early days was the computation of periodic terms in the motion of the moon. For extensive calculations several machines are required; the most important (apart from the usual machines for punching, verifying, interpreting, sorting and collating) being the tabulator, which is a multiregister adding and printing machine, and the

* For more detailed descriptions of these machines see D. R. Hartree, *Calculating Instruments and Machines* (Cambridge, 1950); B. V. Bowden (ed.), *Faster than Thought* (Pitman, 1953); R. S. Casey, J. W. Perry, M. M. Berry and A. Kent (editors), *Punched Cards: Their Applications to Science and Industry*, 2nd ed. (Chapman and Hall, 1959); W. W. Soroka, *Analog Methods in Computation and Simulation* (McGraw-Hill, 1954); A. D. Booth and K. H. V. Booth, *Automatic Digital Calculators*, 2nd ed. (Butterworth, 1956); M. V. Wilkes, *Automatic Digital Computers* (Methuen, 1956); F. L. Alt, *Electronic Digital Computers* (Academic Press, 1958); S. H. Hollingdale, *High-speed Computing: Methods and Applications* (English Universities Press, 1959).

multiplying punch which forms and prints the product of numbers punched on two cards. These punched card machines, which owe their origin to the pioneer work of H. Hollerith in the 1880's, have proved to be invaluable for many kinds of information processing and their use has become worldwide through the activities of I.B.M., I.C.T. (a Hollerith-Powers-Samas combination), Compagnie Bull, and other manufacturing companies. In the 1940's some electronic devices were added to assist those applications in which computing was required, but this was mainly a passing phase during the development of the fast electronic computers to be described in the next section. Punched cards are now an important medium for conveying information into and out of these computers, and in many computer installations the card machines perform useful ancillary functions.

3. AUTOMATIC DIGITAL COMPUTERS

An appreciable increase in computing speed over the usual desk calculator can be achieved by using electromagnetic relays, and in the 1940's a number of quite large relay machines were developed. The time required to multiply two 10 decimal numbers was about 1 second, compared with about 10 seconds on a Marchant desk calculator.

Far more spectacular results are possible using electronic circuits and pulse techniques, and the two decades from about 1943 have seen the construction of digital computers in which the number of internal operations (arithmetical, logical and transfer operations) which can be performed per second has risen progressively to 1,000, to 10,000 and thence to about 1 million. Even this does not represent the foreseeable limit of speed.

There are obvious difficulties in using these high internal speeds effectively, mainly because the passage of information into and out of a computer normally involves electromechanical equipment which is many times slower. These difficulties are overcome in what is called the "stored-program computer" in three ways.

First the "program," which defines the computation as a sequence of simple operations and which must be read into the store of the computer, is kept as short as possible. A compact language (or "autocode") suited to the type of problem may be used in writing the program, and the statements or instructions in this language are expanded to a larger number of more elementary instructions inside the machine. Also it is arranged that instructions can be modified inside the computer so that one instruction will suffice for many similar operations. The operations finally carried out may therefore exceed the number of "written" instructions by a factor of many hundreds or thousands.

Secondly the computer has a large store in which both the encoded instructions and data for the problem can be retained until wanted. The program is converted during input into a form which the computer control will accept, and is stored as a whole before execution begins. The store may be in several parts: one section to which access is as rapid as possible, and one or more sections with relatively long access times but able to hold long programs or large bodies of data or intermediate results.

Thirdly it is possible to arrange that several peripheral units, including those for input and output, can be operating simultaneously and independently of the central computer in which fast arithmetic and other operations are taking place. In some of the faster computers several programs may in fact be using the arithmetic unit in rapid succession. By these various means the input of instructions and data, and the output of results, can be achieved in a time not greatly in excess of the total time occupied by the actual computation.

Clearly the complete electronic computer, consisting of control, store and arithmetic unit, with peripheral equipment for input, output and auxiliary storage, is a complicated structure, although the arithmetic unit itself may be quite simple, with registers not unlike those of a desk calculator. Many technical problems have arisen, particularly in the development of suitable forms of storage, and much research is in progress to develop faster, smaller and cheaper storage elements for the central computer. For the preliminary coding of information to be fed into the machine both punched paper tape and cards are widely used, and magnetic tape is an auxiliary medium for storing large quantities of information. Various devices have been called into play for the rapid printing of results, including line printers, xerographic printers, and photographic recording from cathode ray tubes.

The users of high-speed computers are often faced with special difficulties in the choice of numerical techniques for the solution of their problems. It has not been possible to consider these to any extent in this volume and first priority has been given to the needs of those using desk calculators.

4. ANALOGUE MACHINES

All machines so far considered deal with numbers in digital form. In analogue machines numbers are represented by a continuously variable physical quantity (e.g. length, as in a slide-rule) and the precision of the machine is controlled by the precision with which this quantity can be measured. They are therefore more akin to physical instruments. It is characteristic of analogue computers that to increase the accuracy by a factor of 10 may introduce a similar factor into their cost, whereas the cost of digital computers is roughly proportional to the number of digits used.

(a) *Differential Analysers.* These form an important class, and are used primarily to solve systems of ordinary differential equations, although methods have been found of using them to solve some types of partial differential equations and even linear algebraic equations. The earlier machines were wholly mechanical, being based on a mechanical principle of integration suggested by Kelvin in 1876, and given practical shape by V. Bush in 1931. With 15–20 integrators such machines were capable of solving several coupled equations, linear or non-linear.

Later forms of differential analyser have used electromechanical devices or feed-back amplifiers to effect integration, and servo-driven potentiometers or electronic circuits for multiplication. Some elaborate installations, with a hundred or more amplifiers, can solve large sets of differential equations at high speed. They may also be used to simulate complex physical systems. The precision claimed for results obtained from d.c. analogue machines is rarely better than 1 part in 10,000, although for many applications this is more than adequate.

(b) *Network Analysers.* The use of d.c. networks, with resistance-capacitance elements, has long been an economical way of solving simultaneous linear equations and allied problems with latent roots, and also certain types of differential equation, provided an accuracy of 1–2 per cent is acceptable. A.c. networks, with inductance elements added, are used for similar purposes.

(c) *Special Purpose Computers.* Many machines both mechanical and electronic have been built for more specific purposes. A mechanical device known as the "isograph" is able to estimate the roots, real and complex, of polynomial equations; it is equally suited to the Fourier analysis of periodic functions, and the synthesis of the harmonic components (see § 9.11). Some versions of this use electronic units. The "cinemaintegraph" is a photoelectric device which can form matrix products, and evaluate integrals of the form

$$\int_a^b K(x,\, \xi)\, f(\xi)\, d\xi$$

Mention should also be made of the increasing number of ancillary machines to convert information from analogue to digital form and vice versa.

It might appear from the variety of large, fast and versatile computing machines which are being produced, and soon to be numbered in tens of thousands, that computing with pencil, paper and a desk calculator will cease to be a worthwhile activity. For many large routine calculations, and for research problems which would otherwise remain unsolved, there is no question that the advantage is with the automatic computer. However, there are two reasons why hand computing will continue to be important. First there is still a vast amount of computing on a small- or medium-scale which is most conveniently done by hand. This includes much exploratory work and test calculation which may precede a large computation to be carried out on an automatic machine. Secondly, hand calculations provide an almost essential background of experience for anyone wishing to acquire an understanding of numerical processes and related questions of convergence and error propagation. This experience is particularly necessary for those who may subsequently use automatic computers in which so much calculation proceeds invisibly. Certainly this is the principal reason for giving priority in this book to methods of hand computing, although there is of course a great deal of numerical analysis which is common to all fields of computing.

EXERCISES 1

1. Compare the possible rounding errors of linear interpolation in a table of values of $f(x)$, rounded to nD, using (a) differences of the tabulated values, (b) differences of unrounded values of $f(x)$, rounded to nD. Show that the maximum error of interpolation due to rounding errors is greater in (b) than in (a).

2. If a, b, c are numbers which do not exceed about one-third of the setting register capacity of a hand calculator, show that b/c and ab/c can be formed in one operation using build-up division.

3. If a_k, b_k are pairs of numbers which are not too large, show that
   (i) Σa_k and $\Sigma a_k b_k$ can be formed in one unit calculation;
   (ii) $\Sigma a_k b_k$ and Σa_k^2 likewise. To what extent can the results be checked?

CHAPTER 2

SUMS AND DIFFERENCES OF POLYNOMIALS

In later chapters the difference table derived from a function tabulated at constant intervals of the argument assumes considerable importance; we therefore need a convenient notation for these differences, and for the sums which can also be formed from a set of tabular values. Unfortunately a single notation does not always suffice; in fact, to meet even the simplest of needs, three notations for the same quantities are commonly used. This is not as absurd as may appear at first, as each notation appropriately used shows up certain formulas to the best advantage, and brings out their meaning most clearly. It is therefore worth acquiring an understanding of all three, and actually this does not require much effort.

As polynomials form the basis of nearly all the approximate representations of functions used in this book, the sums and differences of polynomials are important. This introduces the class of polynomials known as factorials, which are considered in detail in the second half of this chapter, with some of their simple applications.

Forward and Backward Differences and Sums

Two of the notations to be described are essentially similar, and these we shall call the *forward difference* and *backward difference* notation respectively. If the first is described in some detail, the second will require only cursory mention.

2.1. Forward Differences and Backward Sums

Suppose the function $f(x)$ is tabulated for values of x at intervals of w, say $x_0 + w$, $x_0 + 2w$, etc. It may also be tabulated for $x_0 - w$, $x_0 - 2w$, etc., but this will not be assumed. It is convenient to write

$$f(x_0 + rw) = u(r)$$

and to denote the values of $f(x_0 + kw)$ or $u(k)$, where k is an *integer*, by u_k. The tabular values are therefore u_0, u_1, u_2, etc. Then the equations

$$\left.\begin{aligned}
\Delta u_k &= u_{k+1} - u_k \\
\Delta^2 u_k &= \Delta u_{k+1} - \Delta u_k
\end{aligned}\right\} \tag{2.1}$$

define the first and second forward differences of u_k, and differences of higher order can be defined in an obvious way. These differences are shown in the following table to the right of the tabular values $u_0, \ldots, u_4$.

$\mathfrak{Z}^3 u$	$\mathfrak{Z}^2 u$	$\mathfrak{Z} u$	u	Δu	$\Delta^2 u$	$\Delta^3 u$	$\Delta^4 u$
			u_0				
		$\mathfrak{Z} u_1$		Δu_0			
	$\mathfrak{Z}^2 u_2$		u_1		$\Delta^2 u_0$		
$\mathfrak{Z}^3 u_3$		$\mathfrak{Z} u_2$		Δu_1		$\Delta^3 u_0$	
	$\mathfrak{Z}^2 u_3$		u_2		$\Delta^2 u_1$		$\Delta^4 u_0$
$\mathfrak{Z}^3 u_4$		$\mathfrak{Z} u_3$		Δu_2		$\Delta^3 u_1$	
	$\mathfrak{Z}^2 u_4$		u_3		$\Delta^2 u_2$		
$\mathfrak{Z}^3 u_5$		$\mathfrak{Z} u_4$		Δu_3			
	$\mathfrak{Z}^2 u_5$		u_4				
$\mathfrak{Z}^3 u_6$		$\mathfrak{Z} u_5$					
	$\mathfrak{Z}^2 u_6$						
$\mathfrak{Z}^3 u_7$							

In the same table, to the left of the function values, are shown *sums* which can be formed from them. These quantities are related in exactly the same way as the differences; the function values being differences of the first sums, the first sums being differences of the second sums, and so on,

i.e.
$$\left.\begin{array}{c} \mathfrak{Z} u_{k+1} - \mathfrak{Z} u_k = u_k \\ \mathfrak{Z}^2 u_{k+1} - \mathfrak{Z}^2 u_k = \mathfrak{Z} u_k \end{array}\right\} \qquad (2.2)$$

Unlike differences, however, sums are not uniquely determined in terms of the u's by (2.2), since all such difference relations are still satisfied if we add to all sums of a particular order an arbitrary constant (or any function whose differences are all zero, e.g. $\sin(\alpha + 2\pi r)$). So long as such constants remain unspecified, the sums $\mathfrak{Z} u_k$, $\mathfrak{Z}^2 u_k \ldots$ are indefinite in the same way that the integrals

$$\int^k u(r)dr, \qquad \int^k \int^r u(r)dr^2, \ldots$$

are indefinite when the lower limits of integration are unspecified. It is therefore appropriate to call them *indefinite sums*.

In practice this arbitrariness is usually removed by defining the values of certain sums. Thus in a table beginning with u_0, it may be convenient to define

$$\mathfrak{Z}^k u_k = u_0 \qquad (2.3)$$

which means that all sums in the diagonal, starting from u_0 and sloping down to the left, have the same value. Then sums up to any order are uniquely determined by the difference relations, and are formed starting at the top of the table and proceeding downwards. This corresponds to defining the lower limit of an integral; thus if

$$U(r) = \int_0^r u(r)dr$$

which is a fully defined function of the upper limit, the sums Σu_k correspond to, though they do not equal, the particular values $U(k)$.

A further glance at the table will show that sums and differences on a diagonal sloping down from left to right carry the same suffix. For this reason they are often called *descending differences* and *ascending sums*, though we shall more often use the terms *forward differences* and *backward sums*.

We describe next the alternative notation, which is particularly appropriate at the end of a table.

2.2. Backward Differences and Forward Sums

Suppose the function $u(r)$ is tabulated for integral values of r up to n. Then it is possible to form the following table of backward differences and forward sums, the symbols ∇ and Σ replacing Δ and Σ.

Σ^3	Σ^2	Σ	u	∇	∇^2	∇^3	∇^4
$\Sigma^3 u_{n-7}$							
	$\Sigma^2 u_{n-6}$						
$\Sigma^3 u_{n-6}$							
	$\Sigma^2 u_{n-5}$	Σu_{n-5}					
$\Sigma^3 u_{n-5}$			u_{n-4}				
	$\Sigma^2 u_{n-4}$	Σu_{n-4}		∇u_{n-3}			
$\Sigma^3 u_{n-4}$			u_{n-3}		$\nabla^2 u_{n-2}$		
	$\Sigma^2 u_{n-3}$	Σu_{n-3}		∇u_{n-2}		$\nabla^3 u_{n-1}$	
$\Sigma^3 u_{n-3}$			u_{n-2}		$\nabla^2 u_{n-1}$		$\nabla^4 u_n$
	$\Sigma^2 u_{n-2}$	Σu_{n-2}		∇u_{n-1}		$\nabla^3 u_n$	
			u_{n-1}		$\nabla^2 u_n$		
		Σu_{n-1}		∇u_n			
			u_n				

Equations (2.1) and (2.2) are now replaced by

$$u_{k+1} - u_k = \nabla u_{k+1} \tag{2.4}$$

$$\Sigma u_{k+1} - \Sigma u_k = u_{k+1} \tag{2.5}$$

and, as a consequence, the constant suffix appears on a backward (or ascending) diagonal for differences, and a forward (or descending) diagonal for sums.

Sums are again indefinite unless the constants of summation are specified. One way of making the sums definite is to assume that

$$\Sigma^m u_{n-m} = (-1)^m u_n \tag{2.6}$$

and sums are then formed from the bottom of the table upwards. Inclusion of the factor $(-1)^m$ in (2.6) leads to forward sums which are exactly similar to the backward sums based on (2.3), as the reader can easily verify.

Using the analogy with the infinitesimal calculus as before the first order sums correspond to the integral

$$U_1(r) = \int_r^n u(r)dr$$

in which the lower limit varies; in particular $-\Sigma u_k$ corresponds to $U_1(k)$. Differences are likewise analogous to derivatives.

Summation from the bottom of the table rather than from the top may often be preferable for numerical reasons, e.g. when the function is decreasing rapidly so that the numbers at the end of the table are much smaller than those at the top.

2.3. Relations with Tabular Values

Since differences depend only on tabular values they can obviously be expressed as simple combinations of these values. One finds easily enough that

$$\Delta^2 u_0 = u_0 - 2u_1 + u_2$$

and $\qquad (-1)^3 \Delta^3 u_0 = u_0 - 3u_1 + 3u_2 - u_3$

and it is clear that the coefficients are in fact those in the binomial expansions of $(1-r)^2$, $(1-r)^3$. The general result, which can be proved by induction, is that

$$(-1)^m \Delta^m u_0 = u_0 - mu_1 + m_{(2)}u_2 - m_{(3)}u_3 + \ldots + (-1)^m u_m \quad (2.7)$$

where $m_{(k)}$ is the usual binomial coefficient, sometimes written $\binom{m}{k}$.

A particular tabular value, say u_m, can also be expressed in terms of u_0 and its leading differences. Thus

$$u_2 = u_0 + 2\Delta u_0 + \Delta^2 u_0$$
$$u_3 = u_0 + 3\Delta u_0 + 3\Delta^2 u_0 + \Delta^3 u_0$$

and, in general

$$u_m = u_0 + m\Delta u_0 + m_{(2)}\Delta^2 u_0 + m_{(3)}\Delta^3 u_0 + \ldots + \Delta^m u_0 \quad (2.8)$$

Similar formulas can be derived relating tabular values with their backward differences.

Definite sums can also be expressed in terms of tabular values. Starting from (2.3), it is obvious that

$$\mathfrak{Z}u_k = u_{k-1} + u_{k-2} + \ldots + u_0$$

$$\mathfrak{Z}^2 u_k = u_{k-2} + 2u_{k-3} + 3u_{k-4} + \ldots + (k-1)u_0$$

The general expression for the mth sum is less easily proved, and will only be stated at the moment; it is that, when $k \geqslant m$,

$$\mathfrak{Z}^m u_k = u_{k-m} + mu_{k-m-1} + (m+1)_{(2)}u_{k-m-2}$$
$$+ \ldots + (k-1)_{(m-1)}u_0$$

or
$$\mathfrak{Z}^m u_k = \sum_{r=0}^{k-m} (k-r-1)_{(m-1)}u_r \qquad (2.9)$$

In comparing these two forms it should be remembered that, when r is integral,

$$(k-r-1)_{(m-1)} = (k-r-1)_{(k-m-r)}$$

It is easily verified that (2.9) reduces to (2.3) when $k = m$, and that in general it satisfies a difference relation of type (2.2).

Similarly, for summation from the bottom of the table, with the condition (2.6),

$$-\Sigma u_k = u_{k+1} + u_{k+2} + \ldots + u_n$$

$$\Sigma^2 u_k = u_{k+2} + 2u_{k+3} + \ldots + (n-k-1)u_n$$

and, in general when $n \geqslant k + m$,

$$(-1)^m \Sigma^m u_k = u_{k+m} + mu_{k+m+1} + (m+1)_{(2)}u_{k+m+2}$$
$$+ \ldots + (n-k-1)_{(m-1)}u_n$$

or
$$(-1)^m \Sigma^m u_k = \sum_{r=k+m}^{n} (r-k-1)_{(m-1)}u_r \qquad (2.10)$$

The application of these expansions to the evaluation of factorial moments and power moments of a tabular function will be discussed in § 2.9.

Central Differences and Sums

The central notation arises naturally enough if one regards u_0 as some entry in the centre of a table which extends indefinitely above and below u_0. The following table representing central differences and sums, with symbols δ and σ respectively, should by now be self-explanatory.

$$
\begin{array}{cccccccc}
 & & \sigma^2 u_{-2} & & u_{-2} & & & \\
\sigma^3 u_{-3/2} & & & \sigma u_{-3/2} & & \delta u_{-3/2} & & \\
 & \sigma^2 u_{-1} & & & u_{-1} & & \delta^2 u_{-1} & \\
\sigma^3 u_{-1/2} & & & \sigma u_{-1/2} & & \delta u_{-1/2} & & \delta^3 u_{-1/2} \\
 & \sigma^2 u_0 & & & u_0 & & \delta^2 u_0 & & \delta^4 u_0 \\
\sigma^3 u_{1/2} & & & \sigma u_{1/2} & & \delta u_{1/2} & & \delta^3 u_{1/2} \\
 & \sigma^2 u_1 & & & u_1 & & \delta^2 u_1 & \\
\sigma^3 u_{3/2} & & & \sigma u_{3/2} & & \delta u_{3/2} & & \\
 & & \sigma^2 u_2 & & u_2 & & & \\
\end{array}
$$

It will be seen that the relations corresponding to (2.1) and (2.2) are

$$u_{k+1} - u_k = \delta u_{k+1/2} \qquad (2.11)$$

$$\sigma u_{k+1/2} - \sigma u_{k-1/2} = u_k \qquad (2.12)$$

In this notation the constant suffix appears along horizontal lines in the table. It is often helpful to use an abbreviation for *mean differences* and *mean sums*. Thus the quantities δu_0, $\delta^2 u_{1/2}$, . . ., which do not occur naturally* in the table, are conveniently defined by the equations

$$\delta u_0 = \tfrac{1}{2}(\delta u_{-1/2} + \delta u_{1/2}), \quad \delta^2 u_{1/2} = \tfrac{1}{2}(\delta^2 u_0 + \delta^2 u_1) \qquad (2.13)$$

with obvious generalizations to $\delta^{2s+1} u_k$, $\delta^{2s} u_{k+1/2}$. Mean sums are represented similarly. It may even be useful to write $u_{1/2}$ for $\tfrac{1}{2}(u_0 + u_1)$, though there is a danger of confusion with the actual mid-value of the function, i.e. $f(x_0 + \tfrac{1}{2}w)$ or $u(\tfrac{1}{2})$.

2.4. Abbreviated Notation

The inclusion of the symbol denoting the function is not always necessary; if there is no likely confusion as to what function is being summed or differenced, we shall write

$$\delta^{2s+1} u_{k+1/2} = \delta^{2s+1}{}_{k+1/2}; \quad \delta^{2s} u_k = \delta^{2s}{}_k$$

and similarly for sums. This applies equally to the other notations; thus

$$\Delta^m u_k = \Delta^m{}_k; \quad \nabla^m u_k = \nabla^m{}_k$$

* This assumes that the tabular values u_k correspond to *integral* values of r. It is sometimes desirable to tabulate $u(r)$ for *half-integral* values of r; then in the central notation the naturally occurring quantities are δu_0, $\delta^2 u_{1/2}$, σu_0, $\sigma^2 u_{1/2}$, etc., and $\delta u_{1/2}$, $\delta^2 u_0$, etc., represent mean differences. Any possible confusion on this score can be removed by prefacing all mean quantities with a special symbol, e.g., the common practice, due to Sheppard, of using μ in this way, as $\mu \delta u_0$, $\mu \delta^2 u_{1/2}$, and so on. We shall not normally do this (see, however, Chapter 6), as it may be taken for granted that the tabulation is for integral k unless the contrary is emphasized.

The following identities should be remembered—

$$\Delta^m{}_k = \nabla^m{}_{k+m} = \delta^m{}_{k+m/2} \tag{2.14}$$

$$\mathbf{Z}^m{}_k = \Sigma^m{}_{k-m} = \sigma^m{}_{k-m/2} \tag{2.15}$$

In (2.15) of course the equivalence refers only to *position* in the table of sums, as numerical values may differ with different choice of the constants of summation.

Factorials

The importance of polynomials, and factorials in particular, has already been stressed. Of the various types of factorial, those known as descending and ascending factorials are already familiar in the guise of binomial coefficients, and will be discussed first; central factorials are perhaps less well known.

2.5. Descending and Ascending Factorials

We begin with the following definitions, in which r is not necessarily an integer.

Descending factorial of order m

$$r^{(m)} = r(r-1)(r-2) \ldots (r-m+1) \tag{2.16}$$

Ascending factorial of order m

$$^{(m)}r = r(r+1)(r+2) \ldots (r+m-1) \tag{2.17}$$

Obviously two notations are not essential here, although sometimes convenient, as the ascending factorial is readily expressed as a descending factorial and vice versa.

Thus

$$^{(m)}r = (r+m-1)^{(m)} \quad \text{or} \quad (-1)^m(-r)^m \tag{2.18}$$

There is no accepted notation for ascending factorials, and in practice it is preferable to use the notation for descending factorials throughout, as we shall usually do.

We also define

$$r_{(m)} = r^{(m)}/m!, \quad {}_{(m)}r = {}^{(m)}r/m! \tag{2.19}$$

and call these *reduced* factorials. Thus the binomial coefficient $n_{(m)}$ is simply an example of a reduced descending factorial. Incidentally $m^{(m)} = m!$.

We consider first the sums and differences of descending factorials, for unit changes* in the variable r.

DIFFERENCES

$$\Delta r^{(m)} = (r + 1)^{(m)} - r^{(m)}$$
$$= (r + 1)r^{(m-1)} - r^{(m-1)}(r - m + 1)$$
$$= mr^{(m-1)} \tag{2.20}$$

It follows that $\qquad\qquad \Delta^m r^{(m)} = m\,!$

and also $\qquad\qquad \Delta r_{(m)} = r_{(m-1)}, \ \Delta^m r_{(m)} = 1$

SUMS

The inverse process to forward differencing is backward summation.

Since $\qquad\qquad \Delta r^{(m+1)} = (m + 1)r^{(m)}$

it follows that the indefinite sum

$$\left.\begin{array}{l} \mathcal{Z}r^{(m)} = \{1/(m + 1)\}r^{(m+1)} \\[2mm] \mathcal{Z}r_{(m)} = r_{(m+1)} \end{array}\right\} \tag{2.21}$$

and

As an example of a definite sum, we note that

$$\sum_{r=0}^{n-1} r^{(m)} = \mathcal{Z}n^{(m)} - \mathcal{Z}0^{(m)} = \{1/(m + 1)\}n^{(m+1)}$$

The process of repeated summation is fairly obvious.

INVERSE FACTORIALS

The extension of our definition to include factorials of negative order is not difficult. When $m = 0$, the recurrence relation

$$r^{(m)} = (r - m + 1)r^{(m-1)}$$

gives $\qquad\qquad r^{(-1)} = 1/(r + 1)$

---

* The definition of factorials can be widened, thus corresponding to discrete intervals of w in a variable x, the descending factorial—

$$x^{(m,\ w)} = x(x - w)(x - 2w) \ldots (x - mw + w)$$

This brings out clearly the parallelism between the difference and sum rules for a factorial, and those for the differentiation and integration of x^m; thus—

$$(d/dx)x^m = mx^{m-1}, \ \int x^m dx = x^{m+1}/(m + 1)$$

follow naturally from the rules for $x^{(m,\ w)}$ when w tends to zero; cp. (2.20) and (2.21).

and repeated use of the relation with $-2, -3, \ldots$ for m leads to the general definition

$$r^{(-m)} = \frac{1}{(r+1)(r+2)\ldots(r+m)} = \frac{1}{(r+m)^{(m)}} \qquad (2.22)$$

The denominator may also be regarded as an ascending factorial.*

ADDITION THEOREM

A useful result, not difficult to prove, is that for all integral values of k and m, positive and negative,

$$r^{(m)}(r-m)^{(k)} = r^{(m+k)} \qquad (2.23)$$

(2.22) is a special case of this.

It is only necessary to quote the corresponding properties of ascending factorials—

Differences $\nabla^{(m)}r = m \cdot {}^{(m-1)}r, \ \nabla_{(m)}r = {}_{(m-1)}r$ (2.24)

Sums $\Sigma^{(m)}r = \dfrac{{}^{(m+1)}r}{m+1}, \ \sum\limits_{r=1}^{n} {}^{(m)}r = \dfrac{{}^{(m+1)}n}{m+1}$ (2.25)

Inverse Factorials

$${}^{(-m)}r = \frac{1}{(r-1)(r-2)\ldots(r-m)} = \frac{1}{(r-1)^{(m)}} \qquad (2.26)$$

Addition Theorem

$${}^{(m)}r \cdot {}^{(k)}(r+m) = {}^{(m+k)}r \qquad (2.27)$$

2.6. Central Factorials

The fact that descending and ascending factorials are intimately associated with descending and ascending differences respectively suggests that there are other factorials similarly linked with central differences. In showing how this is so, we follow Aitken and distinguish two types, called central and mean central factorials, defined as follows—

Central Factorials

Order $2p$
$$r^{\{2p\}} = (r^2 - 1/4)(r^2 - 9/4)\ldots(r^2 - (p-1/2)^2)$$

Order $2p+1$
$$r^{\{2p+1\}} = r(r^2 - 1)(r^2 - 4)\ldots(r^2 - p^2)$$

$\left.\vphantom{\begin{array}{c}1\\1\\1\\1\end{array}}\right\}$ (2.28)

---

* Some writers, e.g. Steffensen, use $r^{(-m)}$ to represent an ascending factorial.

Mean Central Factorials

Order $2p$ $r^{[2p]} = r \cdot r^{\{2p-1\}}$

Order $2p + 1$ $r^{[2p+1]} = r \cdot r^{\{2p\}}$ (2.29)

The notation $r^{\{\ \}}$ seems to have been introduced by Aitken, and $r^{[\ ]}$ by Steffensen. One or other is sometimes avoided by writing $r^{[m+1]} = r^{\{m\}+1}$ or $r^{\{m-1\}} = r^{[m]-1}$. Reduced central or mean factorials are defined, as in (2.19), by

$$r_{\{m\}} = r^{\{m\}}/m!, \quad r_{[m]} = r^{[m]}/m! \qquad (2.30)$$

Central factorials are of course expressible as descending (or ascending) factorials, and we should note the relations

$$r^{\{2p\}} = (r + p - \tfrac{1}{2})^{(2p)} \quad \text{and} \quad r^{\{2p+1\}} = (r + p)^{(2p+1)}$$

which may be combined into a single identity

$$r^{\{m\}} = (r + \tfrac{1}{2}m - \tfrac{1}{2})^{(m)} \qquad (2.31)$$

By means of (2.31) we can easily show the reason for using the term "mean central factorial," which arises because

$$\tfrac{1}{2}\{(r + \tfrac{1}{2})^{\{m\}} + (r - \tfrac{1}{2})^{\{m\}}\}$$
$$= \tfrac{1}{2}\{(r + \tfrac{1}{2}m)^{(m)} + (r + \tfrac{1}{2}m - 1)^{(m)}\}$$
$$= \tfrac{1}{2}\{(r + \tfrac{1}{2}m) \cdot (r + \tfrac{1}{2}m - 1)^{(m-1)}$$
$$\qquad\qquad + (r + \tfrac{1}{2}m - 1)^{(m-1)} \cdot (r - \tfrac{1}{2}m\}$$
$$= r(r + \tfrac{1}{2}m - 1)^{(m-1)}$$
$$= r^{[m]} \qquad (2.32)$$

Thus $r^{[m]}$ is the mean of the two central factorials of the same order whose arguments differ from r by $\pm \tfrac{1}{2}$.

DIFFERENCES

From the definition of a central difference (2.11)

$$\delta r^{\{m\}} = (r + \tfrac{1}{2})^{\{m\}} - (r - \tfrac{1}{2})^{\{m\}}$$
$$= m(r + \tfrac{1}{2}m - 1)^{(m-1)}$$
$$= mr^{\{m-1\}} \qquad (2.33)$$

By a similar argument it can be shown that

$$\delta r^{[m]} = mr^{[m-1]} \qquad (2.34)$$

Thus both central and mean central factorials satisfy a rule for differencing similar to that for descending and ascending factorials. Likewise, for the reduced factorials

$$\delta r_{\{m\}} = r_{\{m-1\}}, \quad \delta r_{[m]} = r_{[m-1]} \tag{2.35}$$

SUMS

By considering summation as the inverse of differencing one finds that the indefinite sum

$$\sigma r_{\{m\}} = r_{\{m+1\}} \tag{2.36}$$

In interpreting this result, it must be remembered that

$$\sigma u(r) = \ldots + u(r - \tfrac{5}{2}) + u(r - \tfrac{3}{2}) + u(r - \tfrac{1}{2})$$

so that (2.36) is rather more complicated than it appears. Examples are provided by the definite sums

$$\sum_{r=1}^{n} (r - \tfrac{1}{2})_{\{m\}} = \sigma n_{\{m\}} - \sigma 0_{\{m\}} = n_{\{m+1\}} - 0_{\{m+1\}}$$

and

$$\sum_{r=1}^{n} r_{\{m\}} = \sigma(n + \tfrac{1}{2})_{\{m\}} - \sigma(\tfrac{1}{2})_{\{m\}} = (n + \tfrac{1}{2})_{\{m+1\}} - (\tfrac{1}{2})_{\{m+1\}}$$

The way in which (2.35) and (2.36) operate is probably made clearer by looking at a section of the sum and difference table of $r_{\{m\}}$—

Sums		Differences	
$(r-1)_{\{m+2\}}$	$(r-1)_{\{m\}}$	$(r-1)_{\{m-2\}}$	
$(r-\tfrac{1}{2})_{\{m+1\}}$	$(r-\tfrac{1}{2})_{\{m-1\}}$		$(r-\tfrac{1}{2})_{\{m-3\}}$
$r_{\{m+2\}}$	$r_{\{m\}}$	$r_{\{m-2\}}$	
$(r+\tfrac{1}{2})_{\{m+1\}}$	$(r+\tfrac{1}{2})_{\{m-1\}}$		$(r+\tfrac{1}{2})_{\{m-3\}}$
$(r+1)_{\{m+2\}}$	$(r+1)_{\{m\}}$	$(r+1)_{\{m-2\}}$	

The table for $r_{[m]}$ is exactly similar.

Applications of Factorials

Among the simple applications of factorials is the formation of sums and differences of polynomials, and the evaluation of power moments. We shall consider these with numerical examples.

2.7. Differences and Sums of Polynomials

The power series form of a polynomial is the natural one if its derivatives or integrals are required. Similarly we might expect that for easy calculation of differences or sums, the polynomial is better expressed as a series of factorials. Thus if we are given that

$$p(r) = a_0 + a_1 r + a_2 r^2 + \ldots + a_n r^n \qquad (2.37)$$

and want forward differences of $p(r)$, the first step is to express it in the form

$$p(r) = c_0 + c_1 r^{(1)} + c_2 r^{(2)} + \ldots + c_n r^{(n)} \qquad (2.38)$$

The transformation from (2.37) to (2.38) might be made in two ways. An elementary method is to divide $p(r)$ in succession by $r, r-1, r-2$, etc., and the remainders from successive divisions are then c_0, c_1, c_2, etc. The divisions can be made by Horner's method using detached coefficients (see § 2.8). On the other hand, a direct calculation is possible if we have in advance a table of coefficients representing the expansion of each power of r, up to the nth, as a series of descending factorials. To make this explicit, let

$$r^m = s_m{}^1 r^{(1)} + s_m{}^2 r^{(2)} + \ldots + s_m{}^m r^{(m)} \qquad (2.39)$$

Then obviously
$$c_n = a_n s_n{}^n$$
$$c_{n-1} = a_n s_n{}^{n-1} + a_{n-1} s_{n-1}{}^{n-1}$$

and in general
$$c_j = \sum_{m=j}^{n} a_m s_m{}^j$$

We need not be concerned at present how the coefficients $s_m{}^j$, usually known as Stirling numbers of the second kind, are derived; this is considered in Appendix 1, where they are tabulated up to $m = 12$. The following simple example illustrates their use.

EXAMPLE 2.1. Find the forward differences (at unit interval) of the polynomial $p(r) = 2r^4 - 5r^3 - 8r^2 + 17r + 2$.

Using the coefficients in Appendix 1, Table 3, we find
$$2r^4 = 2r^{(4)} + 12r^{(3)} + 14r^{(2)} + 2r$$
$$-5r^3 = \qquad\quad - 5r^{(3)} - 15r^{(2)} - 5r$$
$$-8r^2 = \qquad\qquad\qquad\quad - 8r^{(2)} - 8r$$
$$17r = \qquad\qquad\qquad\qquad\qquad\qquad 17r$$

and hence
$$p(r) = 2r^{(4)} + 7r^{(3)} - 9r^{(2)} + 6r + 2$$
$$\Delta p(r) = 8r^{(3)} + 21r^{(2)} - 18r + 6$$
$$\Delta^2 p(r) = 24r^{(2)} + 42r - 18$$
$$\Delta^3 p(r) = 48r + 42$$
$$\Delta^4 p(r) = 48$$

Also
$$\sum_0^{n-1} p(r) = (2/5)n^{(5)} + (7/4)n^{(4)} - 3n^{(3)} + 3n^{(2)} + 2n$$

To express these differences or sums of $p(r)$ in powers of r, the inverse expansion of factorials in powers is needed, i.e. the coefficients $S_m{}^j$ such that

$$r^{(m)} = S_m{}^1 r + S_m{}^2 r^2 + \ldots + S_m{}^m r^m \qquad (2.40)$$

These, the Stirling numbers of the first kind, are given in Appendix 1, Table 1, for m up to 12. The same coefficients are useful if derivatives or integrals of factorials are wanted, as the first step is then conversion to a power series.

In Example 2.1, we find easily, by means of (2.40), that

$$\sum_{r=0}^{n-1} p(r) = (2/5)n^5 - (9/4)n^4 + (1/2)n^3 + (45/4)n^2 - (79/10)n$$

Let us consider next the problem of finding central differences of a polynomial. It is natural to convert to central factorials, using an expansion of the form

$$r^m = t_m{}^1 r^{[1]} + t_m{}^2 r^{[2]} + \ldots + t_m{}^m r^{[m]} \qquad (2.41)$$

with its inverse

$$r^{[m]} = T_m{}^1 r + T_m{}^2 r^2 + \ldots + T_m{}^m r^m \qquad (2.42)$$

Though we have written mean factorials here, the same coefficients of course occur in the expansion of r^{m-1} in terms of $r^{\{j\}}$, and of $r^{\{m-1\}}$ in powers of r.

EXAMPLE 2.2. Find central differences of the polynomial

$$p(r) = 2r^4 - 5r^3 - 8r^2 + 17r + 2$$

tabulated for *integral* values of r.

For a reason which will soon be clear we shall use central factorials for odd powers, and mean central factorials for even powers. Using values of $t_m{}^j$ in Appendix 1, Table 4,

$$
\begin{aligned}
2r^4 &= 2r^{[4]} && + 2r^{[2]} \\
- 5r^3 &= && - 5r^{\{3\}} && - 5r^{\{1\}} \\
- 8r^2 &= && && - 8r^{[2]} \\
17r &= && && && 17r^{\{1\}}
\end{aligned}
$$

therefore

$$
\begin{aligned}
p(r) &= 2r^{[4]} - 5r^{\{3\}} - 6r^{[2]} + 12r + 2 \\
\delta p(r) &= 8r^{[3]} - 15r^{\{2\}} - 12r + 12 \\
\delta^2 p(r) &= 24r^{[2]} - 30r - 12 \\
\delta^3 p(r) &= 48r - 30 \\
\delta^4 p(r) &= 48
\end{aligned}
$$

We note that when $p > 0$,

$$0^{\{2p+1\}} = 0^{[2p]} = 0, \quad (\tfrac{1}{2})^{\{2p\}} = (\tfrac{1}{2})^{[2p+1]} = 0$$

and hence the required differences are

$$\delta p_{1/2} = 6, \quad \delta^2 p_0 = -12, \quad \delta^3 p_{1/2} = -6, \quad \delta^4 p_0 = 48$$

If $p(r)$ were tabulated for half integral values of r, the differences δp_0, $\delta^2 p_{1/2}$, etc., would be most easily obtained by using central factorials for even powers, and mean central factorials for odd powers.

2.8. Tabulating a Polynomial

A polynomial may be tabulated by direct evaluation for each value of the argument, but this is generally tedious and shortcuts are very desirable. If only a few values are wanted, Horner's method of division may be preferable to using tables of powers of r. This method depends on the fact that if $p(r)$ is divided by $(r - k)$, the remainder is necessarily $p(k)$, i.e.

$$p(r) = (r - k)q(r) + p(k)$$

The division is usually carried out omitting the powers of r, and writing only the coefficients, as follows—

$p(r)$	a_n	a_{n-1}	$a_{n-2} \ldots a_1$	a_0
		ka_n	$kb_{n-1} \ldots kb_2$	kb_1
$q(r)$	a_n	b_{n-1}	$b_{n-2} \ldots b_1$	$b_0 = p(k)$

Note that $b_{n-1} = a_{n-1} + ka_n$, $b_{n-2} = a_{n-2} + kb_{n-1}$, etc.

EXAMPLE 2.3.   Evaluate $p(\tfrac{1}{2})$, using the polynomial of Example 2.1.

The calculation is as follows—

2	-5	-8	17	2
	1	-2	-5	6
2	-4	-10	12	$8 = p(\tfrac{1}{2})$

This method of division can be used in converting polynomials to factorials, as suggested above. With a machine having a product transfer mechanism, the process is a continuous one, even for awkward values of r. Care must be taken, however, to avoid accumulation of error.

When a long table of the polynomial is needed at regular

intervals of r, it may be better to build up the function from differences. This is best illustrated by a numerical example.

EXAMPLE 2.4. Tabulate the polynomial of Example 2.1 for $r = 0(1)10$.

It is obvious from Example 2.1 that when $r = 0$, the leading differences of $p(r)$ are

$$\Delta^1_0 = 6, \quad \Delta^2_0 = -18, \quad \Delta^3_0 = 42, \quad \Delta^4_0 = 48$$

Hence we build up the following table from constant 4th differences.

r	$p(r)$				
0	2				
		6			
1	8		−18		
		−12		42	
2	−4		24		48
		12		90	
3	8		114		48
		126		138	
4	134		252		48
		378		186	
5	512		438		48
		816		234	
6	1328		672		48
		1488		282	
7	2816		954		48
		2442		330	
8	5258		1284		48
		3726		378	
9	8984		1662		
		5388			
10	14372				

Equally well a start might have been made with central differences using the information obtained in Example 2.2, though the method does not offer any marked advantage over the above, except perhaps when the table has to be extended to negative values of r. A few entries are given below to indicate how the building-up process is begun, the differences initially known being in heavy type.

r	$p(r)$				
−2	8				
		−24			
−1	−16		42		48
		18		−54	
0	2		−12		48
		6		−6	
1	8		−18		48
		−12			
2	−4				

The reader is at liberty to omit the remainder of this chapter for the time being, at least until the fitting of data by polynomials is discussed in Chapter 10.

2.9. Calculation of Descending and Ascending Factorial Moments

It is often necessary, particularly in statistical work, to calculate power moments. Thus, for a set of values u_0, u_1, . . ., u_n, the mth power moment about the point $r = 0$ is given by

$$M_m(0) = \sum_{r=0}^{n} r^m u_r$$

The moment about any other point, say $\bar{r}$, is obtained by replacing r^m by $(r - \bar{r})^m$, and may be denoted by $M_m(\bar{r})$. For convenience we continue to use the symbol r as in previous sections, but it must be remembered that in the present context the values of r are limited to integers.

To evaluate $M_m(0)$, an alternative to direct summation of the products $r^m u_r$ is the expansion of r^m in descending or ascending factorials, and calculation of the factorial moments

$$M^{(j)}(0) = \sum_{r=0}^{n} r^{(j)} u_r \quad \text{or} \quad {}^{(j)}M(0) = \sum_{r=0}^{n} {}^{(j)}r \cdot u_r$$

It follows from (2.39) that

$$M_m(0) = \sum_{j=1}^{m} s_m{}^j M^{(j)} \quad \text{or} \quad \sum_{j=1}^{m} |s_m{}^j| {}^{(j)}M \qquad (2.43)$$

A knowledge of all the factorial moments up to the mth is therefore sufficient to give all power moments up to the mth.

"Reduced" factorial moments are conveniently defined as

$$M_{(j)} = M^{(j)}/j! \quad \text{and} \quad {}_{(j)}M = {}^{(j)}M/j! \qquad (2.44)$$

The calculation of $M_{(j)}$ is achieved quite simply by repeated summation of the u_r's from the bottom of the table. Thus, adapting the general formula (2.10)

$$(-1)^{j+1}\Sigma^{j+1}u_k = \sum_{r=k+j+1}^{n} (r - k - 1)_{(j)} u_r$$

$$= M_{(j)}(k + 1)$$

and when $k = -1$

$$M_{(j)}(0) = (-1)^{j+1}\Sigma^{j+1}u_{-1} \qquad (2.45)$$

Note that u_0, . . ., u_{j-1} do not contribute to this moment because the multiplying factorial is zero.

When calculating moments with ascending factorials it is

preferable to begin the summation from the top of the table. If the given values are now represented by

$$u_{-n}, u_{-n+1}, \ldots, u_{-1}, u_0$$

formula (2.9) gives

$$\daleth^{j+1}u_k = \sum_{r=-n}^{k-j-1} (k - r - 1)_{(j)} u_r$$

subject to the condition

$$\daleth^{j+1}u_{-n+j+1} = u_{-n} \qquad\qquad \text{(cp. (2.3))}$$

In particular, when $k = 1$

$$\daleth^{j+1}u_1 = \sum_{r=-n}^{-j} (- r)_{(j)} u_r$$

and since the ascending factorial $_{(j)}r = (-1)^j(-r)_{(j)}$ the required moment

$$_{(j)}M(0) = (-1)^j \daleth^{j+1}u_1 \qquad\qquad (2.46)$$

Moments with descending factorials can also be calculated by summation from the top of the table, but this can be shown to involve more summation than with ascending factorials. If the ultimate end is to obtain power moments, it is immaterial whether ascending or descending factorials are used, and it is natural to choose the more economical.

The practical procedure is illustrated by the following examples.

EXAMPLE 2.5. Given

r	0	1	2	3	4	5
u_r	102	146	150	166	155	77

find descending factorial moments about $r = 0$.

					u_r	r
				− 796		
			1949		102	0
		− 2348		− 694		
	1556		1255		146	1
− 540		− 1093		− 548		
	463		707		150	2
− 77		− 386		− 398		
	77		309		166	3
		− 77		− 232		
			77		155	4
				− 77		
					77	5

By application of (2.45)

$$M_{(1)} = 1949 \qquad\qquad M^{(1)} = 1949$$
$$M_{(2)} = 2348 \qquad\qquad M^{(2)} = 4696$$
$$M_{(3)} = 1556 \qquad\qquad M^{(3)} = 9336$$
$$M_{(4)} = 540 \qquad\qquad M^{(4)} = 12960$$

In the above calculation the negative signs in odd sums have been retained to keep the structure of a difference table, but obviously they play no effective part, and the computer soon gets accustomed to omitting them (and may also alter the *shape* of the table to suit his convenience).

EXAMPLE 2.6. Given

r	-5	-4	-3	-2	-1	0
u_r	32	67	75	79	84	102

find ascending factorial moments about $r = 0$.

						u_r	r
						32	-5
					32		
				32		67	-4
			32		99		
		32		131		75	-3
	32		163		174		
32		195		305		79	-2
227		468		253			
	663		558		337	84	-1
		1026		895		102	0
					439		

Summing from the top of the table, and applying (2.46),

$$_{(1)}M = -895 \qquad {}^{(1)}M = -895$$
$$_{(2)}M = 1026 \qquad {}^{(2)}M = 2052$$
$$_{(3)}M = -663 \qquad {}^{(3)}M = -3978$$
$$_{(4)}M = 227 \qquad {}^{(4)}M = 5448$$

EXAMPLE 2.7. Derive the first four power moments about $r = 0$ of the data given in Examples 2.5 and 2.6.

Using the values of $s_m{}^j$ given in Appendix 1, Table 3, we find that

$$M_1 = M^{(1)} = {}^{(1)}M$$
$$M_2 = M^{(1)} + M^{(2)} = -{}^{(1)}M + {}^{(2)}M$$
$$M_3 = M^{(1)} + 3M^{(2)} + M^{(3)} = {}^{(1)}M - 3{}^{(2)}M + {}^{(3)}M$$
$$M_4 = M^{(1)} + 7M^{(2)} + 6M^{(3)} + M^{(4)} = -{}^{(1)}M + 7{}^{(2)}M$$
$$- 6{}^{(3)}M + {}^{(4)}M$$

Hence, combining the descending and ascending moments of Examples 2.5 and 2.6 respectively, we obtain the power moments for the complete set of data—

$$M_1 = 1949 - 895 = 1054$$
$$M_2 = (1949 + 895) + (4696 + 2052) = 9592$$
$$M_3 = (1949 - 895) + 3(4696 - 2052) + (9336 - 3978)$$
$$= 14344$$
$$M_4 = (1949 + 895) + 7(4696 + 2052) + 6(9336 + 3978)$$
$$+ (12960 + 5448)$$
$$= 148372$$

2.10. Central Factorial Moments

The calculation of central factorial moments differs little in practice from the process just described, although from the theoretical aspect it is slightly more complicated. As in the previous section we consider first summation from the bottom of the table, and then from the top.

SUMMATION FROM THE BOTTOM OF THE TABLE

To derive the formula for central moments it is desirable to express (2.10) in central notation. It becomes

$$(-1)^{j+1}\sigma^{j+1}u_{k+(j+1)/2} = \sum_{k+j+1}^{q} (r - k - \tfrac{1}{2}j - \tfrac{1}{2})_{\{j\}}u_r \quad (2.47)$$

where it is assumed that the final entry in the table is u_q. It is important now to distinguish odd and even values of j; at the same time we can pick out sums which represent moments about a mid-point of tabulation as well as about a tabular point, as the following analysis shows.

(a) $j = 2p + 1$

$$\left.\begin{array}{l} k = -(p+1), \ \sigma^{2p+2}u_0 = \sum_r r_{\{2p+1\}}u_r = M_{\{2p+1\}}(0) \\[2mm] k = -p \qquad , \ \sigma^{2p+2}u_1 = \sum_r (r-1)_{\{2p+1\}}u_r = M_{\{2p+1\}}(1) \end{array}\right\} \quad (2.48)$$

Taking means, and using (2.32),

$$\sigma^{2p+2}u_{1/2} = \sum_r (r - \tfrac{1}{2})_{[2p+1]}u_r = M_{[2p+1]}(\tfrac{1}{2}) \quad (2.49)$$

(b) $j = 2p$

$$\left.\begin{array}{l} k = -(p+1), \\[1mm] -\sigma^{2p+1}u_{-1/2} = \sum_r (r + \tfrac{1}{2})_{\{2p\}}u_r = M_{\{2p\}}(-\tfrac{1}{2}) \\[2mm] k = -p, \\[1mm] -\sigma^{2p+1}u_{1/2} = \sum_r (r - \tfrac{1}{2})_{\{2p\}}u_r = M_{\{2p\}}(\tfrac{1}{2}) \end{array}\right\} \quad (2.50)$$

Taking means,

$$-\sigma^{2p+1}u_0 = \sum_r r_{[2p]}u_r = M_{[2p]}(0) \quad (2.51)$$

In every case the summation for r may be assumed to run from 0 to q, though entries up to u_{p+1} or u_p do not in fact contribute because the factorial is zero.

SUMMATION FROM THE TOP OF THE TABLE

Conversion of (2.9) to central notation gives

$$(-1)^j \sigma^{j+1} u_{k-(j+1)/2} = \sum_{r=-q'}^{k-j-1} (r - k + \tfrac{1}{2}j + \tfrac{1}{2})_{\{j\}} u_r \quad (2.52)$$

the initial entry in the table now being $u_{-q'}$.

(a) $j = 2p + 1$

$$k = p + 1, \quad -\sigma^{2p+2} u_0 = \sum_r r_{\{2p+1\}} u_r = M_{\{2p+1\}}(0)$$

$$k = p + 2, \quad -\sigma^{2p+2} u_1 = \sum_r (r-1)_{\{2p+1\}} u_r = M_{\{2p+1\}}(1) \left.\right\} \quad (2.53)$$

Taking means,

$$-\sigma^{2p+2} u_{1/2} = \sum_r (r - \tfrac{1}{2})_{[2p+1]} u_r = M_{[2p+1]}(\tfrac{1}{2}) \quad (2.54)$$

(b) $j = 2p$

$$k = p \quad ,$$

$$\sigma^{2p+1} u_{-1/2} = \sum_r (r + \tfrac{1}{2})_{\{2p\}} u_r = M_{\{2p\}}(-\tfrac{1}{2})$$

$$k = p + 1,$$

$$\sigma^{2p+1} u_{1/2} = \sum_r (r - \tfrac{1}{2})_{\{2p\}} u_r = M_{\{2p\}}(\tfrac{1}{2}) \left.\right\} \quad (2.55)$$

Taking means,

$$\sigma^{2p+1} u_0 = \sum_r r_{[2p]} u_r = M_{[2p]}(0) \quad (2.56)$$

The summation for r now runs from $-q'$ to 0.

In practice the point $r = 0$ or $1/2$ usually lies in the middle of a table in which the entries run from $u_{-q'}$ to u_q, and it is necessary to combine the results of summation from top and bottom of the table. We therefore summarize the results of the above analysis accordingly, for the first four moments.

	Moment	$M_{\{1\}}$	$M_{[2]}$	$M_{\{3\}}$	$M_{[4]}$
Moments about $r = 0$	Sum from top	$-\sigma^2_0$	σ^3_0	$-\sigma^4_0$	σ^5_0
	Sum from bottom	σ^2_0	$-\sigma^3_0$	σ^4_0	$-\sigma^5_0$
	Moment	$M_{[1]}$	$M_{\{2\}}$	$M_{[3]}$	$M_{\{4\}}$
Moments about $r = 1/2$	Sum from top	$-\sigma^2_{1/2}$	$\sigma^3_{1/2}$	$-\sigma^4_{1/2}$	$\sigma^5_{1/2}$
	Sum from bottom	$\sigma^2_{1/2}$	$-\sigma^3_{1/2}$	$\sigma^4_{1/2}$	$-\sigma^5_{1/2}$

It will be observed how central and mean central moments always occur alternately, the mean moments being given by mean sums. In practice the negative signs associated with odd order sums from the bottom of the table can be ignored, just as for descending factorial moments. Examples 2.8–2.10 illustrate the use of the above table.

EXAMPLE 2.8. Calculate central factorial moments about $r = 0$ for the 11 values of u_r used in Examples 2.5 and 2.6.

We arrange the summation as follows; mean sums being given in brackets.

					u_r	r
				32	32	− 5
			32			
		32		99	67	− 4
	32		131			
32		163		174	75	− 3
	195		305			
227		468		253	79	− 2
	663		558			
890		1026		337	84	− 1
	1689		895			
(1734·5)		(1473·5)		(388)	102	0
·	·	·	·	·	·	·
(− 4048)	3904	(− 3322·5)	1949	(− 745)	102	0
− 2096		− 2348		− 694	146	1
	1556		1255			
− 540		− 1093		− 548	150	2
	463		707			
− 77		− 386		− 398	166	3
	77		309			
		− 77		− 232	155	4
			77	− 77	77	5

It follows that

$$M_{\{1\}} = 1949 - 895 = 1054$$
$$M_{[2]} = 3322{\cdot}5 + 1473{\cdot}5 = 4796$$
$$M_{\{3\}} = 3904 - 1689 = 2215$$
$$M_{[4]} = 4048 + 1734{\cdot}5 = 5782{\cdot}5$$

EXAMPLE 2.9. Derive the power moments of the same data about $r = 0$.

For this purpose we expand powers of r in terms of central and mean central factorials, to make use of the moments already obtained. We find by means of Appendix 1, Table 4, that

$$M_1 = M^{\{1\}} = M_{\{1\}}$$
$$M_2 = M^{[2]} = 2M_{[2]}$$
$$M_3 = M^{\{1\}} + M^{\{3\}} = M_{\{1\}} + 6M_{\{3\}}$$
$$M_4 = M^{[2]} + M^{[4]} = 2M_{[2]} + 24M_{[4]}$$

From the results of Example 2.8

$$M_1 = 1054 \qquad M_3 = 1054 + 13290 = 14344$$
$$M_2 = 9592 \qquad M_4 = 9592 + 138780 = 148372$$

This confirms the results of Example 2.7.

EXAMPLE 2.10. Calculate central moments about $r = \tfrac{1}{2}$ for the same data, omitting the value for $r = -5$.

When the number of entries in the table is even, the mean value of their arguments occurs at a mid-point of tabulation. If moments are wanted about this point, we proceed as in this example.

					u_r	r
					67	− 4
				67		
			67		75	− 3
		67		142		
	67		209		79	− 2
		276		221		
67	343		430		84	− 1
		706		305		
410	1049		735		102	0
1459		1441		407		
	(1769·5)		(938·5)			
· · ·	· · ·	· · ·	· · ·	· · ·	· · ·	· · ·
− 2096	(2730)	− 2348	(1602)	− 694		
	1556		1255		146	1
− 540		− 1093		− 548	150	2
	463		707		166	3
− 77		− 386		− 398		
	77		309		155	4
		− 77	77	− 232		
				− 77	77	5

$$M_{[1]}(\tfrac{1}{2}) = 1602 - 938{\cdot}5 = 663{\cdot}5$$
$$M_{\{2\}}(\tfrac{1}{2}) = 2348 + 1441 = 3789$$
$$M_{[3]}(\tfrac{1}{2}) = 2730 - 1769{\cdot}5 = 960{\cdot}5$$
$$M_{\{4\}}(\tfrac{1}{2}) = 2096 + 1459 = 3555$$

Power moments about $r = \tfrac{1}{2}$ can readily be derived using the coefficients of Appendix 1, Table 4 (m odd).

We conclude these illustrations of the use of factorials with the obvious remark that such methods of calculating power moments will appeal most to those possessing a simple or multi-register adding machine. With a calculator which multiplies, direct methods of evaluating moments may well be preferred.

EXERCISES 2

1. If $P(x) = a_0 x^n + a_1 x^{n-1} + \ldots + a_n = Q(x)(x - X) + P(X)$,

where $\quad Q(x) = b_0 x^{n-1} + b_1 x^{n-2} + \ldots + b_{n-1}$,

and $\quad\quad b_k = a_k + b_{k-1}X$, as in synthetic division,

show that

(i) if $b'_0 = b_0$ and $b'_k = b_k + b'_{k-1}X$, then $b'_{n-1} = P'(X)$;

(ii) if $b''_0 = b'_0$ and $b''_k = b'_k + b'_{k-1}X$, then $2b''_{n-2} = P''(X)$.

CHAPTER 3

LAGRANGIAN METHODS OF INTERPOLATION, DIFFERENTIATION AND INTEGRATION

The Problem of Interpolation

WHEN a function is tabulated for a finite number of values of the argument, either at regular or irregular intervals, and nothing further is known about it, the problem of finding its value at intermediate points is obviously insoluble. In fact *any* value could be inserted at such a point without contradiction. It follows that some hypothesis about its general behaviour must be made, if interpolation is to be possible, even approximately. First, little progress can be made unless the function is assumed to vary continuously, i.e. to make no sudden jumps, or indeed very rapid variations, between two given values. Secondly, it is desirable that the function should be one which can be replaced if necessary, with sufficient accuracy, by a mathematical function, or combination of functions, of simple form.

At this point we may recall well-known theorems, such as those of Weierstrass, which state that any function, continuous in a certain range of its argument, can be approximated to any desired accuracy either by a polynomial of *some* degree, or by a trigonometrical series containing a *finite* number of terms of the form sin nx, cos nx. Such theorems, however, though encouraging, hardly meet the present need, which is to ensure that the necessary accuracy is achieved if the function is represented by a polynomial of *acceptably low* degree (perhaps of the 8th, or 6th, or lower degree), or by a trigonometrical series with a *restricted* number of terms. At the same time it is very undesirable, and in fact unnecessary, to restrict the formal analysis to functions of a particular type, such as polynomials of a certain degree.

Let us therefore state as precisely as possible the assumption to be made in following chapters about any tabular function, denoted by $f(x)$. Unless the contrary is stated $f(x)$ means

"a real, single-valued function, continuous in a closed interval, say $a \leqslant x \leqslant b$, and possessing in this interval a continuous differential coefficient of a certain order $n + 1$."

69

It then follows, by the well-known expansion of Taylor, that

$$f(x) = f(a) + hf^{(1)}(a)$$
$$+ \frac{h^2}{2!} f^{(2)}(a) + \ldots + \frac{h^n}{n!} f^{(n)}(a) + R_{n+1} \qquad (3.1)$$

where $x = a + h$, and R_{n+1} is a remainder which can be expressed in various ways, including the differential form

$$R_{n+1} = \frac{h^{n+1}}{(n+1)!} f^{(n+1)}(\xi)$$

where ξ is some value of x between a and b; and the integral form

$$R_{n+1} = (1/n!) \int_a^x f^{(n+1)}(\xi)(x - \xi)^n d\xi$$

Since (3.1) does not introduce derivatives beyond the $(n + 1)$th it is unnecessary for these to exist. The main point to notice is that the terms preceding R_{n+1} constitute a polynomial in x of degree n, which can be regarded as an approximate form for $f(x)$ assuming that the remainder is small. If the variation of $f^{(n+1)}$ within the range (a, b) is known, then limits can be placed on the error which results from omitting the remainder; if it is not known, we may have good reasons, e.g. from the behaviour of the differences of the tabulated values of $f(x)$, for believing that R_{n+1} can be ignored.

Thus in the theory of interpolation, used in the wider sense which includes integration and differentiation of a function, the approximation by polynomials arises naturally, although it is by no means essential. It has obvious limitations, particularly if the function is to be approximated over a very large, perhaps infinite, range of x. However, when $f(x)$ is a known mathematical function there is probably little difficulty in assessing the error of interpolating by means of a polynomial, and, even when the table is the result of experimental work or statistical analysis, it is often reasonable to suppose that it represents a function which behaves in a regular way, and to which a polynomial is a good approximation. The field of application is therefore large.

In this volume it is not possible to deal adequately with the use of trigonometrical functions for interpolation. Some references to works dealing with this are given in § 10.11. We shall for the present, in the following two sections of this chapter, be concerned with various direct applications of polynomials, and in the last section some preliminary consideration is given to the errors involved in this type of approximation.

Lagrange's Interpolation Polynomial

Suppose the function $f(x)$ is specified for $(n + 1)$ distinct values of x; thus let the values of $f(x)$ corresponding to

$$x_0 \qquad x_1 \qquad x_2 \ldots x_n$$

be

$$f_0 \qquad f_1 \qquad f_2 \ldots f_n$$

$f(x_k)$ being written briefly as f_k. These values of x may or may not be in numerical sequence. Then it is possible to find a unique polynomial of degree not greater than n which assumes the value f_k when x has the value x_k, for each of the $(n + 1)$ values of k. Various forms can be found for this polynomial; one, which is associated with Lagrange, is

$$p_n(x) = L_0(x)f_0 + L_1(x)f_1 + L_2(x)f_2 + \ldots + L_n(x)f_n \quad (3.2)$$

where

$$L_k(x) = \frac{(x - x_0)(x - x_1) \ldots (x - x_{k-1})(x - x_{k+1}) \ldots (x - x_n)}{(x_k - x_0)(x_k - x_1) \ldots (x_k - x_{k-1})(x_k - x_{k+1}) \ldots (x_k - x_n)}$$

It will be seen that each of the given values of $f(x)$ is multiplied by a polynomial of degree n in x. In the numerator of $L_k(x)$, the factor $(x - x_k)$ is missing, and the denominator repeats the numerator except that x_k everywhere replaces x. Obviously, when $x = x_k$, $L_k = 1$ and all other L's are zero; hence $p_n(x_k) = f_k$. Thus (3.2) is a polynomial of degree certainly not greater than n (it may be less) with the required property, which it can be shown to share with no other polynomial of like degree.

It is often convenient to define

$$\phi(x) = (x - x_0)(x - x_1) \ldots (x - x_n)$$

and then an alternative expression for L_k is

$$L_k(x) = \phi(x)/\{(x - x_k)\phi^{(1)}(x_k)\} \quad (3.3)$$

where $\phi^{(1)}(x_k)$ represents the derivative of $\phi(x)$ when $x = x_k$.

Lagrange's formula for the interpolation polynomial is easily

seen to be equivalent to Euler's expression for the expansion of
$p_n(x)/\phi(x)$ in partial fractions, which is

$$p_n(x)/\phi(x) = \sum_{k=0}^{n} f_k/\{(x - x_k)\phi^{(1)}(x_k)\}$$

In general we shall write

$$f(x) = p_n(x) + R_{n+1}(x) \qquad (3.4)$$

so that $R_{n+1}(x)$ represents the remainder, or error remaining after
the function has been approximated to by a polynomial of the nth
degree. The efficacy of this approximation obviously depends on
the remainder being negligible, and this we shall for the time being
assume to be so.

3.1. Calculation of Lagrange's Polynomial

If we can assume that (3.2) is an adequate approximation to
$f(x)$, the problem of interpolation is the direct one of applying the
formula. Unless this is systematically done there is danger of error,
particularly in deriving the signs of the Lagrangian coefficients.
The following method is thought to be the most satisfactory.

As an illustration take a function specified at five points, in
numerical order x_0, x_1, x_2, x_3, x_4, the interpolate being required
at x between x_1 and x_2. First the quantity

$$N = |\phi(x)| = (x - x_0)(x - x_1)(x_2 - x)(x_3 - x)(x_4 - x)$$

is evaluated, and then this table prepared—

		Numerator	Denominator		
x_0	$x - x_0$	$N/(x - x_0)$	$(x_1 - x_0)(x_2 - x_0)(x_3 - x_0)(x_4 - x_0)$	$- \|L_0\|$	f_0
x_1	$x - x_1$	$N/(x - x_1)$	$(x_1 - x_0)(x_2 - x_1)(x_3 - x_1)(x_4 - x_1)$	$+ \|L_1\|$	f_1
x_2	$x_2 - x$	$N/(x_2 - x)$	$(x_2 - x_0)(x_2 - x_1)(x_3 - x_2)(x_4 - x_2)$	$+ \|L_2\|$	f_2
x_3	$x_3 - x$	$N/(x_3 - x)$	$(x_3 - x_0)(x_3 - x_1)(x_3 - x_2)(x_4 - x_3)$	$- \|L_3\|$	f_3
x_4	$x_4 - x$	$N/(x_4 - x)$	$(x_4 - x_0)(x_4 - x_1)(x_4 - x_2)(x_4 - x_3)$	$+ \|L_4\|$	f_4
				$\Sigma L_k = 1$	

Throughout the table (excluding the last column containing f_k)
all quantities are first specified regardless of signs. These are,
however, inserted in the column containing $|L_k|$ according to this
simple rule: a $+$ sign opposite the two arguments enclosing x,
then $-$ and $+$ signs alternately up and down the column. A

numerical check is made to confirm that $\Sigma L_k = 1$, and then $f(x)$ evaluated by the formula $f(x) = \Sigma L_k y_k$.

EXAMPLE 3.1. Estimate $f(x)$ when $x = 18$ from the following data—

x	10	16	20	22	30
$f(x)$	24647	93527	204487	289847	933527

x_k	$\lvert x - x_k \rvert$	Numerator	Denominator	L_k	f_k
10	8	192	$6 \times 10 \times 12 \times 20 = 14400$	$- \ 0{\cdot}013333$	24647
16	2	768	$6 \times 4 \times 6 \times 14 = 2016$	$+ \ 0{\cdot}380952$	93527
20	2	768	$10 \times 4 \times 2 \times 10 = 800$	$+ \ 0{\cdot}960000$	204487
22	4	384	$12 \times 6 \times 2 \times 8 = 1152$	$- \ 0{\cdot}333333$	289847
30	12	128	$20 \times 14 \times 10 \times 8 = 22400$	$+ \ 0{\cdot}005714$	933527

Sum $= 1{\cdot}000000$

$\lvert \phi \rvert = 1536$

Hence $$f(18) = \sum_0^4 L_k f_k = 140327$$

It is preferable to calculate the numerator of each L_k by division of $\phi(x)$ rather than by building up each set of products, as the number of operations is thereby reduced, particularly if n exceeds 3 and the values of x are less simple than in this example. If necessary, divisions can be avoided by using reciprocal tables for $1/(x - x_k)$ and multiplying.

3.2. Inverse Interpolation

Inverse interpolation may be described simply as the problem of finding the value of x corresponding to a specified value of $f(x)$, from a given set of data. Lagrange's polynomial may be used for this purpose if the roles of x and $f(x)$ are interchanged, i.e. we write the approximate equation

$$x = \Sigma L_k(p) x_k$$

where $$L_k(p) = \psi(p)/\{(p - f_k)\psi^{(1)}(f_k)\}$$
$$\psi(p) = (p - f_0)(p - f_1) \ldots (p - f_n)$$

The process is now one of direct interpolation for x. The method is not one to be especially recommended, particularly if the arguments x_k are regularly spaced, for then it replaces a function $f(x)$ tabulated at regular intervals of x by a function $x(p)$ tabulated at irregular intervals of p. To meet such cases there are methods simpler and more direct (see Chapter 5).

At this first consideration of inverse interpolation, we should mention some of the attendant dangers, particularly in methods which interchange the dependent and independent variables.

1. Although it has been stipulated that $f(x)$ should have one value only for a given x, it is possible that two or more values of x may correspond to the same value of $f(x)$. It is essential to restrict the range of x sufficiently to ensure that only one value of x corresponding to the given $f(x)$—and that the required value—is contained therein. To achieve this it may be necessary first to *interpolate* additional values of $f(x)$ in this region before proceeding with the inverse process.

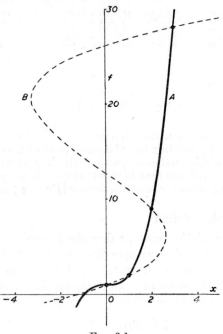

Fig. 3.1

2. It may be that $f(x)$ is well approximated by a polynomial in x, but the converse is not true. Anyone familiar with the reversion of series, which is essentially what is being attempted here, will appreciate the limitations imposed by polynomials of low degree. This point is further brought home by the example illustrated in Fig. 3.1 and based on the following information—

x	0	1	2	3
f	1	2	9	28

These values are in fact consistent with the polynomial relation

$$f = p = 1 + x^3 \qquad (A)$$

but x can also be represented by a Lagrange polynomial in powers of f, which has the approximate form

$$x = 0 \cdot 0038397 f^3 - 0 \cdot 15322 f^2 + 1 \cdot 43278 f - 1 \cdot 2834 \qquad (B)$$

Visual comparison of these two cubics makes it clear what different results can be obtained by direct and by inverse interpolation with polynomials; this example, though a little extreme because of the dominance of the cubic terms, is by no means unlikely. Such divergence of result should not be surprising, in view of the multitude of simple curves which can be made to pass through 4 points, but at the moment we wish to emphasize one reason for this uncertainty, which is that we have not as yet evolved any *guiding principle* by which to pick and choose between different representations in the absence of detailed information about the function tabulated. Without such knowledge in the above example we have no cause to prefer (A) to (B), and this uncertainty is not lessened by considering that the given data are equally consistent with the family of quartic polynomials

$$f = 1 + x^3 + Cx(x - 1)(x - 2)(x - 3)$$

where C is arbitrary.

With these cautionary remarks in mind, we pursue the application of Lagrange polynomials to a further stage.

3.3. Polynomials Using a Constant Interval

When the arguments of a tabular function are regularly spaced some simplification of the Lagrange coefficients is obviously possible. As in the previous chapter, it is an advantage to use the variable r, defined by $x = x_0 + rw$, instead of x, and the function $u(r)$, tabulated at unit intervals in r, instead of $f(x)$.

(a) Let us consider first the Lagrange polynomial through the $(n + 1)$ points corresponding to $x_0, x_1, \ldots, x_n$ or $r = 0, 1, \ldots, n$. The polynomial in (3.4) then becomes

$$p_n = \sum_{k=0}^{n} L_k(r) u_k \qquad (3.5)$$

where

$$L_k(r) = \frac{r(r - 1) \ldots (r - k + 1)}{k(k - 1) \ldots (1)} \cdot \frac{(r - k - 1) \ldots (r - n)}{(-1) \ldots -(n - k)}$$

In terms of descending factorials

$$L_k(r) = r_{(k)}(n - r)_{(n-k)} \qquad (3.6)$$

(b) An alternative expression is obtained by taking the $(n + 1)$ points to correspond to the values $r = -q + 1, -q + 2, \ldots, 0, \ldots, q$ where $2q = n + 1$. We can then write

$$p_n = \sum_{p=-q+1}^{q} L_p(r) u_p \qquad (3.7)$$

where

$$L_p(r) = \frac{(r + q - 1) \ldots (r - p + 1)}{(p + q - 1) \ldots (1)} \cdot \frac{(r - p - 1) \ldots (r - q)}{(-1) \ldots (p - q)}$$

$$= (r + q - 1)_{(p+q-1)} \cdot (q - r)_{(q-p)} \qquad (3.8)$$

(c) Yet another form is obtained if the polynomial is assumed to pass through the points corresponding to the values $r = -q, \ldots, 0, \ldots, q$. This time $n = 2q$, and

$$p_n = \sum_{p=-q}^{q} L_p(r) u_p \qquad (3.9)$$

where

$$L_p(r) = \frac{(r + q) \ldots (r - p + 1)}{(p + q) \ldots (1)} \cdot \frac{(r - p - 1) \ldots (r - q)}{(-1) \ldots (p - q)}$$

$$= (r + q)_{(p+q)} \cdot (q - r)_{(q-p)} \qquad (3.10)$$

The differences between these three forms for the same polynomial are quite trivial, arising solely from changes in the origin chosen for r; it will be seen that in (b) the tabular points are symmetrically placed about $r = 1/2$, and in (c) about $r = 0$. However, it is convenient to have the three expressions, for a reason which is discussed in the following section dealing with their application to the interpolation of a function tabulated at constant intervals.

3.4. Interpolation

One consequence of constant intervals is that it becomes practicable to tabulate Lagrange coefficients (as functions of r) for cases of frequent application. At first sight it might be considered necessary to tabulate L_k as given by (3.6) for various values of n, and for $0 < r < n$. But in making an interpolation it is usually advantageous to use tabular values of the function symmetrically placed about the interval containing the interpolate. This condition is met for instance in (3.7), if it be understood that the interpolated argument lies between 0 and 1; and it is then necessary to tabulate L_p as given by (3.8) for $0 < r < 1$

only. Or, if an odd number of values from the table is preferred, we can use (3.9), with L_p given by (3.10) and tabulated for $-1/2 < r < 1/2$. Only towards the beginning and end of a table will it be necessary to revert to (3.5) and (3.6), with values of r or $(n - r)$ which may sometimes exceed 2 or 3 if circumstances require it.

The Lagrangian interpolation formulas most commonly used, however, are of the symmetrical type, either requiring $2q$ values, e.g. 4-point, 6-point, etc., formulas, or requiring $(2q + 1)$ values, e.g. 5-point, 7-point, etc., formulas. Such formulas are very simply applied with the aid of a calculating machine.

Two formulas only will be quoted here, and these because of the very frequent need for "half-way" interpolation. They are the 4- and 6-point formulas—

$$u(\tfrac{1}{2}) = (1/16)(- u_{-1} + 9u_0 + 9u_1 - u_2) \qquad (3.11)$$

$$u(\tfrac{1}{2}) = (1/256)(3u_{-2} - 25u_{-1} + 150u_0 + 150u_1 - 25u_2 + 3u_3) \qquad (3.12)$$

The following tables of Lagrange coefficients may be found useful—

I.A.T. (1948 edition)	4-pt. formula, $r = 0(0\cdot01)$ 1
Chambers [6]	4-, 6-pt. formulas, $r = 0(0\cdot01)$ 1
NBS tables (Lagrangian coefficients)	3-, 4-pt. formulas, $r = 0(0\cdot0001)$ 1 5- to 8-pt. formulas, $r = 0(0\cdot001)$ 1 and at various intervals for $r > 1$.

Some tables of coefficients for end-of-table interpolation are to be found in the literature.

A method of avoiding interpolation in the tabulated Lagrange coefficients themselves, when the interval in r is too large, is described in Chambers [6] (Vol. 2, p. 542).

3.5. Differentiation

Differentiation of the Lagrange polynomial, whether for points equally spaced in argument or otherwise, is straightforward, and provides approximate derivatives of the function represented, either at the tabular points or intermediate points. The general formula for the mth derivative is

$$d^m f/dx^m = (1/w^m)d^m u/dr^m \simeq (1/w^m)\sum_k (d^m L_k/dr^m)u_k \qquad (3.13)$$

where the summation over k may correspond to (3.6), (3.8) or (3.10), and remainder terms are omitted.

Tabular Points. The need often arises for derivatives to be evaluated at the tabular points, and it is then sufficient to insert the appropriate integral value of r in the coefficient of each in (3.13); thus in using the symmetrical type of polynomial (3.9), one would make r zero to obtain derivatives at x_0.

At the beginning of a table it may be necessary to use (3.5) with L_k given by (3.6).

Mid-points. If derivatives are needed midway between tabular points, it is possible to use (3.5) with half-integral values of r, or preferably (3.7) with $r = 1/2$.

A selection of Lagrangian formulas for derivatives is given in Appendix 3.

Integration

The integral of a tabulated function over any required range of the argument is given approximately by the integral of the corresponding Lagrange polynomial. Thus from (3.2) and (3.3) we obtain

$$\int_a^b p_n(x)dx = \sum_{k=0}^n H_k f_k \qquad (3.14)$$

where $\quad H_k = \int_a^b L_k dx = \{1/\phi^{(1)}(x_k)\} \int_a^b \{\phi(x)/(x - x_k)\}dx \qquad (3.15)$

Any integral obtained in this way is a linear combination of the specified values f_k.

Integral formulas of the Lagrange type can be broadly classified in three groups—

1. *Closed-type Formulas.* The limits of the integral are taken to coincide with x_0, x_n, the extreme arguments of the function values used in the formula. Such formulas are particularly suited to quadrature.

2. *Open-type Formulas.* The limits of integration are taken *outside* the range (x_0, x_n) of the data, so that the integrand is extrapolated beyond this range, at one or both ends, by means of the polynomial. This has a special application in the solution of differential equations, though the accuracy is generally less than for a closed-type formula.

3. *Partial Range Formulas.* One or both of the limits of integration are *within* the range of the data, so that knowledge of the integrand outside the range of the integral is used in its evaluation. This normally provides greater accuracy than a closed-type formula.

When the tabular values of $f(x)$ are irregularly spaced, the coefficients H_k must be evaluated according to the needs of the particular problem, and little further can be usefully added here. For constant intervals, however, there are many simple and useful results which we shall describe in accordance with the above classification—their accuracy will be discussed in sections 3.10–3.14.*

3.6. Closed-type Formulas

When $f(x)$ is specified for $x_0, x_1, \ldots, x_n$, these values being at a constant interval w, then in the constant interval notation

$$\int_{x_0}^{x_n} f(x)dx = w \int_0^n u(r)dr = w \sum_{k=0}^n h_k u_k \qquad (3.16)$$

where, according to (3.6),

$$h_k = \int_0^n L_k(r)dr = \int_0^n r_{(k)}(n-r)_{(n-k)}dr \qquad (3.17)$$

The coefficients in (3.16) thus depend only on n and k. The formula corresponding to a subdivision of the range of integration into n equal intervals is usually known as the Newton-Cotes formula of order n.† When $n = 2$, we obtain the familiar and extremely useful formula known as *Simpson's rule*.

Thus
$$h_0 = (1/2)\int_0^2 (2-r)(1-r)dr = 1/3$$

$$h_1 = \int_0^2 r(2-r)dr = 4/3$$

$$h_2 = (1/2)\int_0^2 r(r-1)dr = 1/3$$

and hence
$$\int_0^2 u(r)dr \simeq (1/3)(u_0 + 4u_1 + u_2) \qquad (3.18)$$

* However, H. O. Hartley, in *Proc. Camb. Phil. Soc.*, **48**, (1952), 436, has shown that when the distances between successive arguments do not alter too abruptly it may be practicable to apply a transformation $x = \phi(t)$, where ϕ is a polynomial, such that the given arguments x_j correspond to integer values of t.

Then
$$\int_a^b f(x)dx = \int_0^n f\{\phi(t)\}\phi^{(1)}(t)dt \simeq \sum_{k=0}^n h_k \phi_k^{(1)} f_k$$

where h_k are the Newton-Cotes coefficients depending only on n and k, and the quantities $\phi_k^{(1)}$ are simple linear combinations of the x_j's. Hartley has given tables to facilitate this method of quadrature when $n \leqslant 10$ (see also Exercises 3, No. 2).

† First derived by Newton in 1676, and later by Cotes in 1722.

This corresponds of course to passing a parabola through the three points.

The formulas corresponding to 3, 4 and 6 intervals are as follows—

$$\int_0^3 u(r)dr \simeq (3/8)(u_0 + 3u_1 + 3u_2 + u_3)$$
$$\text{(Simpson's three-eighth's rule)} \qquad (3.19)$$

$$\int_0^4 u(r)dr \simeq (2/45)(7u_0 + 32u_1 + 12u_2 + 32u_3 + 7u_4)$$
$$\text{(Boole's rule)} \qquad (3.20)$$

$$\int_0^6 u(r)dr \simeq (1/140)(41u_0 + 216u_1 + 27u_2 + 272u_3$$
$$+ 27u_4 + 216u_5 + 41u_6) \qquad (3.21)$$

The last of these has cumbersome coefficients for practical purposes, but a much simpler formula of the same kind, and only slightly inferior in accuracy, is *Weddle's rule*—

$$\int_0^6 u(r)dr \simeq (3/10)(u_0 + 5u_1 + u_2 + 6u_3 + u_4 + 5u_5 + u_6) \quad (3.22)$$

(See Exercises 5, No. 4 (*b*).)

3.7. Quadrature by Newton-Cotes Formulas

The principal application of Newton-Cotes formulas is in numerical quadrature, i.e. the direct evaluation of integrals in which the integrand is a known mathematical function or is tabulated. When the range of integration is extensive it is of course possible to subdivide it so that the chosen formula can be applied several times, the coefficients of the u's being adjusted accordingly. Thus repeated application of Simpson's rule over a range of $2n$ intervals gives

$$\int_0^{2n} u(r)dr \simeq (1/3)\{u_0 + 4(u_1 + u_3 + \ldots + u_{2n-3} + u_{2n-1})$$
$$+ 2(u_2 + u_4 + \ldots + u_{2n-4} + u_{2n-2}) + u_{2n}\} \quad (3.23)$$

In this connexion the *trapezoidal rule* should be mentioned; this may be called the Newton-Cotes formula of the first order, and it gives on repetition

$$\int_0^n u(r)dr \simeq \tfrac{1}{2}u_0 + u_1 + \ldots + u_{n-1} + \tfrac{1}{2}u_n \qquad (3.24)$$

It is of course inferior to (3.23).

As numerical illustrations we shall take several simple mathematical functions, so that comparison with analytical results is possible. The chosen integrals are

$$(a) \int_0^{1 \cdot 2} \sin x dx \qquad (b) \int_0^{1 \cdot 2} e^x dx$$

$$(c) \int_{0 \cdot 2}^{1 \cdot 4} \log_e x dx \qquad (d) \int_0^{1 \cdot 2} dx/(1 + x^2)$$

In each of these an interval of 0·1 in x is adopted, since 12 intervals provide a convenient comparison of the various formulas. We can apply Simpson's rule 6 times, the three-eighths rule 4 times, Boole's rule 3 times and Weddle's rule twice. The following table contains the data used in these calculations.

TABLE 3.1

x	$\sin x$	e^x	$\log x$	$1/(1 + x^2)$
0·0	0·000 000	1·000 000		1·0000 0000
0·1	0·099 833	1·105 171		0·9900 9901
0·2	0·198 669	1·221 403	− 1·609 438	0·9615 3846
0·3	0·295 520	1·349 859	− 1·203 973	0·9174 3119
0·4	0·389 418	1·491 825	− 0·916 291	0·8620 6900
0·5	0·479 426	1·648 721	− 0·693 147	0·8000 0000
0·6	0·564 642	1·822 119	− 0·510 826	0·7352 9412
0·7	0·644 218	2·013 753	− 0·356 675	0·6711 4094
0·8	0·717 356	2·225 541	− 0·223 143	0·6097 5610
0·9	0·783 327	2·459 603	− 0·105 360	0·5524 8619
1·0	0·841 471	2·718 282	− 0·000 000	0·5000 0000
1·1	0·891 207	3·004 166	+ 0·095 310	0·4524 8869
1·2	0·932 039	3·320 117	0·182 322	0·4098 3607
1·3			0·262 364	
1·4			0·336 472	

Details of the computations need not be given, and in Table 3.2 we merely state the results, giving in each case one decimal more than is used in the integrand.

The correction required to give the exact result (to the same number of decimals) is shown in line (a) under each value. The results are in error from two sources: (1) rounding off the tabular values, (2) the polynomial approximation. Since rounding-off errors may be assumed to be random, they tend to cancel in the summation process, and their net contribution can reasonably be expected not to exceed 2 or 3 units of the last decimal retained above, remembering that $w = 0·1$. This justifies the retention of an additional decimal. Errors in excess of this may fairly be ascribed to the approximation involved in the formula.

TABLE 3.2

	$\int_0^{1\cdot2} \sin x\,dx$	$\int_0^{1\cdot2} e^x dx$	$\int_{0\cdot2}^{1\cdot4} \log x\,dx$	$\int_0^{1\cdot2} \dfrac{dx}{1+x^2}$
Exact	0·6376 422	2·3201 169	− 0·4070 513	0·87605 8051
Trapezoidal	0·6371 107	2·3220 501	− 0·4105 902	0·87572 2174
(a)	+ 5 315	− 19 332	+ 35 389	+ 33 5877
(b)	(+ 5 32)	(− 19 334)	(+ 35 710)	(+ 33 59)
Simpson	0·6376 425	2·3201 183	− 0·4071 589	0·87605 7850
(a)	− 3	− 14	+ 1 076	+ 199
(b)	(− 3)	(− 13)	(+ 1 390)	(+ 199)
Three-eighths	0·6376 429	2·3201 199	− 0·4072 591	0·87605 7588
(a)	− 7	− 30	+ 2 078	+ 463
(b)	(− 8)	(− 29)	(+ 3 120)	(+ 447)
Boole	0·6376 422	2·3201 170	− 0·4070 892	0·87605 8078
(a)	0	− 1	+ 379	− 27
(b)	(0)	(0)	(+ 1 590)	(− 15)
Weddle	0·6376 422	2·3201 170	− 0·4070 787	0·87605 8060
(a)	0	− 1	+ 274	− 9
(b)	(0)	(0)	(+ 1 340)	(− 9)

(a) Actual defects.
(b) Defects estimated from the approximate formula (3.38).

In each example the trapezoidal rule gives a comparatively large error, and can clearly be ruled out for practical purposes except where crude results are sufficient. In each example, too, the three-eighths rule is less accurate than Simpson (for a reason to be disclosed in § 3.12), and Weddle's rule is on balance the most accurate.

Thus, on empirical grounds alone, we should be justified in using Simpson's rule for its simplicity whenever the accuracy involved is adequate; and if greater accuracy is needed, Weddle's rule is preferred to that of Boole, both for simplicity and accuracy. The three-eighths rule can be ignored (in common with other Newton-Cotes formulas of odd order).

3.8. Open-range Formulas of Steffensen

If the polynomial (3.5) is integrated between $x_0 - w$ and $x_0 + (n + 1)w$ instead of between x_0 and x_n, for different values of n, a group of formulas of open type is obtained, given in the first instance by Steffensen. A convenient example is that for $n = 2$, when the range of integration covers 4 intervals, and

$$h_0 = (1/2)\int_{-1}^{3} (2 - r)(1 - r)dr = 8/3$$

$$h_1 = \int_{-1}^{3} r(2 - r)dr = -4/3$$

$$h_2 = (1/2)\int_{-1}^{3} r(r - 1)dr = 8/3$$

Hence $$\int_{-1}^{3} u(r)dr \simeq (4/3)(2u_0 - u_1 + 2u_2) \qquad (3.25)$$

This is known as *Milne's formula*, and actually has the accuracy of a cubic approximation, not quadratic as would appear. Thus if a cubic is assumed to pass through the points corresponding to $r = -1, 0, 1, 2$, its integral is independent of u_{-1} and again leads to (3.25).

A selection of Steffensen and other open-range formulas is given in Appendix 3. They may be used for quadrature in the same way as Newton-Cotes formulas, but they have a further application which is deferred to a later chapter.

3.9. Partial-range Formulas

The diversity of partial-range formulas is immense, and they are usually devised to meet special circumstances, making best use of available data. A selection is given in Appendix 3.

The Accuracy of Lagrangian Formulas

It has been emphasized already that the results of treating a function which is not a polynomial as if it were, or indeed of treating a polynomial as if it were a polynomial of lesser degree, must not be accepted too readily. We shall now show that it is possible to obtain an analytical expression for the error of the polynomial approximation used in any Lagrangian formula, whether for interpolation, differentiation or integration. Thus whenever a mathematical form can be given to the function concerned, the error of the calculation can usually be defined within certain limits.

3.10. Error of Interpolation

The case of unequally spaced arguments shall be considered first, and for this we introduce a function $g(X)$, defined by

$$g(X) = f(X) - p_n(X) - \phi(X)\{f(x) - p_n(x)\}/\phi(x) \quad (3.26)$$

where the functions f, p_n and ϕ have the significance attached to them hitherto; and it is also assumed that $f(x)$ and all its derivatives, up to the $(n + 1)$th inclusive, exist and are continuous in the range of the argument which includes x, x_0, . . ., x_n. The same is necessarily true of $g(X)$. We observe that $g(X)$ is zero when X has any one of these $(n + 2)$ values, and therefore, the conditions of Rolle's theorem* being met, it follows that the first derivative of $g(X)$ vanishes at least $(n + 1)$ times in the same range of X. Similarly $g^{(2)}(X)$ vanishes at least n times, and finally $g^{(n+1)}(X)$ vanishes for at least one value of X, which we can denote by ξ.

Now $p_n(X)$ and $\phi(X)$ are polynomials in which the terms with the highest powers of X are X^n and X^{n+1} respectively; therefore

$$p_n{}^{(n+1)}(X) = 0, \quad \phi^{(n+1)}(X) = (n + 1)!$$

and $\quad g^{(n+1)}(X) = f^{(n+1)}(X) - (n + 1)!\{f(x) - p_n(x)\}/\phi(x)$

Hence, when $X = \xi$,

$$R_{n+1}(x) = f(x) - p_n(x) = \{\phi(x)/(n + 1)!\}f^{(n+1)}(\xi) \quad (3.27)$$

This is the error of representing $f(x)$ by the polynomial p_n. When all the values x_0, . . ., x_n coincide and are equal to a, (3.27) reduces to the differential form of the remainder in Taylor's expansion (3.1).

When the arguments are at equal intervals, the remainder belonging to the polynomial (3.5) is easily derived from (3.27) and takes the form

$$R_{n+1} = r_{(n+1)}u^{(n+1)}(\rho) \quad (3.28)$$

where ρ lies within the shortest range which includes 0, n and the argument r.

Likewise for the polynomials (3.7) and (3.9)

$$R_{2q} = (r - \tfrac{1}{2})_{\{2q\}}u^{(2q)}(\rho) \quad (3.29)$$

$$R_{2q+1} = r_{\{2q+1\}}u^{(2q+1)}(\rho) \quad (3.30)$$

---

* *Rolle's theorem.* If $f(x)$ vanishes when $x = a$, b, is continuous when $a \leqslant x \leqslant b$, and differentiable when $a < x < b$, then it is possible to find at least one value ξ, where $a < \xi < b$, such that $f'(\xi) = 0$.

3.11. Error of Differentiation

The error of a polynomial approximation to $f^{(1)}(x)$ at a tabular point, say x_0, is obtained easily by using the definition

$$f^{(1)}(x_0) = \lim_{x \to x_0} \frac{f(x) - f(x_0)}{x - x_0}$$

With unequal intervals, the remainder (3.27) then gives, for the first derivative,

$$R_{n+1} = \lim \frac{\phi(x)}{x - x_0} \times \frac{f^{(n+1)}(\xi)}{(n+1)!}$$

$$= \{(-1)^n x_1 x_2 \ldots x_n/(n+1)!\} f^{(n+1)}(\xi) \tag{3.31}$$

With equal intervals, the corresponding error in $u^{(1)}(0)$ is

$$R_{n+1} = \{(-1)^n/(n+1)\} u^{(n+1)}(\rho) \tag{3.32}$$

There is no difficulty in deriving expressions for the error of the first derivative obtained from (3.7) or (3.9); thus from (3.9) the error in $u^{(1)}(0)$ is

$$R_{2q+1} = \{(-1)^q (q!)^2/(2q+1)!\} u^{(2q+1)}(\rho) \tag{3.33}$$

A general expression can be obtained for the error in the mth derivative. It must be remembered that we cannot get far by using (3.27), because ξ depends on the interpolated argument x in a way which is not known; $f^{(n+1)}(\xi)$ is implicitly a function of x, and this must be allowed for in differentiating or integrating $R_{n+1}(x)$.

3.12. Error of Integration

We should next consider the errors of some of the simpler integral formulas given in § 3.6 and § 3.8, and this is conveniently done in the first instance by a simple application of the Maclaurin series expansion for $u(r)$, which is

$$u(r) = u_0 + r u^{(1)}{}_0 + (r^2/2!) u^{(2)}{}_0 + (r^3/3!) u^{(3)}{}_0 + \ldots$$

We assume temporarily that $u(r)$ possesses continuous derivatives of any order.

The method is made quite clear by applying it to Simpson's rule in the form

$$\int_{-1}^{1} u(r) dr = (1/3)(u_{-1} + 4u_0 + u_1) + R$$

R being the required correction. For the left side of this equation we have from Maclaurin's series,

$$2\{u_0 + (1/3\,!)u^{(2)}{}_0 + (1/5\,!)u^{(4)}{}_0 + (1/7\,!)u^{(6)}{}_0 + \ldots\}$$

as the odd terms vanish on integration.

Moreover

$$u_{-1} = u_0 - u^{(1)}{}_0 + (1/2\,!)u^{(2)}{}_0 - (1/3\,!)u^{(3)}{}_0 + (1/4\,!)u^{(4)}{}_0 - \cdots$$
$$u_0 = u_0$$
$$u_1 = u_0 + u^{(1)}{}_0 + (1/2\,!)u^{(2)}{}_0 + (1/3\,!)u^{(3)}{}_0 + (1/4\,!)u^{(4)}{}_0 + \cdots$$

and therefore

$$\tfrac{1}{3}(u_{-1} + 4u_0 + u_1)$$
$$= 2\left\{u_0 + \frac{1}{3\,.\,2!}\,u^{(2)}{}_0 + \frac{1}{3\,.\,4!}\,u^{(4)}{}_0 + \frac{1}{3\,.\,6!}\,u^{(6)}{}_0 + \cdots\right\}$$

We thus obtain for the correction

$$R = -\,(1/90)\{u^{(4)}{}_0 + (1/21)u^{(6)}{}_0 + (1/1008)u^{(8)}{}_0 + \ldots\} \quad (3.34)$$

The important term in this expression is the first. By a more elaborate argument (e.g. Steffensen, p. 155), not involving the existence of derivatives of $u(r)$ beyond the fourth, it can be shown that

$$R = -\,(1/90)u^{(4)}(\rho)$$

where ρ is some value of r within the limits of integration. It follows that the error of Simpson's rule applied to the integral

$$\int_{x_0}^{x_0+2w} f(x)dx \quad \text{is} \quad -\,(w^5/90)f^{(4)}(\xi) \quad (3.35)$$

Similar treatment of other formulas for integrals of the type $\int_{x_0}^{x_0+nw} f(x)dx$ gives the following expressions for their correction terms—

Trapezoidal rule ($n = 1$)
  correction $= -\,(w^3/12)f^{(2)}(\xi)$

Three-eighths rule ($n = 3$)
  correction $= -\,(3w^5/80)f^{(4)}(\xi)$

Boole's rule $(n = 4)$

correction $= - (8w^7/945)f^{(6)}(\xi)$

Newton-Cotes rule $(n = 6)$

correction $= - (9w^9/1400)f^{(8)}(\xi)$

Weddle's rule $(n = 6)$

correction $= - (w^7/140)\{f^{(6)}(\xi_1) + 0{\cdot}9w^2f^{(8)}(\xi_2)\}$

and Milne's rule $(n = 4)$

correction $= + (14w^5/45)f^{(4)}(\xi)$

The numerical coefficient in each case can be obtained by using Maclaurin's series as above; ξ always lies within the limits of the integral.

It will be observed that, *for a given value of w*, the errors of Simpson's one-third and three-eighths rules are the same in form, but with coefficients in the ratio of 8:27. This is a compelling reason for the disregard which should be given to the three-eighths rule; and for the same reason other Newton-Cotes formulas using an odd number of intervals are properly ignored. Boole's rule is only slightly inferior to Weddle's, assuming that $f^{(8)}$ does not contribute a large portion of the error. We have therefore some justification for the empirical conclusion of § 3.7.

It is also interesting to compare the rules of Simpson and Milne, both "3-point" formulas, applied to the integral between x_0 and $x_0 + 2w$. In such a case, Milne's formula is used with an interval $w/2$, and the coefficients of the two corrections are in the ratio 8:7, i.e. slightly in favour of Milne's formula.* However, for repeated use over a wide range of the argument, Simpson's rule is normally more convenient. Alternative forms for the error of Simpson's rule will be given in Chapter 5.

3.13. Estimation of Quadrature Error, Using a 'Repeated' Formula

Although the expressions which have just been given for the errors of various formulas for interpolation, etc., are valuable as a guide to the *order of magnitude* of the error, their advantage is often illusory when a closer estimate of the *actual error* of a particular calculation is wanted. This is because the derivative which

---

* This advantage of the open-type formula over the closed-type does not persist for formulas of higher order.

occurs in the expression for the error may lie between wide numerical limits, and often the upper limit grossly overestimates the actual error.

There is one type of calculation in which a closer estimate of the actual error may be obtained, and this is when a simple integral formula is used repeatedly to cover an extended range of the argument, as in (3.23) or (3.24). Thus suppose Simpson's rule is applied m times, the integral extending over $2m$ intervals. The total error of the value of the integral so obtained may be written as

$$R_t = -\ (w^4/180)\{2wf^{(4)}(\xi_1) + 2wf^{(4)}(\xi_2) + \ldots + 2wf^{(4)}(\xi_m)\}$$

(3.36)

where each of the ξ's is restricted to a pair of intervals, i.e.

$$x_0 \leqslant \xi_1 \leqslant x_0 + 2w \leqslant \xi_2 \leqslant x_0 + 4w, \text{ etc.}$$

Now the sum in brackets can be replaced approximately by

$$\int_a^b f^{(4)}(x)dx \quad \text{or} \quad f^{(3)}(b) - f^{(3)}(a)$$

if we write a, b for x_0, $x_0 + 2mw$ respectively; so

$$R_t = -\ (w^4/180)\{f^{(3)}(b) - f^{(3)}(a)\} \text{ approximately} \qquad (3.37)$$

This result for Simpson's rule was given by Chevilliet.[*]

The same argument applied to a formula using n intervals and in which the error of a single application is $Cw^{k+2}f^{(k+1)}(\xi)$ gives

$$R_t = (Cw^{k+1}/n)\{f^{(k)}(b) - f^{(k)}(a)\} \qquad (3.38)$$

In particular we obtain for various rules—

Trapezoidal: $\quad R_t \simeq -\ (w^2/12)\{f^{(1)}(b) - f^{(1)}(a)\}$

Three-eighths: $\quad R_t \simeq -\ (w^4/80)\{f^{(3)}(b) - f^{(3)}(a)\}$

Boole: $\quad R_t \simeq -\ (2w^6/945)\{f^{(5)}(b) - f^{(5)}(a)\}$

Weddle: $\quad R_t \simeq -\ (w^6/840)\{f^{(5)}(b) - f^{(5)}(a)$
$$+\ 0 \cdot 9w^2(f^{(7)}(b) - f^{(7)}(a))\}$$

As an application of these results to the direct estimate of errors, we consider the integrals evaluated in § 3.7. The numerical values can be seen by referring again to Table 3.2, which contains

[*] *Comptes Rendus*, **78** (1874), p. 1841.

both estimated and actual defects for each integral, and which shows that Chevilliet's formula gives excellent estimates of the defect associated with the first three rules. It is much less convincing, for the integrals under consideration, when applied to Boole and Weddle, mainly because the conditions for replacing the sum in (3.36) by an integral are barely satisfied, the sums containing only 3 and 2 terms respectively. This difficulty is aggravated in integral (c), where the higher derivatives are varying very rapidly at the beginning of the range, and, if a correction were made based on the estimated error, the more powerful formulas would actually give progressively worse results. The real trouble here is that the interval of 0·1 is too great near the lower limit.

In general, however, estimates based on (3.38) show up very favourably when compared with the uncertain results of using (3.35) and similar expressions alone. For example, the defect of integral (c) given by Boole, might be anywhere between 2 and 1600×10^{-6}; and for the defect of Simpson's estimate of (d), a rather tedious calculation shows that it certainly lies between -2200 and $+2600 \times 10^{-9}$, but does not define it more closely. The reason why the actual errors of estimates of (d) are comparatively small is that the higher derivatives of $1/(1 + x^2)$ are oscillatory; and positive and negative errors tend to cancel. Equation (3.38) allows for this by averaging the derivative concerned, but such close agreement as that obtained for integral (d) must not be relied upon.

In conclusion, let it be quite clear that the *primary purpose* of estimating errors in this way is to determine the extent to which a given result is significant, and is not to render it more accurate. To attempt this may lead to disaster, as a glance at the results for integral (c) will show.

3.14. Method of Improving Estimates of Integrals

Direct estimation of the error in evaluating an integral by the methods just described is a luxury which may be indulged in when the mathematical form of the integrand is known. But suppose this is not known, and a simple formula such as Simpson's has been used to evaluate the integral. Then Chevilliet's rule suggests a method of improving the value so obtained, without attempting to tabulate the integrand at so fine an interval that the error of integration is negligible.

Suppose the integral $I = \int_a^b f(x)dx$ is evaluated, first by m_1 applications of a formula needing n intervals, and then by $m_2 (> m_1)$ applications of the same formula. The intervals are therefore $(b - a)/nm_1$ and $(b - a)/nm_2$ respectively. We may represent the two estimates of the integral I by I_1 and I_2, and their respective errors by E_1 and E_2. Then, according to (3.38), these errors are proportional to a certain power of the interval, s say, or

$$E_1/E_2 = (m_2/m_1)^s$$

Since $I = I_1 - E_1 = I_2 - E_2$

it follows that $- E_2 = (I_2 - I_1)/\{(m_2/m_1)^s - 1\}$ (3.39)

By adding this to I_2, a closer value of the integral should be obtained, provided m_1 is not so small that (3.38) is quite inapplicable.

In particular, when $m_2 = 2m_1$, the correction to be made to I_2 is

$$(I_2 - I_1)/(2^s - 1)$$ (3.40)

Some applications of this rule merely lead to known formulas of a higher order. Thus for the trapezoidal rule, $s = 2$, and from (3.40) we obtain

$$I = I_2 + (1/3)(I_2 - I_1)$$ (3.41)

which, as a little algebra shows, is equivalent to Simpson's rule. Again, for Simpson's rule $s = 4$, and the better approximation

$$I = I_2 + (1/15)(I_2 - I_1)$$ (3.42)

is the same as Boole's rule. It is not generally true, however, that this type of correction leads to a Newton-Cotes formula of higher order. The corresponding improvement to Boole's rule (with $s = 6$) is not susceptible of any simple interpretation, though the resulting error is probably proportional to w^8.

The principle which is involved in (3.39) is susceptible of much wider applications than the particular one considered here, as will be discovered in later chapters. The idea is generally ascribed to L. F. Richardson,* and described as the "deferred approach to the limit."

* L. F. Richardson, *Phil. Trans. Roy. Soc.*, **226** (1927), 300.

EXERCISES 3

1. If $p(x)$ is a polynomial of degree n, and $p_k = p(x_0 + kw) \neq 0$ for $k = 0, 1, \ldots, n$, show that the roots of $p(x) = 0$ are given by the roots of

$$q(r) = \sum_{k=0}^{n} A_k/(r - k) = 0$$

where $x = x_0 + rw$ and $A_k = (-1)^{n-k} n_{(k)} p_k$

Compare the ease of tabulating $q(r)$ at equal intervals over a short range of r with that of tabulating $p(x)$ by synthetic division for the corresponding values of x.   (Lucas, 1888; Salzer, 1952)

2. If x_j ($j = 0, 1, \ldots, n$) are a set of irregularly spaced arguments, and $\phi(t)$ is the Lagrange polynomial

$$\phi(t) = \sum_{j=0}^{n} x_j \{\psi(t)/(t - j)\psi^{(1)}(j)\}$$

where $\psi(t) = t(t - 1) \ldots (t - n)$, show that

$$\int_{x_0}^{x_n} f(x)dx = \int_0^n f(\phi(t))\phi^{(1)}(t)dt \simeq \sum_{k=0}^{n} h_k \phi^{(1)}{}_k f_k$$

where h_k are the Newton-Cotes coefficients for quadrature over n intervals,

$$\phi^{(1)}{}_k = \sum_{j=0}^{n} a_{jk} x_j$$

and $a_{jk} = (-1)^{j+k} n_{(j)}/\{(k - j)n_{(k)}\}$ when $j \neq k$

$$= \sum_{\substack{s=0 \\ s \neq j}}^{n} 1/(j - s)   \text{ when }   j = k$$

(Hartley, 1952)

CHAPTER 4

NEWTON'S METHOD OF DIVIDED
DIFFERENCES

IN the foregoing chapter the interpolation of a tabular function, together with its differentiation and integration, has been discussed on the basis of the Lagrange interpolation polynomial. We shall now approach these same problems afresh by a method which depends on the use of differences. The development of this owes much to Newton, and, to distinguish it from the Lagrangian method of attack, it is conveniently referred to as the Newtonian method, or method of differences.

This chapter is concerned mainly with functions tabulated at unequal intervals, and the special case of equal intervals is deferred to Chapter 5.

Divided Differences and their Properties

It is first necessary to define a type of difference more general than that described in Chapter 2, and which will be applicable to a function tabulated at unequal intervals of the argument. Such differences, following Newton, are called *divided differences*.

As before, let the values of a function $f(x)$ for arguments

$$x_0 \quad x_1 \quad x_2 \quad x_3 \ldots$$

be denoted by $\quad f_0 \quad f_1 \quad f_2 \quad f_3 \ldots$

(a) *Divided Difference of the First Order.* The first divided difference of f_0 and f_1 is denoted by $[10]$ and defined by

$$[10] = (f_1 - f_0)/(x_1 - x_0)$$

In general $\quad [lk] = (f_l - f_k)/(x_l - x_k)$

(b) *Divided Difference of the Second Order.* Introducing a third value, say f_2, it is possible to define a second divided difference of f^0, f_1 and f_2—

$$[210] = \frac{[21] - [10]}{x_2 - x_0}$$

(c) *Divided Difference of the Third Order.* Introducing f_3,

$$[3210] = \frac{[321] - [210]}{x_3 - x_0}$$

(d) In general, a divided difference of order n can be formed from $(n + 1)$ values of the function, and is expressible as a combination of two differences of order $(n - 1)$; thus

$$[n, n - 1, \ldots, 1, 0]$$
$$= \frac{[n, n - 1, \ldots, 2, 1] - [n - 1, n - 2, \ldots, 1, 0]}{x_n - x_0}$$

It will be seen that the two arguments whose difference forms the denominator always correspond to the symbols which are *not* common to the two divided differences in the numerator. Also, these symbols occupy the two extreme outer positions in the brackets representing the differences, though it will be seen in a moment that this is entirely a matter of convention.

Many notations exist for divided differences, some of them as follows—

	Argument	Function	Divided Differences		
(1)	x_k	$f(x_k)$	$f(x_0, x_1)$,	$f(x_1, x_2)$,	$f(x_0, x_1, x_2)$
(2)	x_k	$f(x_k)$	$[x_0 x_1]$,	$[x_0 x_2]$,	$[x_0 x_1 x_2]$
(3)	$a, b, c, \ldots$	$u_a, u_b, u_c, \ldots$	$\underset{b}{\triangle} u_a$,	$\underset{b}{\triangle} u_c$,	$\underset{bc}{\triangle^2 u_a}$

(1) Steffensen, Whittaker and Robinson.
(2) Milne-Thompson.
(3) Aitken, Freeman.
The notation used in the text is thought to be the simplest to write; it is similar to that of Milne-Thompson, but follows our general practice of omitting the variable where this can be done without confusion.

From a given group of values of $f(x)$ (which may, it should be noted, include some values repeated several times), it is now possible to construct a table of divided differences, similar to those displayed for ordinary differences in Chapter 1.

f_0				
	[10]			
f_1		[210]		
	[21]		[3210]	
f_2		[321]		[43210]
	[32]		[4321]	
f_3		[432]		
	[43]			
f_4				

A numerical example illustrates the formation of such a table—

x	$f(x)$				
0	2				
		$3/1 = 3$			
1	5		$9/3 = 3$		
		$24/2 = 12$		$5/5 = 1$	
3	29		$32/4 = 8$		$12/6 = 2$
		$88/2 = 44$		$65/5 = 13$	
5	117		$219/3 = 73$		
		$263/1 = 263$			
6	380				

A point to be noticed is that a rearrangement of any group of entries in the first two columns does not affect the ultimate divided difference derived from the group. Thus consider the table of d.d.'s formed as follows—

x	$f(x)$			
5	117			
		23		
0	2		7	
		9		1
3	29		3	
		12		3
1	5		21	
		75		
6	380			2

The final difference is again 2; also the third d.d. from the four entries corresponding to $x = 0$, 1, 3, 5 is 1 in each table. Such results arise because all d.d.'s are *symmetrical* in the values of x_k and $f(x_k)$ from which they are constructed; interchange of any pair of these quantities does not affect the value of the d.d.

This symmetrical property is easily proved. It is evident from the definition of [10] that [10] = [01]; and the second and third orders can also, from their definitions, be given symmetrical forms—

$$[210] = \frac{f_0}{(x_0 - x_1)(x_0 - x_2)} + \frac{f_1}{(x_1 - x_0)(x_1 - x_2)}$$
$$+ \frac{f_2}{(x_2 - x_0)(x_2 - x_1)}$$

$$[3210] = \frac{f_0}{(x_0 - x_1)(x_0 - x_2)(x_0 - x_3)}$$
$$+ \frac{f_1}{(x_1 - x_0)(x_1 - x_2)(x_1 - x_3)}$$
$$+ \frac{f_2}{(x_2 - x_0)(x_2 - x_1)(x_2 - x_3)}$$
$$+ \frac{f_3}{(x_3 - x_0)(x_3 - x_1)(x_3 - x_2)}$$

The general expression is obvious, and can be proved by induction. It follows that the order of the symbols within the bracket is immaterial to the value of the difference.

These symmetrical forms also show that d.d.'s obey the usual distributive rules of algebra; thus

nth d.d. of $\{f(x) + g(x)\}$ = nth d.d. of $f(x)$ + nth d.d. of $g(x)$

nth d.d. of $kf(x)$ = $k \times n$th d.d. of $f(x)$

Another important result is that the nth d.d.'s formed from $(n + 1)$ or more values of a polynomial, $p_n(x)$, of degree n, are constant. This may be proved, first by considering differences of x^n, for which the first d.d., formed from x_0^n, x_1^n say, is a homogeneous function of degree $(n - 1)$ in powers of x_0 and x_1. Each stage of differencing reduces by one the degree of the homogeneous polynomial formed of the arguments, till eventually the nth d.d. is a polynomial of degree zero, i.e. a constant. The $(n + 1)$th d.d. is zero. Applying this to the polynomial p_n, the only non-zero contribution to the nth d.d. comes from the term in x^n, and is therefore constant. In this, divided differences resemble ordinary differences.

Having thus derived the principal properties of divided differences, we consider an important theorem given first by Newton (in 1687).

Newton's Expansion of $f(x)$ in Divided Differences

Suppose that $f(x)$ is specified for $(n + 1)$ values of the argument, $x_0, x_1, \ldots, x_n$, which are not necessarily in numerical sequence, and that $f(x)$ is used to represent the value of the function for any other value of the argument. Then the following set of equations can be written down, using the definitions of divided differences—

$$f(x) = f_0 + (x - x_0)[x0]$$
$$[x0] = [01] + (x - x_1)[x01]$$
$$[x01] = [012] + (x - x_2)[x012]$$

$$\cdot \qquad\qquad \cdot$$
$$\cdot \qquad\qquad \cdot$$
$$\cdot \qquad\qquad \cdot$$

$$[x01 \ldots (n-1)] = [012 \ldots n] + (x - x_n)[x012 \ldots n]$$

By successive substitution of each identity in the equation preceding it, we obtain the identity

$$f(x) \equiv f_0 + X_0[01] + X_0X_1[012] + X_0X_1X_2[0123]$$
$$+ \ldots + X_0X_1 \ldots X_{n-1}[012 \ldots n] + R_{n+1} \qquad (4.1)$$

where X_k is written for $x - x_k$, and

$$R_{n+1}(x) = X_0X_1 \ldots X_n[x01 \ldots n] \qquad (4.2)$$

It is easily seen that all the terms on the right side of (4.1) excluding the last constitute a polynomial of degree n in x, and we can therefore write

$$f(x) \equiv p_n(x) + R_{n+1} \qquad (4.3)$$

R_{n+1} itself contains a polynomial of degree $(n + 1)$, viz. the function $\phi(x) = X_0X_1 \ldots X_n$, and may be shown to vanish when x has any one of the values $x_0 \ldots x_n$.

The conclusion that $R_{n+1}(x_k) = 0$ does not follow at once from the presence of the factor X_k because the corresponding value of $[x01 \ldots n]$ might be infinite. However, $R_{n+1}(x) \to 0$ as $x \to x_k$, as befits a continuous function.

Using the symmetrical form, with $\phi(x)$ as in (3.3),

$$[x01 \ldots n] = f(x)/\phi(x) + \sum_{k=1}^{n} f_k/\{(x_k - x)\phi^{(1)}(x_k)\}$$

and we have once again $R_{n+1}(x) = f(x) - \sum_{k=1}^{n} L_k f_k$

When $x \to x_k$, $L_p \to 0$ when $p \neq k$ and $L_k \to 1$

so $R_{n+1}(x) \to f_k - f_k = 0$

as stated above.

It also follows from this identity that the expression (4.2) for

R_{n+1} must be equivalent to (3.27), and hence we obtain the relation

$$[x01 \ldots n] = \{1/(n+1)!\}f^{(n+1)}(\xi) \qquad (4.4)$$

This has an important consequence, because it follows that $f(x)$ and $p_n(x)$ coincide at $(n+1)$ specified points. Since $p_n(x)$ is a polynomial of degree n at most, it must be the unique polynomial through these $(n+1)$ points. It is in fact identical with the Lagrange interpolation polynomial defined in (3.2), though we shall refer to the present form of it in terms of d.d's as Newton's interpolation polynomial.

Further, if $f(x)$ is itself a polynomial of degree n it must coincide with $p_n(x)$ for *all* values of x; therefore $R_{n+1}(x) = 0$ for all x, not only $x_0, x_1, \ldots, x_n$. Thus for a polynomial of degree n, $[x01 \ldots n] \equiv 0$, and we have a further proof that the $(n+1)$th d.d's of such a polynomial are all zero.

4.1. Use of Newton's Interpolation Formula

When $f(x)$ is not a polynomial of degree n or less we must return to the identity (4.3) and see how it may be applied. On the right-hand side, $f(x)$ itself occurs only in the remainder term R_{n+1}, and neglect of this term implies, as for the Lagrange polynomial, that $f(x)$ is being represented by a polynomial of degree n. Without special knowledge of how $f(x)$ behaves between the tabular points, we are still unable, naturally, to place limits on the magnitude of R_{n+1}. Nor is it possible to estimate R_{n+1} by substituting for $f(x)$ the approximate value $p_n(x)$, for such an attempt would only lead to the unsatisfactory conclusion that $R_{n+1} = 0$.

Newton's expression for $p_n(x)$, however, has a considerable advantage over Lagrange's, in that the terms are arranged to give the effect of increasing the degree of the approximating polynomial by one with each term added. If, as often happens, the successive terms decrease steadily in magnitude, it is a good indication—though by no means an infallible one—that the polynomial approximation is satisfactory if carried far enough, and that after sufficient terms have been included the remainder can be neglected. Again, if successive terms show no sign of decreasing, there is evident danger that R_{n+1} is not negligible. Neither conclusion is necessarily correct, for it is easy to manufacture examples in which the last term in the series preceding R_{n+1} is the largest, yet R_{n+1} is zero; or in which the terms decrease rapidly, but R_{n+1} exceeds them all. Polynomials with a large coefficient attached to the highest power may behave like this. Nevertheless in practice it is reasonable enough to pay some attention to the convergence or otherwise of the terms of Newton's polynomials. Newton's formula in fact offers a method of successive approximation that Lagrange's formula lacks.

In using this method of successive approximation, it is well to keep in mind the following rule. It is a sound working principle that information close to the point of interpolation is more important than at points further away. Accordingly, in formulating the series of terms in Newton's polynomial (4.1), it is preferable, when possible, to introduce the given arguments in the order of increasing $|x - x_k|$ rather than of increasing x_k. If the method gives convergence at all, it is then likely to be most evident. This point will be made clearer in the following sections.

4.2. Formation of Interpolation Formulas

It was emphasized when the construction of a table of divided differences was being described that the order in which successive arguments are introduced need not be their numerical order. In deriving practical formulas it is often preferable to introduce them in a special order which is not that of increasing x. The method of doing so we shall illustrate by some simple examples.

Suppose the arguments

$$\ldots x_{-k}, x_{-k+1}, \ldots, x_{-1}, x_0, x_1, \ldots, x_k, \ldots$$

are in strict numerical sequence. From these and the corresponding values of $f(x)$ can be constructed a table of divided differences. We restrict the discussion to formulas which involve only differences appearing in this table, and carry through the formation of the Newton interpolation polynomial with arguments and function values introduced in the following different ways—

(i) $x_0\ x_1\ x_2\ \ldots x_n$ (Newton F)

This only repeats equation (4.1) with R_{n+1} given by (4.2).

(ii) $x_0\ x_{-1}\ x_{-2}\ \ldots x_{-n}$ (Newton B)

$$f(x) = f_0 + X_0[0\ -1] + X_0 X_{-1}[0\ -1\ -2]$$
$$+ X_0 X_{-1} X_{-2}[0\ -1\ -2\ -3] + \ldots + R_{n+1} \quad (4.5)$$

where $R_{n+1} = X_0 X_{-1} X_{-2} \ldots X_{-n}[0\ -1\ -2 \ldots -n\ x]$

$= X_0 X_{-1} X_{-2} \ldots X_{-n}\{1/(n+1)!\}f^{(n+1)}(\xi)$ (4.6)

(iii) $x_0\ x_1\ x_{-1}\ x_2\ x_{-2} \ldots x_q\ x_{-q}$ (Gauss F)

$f(x) = f_0 + X_0[0\ 1] + X_0 X_1[0\ 1\ -1]$

$+ X_0 X_1 X_{-1}[0\ 1\ -1\ 2] + \ldots + R_{2q+1}$ (4.7)

where $R_{2q+1} = X_0 X_1 X_{-1} \ldots X_q X_{-q}[0\ 1\ -1 \ldots q\ -q\ x]$

$= X_0 X_1 X_{-1} \ldots X_q X_{-q}\{1/(2q+1)!\}f^{(2q+1)}(\xi)$ (4.8)

(iv) $x_0\ x_{-1}\ x_1\ x_{-2}\ x_2 \ldots x_{-q}\ x_q$ (Gauss B)

$f(x) = f_0 + X_0[0\ -1] + X_0 X_{-1}[0\ -1\ 1]$

$+ X_0 X_{-1} X_1[0\ -1\ 1\ -2] + \ldots + R_{2q+1}$ (4.9)

where R_{2q+1} is identical with (4.8).

(v) $x_1\ x_0\ x_2\ x_{-1}\ x_3 \ldots x_q\ x_{-q+1}$ (Gauss B_1)

$f(x) = f_1 + X_1[1\ 0] + X_1 X_0[1\ 0\ 2]$

$+ X_1 X_0 X_2[1\ 0\ 2\ -1] + \ldots + R_{2q}$ (4.10)

where $R_{2q} = X_1 X_0 X_2 \ldots X_q X_{-q+1}[1\ 0\ 2 \ldots q(-q+1)x]$

$= X_1 X_0 X_2 \ldots X_q X_{-q+1}\{1/2q!\}f^{(2q)}(\xi)$ (4.11)

The following diagram indicates how, if lines are drawn connecting the d.d.'s in the order in which they appear in these formulas, regular paths are obtained through the table of differences—

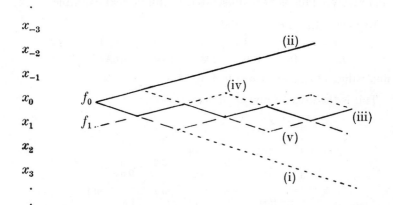

All of these have particular significance, though the titles which have been attached (F, B standing for "forward" and "backward")

refer rather to the counterparts of these formulas when the arguments are equally spaced. These will be considered later, but it is obvious that (i) is suited to interpolation near the beginning of a sequence of values of $f(x)$; (ii) near the end of a sequence; and (iii), (iv), (v), which follow regular zigzag courses, to interpolation near x_0 in the middle of a sequence. Of course, to any path through the table of differences which consists of a sequence of simple diagonal steps there corresponds an interpolation formula of the Newton type, and the construction of such is a useful exercise. The general rule governing the construction of the formula should be noted: *that the argument which appears for the first time in any d.d. determines the factor X_k or $(x - x_k)$ which makes its first appearance in the term following.*

Practical Methods

The practical application of Newton's polynomial to interpolation requires that we evaluate $p_n(x)$. This may or may not be preceded by the formation of a d.d. table; we shall describe methods which make use of d.d.'s, and a valuable method due to Aitken which does not.

4.3. Methods Using the Divided Difference Table

If we wish to take advantage of the successive approximations provided by Newton's polynomial, the most direct method is to prepare a table of d.d.'s and evaluate each term in the polynomial separately. This is best illustrated by numerical examples.

EXAMPLE 4.1. From the data

x	2	3	5	8	9	12
$f(x)$	48	100	294	1080	1630	5824

find values of $f(x)$ when $x = 0, 4, 6, 14$.

This is the table of divided differences—

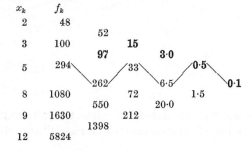

$$
\begin{array}{ccccccc}
x_k & f_k & & & & & \\
2 & 48 & & & & & \\
 & & 52 & & & & \\
3 & 100 & & 15 & & & \\
 & & 97 & & 3{\cdot}0 & & \\
5 & 294 & & 33 & & 0{\cdot}5 & \\
 & & 262 & & 6{\cdot}5 & & 0{\cdot}1 \\
8 & 1080 & & 72 & & 1{\cdot}5 & \\
 & & 550 & & 20{\cdot}0 & & \\
9 & 1630 & & 212 & & & \\
 & & 1398 & & & & \\
12 & 5824 & & & & & \\
\end{array}
$$

To calculate $f(6)$ it is preferable to follow the line of formula (iii) of the previous section, as this takes the arguments in order of increasing $|x - x_k|$. We arrange the calculation as follows—

$$
\begin{array}{rrcr}
6 - x_k & & & \\
 & f(5) = 294 & & 294 \\
1 & 1 \times & 262 & 262 \\
-2 & -2 \times & 33 & -66 \\
3 & -6 \times & 6\cdot5 & -39 \\
-3 & 18 \times & 0\cdot5 & 9\cdot0 \\
4 & 72 \times & 0\cdot1 & 7\cdot2 \\
\hline
 & & & 467\cdot2 = f(6)
\end{array}
$$

The first column contains the X_k factors taking $x_k = 5, 8, 3, 9, 2$, in order; the second contains successive products of these factors with the appropriate d.d's, and the third resultant values of the terms in Newton's series, which are then summed.

Similarly for $f(4)$, we introduce the f_k's in the order of $x_k = 3, 5, 2, 8, 9, 12$, which involves the d.d's in heavy type; for $f(0)$, we take f_k's in order of increasing x_k, and therefore differences along the forward diagonal; for $f(14)$, the f_k's in order of decreasing x_k, and differences along the backward diagonal. The computations are as follows—

$$
\begin{array}{llcr}
f(4) & 4 - x_k & f(3) = 100 & 100 \\
 & 1 & 1 \times & 97 & 97 \\
 & -1 & -1 \times & 15 & -15 \\
 & 2 & -2 \times & 3\cdot0 & -6 \\
 & -4 & 8 \times & 0\cdot5 & 4 \\
 & -5 & -40 \times & 0\cdot1 & -4 \\
\hline
 & & f(4) = & 176
\end{array}
$$

$$
\begin{array}{llcr}
f(0) & -x_k & f(2) = 48 & 48 \\
 & -2 & -2 \times 52 & -104 \\
 & -3 & 6 \times 15 & 90 \\
 & -5 & -30 \times 3\cdot0 & -90 \\
 & -8 & 240 \times 0\cdot5 & 120 \\
 & -9 & -2160 \times 0\cdot1 & -216 \\
\hline
 & & f(0) = & -152
\end{array}
$$

$$
\begin{array}{llcr}
f(14) & 14 - x_k & f(12) = 5824 & 5824 \\
 & 2 & 2 \times 1398 & 2796 \\
 & 5 & 10 \times 212 & 2120 \\
 & 6 & 60 \times 20 & 1200 \\
 & 9 & 540 \times 1\cdot5 & 810 \\
 & 11 & 5940 \times 0\cdot1 & 594 \\
\hline
 & & f(14) = & 13344
\end{array}
$$

If $f(x)$ were a quartic polynomial these results would of course be exact. With more general assumptions, one might say that the convergence of the terms in $f(6)$ and $f(4)$ is good enough for these values to be relied on to within a few digits. The extrapolated values of $f(0)$ and $f(14)$ are obviously likely to be in error by much larger amounts.

As a further exercise the reader may take the data of Example 3.1, evaluate $f(18)$ by Newton's method, and gauge the significance of the result; also find the interpolation polynomial.

When the polynomial representation is known to be adequate, the calculation may with advantage be ordered differently. From the polynomial in (4.1) we can define quantities $v_1, v_2, \ldots, v_n$ by the equations

$$
\left.
\begin{aligned}
p_n(x) &= f_0 + X_0 v_1 \\
v_1 &= [01] + X_1 v_2 \\
v_2 &= [012] + X_2 v_3 \\
&\cdot \\
&\cdot \\
&\cdot \\
v_{n-1} &= [012 \ldots (n-1)] + X_{n-1} v_n \\
v_n &= [012 \ldots n]
\end{aligned}
\right\} \qquad (4.12)
$$

From the prepared table of d.d's, $v_n, v_{n-1}, \ldots, v_1$ are computed, in that order,* and finally $p_n(x)$. This procedure does not allow the relative importance of the terms to be seen. A modification of the method, which may be convenient when several interpolated values are required, is to start from

$$
p_n(x) = f_0 + X_0[01] + X_0 X_1 v_2 \qquad (4.13)
$$

The first two terms correspond to "linear interpolation," and the last term gives the correction thereto. To prepare a set of linearly interpolated values is a simple operation with a machine; the correction to each must be obtained separately, computing v_2 from v_n as above.

4.4. Aitken's Method of Linear Cross-means†

Aitken has applied Newton's polynomial to interpolation in an ingenious way, which avoids the need for a table of divided

---

* This method is conveniently used with a calculating machine which has a device for transferring a number in the product register to the setting register, when the required answer is within the capacity of the machine. The reader may be interested to derive the answer from a single setting on the machine, and without copying down any intermediate results.

† A. C. Aitken, *Proc. Edin. Math. Soc.*, **3** (1932), 56.

differences, yet retains all the advantages of the successive approximations. The method is usually known as the method of linear cross-means.

(i) The first two terms in Newton's formula are

$$f_0 + (x - x_0)[01]$$

and may be written

$$(x_1 - x)/(x_1 - x_0) \times f_0 + (x - x_0)/(x_1 - x_0) \times f_1$$

Denote this by $f(01)$ and call it the linear cross-mean of f_0 and f_1; it is obviously symmetrical in x_0 and x_1. An alternative form uses a determinant—

$$\left. \begin{array}{l} f(01) = \begin{vmatrix} f_0 & x_0 - x \\ f_1 & x_1 - x \end{vmatrix} \div (x_1 - x_0) \\[4mm] \text{Likewise} \quad f(02) = \begin{vmatrix} f_0 & x_0 - x \\ f_2 & x_2 - x \end{vmatrix} \div (x_2 - x_0) \end{array} \right\} \qquad (4.14)$$

(ii) The second Newton approximation, obtained by adding the quadratic term, may be denoted by $f(012)$, where

$$f(012) = f(01) + (x - x_0)(x - x_1)[012]$$

or, by the symmetry property,

$$f(012) = f(02) + (x - x_0)(x - x_2)[012]$$

When [012] is eliminated

$$f(012) = (x_2 - x)/(x_2 - x_1) \times f(01)$$
$$+ (x - x_1)/(x_2 - x_1) \times f(02)$$
$$= \begin{vmatrix} f(01) & x_1 - x \\ f(02) & x_2 - x \end{vmatrix} \div (x_2 - x_1) \qquad (4.15)$$

Thus, according to the definition (4.14), $f(012)$ is the linear cross-mean of $f(01)$ and $f(02)$.

(iii) The third approximation $f(0123)$ may also be written in alternative ways—

$$f(0123) = f(012) + (x - x_0)(x - x_1)(x - x_2)[0123]$$
$$= f(013) + (x - x_0)(x - x_1)(x - x_3)[0123]$$

whence $\quad f(0123) = \begin{vmatrix} f(012) & x_2 - x \\ f(013) & x_3 - x \end{vmatrix} \div (x_3 - x_2) \qquad (4.16)$

The formation of further cross-means, representing higher approximations, needs no elaboration.

The numerical calculations may be laid out as follows—

						Parts
x_0	f_0					$x_0 - x$
x_1	f_1	$f(01)$				$x_1 - x$
x_2	f_2	$f(02)$	$f(012)$			$x_2 - x$
x_3	f_3	$f(03)$	$f(013)$	$f(0123)$		$x_3 - x$
x_4	f_4	$f(04)$	$f(014)$	$f(0124)$	$f(01234)$	$x_4 - x$

The last column gives the values of $x_k - x$, called the "parts," needed in the formation of cross-means, and are so placed that the application of the determinant rule is quite simple. First the means $f(01)$, $f(02)$ . . . in the third column are formed from the second column and the parts; these are used in forming $f(012)$, $f(013)$, . . . and so on. The quantities along the sloping line, $f(01)$, $f(012)$, $f(0123)$, etc., then give the successive approximations to $f(x)$, and show the nature of the convergence. A numerical example will help to make the process clearer.

EXAMPLE 4.2. We use the data of Example 4.1 to evaluate $f(4)$.

As in any other application of Newton's polynomial it is preferable to introduce the arguments in order of increasing $|x - x_k|$, though this is not essential.

x_k	f_k						Parts
3	100						-1
5	294	**197**					$+1$
2	48	152	**182·0**				-2
8	1080	296	164·0	**176·0**			$+4$
9	1630	355	157·5	175·0	**180·0**		$+5$
12	5824	736	120·0	169·6	182·4	**176·0**	$+8$

The successive approximations to $f(4)$, in heavy type, will be found to be identical with those obtained in Example 4.1.

4.5. Quadratic Cross-means

The foregoing method is applicable whatever the intervals in argument may be, but it can be appreciably shortened when the given arguments are symmetrically placed about some point, which is preferably close to the interpolated argument.

Thus suppose the arguments are

$$x_1 \qquad x_2 \qquad x_3 \qquad x_4 \ldots$$

and

$$x_{-1} \qquad x_{-2} \qquad x_{-3} \qquad x_{-4} \ldots$$

subject to restrictions of the form

$$x_k - x_0 = x_0 - x_{-k}$$

The intervals between x_1, x_2, x_3, ... need not be equal, but equal intervals do present a likely special case, and are included in what follows. To simplify the algebra, let a change of variable be made from x to y, where

$$y = x - x_0 \quad \text{and} \quad y_{-k} = -y_k$$

With the previous definition of a cross-mean

$$f(1, -1) = (y_1 - y)/2y_1 \times f_{-1} + (y + y_1)/2y_1 \times f_1 \qquad (4.17)$$

This is symmetrical in y_1 and $-y_1$, and therefore conveniently written as $f(1^2)$. Similarly we can form $f(2^2)$, $f(3^2)$, etc. It is now possible to introduce further terms in the Newton polynomial (written in the Gauss form (4.10)), *two at a time*. Thus, introducing the terms from y_2 and y_{-2}, the cubic approximation is

$$f(1^2, 2^2) = f(1^2) + (y^2 - y_1^2)[-1, 1, -2]$$
$$+ (y^2 - y_1^2)(y + y_2)[-1,1,-2,2] \qquad (4.18)$$

This, by symmetry, is also given by

$$f(1^2, 2^2) = f(2^2) + (y^2 - y_2^2)[-2,2,-1]$$
$$+ (y^2 - y_2^2)(y + y_1)[-1,1,-2,2] \qquad (4.19)$$

Now by taking the difference of (4.18) multiplied by $(y^2 - y_2^2)$ and (4.19) multiplied by $(y^2 - y_1^2)$, and using the definition of $[-1, 1, -2, 2]$ we find

$$f(1^2, 2^2) = \begin{vmatrix} f(1^2) & y_1^2 - y^2 \\ f(2^2) & y_2^2 - y^2 \end{vmatrix} \div (y_2^2 - y_1^2) \qquad (4.20)$$

Thus these quadratic cross-means follow a determinant rule of formation similar to linear cross-means, except that y^2 everywhere replaces y. The next approximation to $f(y)$, given by 6 terms in Newton's polynomial, is

$$f(1^2, 2^2, 3^2) = \begin{vmatrix} f(1^2, 2^2) & y_2^2 - y^2 \\ f(1^2, 3^2) & y_3^2 - y^2 \end{vmatrix} \div (y_3^2 - y_2^2) \qquad (4.21)$$

and so on.

To form a table of quadratic cross-means requires that we first evaluate $f(1^2), f(2^2)$ . . . and the remainder of the calculation is a linear interpolation for $f(y^2)$ which involves little further effort.

                                                   Parts

y_1	$f(1^2)$			$y_1{}^2 - y^2$
y_2	$f(2^2)$	$f(1^2 2^2)$		$y_2{}^2 - y^2$
y_3	$f(3^2)$	$f(1^2 3^2)$	$f(1^2 2^2 3^2)$	$y_3{}^2 - y^2$

As a numerical illustration we take one in which the data are provided by values of a function at constant interval.

EXAMPLE 4.3. Evaluate $\sin 0{\cdot}56$, given $\sin x$ for $x = 0(0{\cdot}2)1{\cdot}0$.

It is convenient here to assume $x_0 = 0{\cdot}5$, and let $y = 100(x - 0{\cdot}5)$. When $x = 0{\cdot}56$, the value of y is 6, and the calculation is as follows—

y_k	$\sin y_k$	$y_k - y$	y_k	$f(y_k{}^2)$			$y_k{}^2 - y^2$
-50	0	-56					
-30	198 669	-36					
-10	389 418	-16	10	**529597·2**			64
$+10$	564 642	$+4$	30	509881·2	531174·5		864
30	717 356	$+24$	50	471223·8	531153·8	**531185·7**	2464
50	841 471	$+44$					

All values of sines have been multiplied by 10^6 for convenience. The value of $\sin 0{\cdot}56$ given in *Chambers* [6] is $0{\cdot}531186$, which agrees to six decimals with the final approximation above.

In this calculation we can place a limit on the remainder to the Newton polynomial. Using (4.11), we find

$$R_6 = \frac{56 \times 36 \times 16 \times 4 \times 24 \times 44}{6!} \cdot 10^{-12} \sin \xi < 0{\cdot}2 \times 10^{-6}$$

since $0 < \xi < 1$. We are quite justified therefore in neglecting this remainder.

In the final stages of an interpolation by Aitken's method, whether using linear or quadratic cross-means, it is often feasible to omit all digits which are no longer varying from the calculation of higher cross-means. Thus in Example 4.3, the digits 5311.. can certainly be dropped at the last stage, and the arithmetic simplified.

4.6. Inverse Interpolation

Since Newton's polynomial does not need arguments to be equally spaced, it can be used for inverse interpolation in the same way as Lagrange's polynomial, by interchange of the dependent and independent variables before the table of d.d's or cross-means is formed. It is liable to the difficulties described in Chapter 3, but any failure of the successive approximations to converge should become apparent in the calculation.

4.7. Differentiation and Integration

The formation of derivatives and integrals of a function can be carried out with Newton's polynomial when arguments are at unequal intervals, though the calculation is likely to be tedious. There is little point in trying to develop general formulas, as any particular problem is best considered on its merits. The application of difference methods when intervals are equal will be developed in the next chapter.

CHAPTER 5

DIFFERENCES AT CONSTANT INTERVAL

WE continue the investigation of difference methods of interpolation, etc., by considering the many problems associated with functions tabulated at constant intervals in the argument. It is again preferable to use instead of x, x_k the quantities r, k defined by

$$x = x_0 + rw, \quad x_k = x_0 + kw$$

together with $\qquad f(x) = u(r), \quad f_k = u_k$

The function $u(r)$ is therefore tabulated at unit intervals in r. With such functions it is possible to dispense with divided differences in favour of the simpler "ordinary" differences defined in Chapter 2.

Interpolation Formulas

We begin by expressing the several forms of Newton's polynomial in § 4.2 in terms of ordinary differences. As an obvious preliminary, the relationship between divided and ordinary differences must be derived.

5.1. Newton Formulas*

With the assumption that the arguments x_0, x_1, . . . are in increasing numerical sequence, and at a constant interval w, it follows that

$$[0\ 1] = (1/w)\Delta^1{}_0, \qquad [1\ 2] = (1/w)\Delta^1{}_1$$
$$[0\ 1\ 2] = (1/2w)\,(\Delta^1{}_1/w - \Delta^1{}_0/w) = (1/2w^2)\Delta^2{}_0,$$
$$[1\ 2\ 3] = (1/2w^2)\Delta^2{}_1$$
$$[0\ 1\ 2\ 3] = (1/3w)\,(\Delta^2{}_1/2w^2 - \Delta^2{}_0/2w^2) = (1/3\,!\,w^3)\Delta^3{}_0$$

and in general $\qquad [0\ 1\ 2\ .\ .\ .\ k] = (1/k\,!\,w^k)\Delta^k{}_0$

Also $\quad X_0 X_1\ .\ .\ .\ X_{k-1} = w^k r(r-1)\ .\ .\ .\ (r-k+1)$
$$= w^k r^{(k)}$$

in factorial notation.

---

* Sometimes called the Gregory-Newton formulas, as they were given by Gregory in 1670, and by Newton about six years later.

When these results are substituted in equations (4.1) and (4.2) there follows at once the *Newton forward formula*

$$u(r) = u_0 + r\Delta^1{}_0 + r_{(2)}\Delta^2{}_0 + \ldots + r_{(n)}\Delta^n{}_0 + R_{n+1} \quad (5.1)$$

where $\quad R_{n+1} = w^{n+1}r_{(n+1)}\left(\dfrac{d^{n+1}f}{dx^{n+1}}\right)_\xi$ or $r_{(n+1)}\left(\dfrac{d^{n+1}u}{dr^{n+1}}\right)_\rho$ $\quad (5.2)$

ρ being some value in the range which includes 0, n and r.

A similar procedure starting with the arguments $x_0, x_{-1}, x_{-2}, \ldots$ leads to the *Newton backward formula*, based upon equations (4.5) and (4.6). The immediate results are that

$$[0, -1, -2, \ldots, -k] = (1/k\,!w^k)\nabla^k{}_0 \text{ (in backward-difference}$$
$$\text{notation)}$$

$$X_0 X_{-1} X_{-2} \ldots X_{-k+1} = w^k r(r+1) \ldots (r+k-1)$$
$$= w^k(-1)^k(-r)^{(k)} \text{ or } w^k(r+k-1)^{(k)}$$

Thus the backward formula may be written in two ways; in terms of r, it is

$$u(r) = u_0 + r\nabla^1{}_0 + (r+1)_{(2)}\nabla^2{}_0 + (r+2)_{(3)}\nabla^3{}_0$$
$$+ \ldots + (r+n-1)_{(n)}\nabla^n{}_0 + R_{n+1} \quad (5.3)$$

where $\qquad\qquad R_{n+1} = (r+n)_{(n+1)}u^{(n+1)}(\rho) \qquad\qquad (5.4)$

Or, if $s = -r$

$$u(s) = u_0 - s\nabla^1{}_0 + s_{(2)}\nabla^2{}_0 - s_{(3)}\nabla^3{}_0 + \ldots$$
$$+ (-1)^n s_{(n)}\nabla^n{}_0 + R_{n+1} \quad (5.5)$$

where $\qquad\qquad R_{n+1} = s_{(n+1)}\left(\dfrac{d^{n+1}u}{ds^{n+1}}\right)_\sigma \qquad (5.6)$

If r is positive (5.3) *extrapolates*; if s is positive (5.5) *interpolates*.

It will be seen that the forward formula involves differences along a diagonal advancing from u_0, the backward formula those along a diagonal receding from u_0. Formula (5.5) may be derived easily from (5.1) (by turning the function table upside-down), from which it differs formally only in the sign of odd differences.

[It is worth noting at this point one of the correspondences between the calculus of finite differences and the infinitesimal calculus. Taylor's series, which may be written

$$f(x_0 + h) = f_0 + hf_0{}^{(1)} + (h^2/2\,!)f_0{}^{(2)} + \ldots + (h^n/n\,!)f_0{}^{(n)}$$
$$+ \{h^{n+1}/(n+1)\,!\}f^{(n+1)}(\xi)$$

the derivatives being evaluated at x_0, is clearly the limiting form of (5.1) when $w \to 0$, but $rw \to h$. In these circumstances

$$w^k r_{(k)} \to h^k / k\,!, \; (1/w^k)\nabla^k_{\;0} \to f_0^{\,(k)} \quad]$$

5.2. Gauss and Stirling Formulas

Equations (4.7) and (4.9) lead to well-known central difference formulas when the intervals are constant. We give first the relevant relations between divided differences and ordinary central differences—

$$[0, 1, -1, \ldots, p, -p, p+1] \; = \frac{1}{(2p+1)!w^{2p+1}} \delta^{2p+1}_{\;1/2}$$

$$[0, 1, -1, \ldots, p, -p] \qquad = \frac{1}{(2p)!w^{2p}} \delta^{2p}_{\;0}$$

$$[0, -1, 1, \ldots, -p, p, -p+1] = \frac{1}{(2p+1)!w^{2p+1}} \delta^{2p+1}_{\;-1/2}$$

Central factorials also arise as follows—

$$X_0 X_1 X_{-1} \ldots X_p X_{-p} = w^{2p+1} r_{\{2p+1\}}$$

$$X_0 X_1 X_{-1} \ldots X_{-p+1} X_p = w^{2p}(r - \tfrac{1}{2})_{\{2p\}}$$

$$X_0 X_{-1} X_1 \ldots X_{p-1} X_{-p} = w^{2p}(r + \tfrac{1}{2})_{\{2p\}}$$

A straightforward application of these results to (4.7) and (4.9) leads to the two Gauss formulas—

Gauss Forward Formula

$$u(r) = u_0 + r\delta^1_{\;1/2} + (r - \tfrac{1}{2})_{\{2\}}\delta^2_{\;0} + r_{\{3\}}\delta^3_{\;1/2} + (r - \tfrac{1}{2})_{\{4\}}\delta^4_{\;0}$$
$$+ \ldots + r_{\{2q-1\}}\delta^{2q-1}_{\;1/2} + (r - \tfrac{1}{2})_{\{2q\}}\delta^{2q}_{\;0} + R_{2q+1} \quad (5.7)$$

Gauss Backward Formula

$$u(r) = u_0 + r\delta^1_{\;-1/2} + (r + \tfrac{1}{2})_{\{2\}}\delta^2_{\;0} + r_{\{3\}}\delta^3_{\;-1/2}$$
$$+ (r + \tfrac{1}{2})_{\{4\}}\delta^4_{\;0} + \ldots + r_{\{2q-1\}}\delta^{2q-1}_{\;-1/2}$$
$$+ (r + \tfrac{1}{2})_{\{2q\}}\delta^{2q}_{\;0} + R_{2q+1} \quad\quad (5.8)$$

More important than either of these formulas is their mean, in which the coefficients of even differences are conveniently written as mean central factorials, using (2.32). This gives the *Stirling formula*

$$u(r) = u_0 + r\delta^1_{\;0} + r_{[2]}\delta^2_{\;0} + r_{\{3\}}\delta^3_{\;0} + \ldots$$
$$+ r_{[2q]}\delta^{2q}_{\;0} + R_{2q+1} \quad (5.9)$$

in which all odd differences are averaged,

i.e. $\qquad\qquad \delta^1_0 = \frac{1}{2}(\delta^1_{-1/2} + \delta^1_{1/2})$, etc.

In (5.7), (5.8) and (5.9)

$$R_{2q+1} = r_{\{2q+1\}}u^{(2q+1)}(\rho) \qquad (5.10)$$

5.3. Bessel and Everett Formulas

A similar transformation of (4.10) leads to the result

$$u(r) = u_1 + (r-1)\delta^1_{1/2} + (r - \tfrac{1}{2})_{\{2\}}\delta^2_1 + (r-1)_{\{3\}}\delta^3_{1/2}$$
$$+ (r - \tfrac{1}{2})_{\{4\}}\delta^4_1 + \ldots + (r - \tfrac{1}{2})_{\{2q-2\}}\delta^{2q-2}_1$$
$$+ (r-1)_{\{2q-1\}}\delta^{2q-1}_{1/2} + R_{2q} \qquad (5.11)$$

where $\qquad\qquad R_{2q} = (r - \tfrac{1}{2})_{\{2q\}}u^{(2q)}(\rho) \qquad (5.12)$

We take the mean of (5.11) and (5.7), the latter being curtailed at the term in $\delta^{2q-1}_{1/2}$, and simplify the coefficients of odd differences by using the relation

$$\tfrac{1}{2}\{(r-1)_{\{2p-1\}} + r_{\{2p-1\}}\} = (r - \tfrac{1}{2})_{[2p-1]}$$

This leads to *Bessel's formula*

$$u(r) = \tfrac{1}{2}(u_0 + u_1) + (r - \tfrac{1}{2})\delta^1_{1/2} + (r - \tfrac{1}{2})_{\{2\}}\delta^2_{1/2}$$
$$+ (r - \tfrac{1}{2})_{[3]}\delta^3_{1/2} + \ldots + (r - \tfrac{1}{2})_{\{2q-2\}}\delta^{2q-2}_{1/2}$$
$$+ (r - \tfrac{1}{2})_{[2q-1]}\delta^{2q-1}_{1/2} + R_{2q} \qquad (5.13)$$

in which it should be noticed that all even differences are averaged, $\delta^2_{1/2} = \frac{1}{2}(\delta^2_0 + \delta^2_1)$, etc. The formula is clearly symmetrical about $r = \frac{1}{2}$, being based on the $2q$ values of u corresponding to $-q+1, -q+2, \ldots, 0, 1, \ldots, q-1, q$. For this reason it is usually curtailed at an odd difference, rather than at an even difference as in Stirling's formula. The remainder in (5.13) is the same as (5.12).

An important modification of Bessel's formula is obtained from it by converting all odd differences into even ones of the previous order. A simpler derivation is from (5.7), in which a pair of adjacent terms can be transformed by recalling from (2.35) that

$$(r - \tfrac{1}{2})_{\{2p\}} = \delta(r - \tfrac{1}{2})_{\{2p+1\}} = r_{\{2p+1\}} - (r-1)_{\{2p+1\}}$$

Hence $\qquad (r - \tfrac{1}{2})_{\{2p\}}\delta^{2p}_0 + r_{\{2p+1\}}\delta^{2p+1}_{1/2}$

$$= (r_{\{2p+1\}} - (r-1)_{\{2p+1\}})\delta^{2p}_0 + r_{\{2p+1\}}(\delta^{2p}_1 - \delta^{2p}_0)$$
$$= r_{\{2p+1\}}\delta^{2p}_1 - (r-1)_{\{2p+1\}}\delta^{2p}_0$$
$$= r_{\{2p+1\}}\delta^{2p}_1 + t_{\{2p+1\}}\delta^{2p}_0, \quad \text{where} \quad t = 1 - r$$

Thus (5.7) leads to *Everett's formula*

$$u(r) = tu_0 + t_{\{3\}}\delta^2{}_0 + t_{\{5\}}\delta^4{}_0 + \ldots + t_{\{2q-1\}}\delta^{2q-2}{}_0$$
$$+ ru_1 + r_{\{3\}}\delta^2{}_1 + r_{\{5\}}\delta^4{}_1 + \ldots + r_{\{2q-1\}}\delta^{2q-2}{}_1 + R_{2q} \quad (5.14)$$

R_{2q} is again given by (5.12) and therefore $2q$ terms of Everett's formula and $2q$ terms of Bessel's formula are exactly equivalent.

The Use of Difference Formulas for Interpolation

Before considering in detail how best to use the foregoing interpolation formulas, we should emphasize the superiority of central difference formulas (Stirling, Bessel, Everett), when suitably applied, over those which contain only forward or backward differences (Newton). It is of course true that if the function interpolated is a polynomial, and the formula is carried to the line of constant differences, then all formulas must lead to the same exact result because they merely reproduce the same polynomial in various guises. But when the series is curtailed at an earlier stage, or the function $f(x)$ is not a polynomial, the interpolated value is necessarily approximate, and the error will vary according to the formula used. In the following comparison it is assumed that the limits usually set in practice are being applied to r (or s)—

Newton (forward)	$0 < r < 1$	⎫ If necessary, r or s
Newton (backward)	$0 < s < 1$	⎭ may be > 1
Bessel (or Everett)	$0 < r < 1$	
Stirling	$-\frac{1}{2} < r < \frac{1}{2}$	

Now it is seen from (5.2), (5.10) and (5.12) that when the first difference neglected is of order $(n + 1)$, the remainder contains two factors, the first a factorial polynomial and the second some value of the $(n + 1)$th derivative of $f(x)$. The appropriate value of the latter will vary from point to point, and from formula to formula, but assuming that this derivative is in fact varying slowly with x, a fair comparison of remainders can be made by comparing the values of the factorials involved. The factorial which occurs in Newton formulas is $r_{(n+1)}$; actually the same factorial occurs in R_{n+1} for the central difference formulas, provided n is odd (and equal to $2q - 1$) in the Bessel or Everett formula, and even $(2q)$ in the Stirling formula, with the essential difference that the range of r lies about $(n + 1)/2$ for these formulas. In Fig. 5.1, therefore, there are shown the factorials $r_{(4)}$, $r_{(5)}$, $r_{(6)}$, $r_{(7)}$, corresponding to the use of 4, 5, 6, 7 tabular values respectively for interpolation, and the appropriate ranges of r for the various formulas (N, B, S) are indicated. From each diagram it is clear that by using data more or less symmetrically distributed about the interval of interpolation the factorial normally contributes a much smaller factor to the error than when they are mainly on one side of it; hence the emphasis placed on this point in the previous chapter.

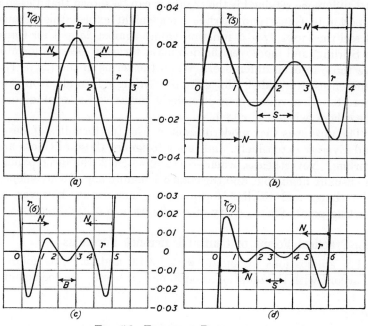

FIG. 5.1. FACTORIAL POLYNOMIALS

Indeed the only reason in practice for using a Newton type of formula is that the differences necessary to the use of a central difference formula are not available, as at the beginning or end of a table.

A further fact which is obvious from Fig. 5.1 is the rapid and unconfined rise in the factorial outside the range of the tabular points used, which causes the error of extrapolation to be much greater than that of interpolation.

5.4. Comparative Accuracy of Central Difference Formulas

We should next consider the relative merits of the various central difference formulas, which are not only less obvious but also less important. A full discussion is hardly worthwhile, and it is sufficient to indicate the conclusion of the argument.*

We note first that formulas curtailed at the same difference are identical, and have the same remainders; thus, to an even difference, Gauss and Stirling are equivalent, and to an odd difference, Gauss and Bessel (or Everett) are equivalent. If the comparison is confined to values of r between 0 and 1, and the last difference retained is the $(2q)$th, it can be shown that Bessel is superior to Gauss and Stirling; one might expect this because Bessel then uses $2q + 2$ function values against $2q + 1$ for Gauss or Stirling, and moreover the dominant terms in Bessel's formula are those in even differences. When the terms in the $(2q + 1)$th differences are added, the gain to Stirling's formula from two more function values gives it a slight but trivial advantage over the others, when $0 < r < 1$.

The upshot is that modern practice uses the formulas of Bessel and Everett extensively, and tends to ignore those of Gauss and Stirling. Nevertheless, when $-1/2 < r < 1/2$, the discrepancies are usually negligible, and the choice is mainly one of convenience. The Gauss and Stirling formulas are important, however, as starting points for a variety of results used in other directions.

5.5. Practical Forms of Central Difference Formulas

For applications we should write (5.13) and (5.14) as follows, to accord with the notation used in most tables of the coefficients.

Bessel

$$u(r) = u_0 + r\delta^1_{1/2} + B^{(2)}(\delta^2_0 + \delta^2_1) + B^{(3)}\delta^3_{1/2}$$
$$+ B^{(4)}(\delta^4_0 + \delta^4_1) + B^{(5)}\delta^5_{1/2} + \cdots \qquad (5.15)$$

Everett

$$u(r) = (1 - r)u_0 + E^{(2)}_0\delta^2_0 + E^{(4)}_0\delta^4_0 + \cdots + ru_1$$
$$+ E^{(2)}_1\delta^2_1 + E^{(4)}_1\delta^4_1 + \cdots \qquad (5.16)$$

where
$$\left.\begin{array}{l} B^{(2)} = (1/4)r(r-1) \\[4pt] B^{(3)} = (1/6)(r - \tfrac{1}{2})r(r-1) \\[4pt] B^{(4)} = (1/12)(r+1)(r-2)B^{(2)} \\[4pt] B^{(5)} = (1/20)(r+1)(r-2)B^{(3)}, \text{ etc.} \end{array}\right\} \qquad (5.17)$$

---

* Anyone interested should consult Whittaker and Robinson, *Calculus of Observations*, p. 49, where further references are given.

and
$$E^{(2)}{}_0 = B^{(2)} - B^{(3)} \qquad E^{(2)}{}_1 = B^{(2)} + B^{(3)}$$
$$E^{(4)}{}_0 = B^{(4)} - B^{(5)} \qquad E^{(4)}{}_1 = B^{(4)} + B^{(5)}, \text{ etc.} \qquad (5.18)$$

The coefficients in these formulas, polynomials in r, have been extensively tabulated, and application is simplicity itself. It should be noted that a Bessel or Everett formula with $2q$ terms, and a symmetrical Lagrange $2q$-point formula, give identical results. Thus the 4-point Lagrange formula,

$$u(r) = L_{-1}u_{-1} + L_0 u_0 + L_1 u_1 + L_2 u_2$$

is equivalent to Bessel, including the $B^{(3)}$ term, and to Everett with second differences; incidentally in this formula, $L_{-1} = E^{(2)}{}_0$ and $L_2 = E^{(2)}{}_1$.

A further point concerns *half-way interpolation*, for which all odd $B^{(k)}$ vanish, and when k is even, $B^{(k)} = E^{(k)}{}_0 = E^{(k)}{}_1$. We therefore have, from either (5.15) or (5.16), a most useful formula.

$$u(\tfrac{1}{2}) = \tfrac{1}{2}(u_0 + u_1) - (\delta^2{}_0 + \delta^2{}_1)/16 + (3/256)(\delta^4{}_0 + \delta^4{}_1) \ldots \qquad (5.19)$$

[Useful tables of interpolation coefficients are as follows—

Bessel: *I.A.T.* $B^{(2)} - B^{(4)}$ $r = 0(0{\cdot}001)1$

   Chambers [6] *Critical Tables for* $B^{(2)}, B^{(3)}$ (4D)

Everett: *I.A.T.* $E^{(2)} - E^{(6)}$ $r = 0(0{\cdot}001)1$

   Thompson   *Tracts for Computers No.* 5
               (Cambridge University Press)
               $E^{(2)} - E^{(8)}$ $r = 0(0{\cdot}001)1$

   Fox   *Math. Tab. Nat. Phys. Lab.,* **2**
               (1958): $E^{(2)}$, and 4th order
               coefficients for use with modi-
               fied differences $r = 0(0{\cdot}0001)1$

Newton: Dwight   *Mathematical Tables*: Up to $r_{(6)}$ $r = 0(0{\cdot}01)1$

   Davis, H. T. *Tables of Higher Mathematical
               Functions,* Vol. 1 (Blooming-
               ton, Indiana, 1933.)
               $n = 2, 3, 4, 5, 6$ $r = 0(0{\cdot}01)1$ to 10S.]

5.6. Numerical Examples

We propose to give two numerical examples of interpolation; one a straightforward example involving the probability integral, the other a rather extreme case of an oscillatory function.

EXAMPLE 5.1. Interpolate $f(x)$ at $x = 0.05$, 0.25, 0.31256 in the following table of $f(x) = \sqrt{(2/\pi)} \int_0^x \exp{(-t^2/2)}dt$.

x	$f(x)$	δ	δ^2	δ^3	δ^4	δ^5
0·0	0		0		0	
		79 656		− 793		27
0·1	0·079 656		− 793		27	
		78 863		− 766		14
0·2	0·158 519		− 1 559		41	
		77 304		− 725		30
0·3	0·235 823		− 2 284		71	
		75 020		− 654		8
0·4	0·310 843		− 2 938		79	
		72 082		− 575		
0·5	0·382 925		− 3 513			
		68 569				
0·6	0·451 494					

Fifth differences are erratic through rounding errors.

Calculation of $f(0.05)$ $r = 0.5$

Newton (forward)		Bessel	
δ^1	$+ 0.5 \quad \times (+ 79656) = 0.039828\ 0$	$+ 0.5 \quad \times (+ 79656) = 0.039828\ 0$	
δ^2	$- 0.125 \times \quad (- 793) = \quad + 99\ 1$	$- 0.0625 \times \quad (- 793) = \quad + 49\ 6$	
δ^3	$+ 0.0625 \times \quad (- 766) = \quad - 47\ 9$		
δ^4	$- 0.0391 \times \quad (+ 41) = \quad - 1\ 6$	$+ 0.0117 \times \quad (+ 27) = \quad + 3$	
δ^5	$+ 0.0273 \times \quad (+ 30) = \quad + 8$		
	$0.039878\ 4$	$0.039877\ 9$	

Exact value (to 6D) = 0·039878

Note the extra decimal to safeguard against accumulation of rounding errors. The answer should be rounded to 6 decimals.

Calculation of $f(0.25)$ $r = 0.5$

Newton (backward)		Bessel	
δ^0	$0.235823\ 0$	$0.158519\ 0$	
δ^1	$- 0.5 \quad \times (+ 77304) = - 38652\ 0$	$+ 0.5 \quad \times (+ 77304) = + 38652\ 0$	
δ^2	$- 0.125 \times \quad (- 1559) = \quad + 194\ 9$	$- 0.0625 \times \quad (- 3843) = \quad + 240\ 2$	
δ^3	$- 0.0625 \times \quad (- 766) = \quad + 47\ 9$		
δ^4	$- 0.0391 \times \quad (+ 27) = \quad - 1\ 1$	$+ 0.0117 \times \quad (+ 112) = \quad + 1\ 3$	
δ^5	$- 0.0273 \times \quad (+ 27) = \quad - 7$		
	$0.197412\ 0$	$0.197412\ 5$	

Exact value (to 7D) = 0·1974126

Calculation of $f(0.31256)$ $r = 0.1256$, $t = 0.8744$

Everett

$\delta^0{}_0$	$0.8744 \times 235823\ 0 =$	$0.206203\ 6$
$\delta^0{}_1$	$+ 0.1256 \times 310843\ 0 =$	$39041\ 9$
$\delta^2{}_0$	$- 0.03432 \times (- 2284) =$	$+ 78\ 4$
$\delta^2{}_1$	$- 0.02062 \times (- 2938) =$	$+ 60\ 6$
$\delta^4{}_0$	$+ 0.0055 \times\ \ (+ 71) =$	$+ 4$
$\delta^4{}_1$	$+ 0.0041 \times\ \ (+ 79) =$	$+ 3$

$$0.245385\ 2$$

Exact value (to 6D) $= 0.245385$

The somewhat better convergence of the central difference formula is obvious; also the advantage of Bessel's formula for half-way interpolation.

EXAMPLE 5.2. Perform half-way interpolation (to 3D) in the following table—

x	$f(x)$	δ	δ^2	δ^3	δ^4	δ^5	δ^6	δ^7	δ^8	δ^9	δ^{10}
0	0		0		0		0		0		0
		1		-2		4		-8		16	
$\pi/2$	1		-2		4		-8		16		-32
		-1		2		-4		8		-16	
π	0		0		0		0		0		0
		-1		2		-4		8		-16	
$3\pi/2$	-1		2		-4		8		-16		32
		1		-2		4		-8		16	
2π	0		0		0		0		0		0

The function is assumed to be periodic with period 2π.

As a typical case, let us interpolate for $\pi/4$ by Newton and Bessel. Contributions from differences up to the tenth are as follows—

	Newton	Bessel	
δ^1	0.5000	0.5000	
δ^2	0.2500	0.1250	
δ^3	0.1250	—	
δ^4	0.0	0.0469	
δ^5	$- 0.1094$	—	
δ^6	$- 0.1641$	0.0195	
δ^7	$- 0.1289$	—	
δ^8	0.0	0.0085	
δ^9	0.1746	—	
δ^{10}	0.2966	0.0038	0.7037

It is clear that the Newton series does not converge, whereas the Bessel series does, giving a sum at this stage of 0·704, and, after a few more terms have been added, 0·707. The significance of this result depends hugely on the properties of $f(x)$; the data are consistent with the assumption that $f(x) = \sin x$ and the Bessel interpolate is in fact $\sin (\pi/4)$. However, the presence of even harmonics, $\sin 2x$, $\sin 4x$, etc., cannot be detected because they contribute nothing to the differences; a term in $\sin 2x$, for instance, would contribute to $f(\pi/4)$ an amount equal to its coefficient.

The example is interesting in showing the ability of a central difference formula to deal with a fairly rapidly oscillating function.

We ought also to consider the use of expressions such as (5.2) and (5.12) for the remainder term, in relation to the above examples.

Example 5.1. Let us estimate the remainders in the interpolation for $f(0·25)$, assuming the series terminated after terms in third differences.

We have that $f^{(4)}(x) = \sqrt{(2/\pi)} \cdot (3 - x^2)xe^{-x^2/2}$

Newton (*Backward*). From (5.4), with $r = -\frac{1}{2}$,

$$R_4 = -(5/128)f^{(4)}(\xi) \times (0·1)^4$$

where $0 \leqslant \xi \leqslant 0·3$. In this range $f^{(4)}(\xi)$ increases from 0 to 0·666, and hence R_4 lies between 0 and $-2·6 \times 10^{-6}$. The actual error is $1·2 \times 10^{-6}$, part of which may be rounding error.

Bessel. From (5.12), $R_4 = (3/128)f^{(4)}(\xi)$ where $0·1 \leqslant \xi \leqslant 0·4$. In this range $f^{(4)}(\xi)$ increases from 0·237 to 0·837, so that R_4 lies between 0·5 and $2·0 \times 10^{-6}$. The actual value is $1·4 \times 10^{-6}$.

Example 5.2. Assuming $f(x) = \sin x$, it is possible to state that $|f^{(n)}(\xi)| < 1$, but the sign of the error can only be guessed from the behaviour of the series. For the Bessel calculation, we can say that

$$|R_{2q}| \leqslant (\pi/2)^{2q} (r + q - 1)_{(2q)}$$

For instance, $|R_{10}| < 0·0110$, $|R_{12}| < 0·0062$

The actual errors are slightly more than half these values.

For the Newton series it is easily shown that the upper limit of $|R_{n+1}|$ increases as n increases beyond 4, a further indication of lack of convergence.

When the remainder is known to lie between two values r, R (with known signs), the addition of $(r + R)/2$ to the estimated value of the interpolate will, in general, reduce the *limits* of error. This might have been done in Example 5.1 above. The practice may be worthwhile if it does not involve much labour, and rounding errors are not serious.

5.7. Neglect of Higher Differences

It is useful to know when differences of a given order may be safely neglected in either Bessel's or Everett's formula. This may be gauged by the maximum value of the appropriate coefficient, $B^{(n)}$ or $E^{(n)}$, e.g. since $B^{(2)}$ never exceeds $1/16$ in magnitude, the condition that $B^{(2)}(\delta^2{}_0 + \delta^2{}_1)$ should not exceed $1/2$ in the last decimal retained implies that the "mean δ^2" must not exceed 4 units of this decimal. Corresponding upper limits on other differences, in units of the last decimal, are as follows—

$$\delta^3 < \quad 60 \qquad \text{Mean } \delta^4 < \quad 20$$

$$\delta^5 < \quad 500 \qquad \text{Mean } \delta^6 < 100$$

$$\delta^7 < 3500 \qquad \text{Mean } \delta^8 < 400$$

The more important restrictions are those on even differences, and these also apply, without appreciable change, to Everett's formula. Of course, if it is considered necessary to limit more severely the terms neglected in the interpolation formula, the above limits on differences must be similarly reduced.

5.8. Use of Modified Differences: Throwback

Approximate allowance for higher differences in Bessel's or Everett's formula can be made by a simple device known as the *throwback*. This is most easily explained in the form in which it is most commonly applied, the modification of second differences to allow for fourth differences.

We have seen that

$$B^{(4)} = (1/12)(r + 1)(r - 2)B^{(2)}$$

and one observes that, if $0 < r < 1$, the ratio $B^{(4)}/B^{(2)}$ varies between $- 0{\cdot}1666$ and $- 0{\cdot}1875$, a comparatively small range. Let (5.15) be written as

$$u(r) = u_0 + r\delta^1{}_{1/2} + B^{(2)}\{\delta^4{}_0 + \delta^2{}_1 - C(\delta^4{}_0 + \delta^4{}_1)\}$$
$$+ B^{(3)}\delta^3{}_{1/2} + T^{(4)}(\delta^4{}_0 + \delta^4{}_1)$$

where $T^{(4)} = B^{(4)} + CB^{(2)}$, and 5th and higher differences are ignored. It is easily verified that if C is chosen to be $0{\cdot}184$, $T^{(4)}$ varies between $\pm 0{\cdot}00023$; hence the last term can be dropped if the mean δ^4 does not exceed 1000 (cp. normal limit of 20). If now

$$M^2{}_0 = \delta^2{}_0 - 0\cdot184\delta^4{}_0, \ M^2{}_1 = \delta^2{}_1 - 0\cdot184\delta^4{}_1 \qquad (5.20)$$

the formula reads

$$u(r) = u_0 + r\delta^1{}_{1/2} + B^{(2)}(M^2{}_0 + M^2{}_1) + B^{(3)}\delta^3{}_{1/2} \qquad (5.21)$$

$M^2{}_0$ and $M^2{}_1$ are known as *modified second differences*. As before the condition for neglecting the last term is that $\delta^3 < 60$.

A similar argument holds for Everett's formula, which becomes

$$u(r) = (1 - r)u_0 + ru_1 + E^{(2)}{}_0 M^2{}_0 + E^{(2)}{}_1 M^2{}_1 \qquad (5.22)$$

The throwback has two considerable advantages—
1. It helps the maker of tables. In many modern tables it is not possible to calculate or print sufficient values of the function to permit linear or even quadratic interpolation, so it would appear that fourth differences should be printed to give proper facilities for interpolation. This can be avoided by modifying second differences as above.
2. It helps the user of tables. By a 4-term formula the effect of several more terms can often be included with comparatively light restrictions on higher differences.

When values of δ^6 exceed 50, but values of δ^4 are less than 1000, a further modification of second differences can be achieved by giving an average value to $B^{(6)}/B^{(2)}$. The modified difference then becomes

$$M^2 = \delta^2 - 0\cdot184\delta^4 + 0\cdot038\delta^6 \qquad (5.23)$$

As the variation of the ratios $B^{(5)}/B^{(3)}$, $B^{(7)}/B^{(3)}$ . . . is likewise small, the procedure can be extended to odd order differences, and the third difference replaced by a modified difference M^3 given by

$$M^3 = \delta^3 - 0\cdot108\delta^5 + 0\cdot016\delta^7 \qquad (5.24)$$

There is a generous upper limit of about 20000 on δ^5, and the last term is superfluous unless δ^7 exceeds 2000. Clearly, if the modification of δ^3 is going to be very significant, it is unlikely that the conditions implied in (5.23) will be satisfied.

Further examples of use of the throwback principle are given in *I.A.T.*.*

---

* It is worth mentioning that the use of modified differences is an example of the approximation of polynomials by Chebyshev polynomials of lower degree; thus in the throwback of fourth differences, the quartic $B^{(4)}$ is replaced by the optimum quadratic.

EXAMPLE 5.3. Given the following 7D values of

$$f(x) = \sqrt{(2/\pi)} \int_0^x \exp\left(-t^2/2\right)dt$$

interpolate $f(0{\cdot}25)$, $f(0{\cdot}475)$ with the help of modified differences.

x	$f(x)$	δ	δ^2	δ^3	δ^4	δ^5	δ^6
0·2	0·1585194		− 15603		459	199	− 19
		773034		− 7224			
0·3	0·2358228		− 22827		658	176	− 23
		750207		− 6566			
0·4	0·3108435		− 29393		834	123	− 53
		720814		− 5732			
0·5	0·3829249		− 35125		957		− 29

Compare this with the table in Example 5.1; the extra decimal has shifted the irregularity from δ^5 to δ^6. When δ^2 and δ^3 are modified the table reads as follows—

x	$f(x)$	δ	M^2	M^3
0·2	0·1585194		− 15688	
		773034		− 7246
0·3	0·2358228		− 22949	
		750207		− 6585
0·4	0·3108435		− 29548	
		720814		− 5745
0·5	0·3829249		− 35302	

Modifications for δ^5 and δ^6 have been included, but are hardly necessary. The interpolations now proceed as usual.

$f(0{\cdot}25)$				$f(0{\cdot}475)$			
			1585194 . 0				3108435 . 0
0·5	×	773034 =	386517 . 0	0·75	×	720814 =	540610 . 5
− 0·0625	× (− 38637) =		2414 . 8	− 0·046875	× (− 64850) =		3039 . 8
				− 0·00781	× (− 5745) =		44 . 9
			1974125 . 8				3652130 . 2

Both results are correct to 7 decimals.

5.9. Subtabulation

Subtabulation is merely systematic interpolation, and as such is very familiar to table-makers wishing to fill in the table of a function from pivotal values at wide intervals. On a large scale this calls for one of the more elaborate calculating machines, with an appropriate technique, but when only a moderate amount of subtabulation is to be done, direct use of a formula such as Everett's is advisable, and indeed quite rapid.

Thus let us take the frequently occurring problem of reducing the interval in a table to one-tenth when the given fourth differences are less than 1000. It is then possible to use second differences modified as in (5.20), and the Everett interpolates, which are worth quoting in full, are as follows—

$$\begin{aligned}
u(0 \cdot 1) &= 0 \cdot 9u_0 + 0 \cdot 1u_1 - 0 \cdot 0285M^2_0 - 0 \cdot 0165M^2_1 \\
u(0 \cdot 2) &= 0 \cdot 8u_0 + 0 \cdot 2u_1 - 0 \cdot 0480M^2_0 - 0 \cdot 0320M^2_1 \\
u(0 \cdot 3) &= 0 \cdot 7u_0 + 0 \cdot 3u_1 - 0 \cdot 0595M^2_0 - 0 \cdot 0455M^2_1 \\
u(0 \cdot 4) &= 0 \cdot 6u_0 + 0 \cdot 4u_1 - 0 \cdot 0640M^2_0 - 0 \cdot 0560M^2_1 \\
u(0 \cdot 5) &= 0 \cdot 5(u_0 + u_1) - 0 \cdot 0625(M^2_0 + M^2_1) \\
u(0 \cdot 6) &= 0 \cdot 4u_0 + 0 \cdot 6u_1 - 0 \cdot 0560M^2_0 - 0 \cdot 0640M^2_1 \\
u(0 \cdot 7) &= 0 \cdot 3u_0 + 0 \cdot 7u_1 - 0 \cdot 0455M^2_0 - 0 \cdot 0595M^2_1 \\
u(0 \cdot 8) &= 0 \cdot 2u_0 + 0 \cdot 8u_1 - 0 \cdot 0320M^2_0 - 0 \cdot 0480M^2_1 \\
u(0 \cdot 9) &= 0 \cdot 1u_0 + 0 \cdot 9u_1 - 0 \cdot 0165M^2_0 - 0 \cdot 0285M^2_1 \\
u(1 \cdot 0) &= 1 \cdot 0u_1 \\
u(1 \cdot 1) &= 0 \cdot 9u_1 + 0 \cdot 1u_2 - 0 \cdot 0285M^2_1 - 0 \cdot 0165M^2_2
\end{aligned}$$ (5.25)

and so on.

Prolonged subtabulation is nowadays often carried out on multi-register adding machines, such as the National Accounting Machine. The process then takes a rather different form, in that the required table is built up from constant differences of some order, but basically it is equivalent to the use of a standard interpolation formula. For instance, in the special case represented by equations (5.25), we see that on the final table all fourth differences are zero, except at trios of points such as 0·9, 1·0, 1·1. It follows that, if the first three forward differences of $u(0)$, which are non-zero, can be derived from the data, all interpolates between u_0 and u_1 can be built up from them, provided enough extra or fictitious decimals are included to guard against cumulative errors of addition (this condition makes the building up very tedious without a suitable machine).

The first need is therefore for equations expressing the leading differences of the interpolates in terms of differences in the original table, and these are easily derived.* One method of subtabulation then consists of a separate building up process from the leading differences thus calculated for each interval in the original table. Though this method has often been used, it is unsatisfactory because it may fail to reproduce the pivotal values exactly, and errors in the building up process are not easily detected. A better method proceeds in this way for the first interval only, and thereafter makes use of the *bridging differences*, e.g. the above-mentioned trio of non-vanishing fourth differences near each pivotal value, which can also be expressed simply in terms of original differences. Once these bridging differences are known, the building up of the final table is a continuous process, the pivotal values are reproduced exactly (hence providing a periodic check on the calculations), and the number of extra decimals can be kept to a minimum. However, it is not within the scope of this book to give details of the method, which can be found in original papers.†

5.10. Inverse Interpolation by Successive Approximation

Methods of inverse interpolation so far described have required an interchange of the dependent and independent variables. By a suitable use of differences, however, this step can be avoided, and when $f(x)$ is tabulated *and* satisfactorily represented by a polynomial the method to be described now is probably the best for solving an equation of the form $f(x) = \text{constant}$.

Bessel's formula provides a convenient illustration of the method. If we write (5.15) as an equation for r—

$$r = \{u(r) - u_0 - B^{(2)}(\delta^2{}_0 + \delta^2{}_1) - B^{(3)}\delta^3{}_{1/2}$$
$$- B^{(4)}(\delta^4{}_0 + \delta^4{}_1) - \ldots\}/\delta^1{}_{1/2} \quad (5.26)$$

it can be solved by successive approximation, because, although the terms in $B^{(2)}$, $B^{(3)}$, etc., depend on r, they represent rapidly diminishing corrections to the first approximation to r, given by

$$r_1 = \{u(r) - u_0\}/\delta^1{}_{1/2}$$

* Some typical relations of this kind are given in Exercises 6, Nos. 1 and 2; lists may also be found in Steffensen's *Interpolation*, and (for central differences) in *Subtabulation* (H.M.S.O., 1958).

† See L. J. Comrie, *J. Roy. Stat. Soc.* (Suppt.), **3** (1936), 87, "Scientific applications of the National Accounting Machine"; or D. R. Hartree, "Numerical Analysis" or *Subtabulation* (H.M.S.O., 1958). Another method of subtabulation, known as the "end-figure process," has been given by Comrie, *Mon. Not. R.A.S.*, **88** (1928), 506 and *Nautical Almanac*, 1931, Appendix.

The second approximation is obtained by including the extra terms on the right side of (5.26), but taking for $B^{(2)}$, $B^{(3)}$, etc., the values corresponding to r_1, as given by tables (two decimals in r_1 are adequate for this purpose). With the new estimate of r, $B^{(2)}$ may require modification, which will again affect the estimate of r; the same applies to $B^{(3)}$, $B^{(4)}$, . . . but, as the later terms are smaller, changes in these coefficients may be deferred until the changes in $B^{(2)}$ produce no further change in the estimate of r. Then it must be verified that corrections to $B^{(3)}$, etc., are not significant; otherwise the approximations must be continued.

From the criteria already obtained for the neglect of higher differences in interpolation, it appears that if we require r correct to N decimals, so that any neglected term in (5.26) should not exceed a $\frac{1}{2}$ unit of the Nth decimal, then the differences must satisfy conditions as follows—

$$\text{mean } \delta^2 < 4 \cdot 10^{-N}\delta^1{}_{1/2} \qquad \delta^3 < 60 \cdot 10^{-N}\delta^1{}_{1/2}$$

$$\text{mean } \delta^4 < 20 \cdot 10^{-N}\delta^1{}_{1/2} \qquad \delta^5 < 500 \cdot 10^{-N}\delta^1{}_{1/2} \text{ and so on.}$$

The use of modified differences is advantageous here as in direct interpolation, the condition being that

$$\text{mean } \delta^4 < 1000 \cdot 10^{-N}\delta^1{}_{1/2}$$

Corresponding to Bessel's equation we have

$$r = \{u(r) - u_0 - B^{(2)}(M^2{}_0 + M^2{}_1) - B^{(3)}\delta^3{}_{1/2}\}/\delta^1{}_{1/2} \quad (5.27)$$

For machine computation this equation is preferably written

$$u_0 + r\delta^1{}_{1/2} = u(r) - B^{(2)}(M^2{}_0 + M^2{}_1) - B^{(3)}\delta^3{}_{1/2} \quad (5.28)$$

so that the extra terms on the right-hand side are in effect a correction to $u(r)$. The machine operation reduces to finding the value of r which equalizes the two sides of the equation. (Details may be found in $I.A.T.$)

EXAMPLE 5.4. Find the value of x for which

$$\sqrt{(2/\pi)} \int_0^x \exp(-t^2/2)dt = 0 \cdot 2453850$$

from the table with modified differences, Example 5.3.

1st approximation: $2358228 + 750207r_1 = 2453850$
whence $r_1 = 0 \cdot 127 \ldots$

2nd approximation: From $I.A.T.$, for $r = 0 \cdot 127$,
$$B^{(2)} = -0 \cdot 027718 \quad \text{and} \quad B^{(3)} = 0 \cdot 00689$$

Hence $2358228 + 750207r_2$
$$= 2453850 - 0 \cdot 027718 \times 52497 + 0 \cdot 00689 \times 6585$$
$$= 2453850 - 1455 + 45$$

and $r_2 = 0 \cdot 12558$

3rd approximation: Revised value of $B^{(2)} = -0 \cdot 027456$

so that $52497\ B^{(2)}$ changes from -1455 to -1441

Hence $r_3 = 0 \cdot 12560$

The correction to $B^{(3)}$ is not significant.

The required value of $x = 0 \cdot 3 + 0 \cdot 1 \times 0 \cdot 12560$
$$= 0 \cdot 312560 \qquad\qquad \text{(cp. Example 5.1)}.$$

5.11. Mixed Interpolation Formulas

A brief mention should be given to circumstances in which central differences may usefully be combined with those along a forward or backward diagonal. This may occur for instance in a few intervals of a table beyond the first, where sufficient central differences are not yet available.

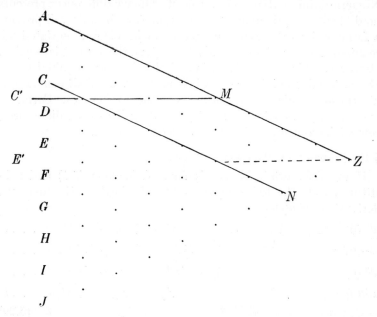

Thus suppose ten values of a function are available, represented in the diagram by A, B, . . ., J, and an interpolate between C

and D is wanted. Bessel's formula would use differences along $C'M$, and therefore only A–F of the given values; Newton's forward formula starting at C would use differences along CN, or the values C–J only. Thus, if the interpolation formula is restricted to values of r less than 1, incomplete use is made of the data. For greater accuracy we may either use a formula with $r > 1$, e.g. central differences along $E'Z$, or forward differences along AZ, or resort to a *mixed* formula, e.g. one using central differences along $C'M$ and forward differences along MZ. Both methods must of course give the same answer, but the mixed formula may be the easier to apply, if all the coefficients for $r > 1$ are not immediately available. It also has a special application to numerical differentiation.

The reader should by now have no difficulty in deriving a mixed formula for any particular circumstances, either directly, or by converting the appropriate formula with divided differences into ordinary differences.

Differentiation

Numerical differentiation in terms of ordinary differences presents no difficulty in principle. Any interpolation formula will provide a formula for a derivative if each coefficient is differentiated the required number of times, and r then given the appropriate value. However, as in most calculations derivatives are required either at the tabular points or at points midway, we shall confine our illustrations of derivative formulas to these two cases. Formulas may be expressed in terms of forward or backward differences, central differences, or if need be, mixed differences.*

5.12. Forward or Backward Differences

If we differentiate Newton's forward formula (5.1) and substitute $r = 0$, the following series are obtained for the first four derivatives of $u(r)$—

$$u^{(1)}(0) = \Delta^1{}_0 - \tfrac{1}{2}\Delta^2{}_0 + \tfrac{1}{3}\Delta^3{}_0 - \tfrac{1}{4}\Delta^4{}_0 + \tfrac{1}{5}\Delta^5{}_0 - \tfrac{1}{6}\Delta^6{}_0 + \cdots$$

$$u^{(2)}(0) = \phantom{\Delta^1{}_0 -} \Delta^2{}_0 - \Delta^3{}_0 + \tfrac{11}{12}\Delta^4{}_0 - \tfrac{5}{6}\Delta^5{}_0 + \tfrac{137}{180}\Delta^6{}_0 - \cdots$$

$$u^{(3)}(0) = \phantom{\Delta^1{}_0 - \Delta^2{}_0 -} \Delta^3{}_0 - \tfrac{3}{2}\Delta^4{}_0 + \tfrac{7}{4}\Delta^5{}_0 - \tfrac{15}{8}\Delta^6{}_0 + \cdots$$

$$u^{(4)}(0) = \phantom{\Delta^1{}_0 - \Delta^2{}_0 - \Delta^3{}_0 -} \Delta^4{}_0 - 2\Delta^5{}_0 + \tfrac{17}{6}\Delta^6{}_0 - \cdots$$

$$(5.29)$$

* If these are extensively required, reference should be made to Bickley and Miller: *Phil. Mag.*, **33** (1942), 1, "Numerical differentiation near the limits of a difference table."

Similarly, when $r = \frac{1}{2}$

$$u^{(1)}(\tfrac{1}{2}) = \Delta^1{}_0 \quad - \tfrac{1}{24}\Delta^3{}_0 + \tfrac{1}{24}\Delta^4{}_0 - \tfrac{71}{1920}\Delta^5{}_0 + \tfrac{31}{960}\Delta^6{}_0 - \cdots$$

$$u^{(2)}(\tfrac{1}{2}) = \quad \Delta^2{}_0 - \tfrac{1}{2}\Delta^3{}_0 + \tfrac{7}{24}\Delta^4{}_0 - \tfrac{3}{16}\Delta^5{}_0 + \tfrac{739}{5760}\Delta^6{}_0 - \cdots$$

$$u^{(3)}(\tfrac{1}{2}) = \quad\quad \Delta^3{}_0 - \Delta^4{}_0 + \tfrac{7}{8}\Delta^5{}_0 - \tfrac{3}{4}\Delta^6{}_0 + \cdots$$

$$u^{(4)}(\tfrac{1}{2}) = \quad\quad\quad \Delta^4{}_0 - \tfrac{3}{2}\Delta^5{}_0 + \tfrac{41}{24}\Delta^6{}_0 - \cdots$$

$$(5.30)$$

Similar results for backward differences are easily derived. It should be remembered that

$$d^k f / dx^k = (1/w^k) d^k u / dr^k$$

so that the above formulas must be multiplied by w^{-k} to obtain derivatives with respect to x.

5.13. Central Differences

To obtain derivatives at tabular points it is convenient to start with Stirling's formula, and at midpoints to start with Bessel's formula. For the first few derivatives we obtain—

$$u^{(1)}(0) = \delta^1{}_0 - (1/6)\delta^3{}_0 + (1/30)\delta^5{}_0 - \cdots$$

$$u^{(2)}(0) = \delta^2{}_0 - (1/12)\delta^4{}_0 + (1/90)\delta^6{}_0 - \cdots$$

$$u^{(3)}(0) = \delta^3{}_0 - (1/4)\delta^5{}_0 + \cdots$$

$$u^{(4)}(0) = \delta^4{}_0 - (1/6)\delta^6{}_0 + \cdots$$

$$(5.31)$$

and

$$u^{(1)}(\tfrac{1}{2}) = \delta^1{}_{1/2} - (1/24)\delta^3{}_{1/2} + (3/640)\delta^5{}_{1/2} - \cdots$$

$$u^{(2)}(\tfrac{1}{2}) = \delta^2{}_{1/2} - (5/24)\delta^4{}_{1/2} + (259/5760)\delta^6{}_{1/2} - \cdots$$

$$u^{(3)}(\tfrac{1}{2}) = \delta^3{}_{1/2} - (1/8)\delta^5{}_{1/2} + \cdots$$

$$u^{(4)}(\tfrac{1}{2}) = \delta^4{}_{1/2} - (7/24)\delta^6{}_{1/2} + \cdots$$

$$(5.32)$$

The obvious advantages of these central difference formulas are the vanishing of alternate terms and the rapidly decreasing coefficients. It should be noticed that alternate derivatives involve mean differences. More extensive results, including derivatives at a general point, and with numerical coefficients for use in applying them, are given in $I.A.T.$, pp. 61–5.

Expressions for remainder terms associated with various formulas for derivatives are given in Appendix 2.

One practical point concerned with the evaluation of derivatives must be mentioned. This is that it is not necessarily an advantage to have the function values at short intervals, because the shorter the interval the greater rounding errors become in proportion to the differences of the function. Such inaccuracies increase with the higher derivatives, especially as they are combined with loss of significant figures. The following simple example will make this clearer.

EXAMPLE 5.5. Evaluate the first and second derivatives of $\sin \theta$ when $\theta = 45°$, from 6-decimal values of $\sin \theta$.

We first compare the differences of $\sin \theta$ in the neighbourhood of $45°$, for intervals of $2°$ and $10°$ in θ, with a view to using a mid-point c.d. formula.

$w = \pi/90 \ (2°)$

θ	$\sin \theta$	δ	δ^2	δ^3
44°	694658		− 845	
		24682		− 32 Third differences
46°	719340		− 877	irregular.

$w = \pi/18 \ (10°)$

40°	642788		− 19532		597	− 29
		123256		− 3743		108
50°	766044		− 23275		705	− 15

The accuracy of the first derivative is determined mainly by the number of significant figures in δ, which is seen to be 6 for $10°$ interval, but only 5 for $2°$. Likewise in δ^2, which determines the second derivative, there are 5 significant figures at $10°$ interval, but only 3 at $2°$. The uncertainty in the last digit due to rounding is the same in each case, so, as a percentage error, it is nearly proportional to $1/w$ for the first derivative, $1/w^2$ for the second, etc.

As the interval is increased, a further cause of error comes in if there is a limit to the number of differences which can conveniently be included in the series for the derivatives, e.g. if the *range* of the data is restricted. In other words, the determining factor is the remainder left on curtailing the series at a particular difference. In this example the position is well shown by the results obtained with four different intervals of θ, ranging from $2°$ to $90°$, the series always being curtailed after the third term. The following table gives the first three terms of the formula, (the first or second of (5.32), multiplied by $1/w$ or $1/w^2$), with their sum in each case.

First Derivative (cos 45°)

w			
2°	0·70709 + 0·00004	=	0·7071(3)
10°	0·706205 + 0·000894 + 0·000003 =		0·707102
30°	0·699056 + 0·007805 + 0·000235 =		0·707096
90°	0·6366 + 0·0531 + 0·0119	=	0·7016

Second Derivative $(-\sin 45°)$

2°	$-0\cdot707$			$=-0\cdot707$
10°	$-0\cdot70264$	$-0\cdot00445$	$-0\cdot00003$	$=-0\cdot7071(2)$
30°	$-0\cdot66755$	$-0\cdot03726$	$-0\cdot00216$	$=-0\cdot70697$
90°	$-0\cdot4053$	$-0\cdot1689$	$-0\cdot0729$	$=-0\cdot6471$

All results are approximations to $1/\sqrt{2}$ or $0\cdot707107$.

It is evident that at 2° intervals, the controlling factor is the number of significant figures; at 90° intervals, it is the remainder of the series. At the optimum interval, probably between 10° and 30° in this example, the error is determined mainly by the random errors in rounding the tabular values to a specified number of decimals.

Integration

The ubiquitous interpolation polynomials provide the starting point of most formulas for numerical integration. We shall begin as usual by considering those which involve forward or backward differences, and then those with central differences. The discussion is confined to integrals which begin and end at tabular points, or occasionally at midpoints. It must be remembered throughout that

$$\int^{x} f(x)dx = w\int^{r} u(r)dr$$

5.14. Formulas Containing Forward or Backward Differences

Newton's forward formula, in terms of differences of u_k, is

$$u(k+r) = u_k + r\Delta^1_k + r_{(2)}\Delta^2_k + r_{(3)}\Delta^3_k + \ldots \quad (5.33)$$

Let $U(r)$ denote the indefinite integral of $u(r)$

i.e. $$U(r) = \int^{r} u(r)dr \quad \text{or} \quad \int^{r-k} u(k+r)dr$$

Then $$U_k = \int^{0} u(k+r)dr, \quad U_{k+1} = \int^{1} u(k+r)dr$$

and $$U_{k+1} - U_k = \int_{0}^{1} u(k+r)dr$$

By integrating each factorial in (5.33) between 0 and 1 it follows that

$$U_{k+1} - U_k = u_k + L_1\Delta^1_k + L_2\Delta^2_k$$
$$+ L_3\Delta^3_k + L_4\Delta^4_k + \ldots \quad (5.34)$$

where $L_1 = 1/2$, $L_2 = -1/12$, $L_3 = 1/24$, $L_4 = -19/720$

Values of further coefficients will be found in Appendix 2. This formula involves u_k, u_{k+1}, u_{k+2}, etc.

Similarly, starting with the backward difference formula (5.5), we obtain

$$U_{k+1} - U_k = u_{k+1} - L_1\nabla^1_{k+1} + L_2\nabla^2_{k+1}$$
$$- L_3\nabla^3_{k+1} + L_4\nabla^4_{k+1} - \ldots \quad (5.35)$$

which involves u_{k+1}, u_k, u_{k-1}, etc.

Equations (5.34) and (5.35) have applications with which we are not concerned at present, but they can also be used to derive a general and sometimes valuable expression for the integral of $u(r)$ over a number of intervals. This is *Gregory's formula*.

5.15. Gregory's Formula

We denote by I the integral

$$\int_0^n u(r)dr = U_n - U_0 \quad (5.36)$$

If the range from 0 to n is divided into n unit intervals, the contribution to I from the kth interval can be represented either

```
                                            - L_4       L_5
                              L_4    (v_0)          L_3
           u_0        - L_3   L_4    (v_1)    u_0         - L_2
          ± L_1  L_2  - L_3   L_4          2u_1    - L_2
          2u_1   2L_2 ± L_3   L_4          2u_1         - L_3
          ± L_1  2L_2 ± L_3   2L_4         2u_2              - L_4
          2u_2   2L_2         2L_4         2u_2                   - L_5
          ± L_1       ± L_3   2L_4         2u_3
          2u_3   2L_2 ± L_3
          .                   2L_4
          .
          .
          .           ± L_3   2L_4
          2u_{n-3} 2L_2 ± L_3  2L_4        2u_{n-3}
          ± L_1       ± L_3   2L_4         2u_{n-2}            - L_5
          2u_{n-2} 2L_2 ± L_3  L_4                        L_4
          ± L_1       L_3    L_4   (v_n)   2u_{n-1}   - L_3
          2u_{n-1} 2L_2      L_4   (v_{n+1}) u_n   L_2   - L_3
          ± L_1  L_2  L_3    L_4           u_n   L_2
          u_n          L_3                       L_2
                       L_3                             L_3
                              L_4                           L_4
                                                                L_5
                 (a)                            (b)
```

FIG. 5.2. CONTRIBUTIONS TO $2I$

by the series (5.34) or by (5.35), or by any linear combination. We shall in fact take for $2I$ a symmetrical combination, consisting of a series of type (5.34) for each interval added to the corresponding series of type (5.35). The resulting formula for $2I$ is shown diagrammatically in Fig. 5.2(a), which is in the form of a difference table, but in the position normally occupied by each difference is placed instead the coefficient which multiplies this difference in the formula.

From the figure it is clear that terms involving many odd differences cancel; those terms which remain can be transformed by replacing the sum of differences in a particular column by a combination of two differences in the column to the left, e.g.

$$\Delta^2_0 + \Delta^2_1 + \ldots + \Delta^2_{n-2} = \nabla^1_n - \Delta^1_0$$
$$\nabla^3_1 + \nabla^3_2 \quad = \Delta^2_0 - \nabla^2_0$$

Proceeding in this fashion it is easily verified that the terms shown in Fig. 5.2 (b) are exactly equivalent to those in Fig. 5.2 (a), and they involve only differences along four sloping lines. At this stage the formula for $2I$ has the form

$$2I = 2T_n + (L_2\nabla^1_n - L_3\nabla^2_n + L_4\nabla^3_n - \ldots)$$
$$+ (L_2\Delta^1_n + L_3\Delta^2_n + L_4\Delta^3_n + \ldots)$$
$$- (L_2\nabla^1_0 - L_3\nabla^2_0 + L_4\nabla^3_0 - \ldots)$$
$$- (L_2\Delta^1_0 + L_3\Delta^2_0 + L_4\Delta^3_0 + \ldots)$$

where $T_n = \tfrac{1}{2}u_0 + u_1 + \ldots + u_{n-1} + \tfrac{1}{2}u_n$, the usual trapezoidal sum.

It can now be shown that for a polynomial the first and second series in brackets are equivalent, and likewise the third and fourth series. For this purpose we introduce the first sums of the u's, $v_0, v_1, \ldots, v_{n+1}$, which satisfy relations of the form, $v_{k+1} - v_k = u_k$, and the corresponding interpolation polynomial $v(r)$. (The positions of v_0 and v_1 in the difference table are shown in Fig. 5.2 (b).)

Then if $V(r) = \int^r v(r)dr$, an application of (5.34) and (5.35) to V instead of U gives

$$V_1 - V_0 = v_0 + \tfrac{1}{2}u_0 + L_2\Delta^1_0 + L_3\Delta^2_0 + L_4\Delta^3_0 + \ldots$$
$$= v_1 - \tfrac{1}{2}u_0 + L_2\nabla^1_0 - L_3\nabla^2_0 + L_4\nabla^3_0 - \ldots$$

Since $v_0 + \frac{1}{2}u_0 = v_1 - \frac{1}{2}u_0$, it follows that

$$L_2\nabla^1{}_0 - L_3\nabla^2{}_0 + L_4\nabla^3{}_0 - \ldots$$
$$= L_2\Delta^1{}_0 + L_3\Delta^2{}_0 + L_4\Delta^3{}_0 + \ldots$$

By a similar argument

$$L_2\nabla^1{}_n - L_3\nabla^2{}_n - L_4\nabla^3{}_n - \ldots$$
$$= L_2\Delta^1{}_n + L_3\Delta^2{}_n + L_4\Delta^3{}_n + \ldots$$

When $u(r)$ is a polynomial all these series do in fact terminate. We can now write

$$I = T_n + L_2(\nabla^1{}_n - \Delta^1{}_0) - L_3(\nabla^2{}_n + \Delta^2{}_0)$$
$$+ L_4(\nabla^3{}_n - \Delta^3{}_0) - L_5(\nabla^4{}_n + \Delta^4{}_0) + \ldots \quad (5.37)$$

This is Gregory's quadrature formula, derived here by a rather protracted argument, but using only simple ideas.

Two points should be noted—

1. Gregory's formula involves differences along two converging lines, and if terminated at or before the term in $(\nabla^n{}_n \pm \Delta^n{}_0)$ it is a *closed* quadrature formula involving only the values

$$u_0, u_1, \ldots, u_n$$

In fact, if curtailed at this term, it is precisely the Newton-Cotes formula of order n, as may be proved easily by expressing all differences in terms of the u's. If carried beyond the nth differences, the formula of course brings in values outside the range of integration.

2. If $u(r)$ corresponds to a polynomial of degree n or less the formula carried to nth differences is necessarily exact. If $u(r)$ is not a polynomial it is necessarily approximate, the error being the same as the corresponding Newton-Cotes formula; moreover, if the series is ended, as it often is in practice, before the nth differences are reached, there is a further error from this curtailment (see Appendix 2).

5.16. Central Differences

Quadrature formulas akin to Gregory's but using central differences can be derived from one or other of the c.d. interpolation polynomials. Their general feature is that they involve values of the integrand outside the range of integration.

For instance, by integrating Bessel's equation for $u(k + r)$

(equation (5.13) with c.d's of $u_{k+1/2}$ replacing those of $u_{1/2}$) between limits of 0 and 1 for r, we obtain

$$U_{k+1} - U_k = \tfrac{1}{2}(u_k + u_{k+1}) + M_2\delta^2_{k+1/2}$$
$$+ M_4\delta^4_{k+1/2} + M_6\delta^6_{k+1/2} + \dots \quad (5.38)$$

where $M_2 = -1/12$, $M_4 = 11/720$, $M_6 = -191/60480$, etc.

Applied to each unit interval of the range $(0, n)$ this leads to the well-known *Gauss-Encke formula* for integral (5.36), in which the total contribution from differences of order $2s$ is

$$M_{2s}\sum_{k=0}^{n-1}\delta^{2s}_{k+1/2} = M_{2s}\{\tfrac{1}{2}\delta^{2s}_0 + \sum_{k=1}^{n-1}\delta^{2s}_k + \tfrac{1}{2}\delta^{2s}_n\}$$
$$= M_{2s}\{\tfrac{1}{2}(\delta^{2s-1}_{1/2} - \delta^{2s-1}_{-1/2}) + (\delta^{2s-1}_{n-1/2}$$
$$- \delta^{2s-1}_{1/2}) + \tfrac{1}{2}(\delta^{2s-1}_{n+1/2} - \delta^{2s-1}_{n-1/2})\}$$
$$= M_{2s}\{\delta^{2s-1}_n - \delta^{2s-1}_0\}$$

Hence, in terms of mean odd differences

$$I = T_n + M_2(\delta^1_n - \delta^1_0) + M_4(\delta^3_n - \delta^3_0)$$
$$+ M_6(\delta^5_n - \delta^5_0) + \dots \quad (5.39)$$

If curtailed after the δ^5 terms, (5.39) involves u's between u_{-3} and u_{n+3} inclusive.

Another procedure is to start with Stirling's formula (5.9) which, when integrated between limits of $-\tfrac{1}{2}$ and $\tfrac{1}{2}$ for r, also gives a result involving even differences only, thus—

$$U(k + \tfrac{1}{2}) - U(k - \tfrac{1}{2}) = u_k + K_2\delta^2_k$$
$$+ K_4\delta^4_k + K_6\delta^6_k + \dots \quad (5.40)$$

where $K_2 = 1/24$, $K_4 = -17/5760$, $K_6 = 367/967680$ and so on.

This leads to the *first Gauss formula*,* in which the range of integration ends at midpoints of tabular points; thus a similar argument to the above shows that

$$\int_{-1/2}^{n+1/2} u(r)dr = U(n + \tfrac{1}{2}) - U(-\tfrac{1}{2})$$
$$= u_0 + u_1 + \dots + u_n$$
$$+ K_2(\delta^1_{n+1/2} - \delta^1_{-1/2}) + K_4(\delta^3_{n+1/2} - \delta^3_{-1/2})$$
$$+ K_6(\delta^5_{n+1/2} - \delta^5_{-1/2}) + \dots \quad (5.41)$$

* It is difficult to avoid confusion in attaching names to formulas; (5.41) and (5.39) are sometimes called the first and second Gauss formulas respectively. (5.39) was certainly known to Gauss in 1812, though published again by Encke in 1837. We shall adhere to the title "Gauss-Encke" for (5.39) and denote (5.41) by Gauss (I).

Provided the integrand is suitably tabulated, this is a much better formula than (5.39), since it converges more rapidly and does not involve mean differences.

Alternatively, Stirling's formula may be integrated between -1 and $+1$ for r, with the result that

$$U_{k+1} - U_{k-1} = 2u_k + N_2\delta^2_k + N_4\delta^4_k + N_6\delta^6_k + \ldots \quad (5.42)$$

where $N_2 = 1/3$, $N_4 = -1/90$, $N_6 = 1/756$, and hence when n is even

$$
\begin{aligned}
I = \int_0^n u(r)dr ={}& 2(u_1 + u_3 + \ldots + u_{n-1}) \\
& + N_2(\delta^2_1 + \delta^2_3 + \ldots + \delta^2_{n-1}) \\
& + N_4(\delta^4_1 + \delta^4_3 + \ldots + \delta^4_{n-1}) \\
& + N_6(\delta^6_1 + \delta^6_3 + \ldots + \delta^6_{n-1}) + \ldots \quad (5.43)
\end{aligned}
$$

This formula, in spite of the sums of differences required, is an attractive and useful alternative to the Gauss-Encke formula. The terms in δ^4 and higher differences are corrections to the "repeated Simpson's rule" (3.24). We shall refer to (5.43) as *Stirling's quadrature formula*.

Further numerical values of the coefficients K_{2s}, M_{2s}, N_{2s} are given in Appendix 2. It should be remembered that although these c.d. formulas are conveniently used as given here—in fact the formation of a difference table is very desirable as a check on the suitability of any proposed formula—each can be expressed in terms of values of u only. Convenient tables of weights associated with tabular values of u are given in *Chambers* [6] (p. 549) for the Gregory and Gauss-Encke formulas, with valuable comments. Similar weights for (5.41) and (5.43) are given in Appendix 3.

5.17. Numerical Examples

For illustrations we shall return to the integrals of simple functions examined in § 3.7. The interval of 0·1 previously used is too fine, however, in relation to these more powerful methods, and we adopt instead an interval of 0·2. Even so, the integrals (a) and (b) are of limited interest; we therefore omit the difference tables of $\sin x$ and e^x, and present only the contributions to the integral from the various terms of each formula.

(a) $\int_0^{1\cdot 2} \sin x\, dx$ $(w = 0\cdot 2)$

Term in	Gregory (5.37)	Gauss-Encke (5.39)	Gauss (I) (5.41)	Stirling (5.43)
δ^0	0·6355151 0	0·6355151 0	0·6387062 0	0·6419128 0
δ^1	+ 18016 8	+ 21113 2	− 10609 6	
δ^2	+ 3455 6			− 42651 4
δ^3	− 140 2	+ 154 4	− 30 0	
δ^4	− 66 0			− 56 6
δ^5	+ 0 8	+ 1 2	− 0 0	
δ^6	+ 1 4			− 0 2
Result	0·6376419	0·6376420	0·6376422	0·6376420
Error	− 3	− 2	0	− 2

(b) $\int_0^{1\cdot 2} e^x\, dx$ $(w = 0\cdot 2)$

Term in	Gregory	Gauss-Encke	Gauss (I)	Stirling
δ^0	2·3278457 0	2·3278457 0	2·3162546 0	2·3047216 0
δ^1	− 63405 4	− 77853 8	+ 38733 0	
δ^2	− 13176 0			+ 154160 6
δ^3	− 470 8	+ 572 8	− 110 0	
δ^4	− 224 6			− 206 2
δ^5	− 3 4	− 4 8	+ 0 6	
δ^6	− 5 4			+ 1 0
Result	2·3201171	2·3201171	2·3201170	2·3201171
Error	+ 2	+ 2	+ 1	+ 2

The small errors remaining in all these computations when sixth differences have been allowed for are traceable directly to rounding errors in the tabular values. There is little to be gained by using central difference formulas for such well behaved functions as these, particularly when one finds that they involve appreciably more labour in differencing, itself a major part of the calculation. The relative importance of the later terms in the various formulas may be noted, however, particularly the magnitude of the δ^4 correction to Simpson's rule.

(c) $\int_{0\cdot 2}^{1\cdot 4} \log x\, dx$. This integral presents difficulties for c.d. formulas, and discussion of it is postponed to the following section.

(d) $\int_0^{1\cdot2} dx/(1 + x^2)$. This is a convenient integral for more detailed comparison of the formulas (5.36)–(5.42). For illustration we give the differences of $1/(1 + x^2)$ at intervals of 0·2, with a restriction to 6 decimals. Since the function is even, the table for negative x is a repetition of that for positive x, save that the sign of odd differences is reversed.

x	$1/(1 + x^2)$	δ	δ^2	δ^3	δ^4	δ^5	δ^6
		+ 38462		− 15917		+ 14050	
0·0	1·000000		− 76924		+ 31834		− 28100
		− 38462		+ 15917		− 14050	
0·2	0·961538		− 61007		+ 17784		− 8892
		− 99469		+ 33701		− 22942	
0·4	0·862069		− 27306		− 5158		+ 14102
		− 126775		+ 28543		− 8840	
0·6	0·735294		+ 1237		− 13998		+ 12103
		− 125538		+ 14545		+ 3263	
0·8	0·609756		+ 15782		− 10735		+ 2236
		− 109756		+ 3810		+ 5499	
1·0	0·500000		+ 19592		− 5236		− 1944
		− 90164		− 1426		+ 3555	
1·2	0·409836		+ 18166		− 1681		− 1937
		− 71998		− 3107		+ 1618	

Results of evaluating the integral are as follows—

Term in	Gregory	Gauss-Encke	Gauss (I)	Stirling
δ^0	0·8747150	0·8747150 0	0·8767292 0	0·8787328 0
δ^1	+ 8617	+ 13513 5	− 6728 5	
δ^2	+ 3451			− 26785 3
δ^3	+ 1578	− 69 2	+ 15 2	
δ^4	+ 596			+ 32 2
δ^5	− 346	− 16 3	+ 1 9	
δ^6	− 550			+ 3 4
Result	0·8760496	0·8760578$_0$	0·8760580$_6$	0·8760578$_3$
Error	− 85	− 2$_5$	0$_1$	− 2$_2$
Rounding Error	− 1$_4$	− 1$_4$	0$_0$	− 2$_3$

A different difference table has been used in applying the Gauss (I) formula. Here the story is quite different when we compare Gregory and the c.d. formulas, the latter showing up much more favourably. The essential reason is that the differences at this interval are not decreasing rapidly enough for the Gregory coefficients to give reasonable convergence. The symmetry of the integrand about $x = 0$ assists the Gauss-Encke formula by causing the rather large odd differences at that point to cancel. Another notable feature is that Simpson's rule gives 0·8760543, a better result than Gregory including 6th differences; this clearly arises from the oscillating differences, so that, although 4th differences are individually large, their net effect is small. Where differences increase monotonically, as in e^x, Gregory shows to greater advantage.

The residual errors in the c.d. formulas are mainly due to rounding, as shown by the rounding errors estimated for the first term in each series.

A calculation with 8-decimal values of $1/(1 + x^2)$, and an interval of 0·1 in x, gives the following results for comparison with Chapter 3, as the reader may verify by a straightforward (though lengthy) calculation—

Gregory (including Δ^{10})	0·87605 8099	Error + 48
Gauss-Encke (including δ^5)	0·87605 8055	Error + 4 (mainly rounding)
Stirling (including δ^6)	0·87605 8054	Error + 3 (mainly rounding) (cp. Simpson, error − 201)

5.18. Some Difficult Integrals

Numerical integration has special difficulties to overcome when the integrand becomes infinite, or has infinite derivatives, either within the range of integration or close to one end of it.

An example of the latter was provided by integral (c) of Chapter 3, in which $\log x$ has an infinity at the origin, and for which the values obtained by Lagrangian methods were not very satisfactory. Before discussing this type of problem in general terms, we should look again at integral (c) through the table of differences shown at the top of page 138.

On seeing the magnitude of differences along the leading diagonals of this table, it is hardly surprising that previous estimates of the integral between 0·2 and 1·4 should have been inaccurate. Moreover, the differences marked X are infinite. An estimate of integral (c) can be made by Gregory's formula, and if curtailed after Δ^6 the result is − 0·4070755, in error by + 242 units of the seventh decimal (slightly better than Weddle); subsequent terms, however, decrease slowly and the series ultimately diverges.

As a further illustration of what is possible in such circumstances without decreasing the interval, we may try to evaluate the integral

x	log x	δ¹	δ²	δ³	δ⁴	δ⁵	δ⁶
		693 147	X				
0·2	− 1·609 438		− 287 682	X			
		405 465		169 899	X		
0·3	− 1·203 973		− 117 783		− 116 654	X	
		287 682		53 245		87 124	X
0·4	− 0·916 291		− 64 538		− 29 530		− 67 656
		223 144		23 715		19 468	
0·5	− 0·693 147		− 40 823		− 10 062		− 14 508
		182 321		12 653		4 960	
0·6	− 0·510 826		− 28 170		− 5 102		− 2 539
		154 151		7 551		2 421	
0·7	− 0·356 675		− 20 619		− 2 681		− 1 284
		133 532		4 870		1 137	
0·8	− 0·223 143		− 15 749		− 1 544		− 546
		117 783		3 326		591	
0·9	− 0·105 360		− 12 423		− 953		− 259
		105 360		2 373		332	
1·0	− 0·000 000		− 10 050		− 621		− 135
		95 310		1 752		197	

of log x between 0·4 and 1·0, using the above table. Contributions to this integral are as follows—

Term in	Gregory	Gauss-Encke	Stirling
δ⁰	− 0·2347296	− 0·2347296	− 0·2310364
δ¹	+ 9815	+ 12923	
δ²	+ 2219		− 24622
δ³	+ 246	− 556	
δ⁴	+ 125		+ 152
δ⁵	+ 18	+ 167	
δ⁶	+ 29		− 2
Result	− 0·2334844	− 0·2334762	− 0·2334836
Error	− 7	+ 75	+ 1

It should be noted that the next term in each of the c.d. formulas would be infinite. Yet if one adopts the common procedure in summing asymptotic series of stopping with only half the smallest term included, even the Gauss-Encke formula gives a reasonably good estimate of the integral.

Nevertheless, these examples do not reach the heart of the problem which is to carry out the numerical process when the integrand becomes infinite, or has an infinite derivative, at a point within the range of integration. Likely examples are

$\log x \cdot f(x)$ or $x^{\pm a} f(x)$, $(0 < a < 1)$, where $f(x)$ is a function finite when $x = 0$, and otherwise well represented by a polynomial, and the integral extends to the origin. We may assume that the nature of the infinity is known, i.e. $\log x$, x^{-a}, etc., and that the integral itself is finite. Then several methods may be practicable.

1. *Change of Variable.* Let the integrand be $s(x)f(x)$, where $s(x)$ or its derivatives has the singular behaviour at $x = 0$.

Then
$$\int_0 s(x)f(x)dx = \int_0 f\{x(t)\}dt$$

where
$$t = \int_0 s(x)dx$$

so that the change of variable from x to t leaves an integrand which is well-behaved.

For example, if $s(x) = t^{-1/3}$ and $f(x) = e^{-x}$

then $\qquad t = (3/2)x^{2/3}$ and $f(x) = f\{(2/3)t^{3/2}\}$

The method obviously depends on $t = t(x)$ being readily soluble for x in terms of t, and for this reason it is not very suitable when $s(x)$ is logarithmic. Although it is most appropriate when $f(x)$ is known as an analytic function, it can be used when $f(x)$ is only tabulated, provided that interpolated values corresponding to regular intervals in t can easily be derived.

2. *Subtraction of the Singularity.* If $f(0)$ is known, we may remove the offending part, which should be integrable analytically, and integrate the remainder numerically. Thus if the infinity is logarithmic, the numerical integration would be applied to $\{f(x) - f(0)\}\log x$. Likewise if the first derivative becomes infinite, one may subtract a function whose derivative behaves similarly, but which can be integrated analytically.

3. Special formulas may be developed for the integral of a function such as $(\log x)$ $(\alpha + \beta x + \gamma x^2 + \ldots)$ over a short range $(0, b)$ say, and ordinary numerical methods used for $x > b$. Typical examples of this approach can be seen in Exercises 5, Nos. 5 and 6.

Hartree (*N.A.*, p. 111) has also described a method which he calls "dividing out the singularity," and which leads to a first-order differential equation for the integral (see Exercises 5, No. 7).

We end with a numerical example of the subtraction method.

EXAMPLE 5.6. Evaluate $\int_0^1 \dfrac{\log x}{(1-x^2)^{1/2}}\, dx$

The integrand is here infinite at the lower limit, and its derivative is infinite at the upper limit. However, the integral is conveniently rewritten as

$$\int_0^{1/2}\left\{\frac{1}{(1-x^2)^{1/2}}-1\right\}\log x\,dx + \int_0^{1/2}\log x\,dx$$

$$+ \int_{1/2}^1\left\{\frac{\log x}{(1-x^2)^{1/2}}-(1/2)\sin^{-1}x\right\}dx + (1/2)\int_{1/2}^1\sin^{-1}x\,dx$$

so that in the first integral the integrand is finite when $x=0$, and in the third the derivative is finite when $x=1$. Let us apply Simpson's rule to these integrals, using an interval of $0\cdot25$ and the following values of the integrands—

x	$\left\{\dfrac{1}{(1-x^2)^{1/2}}-1\right\}\log x$	x	$\dfrac{\log x}{(1-x^2)^{1/2}}-(1/2)\sin^{-1}x$
0·0	0	0·50	− 1·0622
0·25	− 0·0455	0·75	− 1·8590
0·50	− 0·1072	1·00	− 0·7854

The estimates are − 0·0242 and − 0·4403 respectively.

The second and fourth integrals are respectively

$$\left[x\log x - x\right]_0^{1/2} = -0\cdot8466$$

$$\tfrac{1}{2}\left[x\sin^{-1}x - (1-x^2)^{1/2}\right]_{1/2}^1 = +0\cdot2215$$

Hence our estimate of the original integral is

$$-0\cdot0242 - 0\cdot8466 - 0\cdot4403 + 0\cdot2215$$

or $-1\cdot0896$

Cp. correct value, which is $-\tfrac{1}{2}\pi\log_e 2$ or $-1\cdot0888$ to 4 decimals.
Note. If the behaviour of the derivative of the integrand near $x=1$ is ignored, a double application of Simpson's rule gives $-1\cdot0821$, in error by 0·6 per cent. An alternative treatment is to evaluate the equivalent integral $-\int_0^1 (1/x)\sin^{-1}x\,dx$, obtained by integrating by parts, in which the integrand is always finite but its derivative again infinite when $x=1$. If this is ignored, and Simpson's rule used with four intervals, the answer is $-1\cdot1026$; but if the derivative is treated as in the previous case, the answer is $-1\cdot0883$.

EXERCISES 5

1. Derive the following series for $U_{k+1} - U_{k-1}$ from the appropriate Newton polynomial—

$$U_{k+1} - U_{k-1} = 2u_k + (1/3)\nabla^2_k + (1/3)\nabla^3_k + (29/90)\nabla^4_k$$
$$+ (14/45)\nabla^5_k + (1139/3780)\nabla^6_k + \ldots \qquad (a)$$
$$= 2u_k + (1/3)\Delta^2_{k-1} - (1/90)\Delta^4_{k-1} + (1/90)\Delta^5_{k-1}$$
$$- (37/3780)\Delta^6_{k-1} + \ldots \qquad (b)$$
$$= 2u_k + (1/3)\nabla^2_{k+1} - (1/90)\nabla^4_{k+1} - (1/90)\nabla^5_{k+1}$$
$$- (37/3780)\nabla^6_{k+1} - \ldots \qquad (c)$$

2. Show from Newton's backward difference formula that
$$U_{k+1} - U_k = u_k + (1/2)\nabla^1_k + (5/12)\nabla^2_k + (3/8)\nabla^3_k$$
$$+ (251/720)\nabla^4_k + (95/288)\nabla^5_k + (19087/60480)\nabla^6_k + \ldots$$

Note. This formula is the basis of the Adams-Bashforth method, now outmoded, for integrating first-order differential equations.

3. Show that the error of Simpson's rule, applied to $\int_0^n u(r)dr$, where n is an even integer greater than 6, can be expressed in the form
$$- (1/90)\{u_{-1} - 4u_0 + 7u_1 + 8(- u_2 + u_3 - u_4 + \ldots$$
$$+ u_{n-3} - u_{n-2}) + 7u_{n-1} - 4u_n + u_{n+1}\}$$

4. If G_6 is the value of $\int_0^6 u(r)dr$ given by Gregory's formula, terminated at the sixth differences, show that

(a) $G_6 - (9/700)\Delta^6 u_0$ gives Hardy's formula—
$$\int_0^6 u(r)dr = 0\cdot28u_0 + 1\cdot62u_1 + 2\cdot2u_3 + 1\cdot62u_5 + 0\cdot28u_6 + R$$
where $\qquad R = (9/700)\{u^{(6)}(\eta) - \tfrac{1}{2}u^{(8)}(\xi)\}$

(b) $G_6 + (1/140)\Delta^6 u_0$ gives Weddle's rule
$$\int_0^6 u(r)dr = (3/10)(u_0 + 5u_1 + u_2 + 6u_3 + u_4 + 5u_5 + u_6) + R$$
where $\qquad R = - (1/140)\{u^{(6)}(\eta) + 0\cdot9u^{(8)}(\xi)\}$

5. If $u(r) = r^{-a}(A + Br + Cr^2)$, where $0 < a < 1$, show that
$$\int_0^3 u(r)dr = K(c_1u_1 + c_2u_2 + c_3u_3)$$
where $\quad c_1 = (3 + a)3^{1-a}, \; c_2 = - 12a(2/3)^a, \; c_3 = 3 - a + 2a^2$
and $\qquad\qquad K = 3/\{2(1 - a)(2 - a)(3 - a)\}$

6. If $u(r) = \log ar \cdot (A + Br + Cr^2)$, where $a > 0$, show that

$$\int_0^3 u(r)dr = c_1u_1 + c_2u_2 + c_3u_3$$

where $\qquad c_1 = 3(12 \log 3a - 13)/(8 \log a)$, $c_2 = 3/\log 2a$

and $\qquad c_3 = 3(2 \log 3a - 3)/(8 \log a)$

7. If $\displaystyle\int_0^r s(x)f(x)dx = h(x) \int_0^r s(x)dx$

where $s(x)$ or one of its derivatives is singular at the origin but has a finite integral, show that $h(x)$ satisfies the equation

$$\left\{ \frac{1}{s(x)} \int_0^r s(x)dx \right\} \frac{dh}{dx} + h = f(x)$$

and $h(0) = f(0)$. Show also that derivatives of h at $x = 0$ can be expressed in terms of derivatives of f.

Consider the cases in which $s(x) = x^a$ (where a is a non-integer greater than -1), and $s(x) = \log x$.

CHAPTER 6

SYMBOLIC METHODS

MANY results already obtained which express the interpolated values, derivatives and so on of polynomials in terms of ordinary differences can be derived more simply by using what is generally called operational or symbolic analysis. This consists essentially of a separation of the operation, such as differencing, both from the particular function on which the operation is performed and from the result of the operation. As the symbols representing such operations are found to obey the usual rules of algebra, direct manipulation of them leads to much simplification. In developing this method now we shall recover many of the formulas obtained by less sophisticated means in Chapter 5, but at a gain of greater systematization which enables the results to be extended with comparatively little labour.

In its simplest form the symbolic method is applicable to polynomials and to certain functions possessing derivatives of any order. No difficulties are then encountered with regard to remainder terms. It is possible, however, although we shall not pursue the subject so far, to develop remainder terms of the type considered in Chapter 5, by means of suitable operators. The field of applicability is thus extended to functions represented by series of the form (3.1). There is an underlying assumption throughout that the functions to be operated on are tabulated at equal intervals of the argument; the symbolic method is of little value for functions tabulated at unequal intervals.

The second half of the chapter, which deals with summation, uses the symbolic method to introduce several important results for the first time.

Displacement and Difference Operators

A simple operation is the addition of a constant amount to the argument of a function. If the symbol E_w is used for this operation, the defining equation is

$$E_w f(x) = f(x + w)$$

Alternatively it may often be more convenient to use $u(r)$, tabulated at unit intervals in r, in place of $f(x)$. The same equation would then be written

$$\underset{1}{E}\, u(r) = u(r + 1)$$

where the operator $\underset{1}{E}$, though ostensibly different, is in fact the same as $\underset{w}{E}$.

However, subscripts are cumbersome, and we shall omit the subscript whenever possible; this is unlikely to cause confusion if it be understood that when E is applied to a function of x the displacement is normally w, but, when applied to a function of r, the displacement is unity. This concerns, however, not the development of the symbolic algebra itself, but only the application of the results.

Repeated application of E has a cumulative effect, and for k applications we can obviously write

$$E^k f(x) = f(x + kw),\ \ E^k u(r) = u(r + k)$$

Negative powers of E are also covered by these equations. The second of them might also be written $\underset{k}{E}\, u(r) = u(r + k)$.

6.1. Forward and Backward Differences

The operation of displacing the argument is clearly closely related to that of differencing. Taking the forward difference as example, we have

$$\underset{w}{\Delta} f(x) = f(x + w) - f(x) = (\underset{w}{E} - 1)f(x)$$

and $\qquad \underset{1}{\Delta} u(r) = u(r + 1) - u(r) = (\underset{1}{E} - 1)u(r)$

where the significance of $\underset{w}{\Delta}, \underset{1}{\Delta}$ is obvious. Ignoring the subscript, both equations lead to the identities

$$\Delta \equiv E - 1,\ E \equiv 1 + \Delta \qquad\qquad (6.1)$$

The unit numeral here really stands for the identity operator I, but as $I^k = I$ and k is always integral the distinction is not vital.

It is easily verified that the formation of higher differences is equivalent to repeated application of $E - 1$; thus

$$\Delta^2 = E^2 - 2E + 1$$

leads to $\qquad \Delta^2 u_0 = u_2 - 2u_1 + u_0$

in accordance with the usual definition. More generally

$$\Delta^k = (E - 1)^k = E^k - kE^{k-1} + k_{(2)}E^{k-2} - \ldots + (-1)^k$$

whence $\Delta^k u_0 = u_k - k u_{k-1} + k_{(2)} u_{k-2} - \ldots + (-1)^k u_0$

Similarly

$$E^k = (1 + \Delta)^k = 1 + k\Delta + k_{(2)}\Delta^2 + \ldots + \Delta^k$$

so that, on application to u_0

$$u_k = u_0 + k\Delta^1{}_0 + k_{(2)}\Delta^2{}_0 + \ldots + \Delta^k{}_0$$

From these elementary examples it should be clear that E and Δ obey the simple rules of algebra, including that of commutation, i.e. $E\Delta = \Delta E$. Also it should be noted that the symbol Δ, used without a suffix, denotes an *operator*, but with a suffix it represents a *difference*, the result of operating on a function.

Thus far, only integral powers of E have been introduced. An obvious development is to represent the operation of interpolation by E^r, where r is not an integer. Then, using the binomial theorem once again

$$E^r = 1 + r\Delta + r_{(2)}\Delta^2 + r_{(3)}\Delta^3 + \ldots + r_{(k)}\Delta^k + \ldots$$

With this expression for E^r, the equation $u(r) = E^r u(0)$, when $u(r)$ is a polynomial, is exactly the Newton forward formula (5.1) for interpolation, without a remainder. Although the above series appears to have an infinite number of terms, it does in fact end after $(n + 1)$ terms, when $u(r)$ is a polynomial of degree n.

It is now an advantage to introduce a symbol ∇ for forming a backward difference, defined by

$$\nabla f(x) = f(x) - f(x - w) \quad \text{or} \quad \nabla u(r) = u(r) - u(r - 1)$$

Clearly $\qquad\qquad\qquad \nabla \equiv 1 - E^{-1}$

and hence we obtain the relations

$$E = 1/(1 - \nabla) \qquad (6.2)$$

$$\nabla = \Delta/(1 + \Delta) \qquad (6.3)$$

$$\nabla = E^{-1}\Delta, \ \Delta = E\nabla \qquad (6.4)$$

Newton's backward formula follows at once from (6.2).

6.2. Central Differences

When we consider central differences, it is necessary to introduce two further operators. These, in Sheppard's notation, are

(a) the central difference operator, δ, defined by

$$\delta u(r) = u(r + \tfrac{1}{2}) - u(r - \tfrac{1}{2})$$

(b) the averaging operator, μ, defined by

$$\mu u(r) = \tfrac{1}{2}\{u(r + \tfrac{1}{2}) + u(r - \tfrac{1}{2})\}$$

In particular

$$\delta u(k + \tfrac{1}{2}) = u_{k+1} - u_k \quad \text{and} \quad \mu u(k + \tfrac{1}{2}) = \tfrac{1}{2}(u_{k+1} + u_k)$$

The fundamental symbolic relations are

$$\delta = E^{1/2} - E^{-1/2} \tag{6.5}$$

$$2\mu = E^{1/2} + E^{-1/2} \tag{6.6}$$

but from these there follow a number of useful subsidiary relations—

$$E^{1/2} = \mu + \delta/2, \; E^{-1/2} = \mu - \delta/2 \tag{6.7}$$

$$\mu^2 = 1 + \delta^2/4 \tag{6.8}$$

$$2\mu\delta = E - E^{-1} \tag{6.9}$$

$$E = 1 + \mu\delta + \delta^2/2 \tag{6.10}$$

The introduction of μ is necessary for the representation of mean differences. In our previous notation

$$\mu\delta^{2k}u(\tfrac{1}{2}) = \tfrac{1}{2}(\delta^{2k}{}_0 + \delta^{2k}{}_1) = \delta^{2k}{}_{1/2}$$

$$\mu\delta^{2k+1}u(0) = \tfrac{1}{2}(\delta^{2k+1}{}_{1/2} + \delta^{2k+1}{}_{-1/2}) = \delta^{2k+1}{}_0$$

An expression for any central difference in terms of tabular values of u can be obtained by the binomial expansion of δ^k in powers of E.

The derivation of interpolation formulas is slightly more complicated than for forward differences.

(i) *Stirling's Formula.* We expand

$$E^r = (1 + \mu\delta + \delta^2/2)^r \quad \text{or} \quad (\mu + \delta/2)^{2r}$$

by the binomial theorem, using (6.8) where necessary to eliminate even powers of μ and to reduce odd powers to the first only. This gives the result

$$E^r = 1 + r\mu\delta + r_{[2]}\delta^2 + r_{\{3\}}\mu\delta^3 + r_{[4]}\delta^4 + \ldots \quad (6.11)$$

which, applied to a tabular value u_k, gives Stirling's formula.

(ii) *Bessel's Formula.* We require $u(k + r)$ expressed in terms of central differences of $u(k + \frac{1}{2})$, and therefore start from the equation

$$u(k + r) = E^{r-1/2}E^{1/2}u(k) = E^{r-1/2}u(k + \tfrac{1}{2})$$

The expansion of $E^{r-1/2}$ is necessary, and may be obtained either by multiplying the above expansion for E^r by $(\mu - \delta/2)$, or directly as the expansion of $(\mu + \delta/2)^{2r-1}$. By either route

$$E^{r-1/2} = \mu\{1 + (r - \tfrac{1}{2})_{\{2\}}\delta^2 + (r - \tfrac{1}{2})_{\{4\}}\delta^4 + \ldots\}$$
$$+ (r - \tfrac{1}{2})\delta + (r - \tfrac{1}{2})_{[3]}\delta^3 + \ldots \quad (6.12)$$

and Bessel's formula follows. Everett's formula can also be derived directly by symbolic methods (see Exercises 6, No. 3).

Before proceeding to examine the relations between the finite difference operators and those of the ordinary calculus, we should note various relations between δ, μ and Δ, ∇—

$$\delta^2 = \Delta\nabla, \quad \mu\delta = \tfrac{1}{2}(\nabla + \Delta)$$
$$\delta = E^{-1/2}\Delta = E^{1/2}\nabla = \Delta/(1 + \Delta)^{1/2} = \nabla/(1 - \nabla)^{1/2}$$

Relations with Differential and Integral Operators

The use of the differential operator D, and the integral operator I, is familiar to students of the infinitesimal calculus. The link between these and the finite difference operators is provided by Taylor's theorem, which may be written in the form

$$f(x + w) = \underset{w}{E} f(x)$$
$$= \{1 + wD_x + (w^2/2!)D_x{}^2 + (w^3/3!)D_x{}^3 + \ldots\}f(x)$$

where
$$D_x = d/dx$$

This leads to the symbolic equation

$$\underset{w}{E} = 1 + wD_x + (w^2/2!)D_x{}^2 + (w^3/3!)D_x{}^3 + \ldots \quad (6.13)$$

or, in briefer fashion

$$\underset{w}{E} = e^{wD_x}$$

if we understand that the exponential expression merely represents the series in powers of D_x.

If $f(x)$ be replaced by $u(r)$, the same relation would be appropriately written

$$\underset{1}{E} = e^{D_r} \tag{6.14}$$

where $D_r = d/dr$, but, as we shall generally assume functions to be tabulated at unit interval, for the remainder of this chapter, the suffix will be omitted and the symbol D used for D_r.*

Relations between D and other finite difference operators are easily obtained. Thus

$$\Delta = e^D - 1, \quad \nabla = 1 - e^{-D} \tag{6.15}$$

$$\delta = E^{1/2} - E^{-1/2} = 2 \sinh (D/2) \tag{6.16}$$

$$\mu = \tfrac{1}{2}(E^{1/2} + E^{-1/2}) = \cosh (D/2) \tag{6.17}$$

Relations with the integral operator follow at once if we accept the interpretation of I as D^{-1}.

6.3. Differentiation and Integration, Using Forward or Backward Differences

To express derivatives in terms of forward differences it is only necessary to observe that

$$D = \log E = \log (1 + \Delta)$$

and therefore

$$D^k = \Delta^k\{(1/\Delta) \log (1 + \Delta)\}^k$$
$$= \Delta^k\{1 - \Delta/2 + \Delta^2/3 - \Delta^3/4 + \ldots\}^k \tag{6.18}$$

Direct application of (6.18) to any tabular value of $u(r)$, with $k = 1, 2, 3, \ldots$ gives successive derivatives of $u(r)$ at that point. The formulas (5.29) are easily verified in this way, though the Stirling numbers in Appendix 1 actually provide a readier means of evaluating the coefficients in higher derivatives.

To obtain a derivative at an intermediate point, we need only combine (6.18) with an interpolation formula; thus

$$u^{(k)}(r) = D^k E^r u_0$$
$$= \Delta^k\{(1/\Delta) \log (1 + \Delta)\}^k(1 + \Delta)^r u_0 \tag{6.19}$$

* The same simplification is sometimes effected by using an independent symbol, e.g. θ, standing for $wD_x/2$ or $D_r/2$. Then $E = e^{2\theta}$, $\delta = 2 \sinh \theta$.

The analogous formula for backward differences is

$$u^{(k)}(r) = \nabla^k \{- (1/\nabla) \log (1 - \nabla)\}^k (1 - \nabla)^{-r} u_0 \qquad (6.20)$$

The derivation of integral formulas is almost as simple. Thus

$$\int_0^1 u(k + r)dr = \int_0^1 (1 + \Delta)^r dr \cdot u_k$$
$$= \{\Delta/\log (1 + \Delta)\}u_k$$

if the integration is carried out as if Δ were an ordinary quantity. The same result is obtained by treating I as the inverse of D—

$$\int_0^1 u(k + r)dr = Iu_{k+1} - Iu_k = \Delta Iu_k$$
$$= \Delta D^{-1}u_k$$
$$= \{\Delta/\log (1 + \Delta)\}u_k \qquad (6.21)$$

Since

$$\Delta/\log (1 + \Delta) = 1 + (1/2)\Delta - (1/12)\Delta^2$$
$$+ (1/24)\Delta^3 - (19/720)\Delta^4 + \ldots$$

we have verified Laplace's formula (5.34). The same integral, in terms of backward differences, is

$$- \{\nabla/\log (1 - \nabla)\}u_{k+1}$$

A simple extension of this argument leads to Gregory's formula. We first note that the trapezoidal sum

$$T_n = \tfrac{1}{2}u_0 + u_1 + \ldots + u_{n-1} + \tfrac{1}{2}u_n$$
$$= \tfrac{1}{2}(1 + E + E^2 + \ldots + E^{n-1})(u_1 + u_0)$$
$$= \frac{1}{2}\frac{E + 1}{E - 1}(E^n - 1)u_0$$
$$= \frac{1 - \tfrac{1}{2}\nabla}{\nabla} u_n - \frac{1 + \tfrac{1}{2}\Delta}{\Delta} u_0, \text{ from (6.1) and (6.2).}$$

Now

$$\int_0^n u(r)dr = D^{-1}u_n - D^{-1}u_0 = - \{1/\log (1 - \nabla)\}u_n$$
$$- \{1/\log (1 + \Delta)\}u_0$$

if alternative expressions for D^{-1} are used in the two terms, and therefore

$$\int_0^n u(r)dr - T_n$$

$$= - \left\{ \frac{1 - \nabla/2}{\nabla} + \frac{1}{\log(1 - \nabla)} \right\} u_n$$

$$+ \left\{ \frac{1 + \Delta/2}{\Delta} - \frac{1}{\log(1 + \Delta)} \right\} u_0$$

$$= - \{(1/12)\nabla + (1/24)\nabla^2 + (19/720)\nabla^3 + \ldots\}u_n$$

$$+ \{(1/12)\Delta - (1/24)\Delta^2 + (19/720)\Delta^3 - \ldots\}u_0$$

i.e. Gregory's formula.

6.4. Central Differences

The formation of derivatives and integrals in terms of central differences proceeds from the fact that, by (6.16),

$$D = 2 \sinh^{-1}(\delta/2)$$

$$= \delta\{1 - (1/24)\delta^2 + (3/640)\delta^4 - (5/7168)\delta^6 + \ldots\} \quad (6.22)$$

Accordingly, the even and odd derivatives of $u(r)$ at the tabular point $r = 0$ are given by

$$D^{2k}u_0 = \left(\frac{2}{\delta}\sinh^{-1}\frac{\delta}{2}\right)^{2k}\delta^{2k}u_0 \quad (6.23)$$

$$D^{2k+1}u_0 = \left\{\frac{1}{\mu}\left(\frac{2}{\delta}\sinh^{-1}\frac{\delta}{2}\right)^{2k+1}\right\}\mu\delta^{2k}u_0 \quad (6.24)$$

respectively. Note the inclusion of the averager μ in (6.24), necessary if the formula is to contain only quantities appearing in the difference table of the u_k's.

In addition, derivatives at the midpoint $r = 1/2$ are given by

$$D^{2k}u(\tfrac{1}{2}) = \left\{\frac{1}{\mu}\left(\frac{2}{\delta}\sinh^{-1}\frac{\delta}{2}\right)^{2k}\right\}\mu\delta^{2k}u(\tfrac{1}{2}) \quad (6.25)$$

$$D^{2k+1}u(\tfrac{1}{2}) = \left(\frac{2}{\delta}\sinh^{-1}\frac{\delta}{2}\right)^{2k+1}\delta^{2k+1}u(\tfrac{1}{2}) \quad (6.26)$$

where, this time, it is necessary to include the averager in the expression for even derivatives.

Before extending the analysis to integrals, some recapitulation of the meaning of the central difference notation seems desirable, so that the following results shall not be misunderstood. The mth repeated integral of $u(r)$, which is normally written

$$\int^r \cdots \int^r u(r) dr^m$$

we denote by $U^{(m)}(r)$. Then, in terms of the integral operator,

$$U^{(m)}(r) = I^m u(r)$$

Assume now that $U^{(m)}(r)$ is tabulated at the same points as $u(r)$; e.g.

$$U^{(m)}{}_k = I^m u_k = \int^k \cdots \int^r \int^r u(r) dr^m$$

From these values can be formed a difference table in the usual way—

$$
\begin{array}{cccccc}
U^{(m)}{}_0 & & \delta^2 U^{(m)}{}_0 & \cdot & & \delta^{2k} U^{(m)}{}_0 \\
& \delta U^{(m)}{}_{1/2} & & \cdot & & & \delta^{2k+1} U^{(m)}{}_{1/2} \\
U^{(m)}{}_1 & & \delta^2 U^{(m)}{}_1 & \cdot & & \delta^{2k} U^{(m)}{}_1 \\
\end{array}
$$

It is clear that $\delta^{2k} I^m u(0)$ and $\delta^{2k+1} I^m u(\tfrac{1}{2})$ are both quantities which occur naturally in this table.

On the other hand, if $U^{(m)}(r)$ is tabulated at midpoints, $r = 1/2, 3/2$, etc., we get a difference table with a typical section as follows—

$$
\begin{array}{cccccc}
U^{(m)}{}_{-1/2} & & \delta^2 U^{(m)}{}_{-1/2} & \cdot & & \delta^{2k} U^{(m)}{}_{-1/2} \\
& \delta U^{(m)}{}_0 & & \cdot & & & \delta^{2k+1} U^{(m)}{}_0 \\
U^{(m)}{}_{1/2} & & \delta^2 U^{(m)}{}_{1/2} & \cdot & & \delta^{2k} U^{(m)}{}_{1/2} \\
\end{array}
$$

In this table it is the quantities $\delta^{2k} I^m u(\tfrac{1}{2})$ and $\delta^{2k+1} I^m u(0)$ which occur naturally.

We can write down immediately symbolic expressions for four typical quantities, entirely analogous to those above for derivatives. Thus, for integrals at tabular points

$$\delta^{2k} I^{2k} u(0) = \left(\frac{2}{\delta} \sinh^{-1} \frac{\delta}{2} \right)^{-2k} u(0) \tag{6.27}$$

$$\delta^{2k+1} I^{2k+1} u(\tfrac{1}{2}) = \left\{ \frac{1}{\mu} \left(\frac{2}{\delta} \sinh^{-1} \frac{\delta}{2} \right)^{-2k-1} \right\} \mu u(\tfrac{1}{2}) \tag{6.28}$$

and, at midpoints

$$\delta^{2k}I^{2k}u(\tfrac{1}{2}) = \left\{\frac{1}{\mu}\left(\frac{2}{\delta}\sinh^{-1}\frac{\delta}{2}\right)^{-2k}\right\}\mu u(\tfrac{1}{2}) \qquad (6.29)$$

$$\delta^{2k+1}I^{2k+1}u(0) = \left(\frac{2}{\delta}\sinh^{-1}\frac{\delta}{2}\right)^{-2k-1}u(0) \qquad (6.30)$$

We give the formulas in this way, as *differences* of the integrals, pending a detailed discussion of the significance of inverse powers of δ.

In view of the evident importance that attaches to the expansions in powers of δ of

$$\{(2/\delta)\sinh^{-1}(\delta/2)\}^r \quad \text{and} \quad (1/\mu)\{(2/\delta)\sinh^{-1}(\delta/2)\}^r$$

both for positive and negative integral values of r, we give the first few terms in these expansions—

$$\left(\frac{2}{\delta}\sinh^{-1}\frac{\delta}{2}\right)^r = 1 - \frac{r}{24}\delta^2 + \frac{(5+22/r)r^{[2]}}{5760}\delta^4$$

$$- \frac{(35/r)r^{[4]} + (462+1563/r)r^{[2]}}{2903040}\delta^6$$

$$+ \frac{(175+4620/r)r^{[4]} + (40899+124476/r)r^{[2]}}{1393459200}\delta^8 + \cdots$$

$$\frac{1}{\mu}\left(\frac{2}{\delta}\sinh^{-1}\frac{\delta}{2}\right)^r = 1 - \frac{r+3}{24}\delta^2 + \frac{(5+52/r)r^{[2]}+135}{5760}\delta^4$$

$$- \frac{(35/r)r^{[4]} + (777+5784/r)r^{[2]}+14175}{2903040}\delta^6$$

$$+ \frac{(175+6720/r)r^{[4]}+(96969+626496/r)r^{[2]}+1488375}{1393459200}\delta^8 - \cdots$$

The coefficients of higher powers of δ^2 have been written in terms of central factorials. It is then a simple exercise to build up a table of these coefficients for integral r from central differences. A few values are given on page 153.

These tables provide at once the formulas for the first four derivatives of $u(r)$, both at tabular and midpoints, which have been

TABLE 6.1
EXPANSION OF $\{(2/\delta)\sinh^{-1}(\delta/2)\}^r$

r	Numerator in Coefficient of			
	δ^2	δ^4	δ^6	δ^8
-4	4	-8	320	-26240
-3	3	-21	457	-34539
-2	2	-24	496	-36992
-1	$+1$	-17	$+367$	-27859
1	-1	$+27$	-675	$+55125$
2	-2	64	-1728	147456
3	-3	111	-3229	288333
4	-4	168	-5248	490496
Denominator	24	5760	967680	464486400

TABLE 6.2
EXPANSION OF $(1/\mu)\{(2/\delta)\sinh^{-1}(\delta/2)\}^r$

r	Numerator in Coefficient of			
	δ^2	δ^4	δ^6	δ^8
-4	1	7	-457	57565
-3	0	24	-992	110976
-2	-1	51	-1835	195013
-1	-2	88	-3056	319616
0	-3	135	-4725	496125
1	-4	192	-6912	737280
2	-5	259	-9687	1057221
3	-6	336	-13120	1471488
4	-7	423	-17281	1997021
Denominator	24	5760	967680	464486400

given already in (5.31) and (5.32). Corresponding results for the first four integrals at tabular points are as follows—

$$\delta Iu(1/2) = \{1 - (1/12)\delta^2 + (11/720)\delta^4 - (191/60480)\delta^6 + \ldots\}u(1/2) \qquad (6.31)$$

$$\delta^2 I^2u(0) = \{1 + (1/12)\delta^2 - (1/240)\delta^4 + (31/60480)\delta^6 - \ldots\}u(0) \qquad (6.32)$$

$$\delta^3 I^3u(1/2) = \{1 \qquad\quad + (1/240)\delta^4 - (31/30240)\delta^6 + \ldots\}u(1/2) \qquad (6.33)$$

$$\delta^4 I^4u(0) = \{1 + (1/6)\delta^2 - (1/720)\delta^4 + (1/3024)\delta^6 - \ldots\}u(0) \qquad (6.34)$$

and for integrals at midpoints—

$$\delta Iu(0) = \{1 + (1/24)\delta^2 - (17/5760)\delta^4 + (367/967680)\delta^6 - \ldots\}u(0) \qquad (6.35)$$

$$\delta^2 I^2u(1/2) = \{1 - (1/24)\delta^2 + (17/1920)\delta^4 - (367/193536)\delta^6 + \ldots\}u(1/2) \qquad (6.36)$$

$$\delta^3 I^3u(0) = \{1 + (1/8)\delta^2 - (7/1920)\delta^4 + (457/967680)\delta^6 - \ldots\}u(0) \qquad (6.37)$$

$$\delta^4 I^4u(1/2) = \{1 + (1/24)\delta^2 + (7/5760)\delta^4 - (457/967680)\delta^6 + \ldots\}u(1/2) \qquad (6.38)$$

Of these (6.31) and (6.35) are respectively the same as (5.38) and (5.40). Alternate formulas involve mean differences. If integrals of $f(x)$ are required, it is only necessary to include a factor w^m in the series expression for the mth repeated integral.

From any one of (6.31)–(6.38) the integral over a number of intervals is easily derived.

Validity of the Symbolic Method

At this point we should call attention to the rules governing the use of symbols to derive finite difference formulas. First, in using expressions such as $\log (1 + \Delta)$, e^D, $\sinh^{-1} (\delta/2)$, etc., it is understood that these are only abbreviations for the series usually associated with these functions. Secondly, the use of infinite series is certainly permissible provided (a) the series operates on a polynomial, and (b) the terms of the series are ascending powers of a symbol, which, operating on a polynomial, reduces its degree. The infinite series is then, in effect, a finite series, and its later terms have no significance. The symbols Δ, ∇, δ and D satisfy (b), and expansions in powers of these are legitimate; E, μ do not. Thus the operations $\log (1 + \Delta)$, $e^\delta(1 + \delta)^{-1}$ are permissible, whereas $\log \Delta$ is not.

There is little difficulty in showing that functions which possess derivatives of any order, and are represented by infinite but convergent Taylor series, can be included in (a) above. In particular, exponentials of the form e^{ax}, and products of such exponentials with polynomials in x, come into this category for all values of x (see Exercises 6, No. 4). The variety of functions which can be accurately represented by expressions of this kind, at least over a limited range of x, is very large indeed. To this extent the method is certainly free from any need of elaborate justification such as may arise in some operational methods used in the ordinary calculus.

There is, however, a practical point that difference formulas are usually curtailed after a few terms, if only because higher order differences are likely to be dominated by rounding errors in the tabular values. This introduces a truncation error which can be assumed to arise from a remainder term to the Taylor series for the function. Milne* has in fact shown that, starting from the integral form of the remainder to (3.1), operational methods can

* See W. E. Milne, *J. Res. Nat. Bur. Stand.*, **43** (1949), 537; also Milne, *N.C.* paras. 30, 31 and Hartree, *N.A.*, pp. 129–132.

be used to derive remainders to interpolation formulas, etc., thus effectively extending the symbolic method to include functions of the type defined at the beginning of Chapter 3.

Summation

No discussion of symbolic methods would be complete without mention of the operators associated with summation. The formation of sums was discussed briefly in Chapter 2, after which the subject has been somewhat neglected, though a summation operator was implicitly used in the derivation of Gregory's formula in § 6.3. However, we shall now introduce three operators for summation corresponding to Δ, ∇ and δ. These are—

(a) the forward summation operator, Σ, defined by

$$\nabla\Sigma \equiv 1 \quad \text{or} \quad \Sigma u_n - \Sigma u_{n-1} = u_n$$

(b) the backward summation operator, Ξ, defined by

$$\Delta\Xi \equiv 1 \quad \text{or} \quad \Xi u_n - \Xi u_{n-1} = u_{n-1}$$

(c) the central summation operator, σ, defined by

$$\delta\sigma \equiv 1 \quad \text{or} \quad \sigma u_{n+1/2} - \sigma u_{n-1/2} = u_n$$

This notation* is consistent with that used for sums in Chapter 2. It should be observed at once that, although these symbols obey the usual associative and distributive rules of algebra, they do not necessarily commute with the corresponding difference operators. Thus, since $\nabla\Sigma = 1$, Σ is to that extent the inverse of ∇, but in general $\Sigma\nabla \neq 1$ as a little thought will show; in fact $(\Sigma\nabla - \nabla\Sigma)u(r) = u(r_0)$, where $u(r_0)$ is constant or may be replaced by any periodic function with period unity. When we consider the summation operation repeated, the result of $\Sigma^k u(r)$ will be indefinite at least to the extent of a polynomial of degree $k - 1$ in r. For this reason we prefer to introduce the new symbol rather than rely solely on ∇^{-1} to represent forward summation. However, when no question of interchange of Σ and ∇ arises we shall not hesitate to interpret ∇^{-1} as Σ, and vice versa.

Similar arguments apply to the operators Δ and Ξ, δ and σ and of course, D and I.

So far we have been discussing the *indefinite sum*, which

* It is the notation which W. G. Bickley uses in his paper on "Difference and associated operators with some applications," *J. Math. Phys.*, **27** (1948), 183, to which the whole of this chapter owes a great deal.

corresponds to the indefinite integral in infinitesimal calculus. The latter is the limiting result of the former if the interval of the argument is allowed to vary and tend to zero. Corresponding to the definite integral we have the *definite sum*, typified by

$$\Sigma u_n - \Sigma u_0 = u_1 + u_2 + \ldots + u_n$$

or

$$\mathbb{Z} u_n - \mathbb{Z} u_0 = u_0 + u_1 + \ldots + u_{n-1}$$

or

$$\sigma u_{n+1/2} - \sigma u_{-1/2} = u_0 + u_1 + \ldots + u_n$$

The equivalence of Σ and ∇^{-1} in relation to the definite sum can also be seen by writing

$$\begin{aligned}
\nabla^{-1}(u_n - u_0) &= \{E/(E-1)\}(E^n - 1)u_0 \\
&= (E + E^2 + \ldots + E^n)u_0 \\
&= u_1 + u_2 + \ldots + u_n = \Sigma(u_n - u_0)
\end{aligned}$$

Repeated sums, like differences, can be expressed in terms of the tabulated u values if the summation operator is suitably expressed in terms of E. Thus with caution in the use of infinite series, we may use the identities

$$\Sigma = E/(E-1), \quad \mathbb{Z} = 1/(E-1), \quad \sigma = E^{1/2}/(E-1) \quad (6.39)$$

The method of expansion depends on whether summation is intended to proceed from the top of the table downwards, or from the bottom of the table upwards. Thus, in the first case we write for the mth indefinite sum

$$\Sigma^m u_n = \{1/(1 - E^{-1})\}^m u_n = (1 + E^{-1} + E^{-2} + \ldots)^m u_n$$

and, in the second

$$\Sigma^m u_n = \{- E/(1 - E)\}^m u_n = (-1)^m (1 + E + E^2 + \ldots)^m u_{n+m}$$

A similar choice can be made with regard to $\mathbb{Z}$ and σ. Definite sums are obtained if the resulting power series in E or E^{-1} is terminated at a suitable point (see Exercises 6, No. 15).

6.5. Euler-Maclaurin Sum Formulas

Much of the attractiveness of the calculus of finite differences lies in the parallelism between it and the infinitesimal calculus, and the symmetry of the relations between them. In earlier sections we have expressed derivatives and integrals of a function in terms of finite differences, and if undue emphasis has been placed on this type of relation it is because many applications are to functions whose mathematical form is unknown or complicated. But, just as any derivative can be expanded as a series of differences of ascending order, or any integral expressed in terms of sums and a difference series, so any difference can be expanded as a series of derivatives of ascending order, or any sum in terms of integrals and a derivative series. These complementary groups of formulas are sometimes distinguished by the titles "Laplace-type" and "Euler-type" respectively. Hitherto we have been concerned with Laplace-type formulas; now we shall derive one of the best-known and most valuable of the Euler-type, that generally known as the Euler-Maclaurin formula.*

We have seen that

$$u_0 + u_1 + \ldots + u_{n-1} = \{1/(E-1)\}(u_n - u_0)$$
$$= \{1/(e^D - 1)\}(u_n - u_0)$$

by (6.14).

Now the expansion of $s/(e^s - 1)$ in terms of Bernoulli numbers is well known—

$$s/(e^s - 1) = 1 - s/2 + B_2 s^2/2! + B_4 s^4/4! - B_6 s^6/6! + \ldots$$

where $\qquad B_2 = 1/6, \ B_4 = -1/30, \ B_6 = 1/42,$ etc.

(see Appendix 2 for further values).

Hence we may write

$$1/(e^D - 1) = D^{-1} . D/(e^D - 1)$$
$$= D^{-1} - (1/2) + (1/12)D - (1/720)D^3 + (1/30240)D^5 - \ldots$$

and, by operating on $u_n - u_0$

$$\sum_0^{n-1} u_k = \int_0^n u(r)dr - (1/2)(u_n - u_0) + (1/12)(u_n^{(1)} - u_0^{(1)})$$
$$- (1/720)(u_n^{(3)} - u_0^{(3)}) + (1/30240)(u_n^{(5)} - u_0^{(5)}) - \ldots \quad (6.40)$$

When the terms $(1/2)(u_n - u_0)$ are transferred to the other side of the equation, this becomes the trapezoidal sum T_n, and the terms involving derivatives are corrections to the integral approximating to T_n.

---

* Published by Euler in 1738 (though discovered earlier), and independently by Maclaurin in 1742. The joint title conveniently distinguishes it from other theorems of Euler.

A second form* of the Euler-Maclaurin formula is

$$\sum_0^{n-1} u(k + 1/2) = \int_0^n u(r)dr + \frac{B_2(1/2)}{2!}(u_n^{(1)} - u_0^{(1)})$$

$$+ \frac{B_4(1/2)}{4!}(u_n^{(3)} - u_0^{(3)}) + \frac{B_6(1/2)}{6!}(u_n^{(5)} - u_0^{(5)}) + \dots \quad (6.41)$$

where

$$B_2(1/2) = -1/12, \quad B_4(1/2) = 7/240, \quad B_6(1/2) = -31/1344, \text{ etc.}$$

This may be derived by expanding $se^{s/2}/(e^s - 1)$.

Formulas (6.40) and (6.41) may be regarded as complements of the two Gauss formulas, (5.39) and (5.41). They are, however, but special cases of a general theorem relating

$$\sum_{k=0}^{n-1} u(k + t) \quad \text{and} \quad \int_0^n u(r)dr$$

(see Exercises 6, No. 8).

Proof of these results by the symbolic method would strictly limit their application to polynomials, for which the series end after a finite number of terms. Nevertheless they may be terminated at an earlier stage provided a suitable remainder term is included, or applied to more general functions under a similar condition. The proof of the Euler-Maclaurin theorem with remainder (forms of which for (6.40) and (6.41) are given in Appendix 2) is to be found in standard texts (e.g. Steffensen, or Jeffreys, *M.M.P.* p. 279). In general the terms of the series decrease rapidly at first, but subsequently increase, partly because the Bernoulli numbers tend to infinity, and partly because the higher derivatives of many functions not polynomials tend to become large. The series is in fact, like many others used in numerical analysis, an example of an asymptotic expansion, and the most accurate result is obtained, if need be, by taking the sum to one-half of the smallest term.

Applications are obviously limited to functions of which the derivatives can be evaluated without undue labour. The Euler-Maclaurin formula may then be used, either to evaluate the sum, if the integral is known, or, if the sum is easily obtained, to evaluate the integral. In view of its importance we give examples of both these uses.

---

* The coefficients in (6.40) and (6.41) are strictly written $B_n^{(1)}(0)$ and $B_n^{(1)}(1/2)$ (Milne-Thomson's notation), being special values of the Bernoulli polynomials of first order, $B_n^{(1)}(r)$.

EXAMPLE 6.1. Evaluate the sum of the pth powers of the first n integers.

When $u(r) = r^p$, equation (6.40) becomes

$$\sum_1^n k^p = \int_0^n r^p dr + (1/2)n^p - (1/12)\left[pr^{p-1}\right]_0^n$$

$$+ (1/720)\left[p^{(3)}r^{p-3}\right]_0^n - (1/30240)\left[p^{(5)}r^{p-5}\right]_0^n + \cdots$$

$$= n^{p+1}/(n+1) + (1/2)n^p - (1/12)pn^{p-1}$$

$$+ (1/720)p^{(3)}n^{p-3} - (1/30240)p^{(5)}n^{p-5} + \cdots$$

The series terminates when p is a positive integer with a term in n^2 or n.

EXAMPLE 6.2. Evaluate the sum of the infinite series

$$1/101^2 + 1/103^2 + 1/105^2 + \cdots$$

It is here convenient to use (6.41) with $u(r) = 1/(4r^2)$, thus maintaining unit intervals of r in the sum.

$$\sum_{50}^\infty \frac{1}{(2k+1)^2} = \int_{50}^\infty \frac{dr}{4r^2} - \frac{1}{24}\left[-\frac{1}{2r^3}\right]_{50}^\infty$$

$$+ \frac{7}{5760}\left[-\frac{6}{r^5}\right]_{50}^\infty - \frac{31}{157680}\left[-\frac{180}{r^7}\right]_{50}^\infty + \cdots$$

$$= 0{\cdot}00500\ 00000\ 00000 - 0{\cdot}00000\ 01666\ 66667$$

$$+ 0\ 00000\ 00000\ 23333$$

$$- 0{\cdot}00000\ 00000\ 00045$$

$$= 0{\cdot}00499\ 98333\ 56621$$

Other classic examples include the evaluation of Euler's constant, and the derivation of Stirling's asymptotic formula for log $(n!)$. We now give two examples of the evaluation of integrals representing transcendental functions.

EXAMPLE 6.3. Evaluate $\log 1{\cdot}5 = \int_{10}^{{\cdot}15} dr/r$.

If we adopt a unit interval in r, the sum $\Sigma(1/r)$ contains 6 terms. Then from equation (6.40)

$$\frac{1}{20} + \frac{1}{11} + \frac{1}{12} + \frac{1}{13} + \frac{1}{14} + \frac{1}{30} = \log 1{\cdot}5 + \frac{1}{12}\left[-\frac{1}{r^2}\right]_{10}^{15}$$

$$- \frac{1}{720}\left[-\frac{6}{r^4}\right]_{10}^{15} + \frac{1}{30240}\left[-\frac{120}{r^6}\right]_{10}^{15} - \cdots$$

whence log $1{\cdot}5 =$ $0{\cdot}05000\ 00000$
$+\ 0{\cdot}09090\ 90909$ $-\ 0{\cdot}00046\ 29630$
$+\ 0{\cdot}08333\ 33333$
$+\ 0{\cdot}07692\ 30769$ $+\ 0{\cdot}00000\ 06687$
$+\ 0{\cdot}07142\ 85714$
$+\ 0{\cdot}03333\ 33333$ $-\ 0{\cdot}00000\ 00036$
$=\quad 0{\cdot}40592\ 74058$ $-\ 0{\cdot}00046\ 22979$
$=\quad 0{\cdot}40546\ 51079$

Even at this value the logarithmic series requires 17 terms for comparable accuracy, though for the logs of numbers nearer to 2 the Euler expansion shows to greater advantage. We should also note that Gregory's formula, using the above six values, would give log $1{\cdot}5$ correct to six decimals only.

EXAMPLE 6.4. Evaluate $\tan^{-1} 1{\cdot}2 = \displaystyle\int_0^{1{\cdot}2} dx/(1 + x^2)$ to 8 decimals.

This is integral (d) of previous chapters. The trapezoidal sum formed from 8D values of $1/(1 + x^2)$ at intervals of $0{\cdot}2$ is $4{\cdot}373575715$. The odd derivatives vanish at $x = 0$, and have therefore to be evaluated when $x = 1{\cdot}2$ only; we find, using for higher derivatives the formula

$$D^n f(x) = (-1)^n\, \frac{n!\, \sin\, \overline{(n + 1}\ \cot^{-1} x)}{(1 + x^2)^{(n+1)/2}}$$

$f^{(1)}(1{\cdot}2) = -\,0{\cdot}40311744$ $f^{(5)}(1{\cdot}2) = 7{\cdot}07$
$f^{(3)}(1{\cdot}2) = -\,0{\cdot}3575$ $f^{(7)}(1{\cdot}2) = 94$

where $f(x) = 1/(1 + x^2)$. Consequently, allowing for the interval in x being $0{\cdot}2$,

$$\frac{1}{0{\cdot}2}\tan^{-1} 1{\cdot}2 = 4{\cdot}37357\ 5715 + \frac{0{\cdot}2}{12}\,(0{\cdot}40311744)$$

$$-\ \frac{(0{\cdot}2)^3}{720}\,(0{\cdot}3575) - \frac{(0{\cdot}2)^5}{30240}\,(7{\cdot}07)$$

$$+\ \frac{(0{\cdot}2)^7}{1209600}\,(94) - \ \ldots$$

$$= 4{\cdot}37357\ 5715$$
$$+\quad 671\ 8624$$
$$-\qquad 3972$$
$$-\qquad\quad 75$$
$$+\qquad\quad\ 1$$
$$= 4{\cdot}38029\ 0293$$

whence $\tan^{-1} 1{\cdot}2 = 0{\cdot}87605806$

One may conclude that, for simple functions, the rapid initial convergence of the Euler-Maclaurin formula makes it superior to all finite difference formulas both for sums and integrals. The latter are essential, however, for functions whose form is unknown or complicated.

6.6. Euler's Formula for Summation of Alternating Series*

A less important but often useful formula of Euler's is one for summing series of terms which decrease slowly in size but alternate in sign. The series may take the form

$$f(z) = u_0 - u_1 z + u_2 z^2 - u_3 z^3 + \ldots$$

where $u_k > 0$, and if this represents a Taylor series expansion for $f(z)$, then $u_k = (-1)^k f^{(k)}(0)/k!$.

Euler's formula is easily derived symbolically if we first observe that

$$\sum_{0}^{n-1} (-z)^k u_k = \{1 - zE + (zE)^2 - \ldots + (-zE)^{n-1}\} u_0$$

$$= \frac{1 + (-zE)^n}{1 + zE} u_0$$

$$= \{1/(1 + zE)\}\{u_0 + (-z)^n u_n\}$$

Also $1/(1 + zE) = 1/\{1 + z(1 + \Delta)\} = (1 - y)/(1 + y\Delta)$

$$= (1 - y) \sum_{k=0}^{\infty} (-y)^k \Delta^k \quad \text{where} \quad y = z/(1 + z)$$

Hence when u_k tends to zero for large k and the infinite series is convergent

$$\sum_{0}^{\infty} (-z)^k u_k = (1 - y) \sum_{0}^{\infty} (-y)^k \Delta^k u_0 \qquad (6.42)$$

The differences which occur in the sum on the right are thus forward differences of a series of positive coefficients.

---

* A simple method of summing slowly convergent series of positive terms has been suggested by H. E. Salzer, *Journ. Math. Phys.* **33** (1955), 356. If S_k represents the sum of the series to k terms, this can be regarded as one value of the function $S(y)$, where $y = 1/k$. The set of partial sums, $S_n, S_{n-1}, \ldots, S_{n-m}$, can then be represented by a Lagrange polynomial of degree m in the variable y, and the sum of the infinite series estimated by extrapolating this polynomial to $y = 0$. See also Exercises 6, No. 16.

A particular case of (6.42) arises when $z = 1$ and $y = 1/2$, for which

$$\sum_{0}^{\infty} (-1)^k u_k = \sum_{0}^{\infty} (-1)^k \Delta^k u_0 / 2^{k+1}$$

This modification could always be used to sum an alternating series by including the powers of z in the coefficients u_k. The more general formula (6.42) is useful in compiling a table of $f(z)$, since then only one set of differences of u_k need be prepared. For each value of y considered, powers of y are obviously required.

A similar formula in terms of central differences can be derived, but this rarely offers much advantage.

EXAMPLE 6.5.   Evaluate $\tan^{-1} 1\cdot2$ to 7D from the series

$$\tan^{-1} x = \pi/2 - 1/x + 1/3x^3 - 1/5x^5 + \dots$$

This is an alternative expression for the integral used in Example 6.4 and earlier. The series has an obvious advantage over the integral for large values of x, but for moderate values of x it provides a convenient illustration of the use of Euler's formula as well as a comparison of methods. We choose in this instance to sum the first few terms of the series directly, and to form differences of the coefficients from u_5 onwards; thus we write

$$\tan^{-1} x = \frac{\pi}{2} - \frac{1}{x} + \dots - \frac{1}{9x^9} + \frac{1}{x^{11}} \left(\frac{1}{11} - \frac{1}{13x^2} + \frac{1}{15x^4} - \dots \right)$$

Then $z = 1/x^2$ and $y = 1/(1 + x^2)$.

The difference table appears as follows—

u_5 0·0909091							
	− 139860						
u_6 0·0769231		37296					
	− 102564		− 13164				
u_7 0·0666667		24132		5545			
	− 78432		− 7619		− 2646		
u_8 0·0588235		16513		2899		1393	
	− 61919		− 4720		− 1253		− 807
u_9 0·0526316		11793		1646		586	533
	− 50126		− 3074		− 667		− 274
u_{10} 0·0476190		8719		979		312	
	− 41407		− 2095		− 355		
u_{11} 0·0434783		6624		624			
	− 34783		− 1471				
u_{12} 0·0400000		5153					
	− 29630						
u_{13} 0·0370370							

For $x = 1\cdot2$, the table below presents the rest of the calculations.

k	$(-y)^k$	$\Delta^k u_5$	$(-y)^k \Delta^k u_5$
0	$1\cdot0$	$0\cdot0909091$	$0\cdot0909091$
1	$-0\cdot409836$	$-0\cdot0139860$	57320
2	$0\cdot167966$	$0\cdot0037296$	6264
3	$-0\cdot068838$	$-0\cdot0013164$	906
4	$0\cdot028212$	$0\cdot0005545$	156
5	$-0\cdot011562$	$-0\cdot0002646$	31
6	$0\cdot004738$	$0\cdot0001393$	7
7	$-0\cdot001942$	$-0\cdot0000807$	2
8	$0\cdot000796$	$0\cdot0000533$	–
			$S = 0\cdot0973777$

Multiply S by $(1-y)x^{-11}$ $0\cdot0077346_1$ $[(1-y)x^{-11} = 0\cdot0794290]$
Add sum of first 6 terms $0\cdot8683234_5$

$\tan^{-1} 1\cdot2$ $0\cdot8760580_6$

This answer is nearly correct to 8D, the correct eighth digit being 5. Direct summation of the series to this precision would require at least 35 terms for $x = 1\cdot2$, 65 terms for $x = 1\cdot1$, and about 10000 terms for $x = 1$, even when allowance is made for the near cancellation of successive terms. The Euler series is therefore most effective as x approaches unity; even so, because of the slow convergence of the differences of u_k, it becomes cumbersome if $\tan^{-1} x$ is required to many more than 8D, and the integral of $1/(1 + x^2)$ has advantages as an alternative method. In general, when the sum of a slowly convergent alternating series is required, it is worth considering whether there is an equivalent integral expression.

6.7. Lubbock and Woolhouse Formulas

Another summation problem which can arise is that of deriving the sum of values of a function at regular intervals in the argument, using only values at a coarser interval. Without loss of generality we can assume that the required sum consists of n values of the function at unit intervals of the argument, whereas the values available are at intervals of m units, m being a factor of n. The required sum may then be written in the form

$$S = \sum_{p=0}^{mk-1} u(p) \tag{6.43}$$

where $mk = n$. One obvious approximation to S is provided by mS_m, where

$$S_m = \sum_{p=0}^{k-1} u(pm) \tag{6.44}$$

i.e. the sum of k values at interval m, starting with $u(0)$.

Corrections to this estimate may be expressed either in terms of derivatives of $u(r)$, in which case we get a Woolhouse type formula, or in terms of differences of $u(r)$ at interval m, which gives a formula of Lubbock's type. Woolhouse and Lubbock formulas correspond essentially to the Euler and Laplace formulas already mentioned and which arise as limiting cases when m becomes large.

The Woolhouse formula arising from (6.44) can be disposed of first; it is conveniently derived by a double application of the Euler-Maclaurin formula (6.40), first for S and then for S_m—

$$S = \int_0^n u(r)dr - (1/2)(u_n - u_0) + (1/12)(u_n^{(1)} - u_0^{(1)})$$
$$- (1/720)(u_n^{(3)} - u_0^{(3)}) + \ldots$$
$$S_m = (1/m)\int_0^n u(r)dr - (1/2)(u_n - u_0) + (m/12)(u_n^{(1)} - u_0^{(1)})$$
$$- (m^3/720)(u_n^{(3)} - u_0^{(3)}) + \ldots$$

Elimination of the integral gives Woolhouse's formula—

$$S = mS_m + (1/2)(m-1)(u_n - u_0) - \{(m^2 - 1)/12\}(u_n^{(1)} - u_0^{(1)})$$
$$+ \{(m^4 - 1)/720\}(u_n^{(3)} - u_0^{(3)}) - \ldots \qquad (6.45)$$

It should be noted that derivatives of u are with respect to the variable r, and not mr. Except when there is difficulty in integrating $u(r)$, it is usually preferable to evaluate S directly by the Euler-Maclaurin formula.

Formulas of Lubbock's type may be obtained from (6.45) by substituting suitable expressions for the derivatives in terms of differences, or by the symbolic method. As an example of the latter, we derive the formula corresponding to Gregory's.

First
$$S = \{1/(E - 1)\}(u_n - u_0)$$
$$= (1/\nabla - 1)u_n - (1/\Delta)u_0$$

Let the difference operators corresponding to an interval m be denoted by $\underset{m}{\Delta}, \underset{m}{\nabla}$, so that

$$\underset{m}{\Delta} = (1 + \Delta)^{1/m} - 1, \quad \underset{m}{\nabla} = 1 - (1 - \nabla)^{1/m}$$

and

$$S = \left\{ \frac{\underset{m}{\nabla}}{1 - (1 - \underset{m}{\nabla})^{1/m}} \cdot \underset{m}{\nabla^{-1}} - 1 \right\} u_n$$

$$- \left\{ \frac{\underset{m}{\Delta}}{(1 + \underset{m}{\Delta})^{1/m} - 1} \underset{m}{\Delta^{-1}} \right\} u_0 \qquad (6.46)$$

Certain expansions are now required. It is easily verified that

$$s/\{(1+s)^{1/m}-1\} = c_0 + c_1 s - c_2 s^2 + c_3 s^3 - c_4 s^4 + \ldots \qquad (6.47)$$

$$s/\{1-(1-s)^{1/m}\} = c_0 - c_1 s - c_2 s^2 - c_3 s^3 - c_4 s^4 - \ldots \qquad (6.48)$$

where $c_0 = m$ $\qquad\qquad c_3 = (m^2-1)/24m$

$\qquad c_1 = (m-1)/2$ $\qquad c_4 = (m^2-1)(19m^2-1)/720m^3$

$\qquad c_2 = (m^2-1)/12m$ $\qquad c_5 = (m^2-1)(9m^2-1)/480m^3$, etc.

Applying these to (6.46), and remembering that

$$\nabla_m^{-1} u_n - \Delta_m^{-1} u_0 = u_0 + u_m + \ldots + u_{n-m} + u_n$$

$$= S_m + u_n$$

we obtain

$$S = m S_m - \{c_1 + c_2 \nabla_m + c_3 \nabla_m^2 + c_4 \nabla_m^3 + \ldots\} u_n$$

$$- \{c_1 - c_2 \Delta_m - c_3 \Delta_m^2 - c_4 \Delta_m^3 - \ldots\} u_0 \qquad (6.49)$$

This is the required Lubbock formula. Gregory's formula can be derived from it as follows: denote the unit interval by w, so Δ_m becomes Δ_{mw}, etc.; then let $w \to 0$, $m \to \infty$ so that $mw = 1$. Under these conditions $(1/m)S \to \int_0^n u(r)dr$.

Other Lubbock formulas, analogous to the Gauss integral formulas using central differences, are easily derived (Exercises 6, No. 10). Coefficients, including numerical values, are given by Steffensen. Examples of the use of Lubbock formulas, if restricted to simple mathematical functions, are not very convincing, as the sums are usually obtained more easily (and more accurately) by the Euler-Maclaurin formula. In the treatment of numerical (e.g. actuarial) data, however, they find a genuine application.

EXERCISES 6

1. If Δ represents the operation of forward differencing at unit interval, and $\Delta_{(p)}$ at an interval p (< 1), show that

$$\Delta_{(p)} = p\Delta + p_{(2)}\Delta^2 + p_{(3)}\Delta^3 + p_{(4)}\Delta^4 + \ldots$$

$$\Delta_{(p)}^2 = p^2\Delta^2 + 2p \cdot p_{(2)}\Delta^3 + (p/6) \cdot p_{(2)}(7p-11)\Delta^4$$

$$+ (p/2) \cdot p_{(3)}(3p-5)\Delta^5 + \ldots$$

Obtain expressions for $\Delta_{(p)}^3$ and $\Delta_{(p)}^4$, and hence form the leading differences of a function at interval 0·2 from those at unit interval.

2. If δ, $\delta_{(p)}$ are central difference operators at intervals of unity and $p(< 1)$ respectively, show that

$$\delta_{(p)} = \mu\delta\{p + p_{\{3\}}\delta^2 + p_{\{5\}}\delta^4 + p_{\{7\}}\delta^6 + \ldots\}$$

$$\delta_{(p)}{}^2 = \delta^2\{p^2 + 2p_{[4]}\delta^2 + 8p_{[6]}\delta^4 + \ldots\}$$

Note. Use the expansion of $(1 + \mu\delta + \frac{1}{2}\delta^2)^{p/2}$ as in the derivation of Stirling's formula. The results of Nos. 1 and 2 have obvious applications to subtabulation.

3. Show that

$$E^r = \frac{E^{r+1} - E^{-t}}{E - E^{-1}} = \frac{\sinh 2r\theta}{\sinh 2\theta} E + \frac{\sinh 2t\theta}{\sinh 2\theta}$$

where $t = 1 - r$ and $\theta = wD_x/2$, and hence derive Everett's interpolation formula.

Note. Expand $(\sinh 2m\theta)/\cosh \theta$ in powers of $2 \sinh \theta$, i.e. of δ.

(Bickley, 1948)

4. If $F' = f(x, F)$ and $F_k = F(x_0 + kw)$, etc., show that

(a) $F_1 - F_0 = (1/2)w(f_0 + f_1) + \triangle$

where $\triangle = \{- (1/12)\delta^3 + (1/120)\delta^5 - (1/840)\delta^7 + \ldots\}F_{1/2}$

(b) $F_1 - F_0 = (1/2)w(f_0 + f_1) - (1/12)w^2(f_1' - f_0') + \triangle$

where $\triangle = \{(1/720)\delta^5 - (1/3780)\delta^7 + \ldots\}F_{1/2}$

(c) $F_1 - F_0 = (1/2)w(f_0 + f_1) - (1/10)w^2(f_1' - f_0')$
$$+ (1/120)w^3(f_1'' + f_0'') + \triangle$$

where $\triangle = \{- (1/100800)\delta^7 + \ldots\}F_{1/2}$

5. If $G'' = f(x, G)$ and $G_k = G(x_0 + kw)$, etc., show that

$$G_2 - G_1 + G_{-1} + G_{-2} = (1/4)w^2(5f_1 + 2f_0 + 5f_{-1}) + \triangle$$

where $\triangle = w^2\{(17/240)\delta^4 - (53/20160)\delta^6 + \ldots\}f_0$

6. By means of Dirichlet's repeated integral formula

$$U^{(m+1)}(r) = \int_0^r \ldots \int_0^t \int_0^t u(t)dt^{m+1} = (1/m!)\int_0^r (r - t)^m u(t)dt$$

and Stirling's formula for $u(t)$, derive formulas (6.32), (6.34) and (6.37) in the text. Similarly, using Bessel's formula, derive (6.33), (6.36) and (6.38).

Note. The numbers $T_{2s}{}^{2p}$ in Appendix 1 may be used to expand the factorials in the interpolation formulas in powers of t before integration. This orthodox derivation of the integral formulas will emphasize some of the advantages of the symbolic method.

7. By expressing the derivatives in the Euler-Maclaurin formula (6.40) in terms of differences, derive (a) the Gregory formula, (b) the

Gauss-Encke formula. Similarly from the second Euler-Maclaurin formula (6.41) derive the Gauss I formula.

8. Derive the general Euler-Maclaurin summation formula

$$\sum_{k=0}^{n-1} u(k+t) = \int_0^n u(r)dr + \{B_1(t) + (1/2\,!)B_2(t)D$$
$$+ (1/3\,!)B_3(t)D^2 + \ldots\}(u_n - u_0)$$

where $D = d/dr$ and $B_1(t)$, $B_2(t)$, $\ldots$ are the polynomial coefficients in the expansion

$$se^{ts}/(e^s - 1) = \sum_0^\infty (1/k\,!)B_k(t)s^k$$

($B_k(t)$ is the kth Bernoulli polynomial of first order.)

9. Derive the Euler formula for repeated summation

$$\Sigma^2 u(m-1) = \int_m^\infty \int_m^\infty u(r)dr^2 - \{(1/2)B_2 + (1/4.2\,!)B_4 D^2$$
$$+ (1/6.4\,!)B_6 D^4 + (1/8.6\,!)B_8 D^6 + \ldots\}u_m$$

Note. Prove first that $\nabla^{-2}E^{-1} = e^{-D}/(1 - e^{-D})^2$.

10. Derive the Lubbock formulas for the sum S in (6.43).

(a) $S = m\sum_{s=0}^{k-1} u\overline{(s + \tfrac{1}{2}m - \tfrac{1}{2})} + \{P_2\delta_{(m)}{}^1 + P_4\delta_{(m)}{}^3$
$$+ P_6\delta_{(m)}{}^5 + \ldots\}(u_{n-1/2} - u_{-1/2})$$

(b) $S = m\sum_{s=0}^{k-1} u(sm) + \{\tfrac{1}{2}(m-1) + Q_2\delta_{(m)}{}^1 + Q_4\delta_{(m)}{}^3$
$$+ Q_6\delta_{(m)}{}^5 + \ldots\}(u_n - u_0)$$

where m is an integer (> 1) and the coefficients are defined by the expansions

$$\delta^{-1} = m\delta_{(m)}{}^{-1} + P_2\delta_{(m)}{}^1 + P_4\delta_{(m)}{}^3 + P_6\delta_{(m)}{}^5 + \ldots$$
$$\mu\delta^{-1} = m\mu_{(m)}\{\delta_{(m)}{}^{-1} + Q_2\delta_{(m)}{}^1 + Q_4\delta_{(m)}{}^3 + Q_6\delta_{(m)}{}^5 + \ldots\}$$

Show that (a) and (b) reduce to the Gauss I and Gauss-Encke formulas respectively when m is large.

Note. Use $\delta = \{\tfrac{1}{2}\delta_{(m)} + \mu_{(m)}\}^{1/m} - \{\tfrac{1}{2}\delta_{(m)} + \mu_{(m)}\}^{-1/m}$,
$\mu_{(m)}{}^2 = 1 + \delta_{(m)}{}^2/4$.

11. Use the symbolic method to show that

$$\Delta(u_k v_k) = v_k\Delta u_k + u_{k+1}\Delta v_k$$

and likewise prove the general theorem (equivalent to Leibnitz' theorem)

$$\Delta^n(u_k v_k) = v_k\Delta^n u_k + n\Delta v_k\Delta^{n-1}u_{k+1} + n_{(2)}\Delta^2 v_k\Delta^{n-2}u_{k+2}$$
$$+ \ldots + u_{k+n}\Delta^n v_k$$

Note. Write $E = E_1 E_2$ and $\Delta = \Delta_1 + \Delta_2 + \Delta_1\Delta_2$, where E_1 and Δ_1 operate only on $u(r)$, and E_2, Δ_2 only on $v(r)$.

12. If $E = E_1 E_2$ and $\Delta = \Delta_1 + \Delta_2 + \Delta_1\Delta_2$ as in No. 11, prove that

$$\Delta^{-1} = \mathfrak{Z} = \Delta_2^{-1} - \Delta^{-1}(\Delta_1\Delta_2^{-1}E_2)$$

and hence obtain the formula for summation by parts,

$$\mathfrak{Z}(u_k v_k) = u_k \mathfrak{Z} v_k - \mathfrak{Z}(\Delta u_k \mathfrak{Z} v_{k+1})$$

13. By an extension of No. 12, expanding Δ^{-1}, show that

$$\mathfrak{Z}(u_k v_k) = u_k \mathfrak{Z} v_k - \Delta u_k \mathfrak{Z}^2 v_{k+1} + \Delta^2 u_k \mathfrak{Z}^3 v_{k+2} - \cdots$$
$$+ (-1)^n \Delta^n u_k \mathfrak{Z}^{n+1} v_{k+n} + \cdots$$

and in view of the fact that there is only one arbitrary constant on the left, define carefully any restrictions on the sums on the right. Give reasons for expecting the remainder after $(n+1)$ terms to be

$$(-1)^{n+1}\mathfrak{Z}(\Delta^{n+1} u_k \mathfrak{Z}^{n+1} v_{k+n+1})$$

Derive the alternative formula (applicable to summation from the bottom of the table)

$$\mathfrak{Z}(u_k v_k) = u_{k-1}\mathfrak{Z} v_k - \Delta u_{k-2}\mathfrak{Z}^2 v_k + \Delta^2 u_{k-3}\mathfrak{Z}^3 v_k - \cdots$$
$$+ (-1)^n \Delta^n u_{k-n-1}\mathfrak{Z}^{n+1} v_k + \cdots$$

14. Obtain the general formula

$$\mathfrak{Z}^n(u_k v_k) = u_k \mathfrak{Z}^n v_k - n\Delta u_k \mathfrak{Z}^{n+1} v_{k+1} + (n+1)_{(2)}\Delta^2 u_k \mathfrak{Z}^{n+2} v_{k+2}$$
$$- (n+2)_{(3)}\Delta^3 u_k \mathfrak{Z}^{n+3} v_{k+3} + \cdots$$

again explaining the nature of the sums on the right.

15. Derive by the symbolic method the expressions for repeated sums given in equations (2.9) and (2.10).

16. If v_k is a series of decreasing positive terms such that Σv_k converges, and

$$u_k = v_k + 2v_{2k} + 4v_{4k} + 8v_{8k} + \cdots$$

show that

$$v_k = u_k - 2u_{2k}$$

and hence

$$\sum_{k=1}^{\infty} v_k = \sum_{k=1}^{\infty}(-1)^{k-1} u_k \qquad \text{(van Wijngaarden)}$$

Note. This may be used to sum a series of slowly decreasing positive terms, if the Euler transformation is applied to the right-hand side.

CHAPTER 7

SOLUTION OF ORDINARY DIFFERENTIAL EQUATIONS (1)

WE come now to one of the basic problems of numerical analysis, the solution of ordinary differential equations. Analytical methods of solving such equations, as described in any text-book on the subject, have the obvious merit of combining all solutions of the equation in a single explicit mathematical form, so that any particular solution can be obtained by giving suitable values to one or more parameters appearing in the general solution. There is also the obvious demerit that only certain standard forms of equation are soluble in this way, and the variety of non-linear equations included is particularly limited. Numerical methods of solution tend to have the opposite qualities. First, they are applicable to a much wider variety of equations, even those containing functions with no explicit form but tabulated only at a series of points. On the other hand, anything approaching a general solution is not usually possible; what is practicable is the calculation of a few of the infinite family of solutions which comprise the general solution. However, this may not be so significant a restriction in practice, for there are many occasions when only a particular solution is required, and a method which is numerical from the outset may then be preferable. Even when a general solution is available in analytical form, the tabulation of a special case may involve a long tedious computation.

General Considerations

We shall first examine the types of differential equation for which the development of numerical methods of solution is essential. The classification is very much simpler than for analytical methods, because, with one or two exceptions, numerical methods do not distinguish between equations which are linear and those which are not.

Three important types arise—

First-order equation: $\qquad dF/dx = f(x, F)$ $\qquad\qquad$ (7.1)

Simultaneous first-order equations:
$$dF_1/dx = f_1(x, F_1, F_2) \atop dF_2/dx = f_2(x, F_1, F_2) \Big\}$$
$\qquad\qquad$ (7.2)

Second-order equation: $d^2G/dx^2 = f(x, G, dG/dx)$ (7.3)

or $\qquad\qquad\qquad d^2G/dx^2 = f(x, G)$ (7.3a)

It is assumed here that the differential coefficient of highest order can be rationalized; although the function f on the right-hand side may be a non-linear combination of its variables, x, F, etc., it must in general be a single-valued function of them.

In what follows, the capital letters F, G, H, . . . will be commonly used to denote successive integrals of the function f, rather than the notation $F^{(1)}$, $F^{(2)}$, $F^{(3)}$, . . . used in the last chapter. Only F, G will be used extensively, however, and it must then be remembered that

$$F = dG/dx$$

It will also be convenient sometimes to represent differentiation with respect to x by primes attached to capital letters, thus $f = F' = G''$, etc.

7.1. Reduction of Second-order Equations

The first point to observe is that the second-order equation (7.3) can be reduced immediately to a special case of (7.2), since

$$dF/dx = f(x, F, G)$$
$$dG/dx = F \qquad\qquad (7.4)$$

Moreover, any *linear* second-order equation can readily be reduced to the form (7.3a), the so-called "normal form," in which the first derivative is absent. Thus the equation

$$d^2G/dx^2 + p(x)dG/dx + q(x)G = r(x) \qquad (7.5)$$

can be reduced, by a suitable choice of G_1, to

$$d^2G_1/dx^2 + Q(x)G_1 = R(x) \qquad (7.6)$$

If we assume $G = G_1 \exp\left\{-\tfrac{1}{2}\int^x p(x)dx\right\}$, it is easily verified that form (7.6) is obtained with

$$Q(x) = q(x) - \tfrac{1}{2}(dp/dx) - \tfrac{1}{4}\{p(x)\}^2$$
$$R(x) = r(x) \exp\left\{\tfrac{1}{2}\int^x p(x)dx\right\}$$

Alternatively the independent variable x may be changed to z,

where
$$dz/dx = z^{(1)} = \exp\left\{-\int^x p(x)dx\right\}$$

and
$$z^{(2)} = -z^{(1)}p(x)$$
$$(7.7)$$

Then since
$$dG/dx = z^{(1)}(dG/dz), \quad d^2G/dx^2 = z^{(2)}(dG/dz) + (z^{(1)})^2(d^2G/dz^2)$$

equation (7.5) becomes
$$d^2G/dz^2 + Q_1(z)G = R_1(z) \tag{7.8}$$

where
$$Q_1(z) = q(z)/(z^{(1)})^2, \quad R_1(z) = r(x)/(z^{(1)})^2$$

Again the equation has been brought to the normal form.

The following examples illustrate these two methods of transformation.

EXAMPLE 7.1. Convert Bessel's equation
$$x^2 d^2G/dx^2 + x\,dG/dx + (x^2 - n^2)G = 0$$
to normal form by changing the dependent variable.

Let
$$G = G_1 \exp\left\{-\tfrac{1}{2}\int_1^x dx/x\right\} = G_1 \exp\{-\tfrac{1}{2}\log x\} = G_1 x^{-1/2}$$

Then
$$Q(x) = 1 - n^2/x^2 + 1/2x^2 - 1/4x^2$$
so the normal form is
$$d^2G_1/dx^2 + (1 - (n^2 - \tfrac{1}{4})/x^2)G_1 = 0$$

EXAMPLE 7.2. Transform
$$d^2G/dx^2 + (1/x)dG/dx + \{k^2 + q/x - (l + \tfrac{1}{2})^2/x^2\}G = 0$$
to normal form by changing the independent variable.

Let
$$dz/dx = \exp\left(-\int_1^x dx/x\right) = 1/x$$

Then
$$z = \log(x/x_1) \quad \text{or} \quad x = x_1 e^z$$
and the transformed equation is
$$d^2G/dz^2 + \{k^2 x_1^2 e^{2z} + q x_1 e^z - (l + \tfrac{1}{2})^2\}G = 0$$

Alternatively, if $G = x^{-1/2}G_1$, as in Example 7.1,
$$d^2G_1/dx^2 + \{k^2 + q/x - l(l+1)/x^2\}G_1 = 0$$

7.2. Reduction of Equations of nth Order

An equation of the nth order which can be expressed in the form

$$d^n F^{(n)}/dx^n = f(x,\ F^{(1)},\ F^{(2)},\ \ldots,\ F^{(n-1)}) \tag{7.9}$$

where $dF^{(k)}/dx = F^{(k-1)}$, can obviously be replaced by the set of n simultaneous first-order equations—

$$dF^{(n)}/dx = F^{(n-1)}$$
$$dF^{(n-1)}/dx = F^{(n-2)}$$
$$\cdot$$
$$\cdot$$
$$\cdot$$
$$dF^{(2)}/dx = F^{(1)}$$
$$dF^{(1)}/dx = f(x,\ F^{(1)},\ F^{(2)},\ \ldots,\ F^{(n-1)}) \tag{7.10}$$

This is the generalization of (7.4).

Now, in certain circumstances, which will be discussed in a moment, the numerical solution of several first-order equations simultaneously does not differ in principle from the solution of a single equation, though of course it is likely to be much more tedious. Hence, since an nth-order equation can be reduced to a set of first-order equations, it would appear that, from a numerical standpoint, the first-order equation represents the fundamental problem to be solved. However, second-order equations are an important feature of many branches of applied mathematics, and, moreover, can often be expressed easily in normal form. There is good reason to develop direct methods of solving such equations, particularly as these turn out to be no more difficult, and often more reliable, than methods of solving first-order equations. Again it may be convenient to break down higher order equations into several second- rather than first-order equations. For example, the equation

$$d^4 K/dx^4 = n^2 \rho^2(x) K$$

which arises frequently in problems of elasticity, might be replaced with advantage by

$$d^2 K/dx^2 = G,\ d^2 G/dx^2 = n^2 \rho^2(x) K$$

We shall therefore regard (7.1) and (7.3a) as the most important types of equations for which methods of solution are required.

The second-order equation in which the first derivative F, as well as the solution G, is required, is probably next in importance, and is best considered in the form (7.4).

7.3. Boundary Conditions

It has already been stressed that numerical methods normally yield only particular solutions. Another way of expressing this is that the boundary conditions of the particular problem must be stated and used before the process of numerical integration can be satisfactorily begun. For a single first-order equation only one condition need be specified, e.g. the value of F for some value of x, by which the solution is then in general uniquely determined. (Singular solutions, which by definition cannot be derived in this way, must be obtained otherwise.) Two conditions are necessary to pick out a particular solution of a second-order equation, and here it is possible to distinguish two quite different situations—

(a) Both conditions refer to the same value of x, e.g. G and F are both specified for this point.

(b) The conditions refer to different values of x, e.g. G (or F) is specified at two points, or G at one point and F at the other. For ordinary differential equations which arise from physical problems, it is usually possible to express the conditions in a way which involves one or two points only (in contrast to partial differential equations, for which the solution is only determined if conditions are given at an infinite number of boundary points); nevertheless one must be prepared to deal with other forms of condition, e.g. the solution may be required to behave like $\sin x$ or e^{-x} for large values of x, or its integral over a certain range of x may be a minimum, and so on.

The variety of possible boundary conditions clearly becomes greater for equations of order greater than two. In spite of this, although an nth-order equation may involve n conditions, it is still common for these to refer to one or two points only. Both numerically and analytically the treatment of problems in which all conditions refer to a single point (sometimes called "marching conditions") is much simpler, and we shall for the present confine the discussion to these cases.

Under marching conditions, referring to a point x_0, all numerical methods are in a sense extrapolatory, in that they start from this point and develop the solution for a neighbouring point, which provides the basis for the next extension, and so on. There are many methods, but most fall in one of the following classes—

1. Methods using series, usually power series in $(x - x_0)$ or, if the region is that in which x is large, power series in $1/x$.

2. Methods using recurrence relations relating the solution at a succession of equidistant points, these relations being derived from the differential equation.

3. Integration methods, using finite differences (or their equivalent), applied to the integral equation which replaces the differential equation when the starting conditions are known.

Graphical methods, although they will not be pursued here, should also be mentioned, as they are occasionally useful when the accuracy required falls within their scope. A family of solutions can often be sketched out quite rapidly by graphical means.*

The limitations of series methods are usually concerned with the rate of convergence, i.e. the number of terms required to give the solution with required accuracy, rather than theoretical questions of whether the series as a whole is convergent or divergent. Often the most useful series are asymptotic (see sections 7.9–7.12). In (2) and (3) there is always the danger that cumulative computation errors may be important, and that they will introduce, in certain cases, a multiple of some unwanted solution with quite different behaviour to the one desired. This makes constant vigilance essential, particularly in equations of higher order than the second.

As mentioned earlier, when the boundary conditions are of the marching kind, the solution of simultaneous equations of first or second order is in principle the same as for a single equation, though the computation is obviously longer and the danger of build-up errors greater. This is certainly not true when the boundary conditions refer to two or more points, and the numerical problem (as well as the physical) is often quite different. For conditions at two points, two fairly general methods can be mentioned here.

1. Replacement of the differential equation by a finite difference equation, to be solved at a finite (but not too numerous) set of points.

---

* For descriptions of such methods, see Levy and Baggott, *Numerical Studies in Differential Equations* (Watts, 1934), or Willers, *Practical Numerical Analysis* (Dover, 1948).

2. Representation of the solution by a linear combination of relatively simple functions, e.g. polynomials, trigonometrical functions, preferably with certain "orthogonal" properties, their coefficients being determined by a suitable criterion.

Both methods normally lead to a set of simultaneous linear algebraic equations, the solution of which may or may not depend upon giving particular values (proper values) to some parameter in the differential equation. By contrast with the methods used in the previous type of problem, these may be termed "interpolatory," and they are not associated to the same extent with dangerous build-up errors. Discussion of them will be reserved until after the treatment of simultaneous linear equations and determinantal equations in Chapters 11, 12 and 13.

The rest of this chapter will be concerned mainly with the use of series, and is more than usually analytical in character; the following chapter discusses methods (2) and (3) of deriving solutions satisfying one-point conditions.

7.4. General Solution of Linear Second-order Equations

Before the development of series solution is discussed, however, attention should be given to the fact that, for second-order linear equations, numerical methods may suffice to give a general solution. Thus if $G_{(1)}$ is any solution of (7.5) with $r(x)$ absent, possibly in tabular form, a second independent solution is given by

$$G_{(2)} = G_{(1)} \int_{x_0}^{x} \{G_{(1)}\}^{-2} \phi(x) dx$$

where
$$\phi(x) = \exp\left\{-\int^{x} p(x) dx\right\} \qquad (7.11)$$

To obtain a general solution of (7.5) all that is required in addition is a particular integral $G_{(3)}$, which is provided by

$$G_{(3)} = G_{(1)} \int_{x_0}^{x} \{G_{(1)}\}^{-2} \phi(x) \left\{\int_{x_0}^{x} r(x) G_{(1)} (\phi(x))^{-1} dx\right\} dx$$

Then
$$G = A G_{(1)} + B G_{(2)} + G_{(3)} \qquad (7.12)$$

is the required general form, in which A and B may be chosen to satisfy any desired boundary conditions.

In particular, when $p(x)$ is absent

$$G = G_{(1)} \left[A + \int_{x_0}^{x} G_{(1)}^{-2} \left\{B + \int_{x_0}^{x} r(x) G_{(1)} dx\right\} dx\right] \qquad (7.13)$$

Thus, on the basis of a single solution, numerical or analytical, the general solution can be developed by using straightforward numerical integration. See also Exercise 7.2.

Series Solutions

The solution of an equation may sometimes be developed as a series of powers of x over the whole desired range of the variable, although slow convergence may prevent it being a suitable form for computation over a major part of this range. More often a series expression is applied over a short range only, and the solution extended by the use of recurrence relations or finite differences; in this case the series is only a temporary expedient, though necessary for reasons which will be understood later. We shall begin by describing two established methods, those of Taylor and Picard, of developing a series solution about a point x_0.

7.5. Taylor's Series

Let Taylor's series be written as

$$F = F_0 + hf_0 + (h^2/2\,!)f^{(1)}{}_0 + \ldots + (h^{n+1}/(n+1)\,!)f^{(n)}(\xi) \quad (7.14)$$

where $h = x - x_0$, and all derivatives of f, assumed to be finite and continuous, are evaluated at x_0, except the nth, which is evaluated at ξ, lying between x_0 and $x_0 + h$. It has the form of a power series in h, the constant coefficients being provided by the differential equation itself, which can be differentiated as often as necessary. The number of terms to be included is fixed by the permissible error; if this is ε and the term series is curtailed at the term in $f^{(n)}$, then

$$h^{n+1} f^{(n)}(\xi) < (n+1)!\varepsilon$$

For given h, this may determine n; alternatively, if n is specified, it will place an upper limit on h. The following examples show how the method works.

EXAMPLE 7.3. Obtain a series solution of
$$dF/dx = 1 - 2xF \qquad (= f)$$
for which $F = 0$, $x = 0$.

From the equation, $f^{(1)} = -2F \quad -2xf$
$$\begin{aligned} f^{(2)} &= -4f \quad -2xf^{(1)} \\ f^{(3)} &= -6f^{(1)} -2xf^{(2)} \\ f^{(4)} &= -8f^{(2)} -2xf^{(3)} \end{aligned}$$

The extension of this series is obvious. When $x = 0$, all odd derivatives vanish, and

$$f_0 = 1, \quad f^{(2)}{}_0 = -4, \quad f^{(4)}{}_0 = 32, \text{ etc.}$$

In general

$$f^{(2k)}{}_0 = (-1)^k 4 \cdot 8 \cdot 12 \ldots (4k) = (-1)^k k! \, 2^{2k}$$

or $f^{(2k)}{}_0 / (2k + 1)! = (-1)^k 2^k / \{1 \cdot 3 \cdot 5 \ldots (2k + 1)\}$

Hence

$$F = x - (2/3)x^3 + (4/15)x^5 - (8/105)x^7 + (16/945)x^9 - \ldots$$

Since terms are alternating in sign, the error is less than the first term neglected. If the error in F, obtained from 4 terms of the series only, is to be less than 10^{-6} after rounding, then

$$(16/945)x^9 < 5 \times 10^{-7} \quad \text{or} \quad x < 0\cdot314$$

Alternatively, to obtain results correct to 10^{-10} for $x \leqslant 1$, we should require

$$2^k / \{3 \cdot 5 \cdot 7 \ldots (2k + 1)\} < 5 \times 10^{-11}$$

from which it follows that about 25 terms are necessary.

The analytical solution is

$$e^{-x^2} \int_0^x e^{t^2} dt$$

EXAMPLE 7.4. Obtain a series solution of $dF/dx = (xF - 1)^{1/3}$ for which $F = 2$, $x = 1$.

This is preferably rationalized before differentiation, so

$$f^3 = xF - 1$$
$$3f^2 f^{(1)} = xf + F$$
$$3f^2 f^{(2)} + 6f(f^{(1)})^2 = xf^{(1)} + 2f$$
$$3f^2 f^{(3)} + 18f \cdot f^{(1)} f^{(2)} + 6(f^{(1)})^3 = xf^{(2)} + 3f^{(1)}$$
$$3f^2 f^{(4)} + 24f \cdot f^{(1)} f^{(3)} + 18f(f^{(2)})^2 + 36(f^{(1)})^2 f^{(2)} = xf^{(3)} + 4f^{(2)}$$

Hence

$$f_1 = 1, \quad f^{(1)}{}_1 = 1, \quad f^{(2)}{}_1 = -1, \quad f^{(3)}{}_1 = 14/3, \quad f^{(4)}{}_1 = -280/9$$

and

$$F = 2 + h + (1/2)h^2 - (1/6)h^3 + (7/36)h^4 - (7/27)h^5 + \ldots$$

where $h = x - 1$. The use of 5 terms only certainly does not guarantee results accurate to one unit in the fifth decimal unless $h < 0\cdot11$. The example shows that the application of Taylor's series may be tedious.

The application of the method to simultaneous equations or equations of higher order is essentially the same. We must, however, note circumstances which render the method inapplicable.

This occurs if any essential derivative becomes infinite at the point of expansion. Thus neither of the equations of Examples 7.1 and 7.2 could be so solved in the neighbourhood of $x = 0$, at which d^2G/dx^2 is normally infinite. A method of developing series solutions for such equations will be described in § 7.8.

7.6. Tabulation of Solution Using Taylor's Series

The series just developed are generally adequate when the solution is required over a short range of x. For a more extended tabulation, it is preferable to develop the Taylor series at a succession of equidistant points in order to reduce the number of terms required. A convenient method of doing this for a linear first-order equation of the form

$$dF/dx = P_1(x)F(x) + Q_1(x) \qquad (7.15)$$

is as follows.* The kth derivative can be written as

$$d^k F/dx^k = P_k(x)F(x) + Q_k(x) \qquad (7.16)$$

where P_k, Q_k are easily derived by means of recurrence relations

$$P_{k+1} = dP_k/dx + P_1 P_k, \quad Q_{k+1} = dQ_k/dx + Q_1 P_k \quad (7.17)$$

It follows that

$$F(x + h) = P(x, h)F(x) + Q(x, h) \qquad (7.18)$$

where

$$P(x, h) = 1 + hP_1 + (h^2/2\,!)P_2 + (h^3/3\,!)P_3 + \ldots \quad (7.19)$$

$$Q(x, h) = \qquad hQ_1 + (h^2/2\,!)Q_2 + (h^3/3\,!)Q_3 + \ldots \quad (7.20)$$

The functions $P(x, h)$, $Q(x, h)$ can be precalculated at a succession of points x_0, $x_0 + h$, $x_0 + 2h$, etc., and then (7.18) provides the corresponding values of $F(x)$. To obtain a suitable check on the computation, it is an advantage to calculate separately the parts of $P(x, h)$ and $Q(x, h)$ which contain odd and even powers of h, then at each step $F(x - h)$ can be derived, as well as $F(x + h)$, and compared with the value previously used.

To avoid calculating P_k, Q_k at a large number of points, a compromise method may be adopted, in which pivotal values of $F(x)$ are first derived as above at intervals of h, which is chosen so that the number of terms in the series (7.19) and (7.20) is not excessive. Then intermediate values, say $x_k + sw$ where $s = 1$,

* The method has been described by E. M. Wilson, *Quart. J. Mech. Appl. Math.*, **2** (1949), 208.

2, . . ., $(n-1)$ and $nw = h$, can be filled in by using (7.18), (7.19) and (7.20) with $x = x_k$ and h replaced by sw. At the same time, values obtained at an earlier stage for $x_k - sw$ can be checked. The final table gives $F(x)$ at intervals of w in x.

The following example shows the layout of the calculation, and the method of checking.

EXAMPLE 7.5. Tabulate, with 4 decimals, for $x = 0(0{\cdot}1)2{\cdot}0$ the solution of $dF/dx = 1 - 2xF$, for which $F = 0$, $x = 0$.

Using the recurrence relations (7.17), we obtain, with $y = 2x$,

$$P_1 = -y \qquad\qquad\qquad Q_1 = 1$$
$$P_2 = -2 + y^2 \qquad\qquad Q_2 = -y$$
$$P_3 = 6y - y^3 \qquad\qquad Q_3 = -4 + y^2$$
$$P_4 = 12 - 12y^2 + y^4 \qquad Q_4 = 10y - y^3$$
$$P_5 = -60y + 20y^3 - y^5 \qquad Q_5 = 32 - 18y^2 + y^4$$
$$P_6 = -120 + 180y^2 - 30y^4 \qquad Q_6 = -132y + 28y^3 - y^5$$
$$\qquad\quad + y^6$$
$$P_7 = 840y - 420y^3 + 42y^5 \qquad Q_7 = -384 + 348y^2 - 40y^4$$
$$\qquad\quad - y^7 \qquad\qquad\qquad\quad + y^6$$
$$P_8 = 1680 - 3360y^2 + 840y^4 \qquad Q_8 = 2232y - 740y^3 + 54y^5$$
$$\qquad\quad - 56y^6 + y^8 \qquad\qquad\qquad - y^7$$

Let $h = 0{\cdot}5$. The basic table of P_k, Q_k is as follows—

			x			$h^k/k!$			x			
	0	0·5	1·0	1·5	2·0		0	0·5	1·0	1·5	2·0	
P_1	0	− 1	− 2	− 3	− 4	0·5	1	1	1	1	1	Q_1
P_3	0	5	4	− 9	− 40	0·0208333	− 4	− 3	0	5	12	Q_3
P_5	0	− 41	8	117	16	0·0002604	32	15	− 24	− 49	0	Q_5
P_7	0	461	− 464	− 801	3104	$0{\cdot}0000015_5$	− 384	− 75	432	237	2960	Q_7
P_2	− 2	− 1	2	7	14	0·125	0	− 1	− 2	− 3	− 4	Q_2
P_4	12	1	− 20	− 15	76	0·0026042	0	9	12	3	− 24	Q_4
P_6	− 120	31	184	− 201	− 824	0·0000217	0	− 105	− 72	117	240	Q_6
P_8	1680	− 895	− 1648	5217	− 880	$0{\cdot}0000001_0$	0	1545	144	− 2349	480	Q_8

This leads to the following table, in which the values of $P(x_k, \pm h)$, $Q(x_k, \pm h)$ have been obtained from product sums of each column above with the $h^k/k!$ column, odd and even terms being summed separately.

x_k	$P(x_k, h)$	$P(x_k, -h)$	$Q(x_k, h)$	$Q(x_k, -h)$	$F(x_k)$	Check
0·0	(0·77881)	(0·77881)	0·42442	− 0·42442	0·00000	0·00003
0·5	0·47239	1·28399	0·33760	− 0·54498	0·42442	0·42444
1·0	0·28644	2·11704	0·27412	− 0·71472	0·53809	0·53810
1·5	0·17383	3·49037	0·22689	− 0·95665	0·42825	0·42820
2·0	0·10559	5·75431	0·19127	− 1·30575	0·30133	

Five decimals have been used throughout to reduce rounding errors, and it appears that the final values are correct to $0 \cdot 00005$ at least. The first column of $F(x_k)$ is obtained by (7.18) using $P(x_k, h)$, $Q(x_k, h)$ and the check values by using $P(x_k, -h)$, $Q(x_k, -h)$, though because $P(x_k, -h) > 1$ the last figure is not reliable.

The final table requires the insertion of 4 values between each of the above, and therefore $w = 0 \cdot 1$. We omit the values of $P(x_k, \pm sw)$, $Q(x_k, \pm sw)$, obtained similarly with the aid of multiplying columns $(0 \cdot 1s)^k/k!$ ($s = 1, 2, 3, 4$). The results are as follows, the last column giving values (correct to 5D) from tables by Lash Miller and Gordon (*J. Phys. Chem.*, **35** (1931), 2785).

x	$F(x)$	Check	Correct	x	$F(x)$	Check	Correct
0	0·00000		0·00000	1·0	0·53809		
0·1	0·09934	0·09933	0·09934	1·1	0·52621	0·52621	0·52621
0·2	0·19475	0·19474	0·19475	1·2	0·50728	0·50727	0·50727
0·3	0·28263	0·28261	0·28263	1·3	0·48340	0·48340	0·48340
0·4	0·35995	0·35993	0·35994	1·4	0·45652	0·45651	0·45651
0·5	0·42442		0·42444	1·5	0·42825		0·42825
0·6	0·47475	0·47477	0·47476	1·6	0·39994	0·39990	0·39994
0·7	0·51049	0·51052	0·51050	1·7	0·37256	0·37253	0·37256
0·8	0·53209	0·53212	0·53210	1·8	0·34677	0·34674	0·34677
0·9	0·54071	0·54074	0·54072	1·9	0·32297	0·32296	0·32297
1·0	0·53809		0·53808	2·0	0·30133		0·30134

The method can readily be extended to linear second-order equations of the form (7.5). However, compared with methods developed in the next chapter it is decidedly laborious, and not to be recommended except for a few equations to which it is well suited, or when only a few values of the solution are required. For tabulation at a wide interval, similar but more powerful methods are described in Sections 8.10–8.12. It is worth remembering, however, that interpolation using Taylor's series can be very convenient, particularly if the reduced derivatives $F^{(m)}(x)/m!$ are tabulated, as they sometimes are.

7.7. Picard's Method

Before describing this method* it is necessary to replace the differential equation by an integral equation which embodies the boundary condition. This is easily done; thus in place of (7.1) we have

$$F(x) = F_0 + \int_{x_0}^{x} f(x, F)dx \qquad (7.21)$$

* Introduced by Picard in 1890, and developed by Moulton (1926).

Similarly, (7.2) and (7.3a) become

$$F_1(x) = F_{10} + \int_{x_0}^{x} f_1(x,\, F_1,\, F_2)dx \left.\vphantom{\int_{x_0}^{x}}\right\}$$

$$F_2(x) = F_{20} + \int_{x_0}^{x} f_2(x,\, F_1,\, F_2)dx \qquad (7.22)$$

where $F_1 = F_{10}$ and $F_2 = F_{20}$ when $x = x_0$,

and $\qquad G(x) = G_0 + (x - x_0)F_0 + \int_{x_0}^{x} dx \int_{x_0}^{x} f(x,\, G)dx \qquad (7.23)$

where $G = G_0$, $dG/dx = F_0$ when $x = x_0$.

Picard's method is essentially an iterative process of developing a series solution. In solving (7.15) for instance, one obtains a sequence of functions F_0, F_1, F_2, . . ., F_k defined by

$$F_{k+1} = F_0 + \int_{x_0}^{x} f(x,\, F_k)dx \qquad (7.24)$$

i.e. F_1 is derived by substituting F_0 in the integrand, F_2 by substituting F_1 and so on. It can be demonstrated that under certain conditions this sequence converges to a definite limiting function which is the desired solution of the differential equation. The efficacy of the process clearly depends on the sequence being such that the functions $f(x,\, F_k)$ can be integrated without too much difficulty. We give illustrations of its application to equations of each of the three types above.

EXAMPLE 7.6. Obtain, with an error not exceeding 10^{-4} when $x < 0{\cdot}1$, the solution of $dF/dx = 3x^{-1/2} + F - 1$ for which $F = 1$ when $x = 0$.

Taylor's series cannot be used here, because dF/dx is not finite when $x = 0$.

Assuming $F_0 = 1$

then $\qquad F_1 = 1 + \int_0^x 3x^{-1/2}dx = 1 + 6x^{1/2}$

$$F_2 = 1 + \int_0^x (3x^{-1/2} + 6x^{1/2})dx = 1 + 6x^{1/2} + 4x^{3/2}$$

and hence

$$F = 1 + 6x^{1/2} + 4x^{3/2} + (8/5)x^{5/2} + (16/35)x^{7/2} + (32/315)x^{9/2} + \ldots$$

each term being the integral of the preceding one. Although all terms are positive, it is evident that the remainder after the term in $x^{7/2}$ is less than

$$(32/315)x^{9/2}(1 - 2x/11)^{-1}$$

This is less than 5×10^{-5} provided $x < 0.11$, so that the conditions are met by ignoring terms beyond that in $x^{7/2}$.

The solution need not always be expressed in powers of x, fractional or otherwise. Thus if $dF/dx + F = e^{-x}$ and $F = 0$ when $x = 0$, successive approximations to F are

$$1 - e^{-x}$$
$$2(1 - e^{-x}) - x$$
$$3(1 - e^{-x}) - 2x + (1/2)x^2$$
$$4(1 - e^{-x}) - 3x + x^2 - (1/6)x^3 \text{ and so on.}$$

The exact solution is of course xe^{-x}, and Taylor's series leads at once to the expansion of this in powers of x.

The solution of simultaneous equations can be equally direct. Let the successive approximations to F_1, F_2 be F_{10}, F_{11}, F_{12}, $\cdots$ and F_{20}, F_{21}, $F_{22} \cdots$ The recurrence relations can be written in various ways, e.g. the equations

$$\left.\begin{array}{l} F_{1,\,k+1} = F_{10} + \displaystyle\int_{x_0}^{x} f_1(x,\, F_{1k},\, F_{2k})dx \\[2ex] F_{2,\,k+1} = F_{20} + \displaystyle\int_{x_0}^{x} f_2(x,\, F_{1,\,k+1},\, F_{2k})dx \end{array}\right\} \tag{7.25}$$

would allow the sequence of functions to be obtained in the order

$$F_{11},\ F_{21},\ F_{12},\ F_{22},\ F_{13},\ F_{23},\ \cdots$$

EXAMPLE 7.7. Find the solutions of
$$dF_1/dx = (F_1 + F_2)x, \qquad\qquad dF_2/dx = (F_1 - x)F_2$$
for which $F_1 = 0$, $F_2 = 1$ when $x = 0$.

Let $F_{10} = 0$, $F_{20} = 1$

Then
$$F_{11} = \int_0^x x\,dx = (1/2)x^2 + 0(x^3)$$

where $0(x^3)$ denotes that the error of this approximation contains terms in x^3 and higher powers. It follows that

$$F_{21} = 1 + \int_0^x \{-x + (1/2)x^2\}dx = 1 - (1/2)x^2 + (1/6)x^3 + 0(x^4)$$
and hence

$$F_{12} = \int_0^x \{x + (1/6)x^4\}dx = (1/2)x^2 + (1/30)x^5 + 0(x^6)$$

This enables terms in x^4, x^5, x^6 to be added to F_{21} without further change in F_1; thus

$$F_{22} = 1 - (1/2)x^2 + (1/6)x^3 + (1/8)x^4 - (1/12)x^5$$
$$- (1/720)x^6 + 0(x^7)$$

The next approximations are

$$F_{13} = (1/2)x^2 + (1/30)x^5 + (1/48)x^6 - (1/140)x^7$$
$$+ (7/2880)x^8 + 0(x^9)$$

$$F_{23} = 1 - (1/2)x^2 + (1/6)x^3 + (1/8)x^4 - (1/12)x^5 - (1/720)x^6$$
$$+ (1/42)x^7 - (11/1344)x^8 - (13/2880)x^9 + 0(x^{10})$$

Taylor's series leads to the same results, but more laboriously.

Finally we take an example of a second-order equation, using the iterative equation

$$G_{k+1} = G_0 + (x - x_0)F_0 + \int_{x_0}^x dx \int_{x_0}^x f(x, G_k)dx \qquad (7.26)$$

EXAMPLE 7.8. Obtain series solutions of $d^2G/dx^2 = xG$, for which

$$(a)\ G = 0,\ F = 1,\ (b)\ G = 1,\ F = 0, \text{ when } x = 0$$

This is a well-known equation, which leads to Airy's integral.

Case (a) $G_0 = 0,\ G_1 = x$

$$G_2 = x + \int_0^x dx \int_0^x x^2 dx = x + (1/12)x^4$$

Further approximations give

$$G_a = x + (1/12)x^4 + (1/504)x^7 + (1/45360)x^{10} + 0(x^{13})$$

Case (b). Starting with $G_0 = 1$, we obtain easily

$$G_b = 1 + (1/6)x^3 + (1/180)x^6 + (1/12960)x^9 + 0(x^{12})$$

The same results are also given simply by Taylor's series. The general solution for which $G = c_0$, $F = c_1$ when $x = 0$ is

$$G = c_1 G_a + c_0 G_b$$

CONVERGENCE OF PICARD'S METHOD

In general the sequence of approximations obtained by Picard's method converges for only a limited range of x. We shall examine briefly the condition for convergence within a range $(x_0, x_0 + R)$ for a first-order equation.

Define $\varepsilon_k(x) = F_k(x) - F(x)$, F being the true solution.

Then $$\varepsilon_{k+1} = F_{k+1} - F = \int_{x_0}^x \{f(x, F_k) - f(x, F)\}dx$$

$$= \int_{x_0}^x \varepsilon_k(\partial f/\partial F)_{F=\phi}dx$$

where $\phi(x)$ is some function, which for each x has a value between $F(x)$ and $F_k(x)$.

Hence $\quad |\varepsilon_{k+1}| \leqslant \int_{x_0}^{x} |\varepsilon_k| \cdot |(\partial f/\partial F)_\phi| dx < \eta_k M_k (x - x_0)$

where η_k, M_k are the maximum values of $|\varepsilon_k|$ and $|(\partial f/\partial F)_\phi|$ associated with the kth approximation within the range $(x_0, x_0 + R)$. Thus η_k and M_k are independent of x, and the above inequality holds for all values of x within the range; in particular, when $x = x_0 + R$

$$\eta_{k+1} < \eta_k M_k R$$

Assume now that $M_k < M$, independent of k; we have then a sequence of inequalities

$$\eta_{k+1} < \eta_k M R < \eta_{k-1} (MR)^2 < \ldots < \eta_1 (MR)^k$$

Thus, provided $R < 1/M$, η_{k+1} can be made as small as desired by taking sufficient approximations. M is effectively the largest value of $|\partial f/\partial F|$ in the range $(x_0, x_0 + R)$; this may depend upon R, but provided $\partial f/\partial F$ is finite there is always a finite value of R within which the method is convergent. This value of R is of course only a lower limit to the actual radius of convergence.

It must also be shown that the limiting function of the sequence F_k satisfies the differential equation, i.e.

$$|\partial F_{k+1}/\partial x - f(x, F_{k+1})| \to 0$$

when $x_0 < x < x_0 + R$, as k becomes large.

But $\quad |\partial F_{k+1}/\partial x - f(x, F_{k+1})| = |f(x, F_k) - f(x, F_{k+1})|$
$$< |F_k - F_{k+1}| \cdot |(\partial f/\partial F)_\phi|$$
$$< |\varepsilon_k - \varepsilon_{k+1}| \cdot M$$

This certainly tends to zero for large k.

A similar argument, applied to the simultaneous equations (7.22), leads to the condition $R < 1/M$, where M is the maximum value of

$$|\partial f_1/\partial F_1| + |\partial f_2/\partial F_1| \quad \text{or} \quad |\partial f_1/\partial F_2| + |\partial f_2/\partial F_2|$$

whichever is the larger.

The limitations of Picard's method are fairly obvious. It fails in principle if $\partial f/\partial F$ is not finite when $F = F_0$; it fails in practice if the successive integrations cannot be carried out satisfactorily (e.g. Example 7.4). It should, however, be observed that analytical integration is not essential, and that a numerical method may be more effective. Indeed some numerical methods to be described in Chapter 8 are basically applications of Picard's method in a suitable form.

7.8. Series Solutions near a Regular Singularity

An equation of the form

$$\frac{d^2G}{dx^2} + \frac{p(x)}{x}\frac{dG}{dx} + \frac{q(x)}{x^2}\,G = 0 \qquad (7.27)$$

where $p(x) = p_0 + p_1 x + p_2 x^2 + \ldots$

and $q(x) = q_0 + q_1 x + q_2 x^2 + \ldots$

is said to have a regular singularity at the point $x = 0$. If p_0, q_0 and q_1 are not zero, a solution in the form of Taylor's series at $x = 0$ is impossible. Bessel's equation (Example 7.1) is clearly of this type when $n \neq 0$, and so is the equation of Example 7.2. It is always possible, however, to obtain a solution in series form by the following procedure. Assume that

$$G = x^s\{a_0 + a_1 x + a_2 x^2 + \ldots\} \qquad (7.28)$$

where s and the coefficients a_k are initially unknown.

On substitution in (7.27), the lowest power of x arising from each term in the equation is x^{s-2}, the coefficients being

$$a_0 s(s-1), \quad a_0 p_0 s, \quad a_0 q_0$$

For the series to satisfy (7.27) for a continuous range of values of x, the resultant coefficient of x^{s-2} (and of each higher power of x) must be zero; hence we obtain the *indicial equation*

$$s(s-1) + p_0 s + q_0 = 0 \qquad (7.29)$$

which in general determines *two* values of s, on which a series solution can be based.

The corresponding equations for the coefficients of higher powers of x determine the coefficients a_1, a_2, $\ldots$ in terms of a_0, which for a homogeneous equation is arbitrary. Thus the coefficient of x^{s-1}

$$a_0(s p_1 + q_1) + a_1\{(s+1)(s+p_0) + q_0\} = 0$$

and therefore a_1 is given in terms of a_0. Similarly from the coefficient of x^s

$$a_0(s p_2 + q_2) + a_1\{(s+1)p_1 + q_1\}$$
$$+ a_2\{(s+2)(s+1+p_0) + q_0\} = 0$$

which determines a_2, and so on. The expression giving a_k is cumbersome in this general case, but for most equations of interest, a simple recurrence relation between two or three successive coefficients can be obtained.

When (7.29) has two unequal roots, say s_1 and $s_1 - \sigma$, it is generally possible to derive two sets of coefficients, and therefore two independent series solutions of (7.27). If these be denoted by $G_{(1)}$ and $G_{(2)}$ (with $a_0 = 1$ in each case), the general solution has the form

$$G = AG_{(1)} + BG_{(2)}$$

and the constants A, B are fixed by the boundary conditions at $x = 0$. When $\sigma = 0$, only one such series is of course possible, and a similar situation may occur when σ is an integer. This is because, in the series corresponding to $s_1 - \sigma$, the recurrence relation defining a_σ fails, the term in a_σ being

$$a_\sigma \{ s_1(s_1 - 1 + p_0) + q_0 \}$$

which disappears when s_1 satisfies the indicial equation. There are exceptional cases, however, in which the other terms in this equation also vanish, and a second series solution is still possible. Further details are given in Jeffreys and Jeffreys, *M.M.P.* and text-books on differential equations.

When only one series solution exists, denoted by $G_{(1)}$, a second solution of the form

$$G_{(2)} = G_{(1)} \log x + x^{s_1 - \sigma}(b_0 + b_1 x + b_2 x^2 + \ldots) \quad (7.30)$$

can be derived, the coefficients b_k being obtained by recurrence relations provided as before by the differential equation. It turns out that $b_{s_1} = 0$.

The procedure is illustrated in Example 7.9 for Bessel's equation.

It is worth noting the special forms of the indicial equation which arise when (a) $q_0 = 0$ or $q_0 = q_1 = 0$, (b) $p_0 = 0$ or (c) $p_0 = q_0 = 0$.

EXAMPLE 7.9. Obtain series solutions of Bessel's equation

$$d^2G/dx^2 + (1/x)dG/dx + (1 - \nu^2/x^2)G = 0$$

Also derive a second solution when $\nu = 1$.

In this example, $p_0 = q_2 = 1$, $q_0 = -\nu^2$ and all other p_k, q_k are zero. The indicial equation is therefore

$$s^2 - \nu^2 = 0$$

so that

$$s_1 = \nu, \quad s_2 = -\nu$$

When the series (7.28) is substituted in the equation, the coefficient of x^{s+k-2} gives

$$a_{k-2} + \{(k+s)(k+s-1) + k + s - v^2\}a_k = 0$$

and hence
$$a_k = - a_{k-2}/\{k(k+2s)\}$$

The two series solutions corresponding to s_1 and s_2 are then

$$J_v(x) = C_v x^v \left\{1 - \frac{x^2}{2(2v+2)} + \frac{x^4}{2\,.\,4(2v+2)(2v+4)} - \cdots\right\}$$

$$J_{-v}(x) = C_{-v} x^{-v} \left\{1 + \frac{x^2}{2(2v-2)} + \frac{x^4}{2\,.\,4(2v-2)(2v-4)} - \cdots\right\}$$

These are the usual series for the Bessel functions J_v, J_{-v}

if
$$C_v = \{2^v v!\}^{-1}, \quad C_{-v} = \{2^{-v}(-v)!\}^{-1}$$

where $v!$ and $(-v)!$ are values of the factorial (or gamma) function when v is not an integer.

Difficulty arises when v is an integer, say n, as the recurrence relation in the series for J_{-n} breaks down at the term in x^{2n} in the bracket. It can then be proved, with the above definitions of C_v, C_{-v} that $J_{-n} = (-1)^n J_n$, and therefore the two series are effectively identical. It might be expected that the similar difficulty would also arise when v is half an integer (the difference $s_1 - s_2$ being integral), but it does not, this being one of the exceptional cases already mentioned.

Consider now the second solution when $v = 1$, given that

$$J_1(x) = x\{a_0 + a_2 x^2 + a_4 x^4 + \ldots\}$$

$$= \frac{x}{2}\left\{1 - \frac{1}{1!\,2!}\left(\frac{x}{2}\right)^2 + \frac{1}{2!\,3!}\left(\frac{x}{2}\right)^4 - \frac{1}{3!\,4!}\left(\frac{x}{2}\right)^6 + \cdots\right\}$$

Let $\quad G_{(2)}(x) = J_1(x) \log x + x^{-1}(b_0 + b_1 x + b_2 x^2 + \ldots)$

Then $\quad G''_{(2)} + (1/x)G'_{(2)} + (1 - 1/x^2)G_{(2)}$

$$= \{J''_1 + (1/x)J'_1 + (1 - 1/x^2)J_1\}\log x + 2J'_1/x$$
$$- b_1/x^2 + b_0/x + (b_1 + 3b_3) + (b_2 + 8b_4)x$$
$$+ \ldots + \{b_k + (-1 + (k+1)^2)b_{k+2}\}x^{k-1} + \ldots$$
$$= 2\{a_0/x + 3a_2 x + 5a_4 x^3 + \ldots + (k+1)a_k x^{k-1} + \ldots\}$$
$$+ \text{above series in } b_k$$

From coefficients of powers of x,

$$b_1 = b_3 = b_5 = \ldots = 0$$
$$b_0 = -2a_0 = -1$$
$$8b_4 + b_2 + 6a_2 = 0$$
$$24b_6 + b_4 + 10a_4 = 0, \text{ etc.}$$

Thus b_4, b_6, etc., are expressed in terms of b_2, which remains arbitrary since any multiple of J_1 can be added to $G_{(2)}$. (In particular, if $Y^{(1)}$ is the solution for which $b_2 = -1/4$, then the Bessel function of the second kind denoted by Y_1 is equal to $(2/\pi)\{Y^{(1)} - (\ln 2 - \gamma)J_1\}$, where γ is Euler's constant.)

An example involving an inhomogeneous equation is given in § 7.9.

Series Solutions for Large x

When x is large, it is often more convenient to express the solution of a differential equation, or to expand an integral, in a series of ascending powers of $1/x$. Such series may or may not converge to a definite limit as the number of terms increases, but even in the absence of a limit they may still be valuable for computing the function, if the individual terms decrease initially and become sufficiently small before increasing again. Series of this type which, although not convergent in the usual sense, give a good representation of the function under certain circumstances, are termed *asymptotic expansions*. Various methods of deriving asymptotic expansions are available, some involving an extensive mathematical background, though often quite simple in application. The subject is not one which can be treated here in detail,* and we shall describe only a few elementary ways in which some functions, mainly the solutions of linear differential equations, can be expanded for large values of the variable. These include

(a) reciprocation of the equation,

(b) the method of repeated integration,

(c) the Stokes' form of solution, and

(d) the amplitude and phase method.

Of these (c) and (d) in particular apply to linear second-order equations.

7.9. Reciprocation of the Equation

It is obvious that methods already described for obtaining series solutions when $x - x_0$ is small may be equally useful when x is large, if the independent variable is changed from x to $1/x$. The procedure is best explained by a simple example.

EXAMPLE 7.10. Show that

$$e^{x^2}\int_x^\infty e^{-t^2}dt \sim (1/2x)\{1 - 1/(2x^2) + 1\,.\,3/(2x^2)^2 - \,.\,.\,.\}$$

This function satisfies the equation $dF/dx = 2xF - 1$.

* For this, see Bromwich, *Infinite Series*, or Jeffreys, *M.M.P.*, Chap. 17.

Let $$\xi = 1/x$$

Then $$dF/dx = -\xi^2 dF/d\xi = 2F/\xi - 1$$

There is no Taylor's series for F when $\xi = 0$, but we can assume that
$$F = \xi^s(a_0 + a_1\xi + a_2\xi^2 + \ldots)$$

$$\xi^2 dF/d\xi + (2/\xi)F - 1 = \xi^s \sum_{k=0}^{\infty} \{(k+s)a_k\xi^{k+1} + 2a_k\xi^{k-1}\} - 1 = 0$$

A solution of this form is possible if
$$2a_0\xi^{s-1} - 1 = 0, \quad 2a_1\xi^s = 0$$

i.e. $$s = 1, \quad a_0 = 1/2 \quad \text{and} \quad a_1 = 0$$

Higher coefficients are then given by the recurrence relation
$$2a_{k+2} + (k+1)a_k = 0$$

Hence
$$F \sim (1/2)\xi\{1 - (1/2)\xi^2 + (1.3/2^2)\xi^4 - (1.3.5/2^3)\xi^6 + \ldots\}$$
$$= (1/2x)\{1 - 1/(2x^2) + 1.3/(2x^2)^2 - 1.3.5/(2x^2)^3 + \ldots\}$$

This series is asymptotic, because the ratio of the terms in ξ^{2k+2} and ξ^{2k} is $(k + 1/2)\xi^2$ which, however small ξ may be, eventually exceeds unity if k is allowed to increase indefinitely. Yet, since the terms alternate in sign the error of curtailing the series at any term is less than the first term omitted; the best result is obtained by including half the smallest term.

When $x = 2$
$$F(2) \sim 0{\cdot}25\{1 - 0{\cdot}125 + 0{\cdot}046875 - 0{\cdot}029297$$
$$+ 0{\cdot}025635 - 0{\cdot}028839 + \ldots\}$$

so $$F(2) \simeq 0{\cdot}226349$$

From tables of the probability integral
$$(2/\pi^{1/2})\int_0^2 e^{-t^2}dt = 0{\cdot}99532227$$

hence $$F(2) = 0{\cdot}886227 \times (1 - 0{\cdot}99532227)e^4 = 0{\cdot}226338$$

Thus the asymptotic series in this instance gives 4 figures correctly.

A similar analysis of the equation $dF/dx = 1 - 2xF$ (Example 7.5) shows that
$$e^{-x^2}\int_0^x e^{t^2}dt \sim (1/2x)\{1 + 1/2x^2 + 1.3/(2x^2)^2 + 1.3.5/(2x^2)^3 + \ldots\}$$

This is less useful because all terms are positive.

7.10. Method of Repeated Integration

When a function is given as an indefinite integral, an asymptotic series is often generated by repeated integration. The following integral illustrates this very well.

Let
$$E(x, s) = \int_x^\infty e^{-t}t^s dt = e^{-x}x^s + s \int_x^\infty e^{-t}t^{s-1} dt$$
$$= e^{-x}x^s\{1 + s/x + s(s-1)/x^2 + \ldots + s^{(k)}/x^k\}$$
$$+ s^{(k+1)} \int_x^\infty e^{-t}t^{s-k-1} dt$$

Thus far, if the final integral be retained, the result is exact, whatever the value of x. The terms of the series, if $s > 0$, are initially positive but become alternating in sign when $k > s$, or if $s < 0$, they alternate from the beginning. When in addition $x \gg s$ the series is genuinely asymptotic, for the terms decrease in magnitude until $|k - s| \simeq x$ and thereafter increase.

Hence
$$E(x, s) \sim e^{-x}x^s \sum_{k=0} s^{(k)}x^{-k}$$

In this way, we obtain the asymptotic expression for the incomplete factorial function

$$F(x, s) = \int_0^x e^{-t}t^s dt = s! - E(x, s)$$

provided s is not a negative integer. Special cases of importance are the exponential integrals

$$Ei(x) = \int_{-\infty}^x t^{-1}e^t dt, \quad -Ei(-x) = \int_x^\infty t^{-1}e^{-t} dt$$

the latter being $E(x, -1)$.

EXAMPLE 7.11. Derive asymptotic series for the functions

$$C(x, r) = \int_x^\infty \frac{\cos t}{t^r} dt, \quad S(x, r) = \int_x^\infty \frac{\sin t}{t^r} dt$$

when $r > 0$.

By repeated integration

$$\int_x^\infty e^{it}t^{-r} dt = (ie^{ix}/x^r)\{1 - ir/x - (r+1)^{(2)}/x^2 + i(r+2)^{(3)}/x^3$$
$$+ (r+3)^{(4)}/x^4 + \ldots + (i)^{-k}(r+k-1)^{(k)}/x^k\} + R_{k+1}$$

where
$$R_{k+1} = \{(r+k)^{(k+1)}/i^{k+1}\} \int_x^\infty e^{it}t^{-(r+k+1)} dt$$

Then, by separating real and imaginary parts,

$$C(x, r) = P(x, r) \cos x - Q(x, r) \sin x$$
$$S(x, r) = P(x, r) \sin x + Q(x, r) \cos x$$

where

$$P(x, r) \sim x^{-r}\{r/x - (r + 2)^{(3)}/x^3 + (r + 4)^{(5)}/x^5 - \ldots\}$$
$$Q(x, r) \sim x^{-r}\{1 - (r + 1)^{(2)}/x^2 + (r + 3)^{(4)}/x^4 - \ldots\}$$

The series for $P(x, r)$ and $Q(x, r)$ are asymptotic when $x \gg r$ but integral expressions for the remainders after k terms can easily be derived, the form depending somewhat on whether k is even or odd.

Asymptotic expressions for the integrals over the range $(0, x)$ can be derived by using the result

$$\int_0^\infty (e^{it}/t^r)dt = (-r)!\{\cos(\pi/2)(1 - r) + i \sin(\pi/2)(1 - r)\}$$

provided r is not an integer.

The following special cases are worth noting—

$r = 1$. *Sine and Cosine Integrals*

$$\text{Ci}(x) = \int_\infty^x \frac{\cos t}{t} dt \sim - P(x, 1) \cos x + Q(x, 1) \sin x$$

$$\text{Si}(x) = \int_0^x \frac{\sin t}{t} dt \sim \frac{\pi}{2} - P(x, 1) \sin x - Q(x, 1) \cos x$$

$r = 1/2$. *Fresnel Integrals*

$$C(x) = \frac{1}{(2\pi)^{1/2}} \int_0^x \frac{\cos t}{t^{1/2}} dt \sim \frac{1}{2} - P(x, \tfrac{1}{2}) \cos x - Q(x, \tfrac{1}{2}) \sin x$$

$$S(x) = \frac{1}{(2\pi)^{1/2}} \int_0^x \frac{\sin t}{t^{1/2}} dt \sim \frac{1}{2} - P(x, \tfrac{1}{2}) \sin x - Q(x, \tfrac{1}{2}) \cos x$$

The usual variable here is $y = (2x/\pi)^{1/2}$.

7.11. Stokes' Expansion for Second-order Linear Equations

The integrals discussed in § 7.10 are simply related to the solutions of certain second-order linear differential equations, from which their asymptotic forms might have been derived (see Exercises 7, No. 6). For a class of such equations a general method of obtaining solutions for large x can be adopted. Thus consider the equation

$$\frac{d^2G}{dx^2} + p(x)\frac{dG}{dx} + q(x)G = 0 \qquad (7.31)$$

in which, for large x, it can be assumed that

$$p(x) \sim p_0 + p_1/x + p_2/x^2 + \ldots$$
$$q(x) \sim q_0 + q_1/x + q_2/x^2 + \ldots$$

It can be shown that solutions of (7.31) have the asymptotic form*

$$G \sim e^{\lambda x} x^\sigma (1 + c_1/x + c_2/x^2 + \ldots) \qquad (7.32)$$

where

$$\lambda^2 + p_0\lambda + q_0 = 0 \qquad (7.33)$$

and

$$\sigma = -(\lambda p_1 + q_1)/(2\lambda + p_0) \qquad (7.34)$$

and the constants c_1, c_2, etc., depend on the coefficients in $p(x)$ and $q(x)$. As might be expected, the quadratic equation for λ leads to two possible solutions.

We shall consider this in detail for the simpler equation

$$d^2G/dx^2 + q(x)G = 0 \qquad (7.35)$$

The substitution $G(x) = e^{\lambda x} x^\sigma g(x)$ leads to the equation for $g(x)$—

$$d^2g/dx^2 + 2(\lambda + \sigma/x)dg/dx$$
$$+ \{\lambda^2 + 2\lambda\sigma/x + \sigma(\sigma - 1)/x^2 + q(x)\}g = 0$$

If we choose $\lambda^2 = -q_0$, and write

$$q(x) = -\lambda^2(1 + a_1/x + a_2/x^2 + \ldots)$$

then the constant term in the expression multiplying $g(x)$ vanishes, and the term in $1/x$ likewise disappears if

$$2\sigma = \lambda a_1 \qquad (7.36)$$

A slight change to the variable $y = \lambda x$ now gives

$$\frac{d^2g}{dy^2} + 2\frac{dg}{dy} = -\frac{2b_1}{y}\frac{dg}{dy} + \left\{\frac{b_2 - b_1(b_1 - 1)}{y^2} + \frac{b_3}{y^3} + \ldots\right\}g$$

where $b_1 = \lambda a_1/2$, $b_2 = \lambda^2 a_2$, $b_3 = \lambda^3 a_3$, etc.

Let $g(y) = 1 + B_1/y + B_2/y^2 + \ldots \qquad (7.37)$

When this is substituted and the coefficients of y^{-2}, y^{-3}, etc., examined it is easily verified that—

$$2B_1 = b_1(b_1 - 1) - b_2$$
$$4B_2 = \{(b_1 - 1)(b_2 - 2) - b_2\}B_1 - b_3$$
$$6B_3 = \{(b_1 - 2)(b_2 - 3) - b_2\}B_2 - b_3B_1 - b_4, \text{ etc.}$$

* See e.g. Jeffreys, *M.M.P.* p. 519, or Ince, *Differential Equations.*

A second solution is obtained by replacing λ by $-\lambda$ throughout; thus

$$G(x) \sim e^{\lambda x} x^{\lambda a_1/2} g \quad \text{or} \quad e^{-\lambda x} x^{-\lambda a_1/2} g*$$

where
$$g* = 1 + B_1*/y + B_2*/y + \ldots \qquad (7.38)$$

and
$$2B_1* = -b_1(b_1 - 1) + b_2$$
$$4B_2* = \{-(b_1 + 1)(b_1 + 2) + b_2\}B_1* + b_3, \text{ etc.}$$

The general solution will of course behave asymptotically like a linear combination of these two series.

A similar analysis can be pursued when λ^2 is replaced by $-p^2$. This again leads to two independent asymptotic solutions

$$e^{ipx} x^{i\alpha} g \quad \text{and} \quad e^{-ipx} x^{-i\alpha} \bar{g}$$

where $\alpha = pa_1/2$, g is a power series in $1/x$ and $\bar{g}$ the complex conjugate of g. The sum and difference of these provide two solutions in real form, from which there is no difficulty in expressing the general asymptotic solution as

$$C\{P(x) \cos (\theta - \beta) - Q(x) \sin (\theta - \beta)\}$$

where $\theta = px + \alpha \log x$, β is an arbitrary phase, $P(x)$ is an even polynomial in $1/x$ and $Q(x)$ an odd polynomial (see Example 7.13).

EXAMPLE 7.12. Obtain asymptotic forms for the solutions of Whittaker's equation

$$\frac{d^2G}{dx^2} + \left(-\frac{1}{4} + \frac{k}{x} + \frac{1/4 - m^2}{x^2}\right) G = 0$$

Here $\lambda^2 = 1/4$, $\sigma = b_1 = -k$, $b_2 = m^2 - 1/4$

The solutions therefore have the form

$$e^{x/2} x^{-k} g, \quad e^{-x/2} x^k g*$$

where g, $g*$ are given by (7.37) and (7.38) with $y = x/2$. Real oscillatory solutions are possible if the variable is changed to ix.

EXAMPLE 7.13. Derive asymptotic solutions of the equation

$$d^2G/dx^2 + (1 + 1/4x^2) G = 0$$

In this case $p^2 = 1$, $\sigma = 0$ and $b_1 = 0$, $b_2 = 1/4$. Proceeding as above, and assuming that

$$G(x) = e^{ix}(1 + B_1/x + B_2/x^2 + \ldots)$$

it follows that

$$iB_1 = \tfrac{1}{2} b_2 \qquad\qquad = \tfrac{1}{8}$$

$$iB_2 = \tfrac{1}{4}(b_2 + 2)B_1 \quad = -\frac{1^2 . 3^2}{2!\, 8^2} i$$

$$iB_3 = \tfrac{1}{6}(b_2 + 2.3)B_2 = -\frac{1^2 . 3^2 . 5^2}{3!\, 8^3}$$

$$iB_4 = \tfrac{1}{8}(b_2 + 3.4)B_3 = \frac{1^2 . 3^2 . 5^2 . 7^2}{4!\, 8^4} i$$

Hence $$G(x) = e^{ix}(P(x) + iQ(x))$$

where $$P(x) \sim 1 - \frac{1^2 . 3^2}{2!(8x)^2} + \frac{1^2 . 3^2 . 5^2 . 7^2}{4!(8x)^4} - \cdots$$

$$Q(x) \sim -\frac{1}{8x} + \frac{1^2 . 3^2 . 5^2}{3!(8x)^3} - \cdots$$

A second solution is the conjugate function

$$\bar{G}(x) = e^{-ix}(P(x) - iQ(x))$$

and the general solution in real form is obtained from the combination

$$\tfrac{1}{2}C\{(G + \bar{G}) \cos \beta - i(G - \bar{G}) \sin \beta\}$$
$$\sim C\{P(x) \cos (x - \beta) - Q(x) \sin (x - \beta)\}$$

The equation being considered is the normal form of Bessel's equation of order zero, one solution of which is $x^{1/2}J_0(x)$. Since

$$J_0(x) \sim (2/\pi x)^{1/2} \cos (x - \pi/4),$$

as may be proved from the integral expression

$$J_0(x) = (1/\pi)\int_0^\pi \cos (x \sin \phi)d\phi,$$

$J_0(x)$ corresponds to the values $C = (2/\pi)^{1/2}$, $\beta = \pi/4$.

7.12. Amplitude and Phase Method

Some of the examples already considered, in which the asymptotic solutions are oscillatory, strongly suggest that a direct attack in which the solution is characterized by an amplitude and phase which vary with x may be profitable. Let us therefore consider the equation

$$d^2G/dx^2 + \phi^2(x)G = 0 \qquad\qquad (7.39)$$

and assume that it has two independent solutions

$$G_1 = A(x) \sin \theta(x), \quad G_2 = A(x) \cos \theta(x) \qquad\qquad (7.40)$$

where $A(x)$, $\theta(x)$ are the amplitude and phase functions. It is obvious from the differential equation that

$$G_2 G_1'' - G_1 G_2'' = 0$$

and hence

$$G_2 G_1' - G_1 G_2' = \text{const.} \tag{7.41}$$

It is convenient to choose the constant in (7.41) to be unity; then by substitution it follows that

$$A^2 \theta' = 1 \quad \text{or} \quad \theta(x) = \int^x A^{-2} dx$$

and

$$A\theta'' + 2A'\theta' = 0 \tag{7.42}$$

But
$$\begin{aligned} G_1'' &= (A'' - A\theta'^2)\sin\theta + (A\theta'' + 2A'\theta')\cos\theta \\ &= (A'' - A^{-3})\sin\theta \\ &= -\phi^2 A \sin\theta \end{aligned}$$

so

$$A'' + \phi^2 A - A^{-3} = 0 \tag{7.43}$$

This is known as Madelung's transformation.

If $\phi^2 \to k^2$ for large x, the solution of (7.43) is subject to the conditions $A \to k^{-1/2}$ and $A' \to 0$.

To obtain series expressions for A and θ it is advisable to reciprocate (7.43). If $\xi = 1/x$ it is easily shown that

$$\xi^3 (d^2/d\xi^2)(\xi A) + \phi^2 A - A^{-3} = 0 \tag{7.44}$$

and

$$d\theta/d\xi = -1/\xi^2 A^2 \tag{7.45}$$

In many cases of importance it is possible to expand both A and θ as power series in ξ. It should be noted that the validity of (7.42) and (7.43) does not depend on ϕ^2 being always positive (see Exercises 7, No. 7).

EXAMPLE 7.14.   Derive amplitude and phase functions for the solutions of

$$d^2G/dx^2 + (1 - 2\eta/x)G = 0$$

In this example, $\phi^2(x) = 1 - 2\eta/x$. Application of Stokes' method shows that the equation has solutions which behave asymptotically as

$$e^{\pm i(x - \eta \log x)}$$

Let us assume that $\theta(x) = x - \eta \log x + \psi(x) + C$, where the constant C is chosen so that $\psi(\infty) = 0$. Changing to ξ as variable, (7.45) is replaced by

$$\xi^2 (d\psi/d\xi) = 1 - \eta\xi - A^{-2}$$

Assume that $\qquad A = 1 + a_1\xi + a_2\xi^2 + \dots$

$$\psi = \quad b_1\xi + b_2\xi^2 + \dots$$

Then $\quad \phi^2 A = 1 + (a_1 - 2\eta)\xi + (a_2 - 2\eta a_1)\xi^2$
$$+ (a_3 - 2\eta a_2)\xi^3 + \dots$$

$$A^{-3} = 1 - 3a_1\xi + (6a_1{}^2 - 3a_2)\xi^2$$
$$+ (-10a_1{}^3 + 12a_1 a_2 - 3a_3)\xi^3 + \dots$$

$$\xi^3(d^2/d\xi^2)(\xi A) = 2a_1\xi^3 + 6a_2\xi^4 + \dots$$

and hence from (7.44)

$$2a_1 = \eta \qquad\qquad 128a_4 = 195\eta^4 - 184\eta^2$$
$$8a_2 = 5\eta^2 \qquad\qquad 256a_5 = 663\eta^5 - 1456\eta^3 + 192\eta$$
$$16a_3 = 15\eta^3 - 2\eta \qquad\qquad \text{etc.}$$

Likewise, from the above equation for $\psi(\xi)$

$$2b_1 = \eta^2 \qquad\qquad 32b_4 = 7\eta^5 - 55\eta^3 + 12\eta$$
$$4b_2 = \eta^3 - \eta \qquad\qquad 80b_5 = 21\eta^6 - 315\eta^4 + 242\eta^2$$
$$24b_3 = 5\eta^4 - 17\eta^2 \qquad\qquad \text{etc.}$$

The functions whose asymptotic forms have been derived are *Coulomb functions of zero order* (from the term $2\eta/x$, which usually represents a Coulomb potential). The value of C depends on the behaviour of the solutions for small x; in particular if $G_1 = A \sin \theta$ corresponds to the solution which vanishes when $x = 0$, it can be shown that $C = \arg(i\eta)! - \eta \log 2$.

Coulomb functions of order l satisfy the equation

$$G'' + \{1 - 2\eta/x - l(l+1)/x^2\}G = 0$$

which can be treated in the same way; the corresponding value of C is $\arg(l + i\eta)! - \eta \log 2 - \frac{1}{2}l\pi$.

Other Approximate Methods

There are other methods of expanding the solutions of differential equations which are at times a most valuable aid or supplement to numerical methods. Of these we shall describe briefly the perturbation method, and that variously known as Jeffrey's method and the WKB (Wentzel-Kramers-Brillouin) method for second-order equations. The feature which they have in common is that the solution is expanded as a sequence of functions of decreasing importance, not necessarily powers of x, which satisfy certain subsidiary equations. Although the examples chosen are analytical, it must be emphasized that in most practical applications the integrations must be effected numerically.

7.13. The Method of Perturbations

Consider first the equation

$$dF/dx + p(x)F = 0 \qquad (7.46)$$

where $p(x) = p_0(x) + \varepsilon p_1(x) + \varepsilon^2 p_2(x)$, ε being a small quantity. If $F_0(x)$ is a solution of (7.46) with $p_0(x)$ in place of $p(x)$, then it may be possible to expand $F(x)$ in the form

$$F(x) = F_0(x) + \varepsilon F_1(x) + \varepsilon^2 F_2(x) + \ldots \qquad (7.47)$$

Substitution in (7.46) gives

$$F_0' + \varepsilon F_1' + \varepsilon^2 F_2' + \ldots$$
$$+ (p_0 + \varepsilon p_1 + \varepsilon^2 p_2)(F_0 + \varepsilon F_1 + \varepsilon^2 F_2 + \ldots) = 0$$

and hence, picking out terms involving ε^0, ε^1, ε^2, etc., we obtain the equations—

$$\left.\begin{array}{l} F_0' + p_0 F_0 = 0 \\ F_1' + p_0 F_1 = - p_1 F_0 \\ F_2' + p_0 F_2 = - (p_2 F_0 + p_1 F_1) \\ F_3' + p_0 F_3 = - (p_2 F_1 + p_1 F_2), \text{ etc.} \end{array}\right\} \qquad (7.48)$$

Thus if F_0 is known it may be possible to find solutions of these equations which then provide with sufficient accuracy the required solution of (7.46).

It is important to notice that there are two ways of dealing with boundary conditions in this scheme—

(a) F_0 may be a general solution, perhaps in analytical form; and then F_1, F_2, etc., need only be particular integrals of their respective equations, particular boundary conditions being dealt with *after* the series has been developed.

(b) F_0 may satisfy a desired condition, say $F_0(x_0) = A_0$ and it is then necessary that $F_1(x_0) = F_2(x_0) = \ldots = 0$ if the condition is not to be disturbed.

When the development is analytical throughout, (a) is the simpler procedure to follow, but, as will be seen in Chapter 8, (b) is generally better suited to a numerical treatment. The following examples should make clear the difference in method.

EXAMPLE 7.15. Develop the solution of $F' + (1 - \varepsilon x)F = 0$ when $\varepsilon x \ll 1$.

Assume an expansion of the form (7.47). The equation

$$F_0' + F_0 = 0$$

gives

$$F_0 = Ce^{-x}$$

where C is arbitrary. Following method (a), we obtain particular integrals of succeeding equations as follows—

$$F_1' + F_1 = Cxe^{-x}, \quad F_1 = \tfrac{1}{2}Cx^2e^{-x}$$
$$F_2' + F_2 = \tfrac{1}{2}Cx^3e^{-x}, \quad F_2 = \tfrac{1}{8}Cx^4e^{-x} \qquad \text{and so on.}$$

Hence

$$F = Ce^{-x}\left\{1 + \frac{1}{2}\,\varepsilon x^2 + \frac{1}{2\,.\,4}\,\varepsilon^2 x^4 + \frac{1}{2\,.\,4\,.\,6}\,\varepsilon^3 x^6 + \cdots\right\}$$

If now $F(x_0) = A_0$, C is determined by the condition

$$A_0 = Ce^{-x_0}\left\{1 + \frac{1}{2}\,\varepsilon x_0{}^2 + \frac{1}{2\,.\,4}\,\varepsilon^2 x_0{}^4 + \cdots\right\}$$

Method (b) would be applied as follows. We define $F_0 = A_0 e^{-(x-x_0)}$ which satisfies the condition at x_0. To F_1 is then added a multiple of the complementary function, say $B_1 e^{-(x-x_0)}$, and B_1 is chosen so that $F_1(x_0) = 0$; similarly for F_2, etc. The result is that

$$F = A_0 e^{-(x-x_0)}\left\{1 + \frac{1}{2}\varepsilon(x^2 - x_0{}^2) + \frac{1}{2\,.\,4}\,\varepsilon^2(x^2 - x_0{}^2)^2 \right.$$
$$\left. + \frac{1}{2\,.\,4\,.\,6}\,\varepsilon^3(x^2 - x_0{}^2)^3 + \cdots\right\}$$

This procedure would be more natural when the integration of each equation is carried out numerically, using a step-by-step method beginning at x_0.

Taylor's series does not give the solution in quite such a convenient form, but the second form can be derived, with rather more trouble, by Picard's method.

EXAMPLE 7.16. Develop the general solution of

$$G'' - (n^2 + \varepsilon e^{-x})G = 0$$

when $\varepsilon \ll n$.

The transition to second-order equations (in normal form) is trivial, all first derivatives in (7.48) being replaced by second derivatives. We proceed by method (a); assuming

$$G(x) = G_0(x) + \varepsilon G_1(x) + \varepsilon^2 G_2(x) + \cdots$$

where

$$G_0'' - n^2 G_0 = 0, \qquad G_0 = A_0 e^{nx} + B_0 e^{-nx}$$

$$G_1'' - n^2 G_1 = e^{-x}G_0, \quad G_1 = -\frac{A_0}{2n-1}\,e^{(n-1)x} + \frac{B_0}{2n+1}\,e^{-(n+1)x}$$

$$G_2'' - n^2 G_2 = e^{-x}G_1, \quad G_2 = \frac{A_0}{(2n-1)(4n-4)}\,e^{(n-2)x}$$
$$+ \frac{B_0}{(2n+1)(4n+4)}\,e^{-(n+2)x}$$

Hence

$$G(x) = A_0 e^{nx} \left\{ 1 - \frac{\varepsilon e^{-x}}{2n - 1} + \frac{\varepsilon^2 e^{-2x}}{(2n - 1)(4n - 4)} \right.$$

$$\left. - \frac{\varepsilon^3 e^{-3x}}{(2n - 1)(4n - 4)(6n - 9)} + \cdots \right\}$$

$$+ B_0 e^{-nx} \left\{ 1 + \frac{\varepsilon e^{-x}}{2n + 1} + \frac{\varepsilon^2 e^{-2x}}{(2n + 1)(4n + 4)} \right.$$

$$\left. + \frac{\varepsilon^3 e^{-3x}}{(2n + 1)(4n + 4)(6n + 9)} + \cdots \right\}$$

Difficulties obviously arise when n has certain values.

Method (b) is more troublesome. The first step, assuming that A_0 and B_0 are determined by making G_0 conform to the boundary conditions, say $G(0) = a$, $G'(0) = b$, is to add to G_1 the complementary function $C_1 e^{nx} + D_1 e^{-nx}$, and choose C_1 and D_1 so that

$$G_1(0) = G_1{}'(0) = 0$$

i.e. $A_0 + B_0 = a$, $- \dfrac{A_0}{2n - 1} + \dfrac{B_0}{2n + 1} + C_1 + D_1 = 0$

$n(A_0 - B_0) = b$, $- \dfrac{A_0(n - 1)}{2n - 1} - B_0 \dfrac{(n + 1)}{2n + 1} + n(C_1 - D_1) = 0$

The algebra associated with G_2 is more complicated. When the integration is numerical, no difficulty arises when both boundary conditions refer to the same x and not much when they refer to two different values of x.

7.14. Green's-type Solutions (Jeffreys or WKB Method)

The following method has extensive applications to second-order equations with nearly exponential or sinusoidal solutions, and is closely related to the amplitude and phase method discussed in § 7.12.

We begin by considering the equation

$$G'' = \tfrac{1}{4}n^2 X^2(x)G \qquad (7.49)$$

where $X(x)$ varies slowly with x, and n is assumed large. If X were constant the solutions of (7.49) would have the form $\exp\{\pm \tfrac{1}{2}nXx\}$, and when X varies it is reasonable to assume solutions of the form

$$G = \exp \int^x \{\pm \tfrac{1}{2}nX + f_0/X^2 \pm f_1/nX^5$$

$$+ f_2/n^2 X^8 \pm f_3/n^3 X^{11} + \ldots\}dx \quad (7.50)$$

where $f_0, f_1, \ldots$ are functions of x to be determined, and the integrand is a series in powers of $1/n$. From (7.50)

$$G'/G = \pm \tfrac{1}{2}nX + f_0/X^2 \pm f_0/nX^5 + f_2/n^2X^8 \pm \cdots$$

and by a further differentiation G''/G can be derived and substituted in (7.49). By picking out terms involving n^1, n^0, n^{-1}, n^{-2}, etc., the following series of equations is easily derived—

$$\left.\begin{aligned}
f_0 &= -\tfrac{1}{2}XX' \\
f_1 &= -(X^2f_0' + 5f_0^2) \\
f_2 &= -(X^2f_1' + 12f_0f_1) \\
f_3 &= -(X^2f_2' + 18f_0f_2 + f_1^2) \\
f_4 &= -(X^2f_3' + 24f_0f_3 + 2f_1f_2), \text{ etc.}
\end{aligned}\right\} \qquad (7.51)$$

The sequence of functions is thus defined.

Now $\quad \exp\displaystyle\int^x (f_0/X^2)dx = \exp\left(-\tfrac{1}{2}\log X\right) = X^{-1/2}$

so that the general solution of (7.49) can be expressed as

$$G = X^{-1/2}\{A_1e^{n\theta} + A_2e^{-n\theta}\}e^{(\phi/n^2)} \qquad (7.52)$$

where $\quad \theta = \displaystyle\int^x (X/2 + f_1/n^2X^5 + f_3/n^4X^{11} + \cdots)dx$

$$\phi = \int^x (f_2/X^8 + f_4/n^2X^{14} + \cdots)dx$$

Rather simpler expressions for θ and ϕ can be derived by using the relations (7.51) and integrating by parts. One then obtains, including the terms in f_4,

$$\theta = \tfrac{1}{2}\int^x Xdx - \frac{1}{n^2}\left(\frac{f_0}{X^3} - \int^x \frac{f_0^2}{X^5}dx\right)$$

$$-\frac{1}{n^4}\left(\frac{f_2}{X^9} + \int^x \frac{f_1^2}{X^{11}}dx\right) - \cdots \quad (7.53)$$

$$\phi = -\frac{f_1}{X^6} - \frac{1}{n^2}\left(\frac{f_3}{X^{12}} + \int^x \frac{2f_1f_2}{X^{14}}dx\right) - \cdots \qquad (7.54)$$

It is often possible to ignore ϕ and retain only the terms in θ involving f_0 explicitly.

Solutions of this kind were derived by Jeffreys[*] and termed by him Green's-type solutions; something similar was in fact given by G. Green in 1837. Like the Stokes' type (7.32), they are often useful in providing asymptotic series. The above form breaks down at a zero of $X(x)$, but even if X is small the approximation is reliable provided n is large enough.

The treatment of oscillatory solutions is similar. The equation

$$G'' + \tfrac{1}{4}m^2X^2(x)G = 0 \tag{7.55}$$

has solutions of the form

$$G = X^{-1/2}\{A_1e^{im\chi} + A_2e^{-im\chi}\}e^{(-\psi/m^2)} \tag{7.56}$$

where $\quad \chi = \displaystyle\int^x (X/2 - f_1/m^2X^5 + f_3/m^4X^{11} - \ldots)dx$

$$\psi = \int^x (f_2/X^8 - f_4/m^2X^{14} + \ldots)dx$$

and the functions f_1, f_2, etc., are again given by (7.51). Real solutions, involving $\cos m\chi$ and $\sin m\chi$, are obviously obtained if A_1 and A_2 have suitable values (see Example 7.19). The "amplitude" of such solutions is described primarily by $X^{-1/2}$, and the relation to the amplitude-phase method can therefore be clearly seen; if in (7.39) $\phi^2 = m^2X^2/4$, the fact that the amplitude $A \propto X^{-1/2}$ follows at once from (7.43) provided $A'' \ll \phi^2A$.

It should be said that the use of the parameter n in (7.49) and subsequent formulas, and similarly of m, is purely a matter of convenience, and if X^2 itself contains a large dominant term it is then permissible to put n or m equal to unity. The retention or otherwise of contributions from lesser terms in X^2 will be a matter of discretion. The following examples will help to make this clear.

EXAMPLE 7.17. Obtain solutions of $d^2G/dx^2 = xG$ when x is large.

We let $n = 1$, and use (7.51) with $X^2 = 4x$. This gives

$$f_0 = -1, \; f_1 = -5, \; f_2 = -60, \; f_3 = -1105$$

All the integrals in (7.53) and (7.54) are easily evaluated, and the two independent solutions have the form

$$G = x^{-1/4}e^{\pm\theta}e^\phi$$

* H. Jeffreys, *Proc. Lond. Math. Soc.* (2), **23** (1924), 428. The above method of obtaining higher terms in the series was given by C. G. Darwin, *Quart. J. Mech. Appl. Math.* **2** (1949), 311.

where θ and ϕ can be expressed as follows—

$$\theta = \xi + 5/72\xi + (5 \,.\, 221)/(6 \,.\, 72^2\xi^3) + \ldots$$
$$\phi = 5/(2 \,.\, 72\xi^2) + (5 \,.\, 113)/(2 \,.\, 72^2\xi^4) + \ldots, \quad \xi = (2/3)x^{3/2}$$

For comparison the Stokes' expansion is

$$G = x^{-1/4}e^{\pm\xi}[1 \pm (3 \,.\, 5)/(1!\, 216\xi) + (5 \,.\, 7 \,.\, 9 \,.\, 11)/\{2\,!(216\xi)^2\}$$
$$\pm (7 \,.\, 9 \,.\, 11 \,.\, 13 \,.\, 15 \,.\, 17)/\{3\,!(216\xi)^3\} + \ldots]$$

This is neater algebraically, but for computation, particularly of $\log G$, the other may be preferred.

EXAMPLE 7.18. Obtain solutions of $G'' - (n^2 + e^{-x})G = 0$ when $n \gg 1$.

Again let $n = 1$ in (7.53) and (7.54), and write $X^2 = 4(n^2 + e^{-x})$.

We find $\qquad f_0 = e^{-x}$ and $f_1 = 4n^2e^{-x} - e^{-2x}$

and hence

$$\theta = \int^x (n^2 + e^{-x})^{1/2}dx - e^{-x}/\{8(n^2 + e^{-x})^{3/2}\} + 0(n^{-5})$$
$$= \text{const.} + nx - (e^{-x}/2n)(1 + 1/4n^2) + e^{-2x}/8n^3 + 0(n^{-5})$$
$$\phi = \text{const.} + 0(n^{-4})$$

The general solution of the equation may therefore be written

$$G = (1 + e^{-x}/n^2)^{-1/4}\{A_1e^{nx}(1 - e^{-x}/2n + e^{-2x}/8n^2)$$
$$+ A_2e^{-nx}(1 + e^{-x}/2n + e^{-2x}/8n^2) + 0(n^{-3})\}$$

and this should be compared with the result of the perturbation calculation in Example 7.16.

EXAMPLE 7.19. Obtain solutions of $G'' + (m^2 + \cos x)G = 0$ when $m \gg 1$.

Let $m = 1$ in (7.56) and $X^2 = 4(m^2 + \cos x)$.

Then $\qquad\qquad f_0 = \sin x$
$$f_1 = - (X^2 \cos x + 5 \sin^2 x)$$

so $\qquad\qquad \chi = m\int_0^x \{1 + (\cos x)/m^2\}^{1/2}dx + 0(m^{-3})$
$$= mx + (\sin x)/2m + 0(m^{-3})$$
$$\psi = 0(m^{-4})$$

Consequently the solutions have the form

$$\{1 + (\cos x)/m^2\}^{-1/4} \exp \pm i\{mx + (\sin x)/2m + 0(m^{-3})\}$$

The following solutions are obtained by taking the sum and difference of the exponentials with $+$ and $-$ signs—

$$\left(1 + \frac{\cos x}{m^2}\right)^{-1/4} \cos\left(mx + \frac{\sin x}{2m} + 0(m^{-3})\right)$$

$$\simeq \cos mx - \frac{1}{2m}\sin x \sin mx - \frac{1}{4m^2}\cos mx\,(\cos x + \tfrac{1}{2}\sin^2 x) + 0(m^{-3})$$

$$\left(1 + \frac{\cos x}{m^2}\right)^{-1/4} \sin\left(mx + \frac{\sin x}{2m} + 0(m^{-3})\right)$$

$$\simeq \sin mx + \frac{1}{2m}\sin x \cos mx - \frac{1}{4m^2}\sin mx\,(\cos x + \tfrac{1}{2}\sin^2 x) + 0(m^{-3})$$

The first few terms given by the perturbation method are

$$G \simeq A_0\left\{\cos mx - \frac{1}{4m^2 - 1}\,(2m \sin x \sin mx + \cos x \cos mx)\right\}$$

$$+ B_0\left\{\sin mx + \frac{1}{4m^2 + 1}\,(2m \sin x \cos mx - \cos x \sin mx)\right\}$$

which agrees with the above when m is large.

For the method of treating equations in which X^2 has a zero, the reader should consult Jeffreys, *M.M.P.* or Schiff, *Quantum Mechanics* (p. 181), and also R. E. Langer, *Phys. Rev.*, **51** (1937), 669.

Tabulation of Functions

Before concluding this chapter it is worth considering what the tabulation of a mathematical function commonly involves. Let us assume that the values of x for which the function is required run from 0 to ∞. Then the main parts of the computation are—

1. The calculation of pivotal values, i.e. at values of x suitably chosen at regular intervals.

2. Subtabulation to smaller intervals in x, which allow further interpolation (linear, quadratic, etc., as the case may be) to be conveniently done by the user of the table.

We are here concerned with (1), which may also be carried out in stages—

(*a*) tabulation at regular intervals in x, when x is small, using an ascending series;

(*b*) tabulation at regular intervals in $1/x$, when x is large, using an asymptotic series;

(*c*) tabulation over an intervening range of x, if made necessary by poor convergence of the series, by other means, e.g. direct quadrature, if an integral expression is available, or solution of a differential equation.

It is obvious that the development of series expressions, by the various methods considered in this chapter, assumes special importance in the tabulation of such functions. Some of the points which arise are brought out by one or two simple examples.

7.15. Tabulation of $\tan^{-1} x$

Let us start from the familiar integral form

$$\tan^{-1} x = \int_0^x dx/(1 + x^2)$$

Expansion of $(1 + x^2)^{-1}$, first in powers of x and then in powers of $1/x$ and integration term by terms, leads at once to two convergent series—

$$x < 1 \qquad \int_0^x dx/(1 + x^2) = x - (1/3)x^3 + (1/5)x^5 - \ldots \qquad (7.57)$$

$$x > 1 \qquad \int_x^\infty dx/(1 + x^2) = 1/x - 1/3x^3 + 1/5x^5 - \ldots \qquad (7.58)$$

These are alternating series, and as seen in Chapter 6 they can be summed even for values of x near to 1 by using Euler's transformation. Thus the whole range of x might in principle be covered by these two series. However, a more satisfactory alternative might be to confine the use of (7.57) to $x \leqslant 0.6$, say, and of (7.58) to $x \geqslant 1.8$, the exact limits depending on the number of decimals required. The range $(0.6, 1.8)$ could then be covered by direct tabulation of the integral, solving in effect the simple differential equation

$$dF/dx = 1/(1 + x^2)$$

by one of the step-by-step methods described in Chapter 8. The solution, if begun at $x = 0.6$, must join smoothly to the values obtained from the asymptotic series. Even better would be to solve the second-order equation

$$d^2F/dx^2 + 2x/(1 + x^2)^2 = 0$$

treating it as a two-point boundary problem, the values $F(0.6)$ and $F(1.8)$ being given. This may be done by the relaxation method or by matrix inversion (see Example 14.1).

The calculation of pivotal values should of course be carried out to at least 2–3 decimals more than the final table.

7.16. The Exponential Integrals

The functions $Ei(x)$ and $Ei(-x)$ which have been defined already in § 7.10, can be represented both by ascending and asymptotic series—

$$Ei(x) = \gamma + \log x + \sum_{k=1}^{\infty} x^k/(k \cdot k!)$$
$$\sim x^{-1}e^x(1 + 1! \, x^{-1} + 2! \, x^{-2} + \ldots)$$

$$-Ei(-x) = -\gamma - \log x + \sum_{k=1}^{\infty} (-1)^{k-1} x^k/(k \cdot k!)$$
$$\sim x^{-1}e^{-x}(1 - 1! \, x^{-1} + 2! \, x^{-2} - \ldots)$$

Both functions are covered in effect by considering a range of x from $-\infty$ to $+\infty$. Although about 37 terms of the ascending series give the functions to 6 decimals at $|x| = 10$, and 45 terms give them to 10 decimals, the corresponding number of terms at $|x| = 15$ are about 51 and 58, which is becoming cumbersome. On the other hand, for $|x| < 15$ the asymptotic series without modification are more limited in the number of decimals they will provide. There is good reason to look for an alternative to the asymptotic series which will ease the tabulation for $|x| > 10$. This is in fact provided by the function*

$$T = e^{-x}Ei(x) - 1/x$$

which satisfies the equation

$$dT/d\xi - \xi^{-2}T + 1 = 0$$

where $\xi = 1/x$. When $|\xi|$ is small, T behaves like ξ^2 and the equation can be solved both for positive and negative ξ by step-by-step methods starting at $\xi = 0$. Again it is much better, however, to solve the second-order equation

$$d^2T/d\xi^2 - (\xi^{-4} - 2\xi^{-3})T + \xi^{-2} = 0$$

assuming the values of T given by ascending series at, say, $\xi = \pm 0 \cdot 10$. This can be done conveniently by relaxation.

In the final table the function $S = 1 + T/\xi$ is preferable as it leads to easier interpolation.

Other functions may of course require other methods of tabulation but it is interesting to see how often the use of series can be supplemented by direct numerical solution of differential equations.

---

* The use of T is due to L. Fox and J. C. P. Miller, *Math. Tab., Wash.*, **5**, (1951), 163, who tabulated it to 9D for $\xi = -0 \cdot 10(0 \cdot 01)0 \cdot 10$.

EXERCISES 7

1. Show that the solution of equation (7.5) i.e.

$$G'' + p(x)G' + q(x)G = r(x)$$

satisfies the integral equation

$$G = G_0 + (x - x_0)(G'_0 + p_0G_0)$$
$$+ \int_{x_0}^{x} dx \int_{x_0}^{x} \{r + (p' - q)G\}dx - \int_{x_0}^{x} pGdx$$

where $G_0 = G(x_0)$, etc.

2. Show that if $G_1(x)$, $G_2(x)$ are independent solutions of the equation

$$G'' + p(x)G' + q(x)G = 0$$

then the general solution of (7.5) satisfies the Volterra equation

$$G(x) = AG_1 + BG_2 + \int_{x_0}^{x} K(x, t)G(t)dt$$

where

$$K(x, t) = \frac{G_1(x)G_2(t) - G_2(x)G_1(t)}{G_1'(t)G_2(t) - G_2'(t)G_1(t)} r(t)$$

3. Apply Picard's method to obtain series solutions (in ascending powers of x) of the equation

$$G'' - (\lambda^2 + a_1x + a_2x^2 + a_3x^3 + \ldots)G = 0$$

for which

(i) $G(0) = 0$, $G'(0) = 1$; (ii) $G(0) = 1$, $G'(0) = 0$

4. Obtain the general asymptotic solution of the equation

$$G'' - (\lambda^2 + a_1e^{-x} + a_2e^{-2x} + \ldots)G = 0$$

in the form

$$G \sim Ae^{\lambda x}P(x) + Be^{-\lambda x}Q(x)$$

where

$$P(x) = 1 + \frac{a_1}{1 - 2\lambda} e^{-x} + \frac{a_1^2 + a_2(1 - 2\lambda)}{2(1 - 2\lambda)(2 - 2\lambda)} e^{-2x} + \cdots$$

$$Q(x) = 1 + \frac{a_1}{1 + 2\lambda} e^{-x} + \frac{a_1^2 + a_2(1 + 2\lambda)}{2(1 + 2\lambda)(2 + 2\lambda)} e^{-2x} + \cdots$$

Consider what happens when λ is an integer or half-integer. Derive a similar result when λ^2 is replaced by $-p^2$, assuming that

$$G \sim AP_1(x) \sin px + BQ_1(x) \cos px$$

5. If $G_0(x)$ is a known solution of the equation $G'' + q(x)G = 0$, where $q(x)$ is a periodic function with period d, e.g.

$$q(x) = a_0 + a_1 \cos(2\pi x/d) + a_2 \cos(4\pi x/d) + \cdots$$

then the general solution takes the form

$$G = Ae^{\lambda x}\phi_1(x) + Be^{-\lambda x}\phi_2(x)$$

where λ is determined by the equation

$$\cosh \lambda d = \{G_0(x + 2d) + G_0(x)\}/\{2G_0(x + d)\}$$

and ϕ_1, ϕ_2 are the periodic functions

$$\phi_1(x) = e^{-\lambda x}\{G_0(x + d) - e^{-\lambda d}G_0(x)\}$$
$$\phi_2(x) = - e^{\lambda x}\{G_0(x + d) - e^{\lambda d}G_0(x)\}$$

Note. This is Flocquet's theorem. The use of the WBK method to approximate to solutions of this kind has been discussed by L. Brillouin, *Quart. Appl. Math.*, **6** (1948), 167 and **7** (1950), 363.

6. If, as in Example 7.11,

$$C(x, r) = P(x, r) \cos x - Q(x, r) \sin x$$

and

$$S(x, r) = P(x, r) \sin x + Q(x, r) \cos x$$

show that P and Q satisfy the equations

$$d^2P/dx^2 + P = r/x^{r+1}, \quad d^2Q/dx^2 + Q = 1/x^r$$

Use these equations to obtain asymptotic forms for $C(x, r)$ and $S(x, r)$.

7. Let $q(x, \lambda)$ be a continuous function of x in the range

$$- \infty < x < \infty$$

having negative values when $|x|$ is large, for all relevant values of the continuous parameter λ. If the solution of the equation

$$d^2G/dx^2 + q(x, \lambda)G = 0$$

is then expressed in the form

$$G(x) = CA(x) \sin \{\theta(x) - \theta_0\}$$

where the amplitude A satisfies (7.43), and $\theta = \int_{x_0}^{x} A^{-2}dx$, show that solutions satisfying the conditions, $G(\pm \infty) = 0$, are obtained only if λ is such that $\int_{-\infty}^{\infty} A^{-2}dx = n\pi$ ($n = 1, 2, 3, \ldots$).

Note. It should be assumed that q is differentiable with respect to λ, $\partial q/\partial \lambda$ being positive.

(Milne, *Phys. Rev.*, 1930)

CHAPTER 8

SOLUTION OF ORDINARY DIFFERENTIAL EQUATIONS (2)

IN the foregoing chapter the use of series and similar analytical procedures was described fairly fully. This seemed a desirable opening, to encourage a just appreciation of the relative merits of analytical and numerical methods in these problems. It was perhaps clear towards the end of the chapter that although it often happens that series provide all, or nearly all, the solution, yet numerical solution of the differential equation may lighten the task appreciably. There are other equations for which the main burden of the computation may be put on the numerical approach, the use of series being only incidental, as some examples in this chapter will show.

So much progress has been made in recent years in developing numerical methods for solving differential equations that there is now a bewildering variety of such methods for first- and second-order equations, though many of them are closely related. In compiling this chapter some selection has been necessary, but it is hoped that the range of methods available has been shown, and the best included. Broadly speaking there is a division between methods which directly replace the derivatives in the equation by their finite difference equivalents, the recurrence methods described in § 8.1–§ 8.3, and those which begin, like Picard's method, from the integral equation embodying the initial boundary conditions, and then use either Lagrangian or difference quadrature formulas. These integral methods are described in § 8.4–§ 8.9.

Finally there are methods which are best regarded as variations of the Taylor series method described in Chapter 7, and which are briefly discussed in § 8.10–§ 8.14. Those readers who do not require to follow the chapter out in detail are advised to concentrate on the difference methods described in § 8.6–§ 8.9.

The treatment of two-point boundary conditions is only touched upon in this chapter, the main discussion being left to Chapter 14, after the introduction of the relaxation method of solving linear simultaneous equations.

Recurrence Methods for Linear Equations

There is no difficulty in replacing a differential equation by a set of approximate equations relating the solution values at a series of equidistant values of x, i.e. by a set of recurrence relations. Then if the first few values are given, these relations determine the rest. Such a procedure will not necessarily be very accurate if the recurrence relations contain only two or three consecutive values, but Fox and Goodwin* showed that an intelligent combination of its use, with correcting terms provided by higher order differences of the solution, could be quite satisfactory. The manner of doing this for first- and second-order equations we shall now describe. The method is restricted mainly to linear equations.

8.1. First-order Equations

Let us consider the equation

$$F' + p(x)F = q(x) \tag{8.1}$$

Then, from the formula, proved in Exercises 6 No. 4(a),

$$F_1 - F_0 = \tfrac{1}{2}w(F'_1 + F'_0) - (1/12)\delta^3 F_{1/2}$$
$$+ (1/120)\delta^5 F_{1/2} - (1/840)\delta^7 F_{1/2} + \ldots \tag{8.2}$$

it follows at once that

$$\{1 + \tfrac{1}{2}wp_1\}F_1 = \{1 - \tfrac{1}{2}wp_0\}F_0 + \tfrac{1}{2}w(q_0 + q_1) + \triangle \tag{8.3}$$

where $\qquad\qquad p_1 = p(x_1)$, etc.

and $\quad \triangle = \{- (1/12)\delta^3 + (1/120)\delta^5 - (1/840)\delta^7 + \ldots\}F_{1/2}$

A similar relation holds between any pair of consecutive values, the suffices 0, 1 being replaced by k, $k + 1$. If $\triangle$ is ignored, all that is then required to tabulate $F(x_0 + kw)$ is the starting value F_0 and tables of $1 \pm \tfrac{1}{2}wp_k$ and $\tfrac{1}{2}w(q_k + q_{k+1})$.

Of course $\triangle$ may not be negligible, but from such an approximate solution a difference table of F can be prepared and the magnitude of $\triangle$, called the difference correction, estimated at each point. Then if necessary the recurrence relations, with $\triangle$ included, can be reapplied to obtain a more accurate solution. This again can be differenced to see whether $\triangle$ is appreciably

---

* L. Fox and E. T. Goodwin, *Proc. Camb. Phil. Soc.*, **45** (1948), 373; also C. W. Clenshaw and F. W. J. Olver, *Math. Tab., Wash.*, **5** (1951), 34.

altered; when this point is settled, the solution can be continued further.

This method has made use of a simple two-term recurrence relation. A relation between three consecutive values is easily derived by operating on both sides of the equation

$$F'_0 = - p_0 F_0 + q_0$$
$$= \{\delta^1 - (1/6)\delta^3 + (1/30)\delta^5 - (1/140)\delta^7 + \ldots\}F_0 w$$

with $\{1 + (1/6)\delta^2\}$, so eliminating the term in $\delta^3 F_0$. The result is that

$$\{1 + (1/3)wp_1\}F_1 = - (4/3)wp_0 F_0 + \{1 - (1/3)wp_{-1}\}F_{-1}$$
$$+ (1/3)w(q_1 + 4q_0 + q_{-1}) + \triangle \quad (8.4)$$

where $\quad \triangle = \{- (1/90)\delta^5 + (1/315)\delta^7 - \ldots\}F_0$

Apart from $\triangle$, this result could have been written down at once by applying Simpson's rule to the integral of $- pF + q$. It should be noticed that $\triangle$ contains mean differences.

To apply (8.4), two initial values are necessary, the second being calculated in some other way, e.g. by using a power series solution. Otherwise the procedure is the same, and the difference correction is found and applied as before. One feature of (8.4) which should be noted is that F_1 usually depends more on F_{-1} than on F_0. Rounding or other errors therefore tend to be perpetuated through alternate values; indeed two sets of errors, largely independent, are propagated within the calculation. This may lead to rather large oscillations in the difference table, and therefore in $\triangle$, a defect which is absent from (8.3). Formulas similar to (8.3) and (8.4) can easily be derived for two or more simultaneous first-order equations (see Exercises 8, Nos. 1 and 2).

Before giving a numerical example, it is worth mentioning a device which reduces the labour of including the difference correction, when this is moderate in size. This is to calculate the change in F, rather than to recalculate F itself. Suppose $F^{(1)}$ satisfies (8.3) without $\triangle$, and that the next approximation $F^{(2)}$ satisfies (8.3) with $\triangle^{(1)}$, the first estimate of $\triangle$ included. Writing $F^{(2)} = F^{(1)} + \eta^{(1)}$, it follows by subtraction that

$$\{1 + \tfrac{1}{2}wp_1\}\eta^{(1)}_1 = \{1 - \tfrac{1}{2}wp_0\}\eta^{(1)}_0 + \triangle^{(1)}_0 \quad (8.5)$$

The values of η, being small, are easily calculated; the starting value is of course zero. The chance of rounding errors in forming the sum $F^{(1)} + \eta^{(1)}$ can be minimized by keeping a guarding figure, which in any event is desirable when recurrence relations are used. The same device is particularly useful with (8.4).

EXAMPLE 8.1. Calculate, for $x = 0(0\cdot 1)1$, the solution of

$$F' = 1 - 2xF$$

for which $\qquad F = 0, \ x = 0$

(A) We consider the application of (8.3) which becomes

$$(1 + 0\cdot 1x_1)F_1 = (1 - 0\cdot 1x_0)F_0 + 0\cdot 1 + \triangle$$

The calculation is shown below; $F^{(1)}$ is the first approximation from which $\triangle^{(1)}$ is derived; $F^{(2)}$ is obtained when $\triangle^{(1)}$ is included in the recurrence formula, and a further correction $\eta^{(2)}$ is derived from $\triangle^{(2)} - \triangle^{(1)}$, using a formula similar to (8.5). The final solution is not in error by more than $2 \cdot 10^{-6}$, but would normally be rounded to 5D.

x	$F^{(1)}$	δ^3	δ^4	δ^5	$\triangle^{(1)}$	$F^{(2)}$	$\triangle^{(2)}$	$\eta^{(2)}$	Error
0	0		0			0		0	0
		-388		29	32·6		329·2		
0·1	9901		29			99333		3	0
		-359		30	30·2		303·6		
0·2	19414		59			194746		4	-1
		-300		15	25·1		253·9		
0·3	28180		74			282624		6	-1
		-226		19	19·0		189·4		
0·4	35899		93			359938		5	0
		-133		-5	11·1		111·7		
0·5	42345		88			424430		6	0
		-45		-2	3·7		34·9		
0·6	47385		86			474760		3	0
		$+41$		-11	$-3·5$		$-37·8$		
0·7	50974		75			510504		1	$+2$
		116		-25	$-9·6$		$-99·3$		
0·8	53153		50			532103		0	$+2$
		166			$-14·1$		$-144·3$		
0·9	54038					540729		-3	$+2$
					(-16)				
1·0	53795					(538090)			
		Units of 10^{-5}				Units of 10^{-6}			

(B) The same calculation can be performed using the formula (8.4)

$$(3 + 0\cdot 2x_1)F_1 = -0\cdot 8x_0F_0 + (3 - 0\cdot 2x_{-1})F_{-1} + 0\cdot 6 + 3\triangle$$

Note that awkward fractions are removed by the factor 3. $F(0\cdot 1)$ is given by the Taylor series

$$F = x - (2/3)x^3 + (4/15)x^5 - (8/105)x^7 + \dots$$

In this case, only one correction is necessary, $\eta^{(1)}$ being derived directly from $\triangle^{(1)}$ with the first two values zero. It is advisable to include an extra decimal in $\eta^{(1)}$. The final result is slightly better than in (A).

x	$F^{(1)}$	δ^5	δ^6	δ^7	$\triangle^{(1)}$	$\eta^{(1)}$	Error
0	**0**		0		(-3.3)	0	0
		298		-4			
0·1	**99336**		-4		-3.5	0	0
		294		-111			
0·2	194754		-115		-2.6	-3.4	0
		179		$+82$			
0·3	282634		-33		-1.8	-2.4	$+1$
		146		-117			
0·4	359948		-150		-0.8	-4.7	0
		-4		$+118$			
0·5	424439		-32		$+0.2$	-2.6	0
		-36		-97			
0·6	474767		-129		1.1	-3.9	0
		-165		$+134$			
0·7	510505		$+5$		1.8	-0.8	$+1$
		-160		-78			
0·8	532103		-73		2.2	-1.7	0
		-233					
0·9	540723				(2.0)	$+1.7$	$+1$
1·0	538079					(0)	-1
1·1	526204						

Units of 10^{-6} throughout

Normally the quantities $3 \pm 0.2x$, $0.8x$ would be included in the table, but they are omitted here to save space, and the lower-order differences for the same reason.

8.2. Second-order Equations

Consider now the equation

$$G'' + p(x)G' + q(x)G = r(x) \qquad (8.6)$$

From the central difference equivalents of G'_0 and G''_0 (equations (5.32)) it is easily found that

$$\{1 + \tfrac{1}{2}wp_0\}G_1 = (2 - w^2q_0)G_0$$
$$- \{1 - \tfrac{1}{2}wp_0\}G_{-1} + w^2r_0 + \triangle \qquad (8.7)$$

where

$$\triangle = \{(1/12)\delta^4 - (1/90)\delta^6 + \ldots\}G_0$$
$$+ wp_0\{(1/6)\delta^3 - (1/30)\delta^5 + \ldots\}G_0$$

This again is a simple formula to apply, and the difference correction is often small. It does not supply values of G' which must be obtained subsequently by numerical differentiation, but often these are not required.

There is an obvious simplification when $p(x) = 0$ particularly as $\triangle$ does not then involve mean odd differences. When this happens, however, a more accurate recurrence relation is obtained by operating on (8.7) by $(1 + \delta^2/12)$. Then

$$(1 - \phi_1)G_1 = (2 + 10\phi_0)G_0 - (1 - \phi_{-1})G_{-1}$$
$$+ \psi_1 + 10\psi_0 + \psi_{-1} + \triangle \qquad (8.8)$$

where $\phi(x) = - (1/12)w^2q(x), \quad \psi(x) = (1/12)w^2r(x)$

and $\triangle = \{- (1/240)\delta^6 + (13/15120)\delta^8 - \ldots\}G_0$

This is a very attractive formula in view of the small difference correction. Considerable differencing is required, however, to evaluate $\triangle$, and the double summation method described in § 8.7, using essentially the same formula, may be on the whole less laborious. It must be emphasized that the differencing process is essential in this and other applications of the Fox-Goodwin method, even when $\triangle$ is negligible, otherwise there is no check on the final accuracy, nor on the presence of accidental errors. When $\triangle$ is not negligible, the η process can be used to calculate the correction as for first-order equations.

We now give examples of the use of (8.7) and (8.8).

EXAMPLE 8.2. Tabulate, at $x = 0(0 \cdot 5)4 \cdot 5$, 4D values of the solution of $G'' + (1/x)G' + G = 0$, given that $G(0) = 1 \cdot 0$ and $G(0 \cdot 5) = 0 \cdot 9385$.

The solution required is $J_0(x)$. The recurrence formula, with $w = 0 \cdot 5$,

is $(1 + 1/(4x_0))G_1 = 1 \cdot 75G_0 - (1 - 1/(4x_0))G_{-1} + \triangle$

Since $\triangle^{(1)}$ is fairly large, the second approximation $G^{(2)}$ is calculated directly and rounded to 4D at each step. From differences of $G^{(2)} - G^{(1)}$, the difference correction $\triangle^{(2)} - \triangle^{(1)}$ is derived and used to obtain $\eta^{(2)}$. A guarding figure is introduced at this stage; a similar precaution should perhaps be taken in obtaining $G^{(2)}$, but as $G(0 \cdot 5)$ is already rounded to 4D it is hardly worthwhile. The values of $G^{(3)}$ are nearly all correct to 4D, although unit errors in the 4th D are fairly likely.

This is an example of the use of a wide interval.

x	$G^{(1)}$	δ^3	δ^4	δ^5	δ^6	$\Delta^{(1)}$	$G^{(2)}$	$\Delta^{(2)}-\Delta^{(1)}$	$\eta^{(2)}$	$G^{(3)}$	Error of $G^{(3)}$
0	10000						10000		0	10000	0
0·5	9385	+ 76	152	+ 110	+ 220	59	9385	− 5·0	0	9385	0
1·0	7616	338	262	− 124	− 234	47	7655	− 1·6	− 3·4	7652	0
1·5	5031	476	138	− 92	+ 32	33	5124	− 1·1	− 6·1	5118	1
2·0	2106	522	+ 46	− 107	− 15	16	2246	0·0	− 7·6	2238	0
2·5	− 637	461	− 61	− 88	+ 19	1	− 477	+ 0·5	− 7·1	− 484	0
3·0	− 2737	312	− 149	− 60	28	− 12	− 2596	+ 1·5	− 4·6	− 2601	0
3·5	− 3882	+ 103	− 209	− 8	52	− 19	− 3801	+ 1·1	− 0·0	− 3801	0
4·0	− 3969	− 114	− 217	+ 34	42	− 20	− 3976	+ 0·8	+ 5·0	− 3971	0
4·5	− 3112	− 297	− 183			(− 17)	− 3214		+ 9·0	− 3205	
5·0	− 1608						− 1787				

Units of 10^{-4} throughout

EXAMPLE 8.3. Tabulate the solution of $G'' = xG$ for

$$x = 1 \cdot 0(0 \cdot 2)3 \cdot 0$$

given $\qquad G(0 \cdot 8) = 0 \cdot 169846, \; G(1 \cdot 0) = 0 \cdot 135292$

The solution required is $Ai(x)$. This is an example of an exponentially decreasing solution, in which particular care is necessary to avoid introducing error at the start of the integration, and any accumulation of rounding errors. Either of these will add in effect a small multiple of the second solution, which increases exponentially, and therefore eventually dominates. The recurrence formula (8.8) becomes

$$(3 - 0 \cdot 01x_1)G_1 = (6 + 0 \cdot 1x_0)G_0 - (3 - 0 \cdot 01x_{-1})G_{-1} + 3 \triangle$$

x	$G^{(1)}$	δ^4	δ^5	δ^6	$\triangle^{(1)}$	$\eta^{(1)}$	Error of $G^{(2)}$
0·8	**169846**	− 425				**0**	0
			130				
1·0	**135292**	− 295		− 20	+ 0·08	**0**	0
			110				
1·2	106125	− 185		− 18	+ 0·07	+ 0·1	− 1
			92				
1·4	82037	− 93		− 24	+ 0·10	+ 0·2	− 1
			68				
1·6	62535	− 25		− 23	+ 0·10	+ 0·5	− 2
			45				
1·8	47033	+ 20		− 13	+ 0·06	+ 0·9	− 2
			32				
2·0	34920	52		− 17	+ 0·07	+ 1·4	− 3
			15				
2·2	25605	67		− 11	+ 0·05	+ 2·1	− 3
			4				
2·4	18549	71		− 2	+ 0·01	+ 3·0	− 3
			2				
2·6	13280	73				+ 4·3	− 5
2·8	9397						
3·0	6572					$G^{(2)} = G^{(1)} + \eta^{(1)}$	

Units of 10^{-6} throughout

An important point to notice is that, although $\triangle^{(1)}$ does not exceed 0·1 of the 6th D its cumulative effect is quite large. Even so, comparison with values of $Ai(x)$ given in *B.A. Tables* (1946), shows that the error in $G^{(2)}$ is increasing steadily, probably for the reason mentioned above. The type of equation is one in which interpolatory methods, e.g. relaxation, are preferable and can often be used. For negative values of x the solution is oscillatory, and the recurrence method should be quite satisfactory.

When there is need to tabulate G' as well as G, it is possible to replace (8.6) by two first-order equations, as in (7.4). A pair of recurrence relations can then be derived as in Exercises 8, Nos. 1 and 2, each similar to (8.3) or (8.4); these we shall only quote, as their application is obvious.

(*A*) *Similar to* (8.3)

$$\left.\begin{aligned}
(1 + \tau p_1 + \tau^2 q_1)G_1 &= (1 + \tau p_1 - \tau^2 q_0)G_0 \\
&\quad + \tau(2 + \tau p_1 - \tau p_0)F_0 + (1 + \tau p_1)\triangle_G + \tau\triangle_F \\
(1 + \tau p_1 + \tau^2 q_1)F_1 &= - \tau(q_0 + q_1)G_0 \\
&\quad + (1 - \tau p_0 - \tau^2 q_1)F_0 - \tau q_1\triangle_G + \triangle_F
\end{aligned}\right\} \quad (8.9)$$

where
$$\triangle_G = \{- (1/12)\delta^3 + (1/120)\delta^5 - \ldots\}G_{1/2}$$
$$\triangle_F = \{- (1/12)\delta^3 + (1/120)\delta^5 - \ldots\}F_{1/2}$$

and
$$\tau = w/2$$

(*B*) *Similar to* (8.4)

$$\left.\begin{aligned}
(1 + \nu p_1 + \nu^2 q_1)G_1 &= - 4\nu^2 q_0 G_0 \\
&\quad + (1 + \nu p_1 - \nu^2 q_{-1})G_{-1} + 4\nu(1 + \nu p_1 - \nu p_0)F_0 \\
&\quad + \nu(2 + \nu p_1 - \nu p_{-1})F_{-1} + (1 + \nu p_1)\triangle_G + \nu\triangle_F \\
(1 + \nu p_1 + \nu^2 q_1)F_1 &= - 4\nu q_0 G_0 \\
&\quad - \nu(q_1 + q_{-1})G_{-1} - 4\nu(p_0 + \nu q_1)F_0 \\
&\quad + (1 - \nu p_{-1} - \nu^2 q_1)F_{-1} - \nu q_1\triangle_G + \triangle_F
\end{aligned}\right\} \quad (8.10)$$

where
$$\triangle_G = \{- (1/90)\delta^5 + (1/315)\delta^7 - \ldots\}G_0, \ \triangle_F \text{ similarly}$$

and
$$\nu = w/3$$

Alternative methods are described in § 8.5 and § 8.8.

8.3. Extension to Non-linear Equations

Recurrence methods are not in general suitable for use with non-linear equations, but there is a notable exception in equations of the form

$$G'' + p(x)G' - f(x, G) = 0 \quad \text{or} \quad r(x) \quad (8.11)$$

Because q does not occur on the left side of (8.7), this formula can still be used directly if $(2 - w^2 q_0)G_0$ be replaced by $(2G_0 + w^2 f_0)$. The more accurate formula (8.8) leads to a non-linear equation for G_1, since the left side becomes

$$G_1 - (w^2/12)f(x_1, G_1)$$

In some cases this can be solved at each step without excessive trouble, and the effect of including $\triangle$ estimated by using an approximate linear equation for the correction η (see reference, Clenshaw and Olver). Normally, however, one of the procedures described in § 8.5 or § 8.7 seems more appropriate.

Integral Methods not Using Differences

When equations are not linear, it is advisable to use one of the integral forms (7.21), (7.25) or (7.26), introduced in connexion with Picard's method of obtaining series solution by iteration. Established quadrature formulas can then be used which do not depend for their validity on whether the function which forms the integrand is a linear function of the solution. The formulas used may be of the Lagrangian type, as in the methods about to be described, or they may involve differences of the integrand. One feature, however, is common, that two formulas are generally used, one to predict or extrapolate the next value of the solution in terms of those preceding it, and another to use this approximate value so as to check it, and if necessary correct it by a rapid iterative process. Besides being convenient, this use of two formulas for prediction and correction plays an essential role in providing a check on the accuracy of the solution and on the absence of avoidable errors. Development of these methods which do not use differences is largely due to Milne (see Milne, $N.C.$).

8.4. First-order Equations

For equations of the type

$$dF/dx = f(x, F) \quad \text{or} \quad F = F_0 + \int_{x_0}^{x} f(x, F)dx \qquad (8.12)$$

a very useful pair of formulas for prediction and correction are

$$\bar{F}_1 = F_{-3} + (4w/3)(2f_0 - f_{-1} + 2f_{-2}) + (28w^5/90)f^{(4)}(\xi) \quad (8.13)$$

$$F_1 = F_{-1} + (w/3)(\bar{f}_1 + 4f_0 + f_{-1}) - (w^5/90)f^{(4)}(\xi_1) \qquad (8.14)$$

in which the suffices as before refer to any consecutive set of F values. The two formulas are clearly derived from Milne's rule (3.25) and Simpson's rule (3.18), the final terms indicating the nature of the remainder; ξ and ξ_1 lie within the respective ranges of integration.

The bar is used to denote a "predicted" value, which is subject to confirmation, and perhaps correction. It is obvious that if at any stage four consecutive values F_0, F_{-1}, F_{-2}, F_{-3} are available (and therefore f_0, f_{-1}, f_{-2}), (8.13) gives an estimate of F_1, which can be used to calculate $\bar{f}_1$; then (8.14) gives an improved value of F_1, which can be bettered if necessary by iteration. The process is repeated to obtain F_2 and so on.

Four starting values may be obtained by one of the series methods described in § 7.5–§ 7.8. An alternative which does not call for an analytical series to be developed, and is applicable whenever Taylor series can be used, has been suggested by Milne. Beginning with the values F_0, f_0, f'_0, the method is first to use

$$f_1 \simeq f_0 + wf'_0 \quad \text{and} \quad f_{-1} \simeq f_0 - wf'_0$$

to estimate f_1 and f_{-1}, and then to evaluate F_1 and F_{-1} by iteration from the formulas

$$\left. \begin{aligned} F_1 &= F_0 + (w/24)(7f_1 + 16f_0 + f_{-1}) \\ &\qquad + (w^2/4)f'_0 - (w^5/180)f^{(4)}(\xi_+) \\ F_{-1} &= F_0 - (w/24)(f_1 + 16f_0 + 7f_{-1}) \\ &\qquad + (w^2/4)f'_0 + (w^5/180)f^{(4)}(\xi_-) \end{aligned} \right\} \quad (8.15)$$

The integration is continued by predicting F_2 from the formula

$$\bar{F}_2 = F_0 + (2w/3)(5f_1 - f_0 - f_{-1}) \\ - 2w^2f'_0 + (7w^5/45)f^{(4)}(\xi) \quad (8.16)$$

which replaces (8.13) on this occasion. F_2 can be verified by the counterpart of (8.14), and the rest of the calculation follows naturally.

It is necessary, since no differences of F are tabulated as in the Fox-Goodwin methods, to keep an eye on the error of using the truncated quadrature formula (8.14). The following argument suggests how this may be done. The errors of $\bar{F}_k$ and F_k are respectively

$$(28w^5/90)f^{(4)}(\xi), \quad (-w^5/90)f^{(4)}(\xi_1) + \text{small error due to } \bar{f}_k$$

so

$$\text{error of } (\bar{F}_k - F_k) \simeq (29w^5/90)f^{(4)}(\xi')$$

and

$$\text{error of } F_k \simeq (\bar{F}_k - F_k)/29 \quad (8.17)$$

It is assumed that $f^{(4)}$ varies but slowly. It is thus useful to include in the computation a table of $d_k = \bar{F}_k - F_k$, first to ensure that it does not become excessive, and secondly as a help to anticipating corrections when calculating $\bar{f}_k$. It must be remembered that for accurate results $d_k \ll 29$, because truncation errors may in some equations build up over a number of steps. Sudden fluctuations in d_k are a common indication of arithmetical errors. If d_k grows steadily to an unacceptable value, the interval w should be shortened; this usually presents no difficulty beyond interpolating one or two values of f. If w is halved, the error of each step is reduced by 32. Alternatively if d_k seems quite negligible it may be possible to lengthen the interval.

More accurate results may be obtained, or a longer interval used, by using quadrature formulas based on higher degree polynomials. For instance, the Steffensen formula

$$\bar{F}_1 = F_{-5} + (3w/10)(11f_0 - 14f_{-1} + 26f_{-2} - 14f_{-3} + 11f_{-4})$$
$$+ (41w^7/140)f^{(6)} \quad (8.18)$$

may be used for prediction, and for correction Boole's rule

$$F_1 = F_{-3} + (2w/45)(7\bar{f}_1 + 32f_0 + 12f_{-1} + 32f_{-2} + 7f_{-3})$$
$$- (8w^7/945)f^{(6)} \quad (8.19)$$

The labour per step is of course greater.
The following example uses (8.13) and (8.14).

EXAMPLE 8.4.   Find   the   solution   of $F' = (xF - 1)^{1/2}$ for $x = 1(0.2)3$, given that $F(1) = 2$, and taking the negative root.

The solution of this equation has two branches, arising from the two roots, $f_+ = + (xF - 1)^{1/2}$ and $f_- = - (xF - 1)^{1/2}$. We investigate here the decreasing solution, given by f_-, assuming $w = 0.2$. At $x = 1, f_0 = - 1$ and $f'_0 = - 1/2$.
Application of equation (8.15) gives the following sequence of approximations—

	(1)	(2)	(3)	(4)
$f(0.8)$	$- 0.9$	$- 0.8672$	$- 0.86618$	$- 0.86616$
$f(1.2)$	$- 1.1$	$- 1.0714$	$- 1.07253$	$- 1.07250$
$F(0.8)$	2.19	2.18783	2.18780	
$F(1.2)$	1.79	1.79194	1.79188	

From (8.16), $\bar{F}(1.4) = 1.5738$. If F is required to 4D, as in the following integration, it is very desirable at this stage to obtain $F(0.8)$ and $F(1.2)$ correct to 5D.

[Alternatively, the Taylor series may be used; this is

$$F = 2 - h - (1/4)h^2 + (1/4)h^3$$
$$- (3/32)h^4 + (5/64)h^5 - (5/64)h^6 + \ldots$$

where $h = x - 1$]

x	$(w/3)\bar{f}$	$(w/3)f$	$\bar{F}$	F	$\bar{F} - F$
0·8		− 0·05774		2·18780	
1·0		− 0·06667		2·0	
1·2		− 0·07150		1·79188	
1·4	− 0·07313		1·5738		
		− 0·07315		1·57418	− 0·0004
1·6	− 0·07206		1·3552		
		− 0·07208		$1·3557_0$	− 5
1·8	− 0·06861		1·1440		
		− 0·06862		$1·1440_9$	− 1
2·0	− 0·06296		0·9460		
		− 0·06298		$0·9461_6$	− 2
2·2	− 0·05538		0·7682		
		− 0·05538		$0·7681_7$	0
2·4	− 0·04607		0·6156		
		− 0·04606		$0·6156_0$	0
2·6	− 0·03544		0·4933		
		− 0·03541		$0·4931_4$	2
2·8	− 0·02417		0·4041		
		− 0·02410		$0·4038_0$	3
3·0	− 0·01422		0·3485		
		− 0·01377		$0·3475_6$	9

8.5. Second-order Equations

The solution of a second-order equation

$$G'' = f(x, F, G) \qquad (8.20)$$

in its integral form (7.26), can be carried out by a double process of the kind just described, in which both G and F are tabulated. For this purpose three formulas suffice—

$$\bar{F}_1 = F_{-3} + (4w/3)(2f_0 - f_{-1} + f_{-2}) \qquad (8.21)$$

$$\bar{G}_1 = G_{-1} + (w/3)(\bar{F}_1 + 4F_0 + F_{-1}) \to \bar{f}_1 = f(x, \bar{G}_1, \bar{F}_1) \qquad (8.22)$$

$$F_1 = F_{-1} + (w/3)(\bar{f}_1 + 4f_0 + f_{-1}) \qquad (8.23)$$

Assuming as before that four consecutive values are known, (8.21) predicts a value $\bar{F}_1$, which leads by (8.22) to $\bar{G}_1$ and thence to $\bar{f}_1$; (8.23) is now used to give a better value of F_1, and so on.

In practice it is convenient to tabulate G, $wF/3$, $w^2f/9$ rather than G, F, f, as the following example shows.

EXAMPLE 8.5. Find the first zero of the solution of

$$G'' - (1/4)(G')^2 + G = 0$$

for which $G(0) = 1$, $G'(0) = 0$

This is an equation for damped simple harmonic motion, the frictional force being proportional to the square of the velocity. The starting solution is conveniently given by the Taylor series

$$G = 1 - (1/2)x^2 + (1/16)x^4 - (1/160)x^6 + (13/17920)x^8 - \ldots$$

If we choose w to be 0·2, this is used to give G and F for $x = 0·2$, 0·4, 0·6. Writing $v = (w^2/9)f$ it follows that

$$v = -0{\cdot}004444G + (wF/6)^2$$

which is more easily derived if we tabulate $wF/3$. The subsequent computation appears as follows—

x	$\bar{v}$	v	$w\bar{F}/3$	$wF/3$	$\bar{G}$	G	$\dfrac{w(\bar{F}-F)}{3}$
0		− 4444		0		1000000	
0·2		− 4312		− 13201		98010_0	
0·4		− 3931		− 25625		92157_5	
0·6		− 3344		− 36583		82782_0	
0·8	− 2611		− 45524		704094		
		− 2610		− 45542		70407_6	18
1·0	− 1795		− 52153		55691_6		
		− 1795		− 52162		55690_7	9
1·2	− 957		− 56297		39358_9		
		− 957		− 56289		39359_7	− 8
1·4	− 146		− 57939		22165_0		
		− 146		− 57931		22165_8	− 8
1·6	+ 604		− 57242		4834_2		
		+ 604		− 57226		4835_8	− 16
1·8	1271		− 54402		-11957_9		
		1271		− 54390		-11956_7	− 12
2·0	1845		− 49705		-27613_3		
		1844		− 49694		-27612_2	− 11

Units of 10^{-6} throughout

Inverse interpolation shows that $G = 0$ when $x = 1·6566$, which may be compared with $1·5708(= \pi/2)$ for undamped motion.

When F is absent from the equation other formulas may be preferable. Thus if $G'' = f(x, G)$, and F is not required at every point, it is possible to use the following formulas for prediction and checking—

$$\bar{G}_1 = G_0 + G_{-2} - G_{-3} + (w^2/4)(5f_0 + 2f_{-1} + 5f_{-2})$$
$$+ (17w^6/240)f^{(4)} \quad (8.24)$$

$$G_1 = 2G_0 - G_{-1} + (w^2/12)(\bar{f}_1 + 10f_0 + f_{-1})$$
$$- (w^6/240)f^{(4)} \quad (8.25)$$

The first of these is based on the parabola passing through f_0, f_{-1} and f_{-2}, and twice integrated; the second is merely a rearrangement of (8.8), $q(x)G(x)$ being replaced by $-f$, and $\triangle$ by the Taylor series form of the remainder. The sequence of the calculation is obvious, $\bar{G}_1$ leading to $\bar{f}_1$ and thence to G. The remainder in (8.25) can be ignored if $\bar{G}_1 - G_1 \ll 18$ (units of final decimal), by an argument similar to that used in deriving (8.17). Comparison with the recurrence method based on (8.8) shows that for linear equations the two methods should give identical results when, as often happens, the difference correction is negligible. When $\triangle$ is not negligible a somewhat smaller interval is advisable with Milne's method than the Fox-Goodwin method allows. Though (8.24) and (8.25) are easy to apply, and have the advantage that they can be used without modification to non-linear equations, they do not give quite the same clear control over the accuracy of the result that is afforded by the difference table of G.

EXAMPLE 8.6. Solve the equation
$$d^2G/dx^2 + (1 + 1/4x^2)G - 1/G^3 = 0$$
for large values of x, given $G = 0$, $G' = 0$ for $x = \infty$.

This is the amplitude equation for Bessel functions of order zero (cp. equation (7.43)), the solution satisfying the given conditions being
$$(\pi x/2)^{1/2}\{J_0{}^2(x) + Y_0{}^2(x)\}^{1/2}$$
Transforming to $\xi = 1/x$ we obtain (cp. (7.44))
$$d^2M/d\xi^2 + (1/\xi^4 + 1/4\xi^2)M - 1/M^3 = 0$$
where $M = \xi G$. The solution for small ξ is given by an asymptotic series
$$M = \xi\{1 - (1/16)\xi^2 + (53/512)\xi^4 - (17803/32768)\xi^6 + \ldots\}$$
[The reader should investigate the asymptotic solution of
$$d^2G/dx^2 + (1 + \alpha^2/x^2)G - 1/G^3 = 0$$
following the method of Example 7.14).]

Let $w = 0.1$. Then it is convenient to write (8.24) and (8.25) as

$$\bar{G}_1 = G_0 + G_{-2} - G_{-3} + 15v_0 + 6v_{-1} + 15v_{-2}$$
$$G_1 = 2G_0 - G_{-1} + \bar{v}_1 + 10v_0 + v_{-1}$$

where $\quad v = (w^2/12)f = 0.0008333\{M^{-3} - (1/\xi^4 + 1/4\xi^2)M\}$

In the following calculation, the fact that $M(-\xi) = -M(\xi)$ has been used to assist the start.

ξ	$\bar{v}$	v	$\bar{M}$	M	$\bar{M} - M$	$1 - G$
-0.1				-99938.5		
0.0		0		0		0
0.1		-29.7		99938.5		615
0.2		-52.6		199528.1		2360
0.3	-68.6		298499			
		-66.9		298495	4	5017
0.4	-77.3		396669			
		-76.6		396664	5	8340
0.5	-81.0		493914			
		-81.2		493919	-5	12162
0.6	-83.3		590205			
		-83.1		590202	3	16330
0.7	-83.5		695488			
		-83.5		685489	-1	20730
0.8	-82.7		779775			
		-82.7		779775	0	25281
0.9	-81.3		873070			
		-81.3		873069	1	29923
1.0	-79.4		965388			
		-79.4		965388	0	34612

All values multiplied by 10^6

The calculation is not too satisfactory, and would be improved by using a smaller interval at the start. The reason is that the asymptotic series does not converge very well at $\xi = 0.2$, and the value of $M(0.2)$ to 6D involves some guesswork. This may explain the initial erratic behaviour of $\bar{M} - M$. Note that $f(0.2)$ must not be obtained by differentiating the asymptotic series for M. The accuracy of the results can be judged from the following values of $1 - G$ obtained from Bessel function tables—

ξ	0.5	1.0
$1 - G$	0.012168	0.034609

The full computation would include columns giving $\xi^{-4} + (1/4)\xi^{-2}$, $(\bar{M})^{-3}$ and M^{-3}.

Integral Methods with Use of Differences

We turn now to methods which are essentially the same as those just described, but which use difference formulas to effect the integration. As in Milne's methods, two formulas are generally used to complete each step, the calculations being complementary and mutually checking.

8.6. Nyström's Method for First-order Equations

This simple method of solving (8.12) uses backward differences and is based on the following pair of formulas, taken from Exercises 5, No. 1.

For prediction

$$\overline{F}_1 = F_{-1} + w\{2f_0 + (1/3)(\nabla^2 + \nabla^3 + \nabla^4)f_0$$
$$- (1/90)\nabla^4 f_0 + (14/45)\nabla^5 f_0 + \ldots\} \quad (8.26)$$

For correction

$$F_1 = F_{-1} + w\{2f_0 + (1/3)\nabla^2 \overline{f}_1 - (1/90)(\nabla^4 + \nabla^5)\overline{f}_1$$
$$- (37/3780)\nabla^6 \overline{f}_1 + \ldots\} \quad (8.27)$$

It is convenient in (8.26) to ignore $(1/90)\nabla^4 f_0$ and higher differences, thus leaving $\nabla^4 f_0$ with a simple coefficient. If fourth differences can be entirely neglected, (8.27) is equivalent to Simpson's rule, and the correction consists mainly in comparing $(w/3)(\nabla^2 + \nabla^3 + \nabla^4)f_0$ and $(w/3)\nabla^2 \overline{f}_1$. However, if necessary the inclusion of $-(w/90)(\nabla^2 + \nabla^4)\overline{f}_1$ presents little difficulty as these differences are available from $\overline{f}_1$. Further improvement of F_1 can be made by iteration if need be.

The advantage in using an integral formula like Simpson's, which extends over two intervals, is that the coefficients of higher differences are smaller, but there is also the danger that oscillating errors may arise as in the recurrence formula (8.4), which is basically the same. Nyström's method has the disadvantage that five starting values are generally needed. Although it is suitable for non-linear equations, we shall illustrate its use by the same equation as in Example 8.1 to provide a comparison.

EXAMPLE 8.7. Calculate for $x = 0(0 \cdot 1)1 \cdot 0$ the solution of

$$F' = 1 - 2xF$$

for which $F(0) = 0$

x	F	f	∇	∇^2	∇^3	∇^4	∇^5	(a)	(b)	$F - \bar{F}$ (c)	Error of F
0	**0**	**1·00000**									
0·1	**0·099836**	**0·98013**	**− 1987**	**− 3974**	**158**	**316**	− 23	1·84420			0
0·2	**0·194751**	**0·92210**	**− 5803**	**− 3816**	451	293	− 48	− 1114	0·183306	− 11	0
0·3	0·282631	0·83042	− 9168	− 3365	696	245	− 84	1·66084	0·165210	− 18	0
0·4	0·359943	0·71205	− 11837	− 2669	857	161	− 84	− 874	0·141834	− 29	0
0·5	0·424436	0·57556	− 13649	− 1812	934	77	− 105	1·42410	0·114847	− 28	0
0·6	0·474762	0·43029	− 14527	− 878	906	− 28	− 73	− 576	0·086102	− 33	− 1
0·7	0·510503	0·28530	− 14499	+ 28	805	− 101	− 65	1·15112	0·057361	− 22	0
0·8	0·532101	0·14864	− 13666	833	639	− 166	− 37	− 265	0·030240	− 19	0
0·9	0·540724	0·02670	− 12194	1472	436	− 203		0·86058	0·005988	− 9	0
1·0	0·538080	− 0·07616	− 10286	1908				+ 44			0
								0·57059			
								302			
								0·29728			
								512			
								0·05340			
								648			

The subsidiary calculation at each step is shown in columns (a), (b), (c) as follows—

(a) $2f_0$ and $(1/3)(\nabla^2 + \nabla^3 + \nabla^4)f_0$

(b) $\bar{F}_1 - F_{-1} = w\{2f_0 + (1/3)(\nabla^2 + \nabla^3 + \nabla^4)f_0\}$

(c) $F_1 - \bar{F}_1 = w\{(1/3)\nabla^2 f_1 - (1/90)(\nabla^4 + \nabla^5)f_1 - (1/3)(\nabla^2 + \nabla^3 + \nabla^4)f_0\}$

As a final check it is desirable to difference F, but this is not shown.

Starting values are provided by the Taylor series

$$F = x - (2/3)x^3 + (4/15)x^5 - (8/105)x^7$$
$$+ (16/945)x^9 - (32/10395)x^{11} + \ldots$$

This can be used to give values up to $x = 0.4$, although in this instance, since $F(-x) = -F(x)$, it is simpler to use values between -0.2 and 0.2, and this has been done in the calculation on p. 225. The final errors compare favourably with Example 8.1.

As an alternative layout for the integration, $wf/3$ can be tabulated and differenced instead of f. This has obvious advantages.

8.7. Second-order Equations, without First Derivative

The solution of second-order equations of the type

$$G'' = f(x, G)$$

is one in which numerical methods often show to the best advantage. This is because the neglected terms in the integration formula have unusually small coefficients. An excellent method, suggested by Cowell* in 1909 in connexion with astronomical computations, uses a combination of sums and differences and is based on the formula

$$G_k = w^2\{\sigma^2 f_k + (1/12)f_k - (1/240)\delta^2 f_k + \ldots\} \qquad (8.28)$$

This involves the "second sum" $\sigma^2 f$, and follows easily from (6.22) or (6.32). The following table shows that if G_{k-1} and f_{k-1}, and preceding values, are known, the calculation of G_k depends mainly on an estimate of $f_k/12$ being possible, since f_{k-1} is sufficient to give $\sigma^2 f_k$ and $\delta^2 f_k/240$ is usually very small.

G_{k-2}	$\sigma^2 f_{k-2}$		f_{k-2}
		$\sigma f_{k-3/2}$	
G_{k-1}	$\sigma^2 f_{k-1}$		f_{k-1}
		$\sigma f_{k-1/2}$	
G_k	$\sigma^2 f_k$		(f_k)

The extrapolation of $f_k/12$ usually presents no difficulty, and any error, being multplied by w^2, rarely makes much change in G_k. As soon as G_k has been estimated, f_k can of course be checked, and improvements made iteratively.

Two starting values G_0, G_1 are required to set the calculation going. These may both be prescribed, or if the initial conditions define G_0 and G'_0, a series solution can usually be found to give

---

* See J. Jackson, *Mon. Not. R. Astr. Soc.*, **84** (1924), 602.

G_1. Then assuming w is taken small enough to make $\delta^2 f/240$ negligible (and it is advantageous to do this), $\sigma^2 f_0$ and $\sigma^2 f_1$ are given by the equations

$$\sigma^2 f_0 = w^{-2} G_0 - f_0/12, \quad \sigma^2 f_1 = w^{-2} G_1 - f_1/12$$

The calculation of G_2, etc., then proceeds as above.

As a check on the integration, it is desirable and convenient to use the formula (6.32)

$$\delta^2 G_k = w^2 \{ f_k + (1/12)\delta^2 f_k - (1/240)\delta^4 f_k + \ldots \} \quad (8.29)$$

which requires the second differences of G and f to be formed. This generally checks the formation of $\sigma^2 f$ and the derivation of f from G.

It is important to notice that when the equation is linear no extrapolation for $f_k/12$ need be made. Thus, when

$$f(x, G) = - q(x)G + r(x)$$

(8.28) becomes

$$\{1 + w^2 q_k/12\}G_k = w^2 \{\sigma^2 f_k + r_k/12 - \delta^2 f_k/240 + \ldots \} \quad (8.30)$$

so that, ignoring the term in $\delta^2 f_k$, G_k is derived immediately from $\sigma^2 f_k$. It is then an advantage to pretabulate $w^2/\{1 + w^2 q_k/12\}$. Since (8.30) is essentially identical with the recurrence formula (8.8), the two methods should give similar results. There is, however, the distinction that in using (8.30) the effect of the $\delta^2 f$ term can if desired be included in the step-by-step procedure, whereas in the recurrence method it is incorporated later.

Two applications of the Gauss-Jackson method follow, the first to a non-linear, the second to a linear equation.

EXAMPLE 8.8. Find the first zero of the solution of $G'' + \sin G = 0$ for which $G(0) = 0 \cdot 2$, $G'(0) = 0$.

This is the equation for harmonic oscillations with finite amplitude. By Taylor's series

$$G = 0 \cdot 2 - 0 \cdot 1986693(x^2/2\,!) + 0 \cdot 194709(x^4/4\,!)$$
$$- 0 \cdot 167304(x^6/6\,!) + \ldots$$
$$= 0 \cdot 2 - 0 \cdot 0993347 x^2 + 0 \cdot 0081129 x^4 - 0 \cdot 0002324 x^6$$
$$- 0 \cdot 0000016 x^8 - \ldots$$

This is sufficient to give G to 7D for $x \leqslant 1$; in particular

$$G(0 \cdot 9) = 0 \cdot 1247376 \qquad \sin G(0 \cdot 9) = 0 \cdot 12442$$
$$G(1 \cdot 0) = 0 \cdot 1085442 \qquad \sin G(1 \cdot 0) = 0 \cdot 10833$$

Hence, at $x = 0\cdot9$, $\sigma^2 f = 12\cdot47376 + 0\cdot01037 = 12\cdot48413$

$\qquad\qquad\;\; 1\cdot0,\;\; \sigma^2 f = 10\cdot85442 + 0\cdot00903 = 10\cdot86345$

This assumes $w = 0\cdot1$. The step-by-step process is then as follows—

x	$f/12$	$\sigma^2 f$	σf	f	$100G$	$100\delta G$	$100\delta^2 G$	$f + \delta^2 f/12$
0·9	− 103·7	124841·3		− 1244·2	124738			
			− 16206·8			− 16194		
1·0	− 90·3	108634·5		− 1083·3	108544		− 1082	− 1082
			− 17290·1			− 17276		
1·1	− 76·0	91344·4		− 911·4	91268		− 910	− 911
			− 18201·5			− 18186		
1·2	− 60·8	73142·9		− 730·2	73082		− 730	− 730
			− 18931·7			− 18916		
1·3	− 45·1	54211·2		− 541·4	54166		− 541	− 541
			− 19473·1			− 19457		
1·4	− 28·9	34738·1		− 347·0	34709		− 346	− 347
			− 19820·1			− 19803		
1·5	− 12·4	14918·0		− 149·0	14906		− 150	− 149
			− 19969·1			− 19953		
1·6	+ 4·2	− 5051·1		+ 50·5	− 5047		+ 51	+ 50
			− 19918·6			− 19902		
1·7	20·8	− 24969·7		249·4	− 24949		249	249
			− 19669·2			− 19653		
1·8	37·2	− 44638·9		445·9	− 44602			
1·6	4·2	− 1266·0		50·5	− 5047			
			− 9921·7			− 39555		
1·8	37·2	− 11187·7		445·9	− 44602		1777	1778
			− 9475·8			− 37778		
2·0	68·6	− 20663·5		822·9	− 82380			

All values in units of 10^{-4}

Note that $\sin G$ is required to 4D only. By inverse interpolation the zero is found to occur at $x = 1\cdot57467$ (cp. analytical solution $1\cdot57473$).

An important point about the use of the check formula (8.29) is that any discrepancies in the quantities given in the last two columns should alternate in sign. If either sign persists the integration should be carefully examined for errors.

Changing the interval is a little more troublesome in this method than in recurrence methods or those not using differences, as the starting procedure must be applied once again to obtain two basic values of $\sigma^2 f$. This is illustrated above, the interval being increased from 0·1 to 0·2 at $x = 1\cdot8$. At the larger interval the final digit in G is not very reliable.

EXAMPLE 8.9. Tabulate for $x = 1(0\cdot2)3$ the solution of $G'' = xG$ for which $G(0\cdot6) = 0\cdot209800$, $G(0\cdot8) = 0\cdot169846$, $G(1\cdot0) = 0\cdot135292$.

This is similar to Example 8.3 and is subject to the same reservations. With $w = 0\cdot2$, the integration formula (8.30) is conveniently written

$$(300 - x)G = 12\{\sigma^2 f - (1/240)\delta^2 f\}, \quad f = xG$$

At this interval, the $\delta^2 f$ term is not quite negligible with 6D in G. For this reason the value at 0·6 has been assumed (to provide $\delta^2 f_0$), and without this it would be better to begin the integration with

$w = 0.1$. Alternatively the calculation could be started ignoring the $\delta^2 f$ term, and subsequently corrected by a method described later.

The initial values are obtained as follows—

$$x = 0.8 \qquad \sigma^2 f_0 = 1/12 \times 299.2 \times 0.169846 - 0.00004 = 4.23479$$
$$x = 1.0 \qquad \sigma^2 f_1 = 1/12 \times 299.0 \times 0.135292 - 0.00003 = 3.37100$$

The $\delta^2 f$ correction of -0.00003 at $x = 1.0$ has to be confirmed later. Every care must be taken to obtain $\sigma f_{1/2}$ accurately, to avoid subsequent accumulation of error.

x	$\sigma^2 f$	σf	f	δf	$\delta^2 f$	G	δG	$\delta^2 G$	$0.04\{f + \delta^2 f/12\}$
0.8	423479		13588		− 1059	169846		5400	5400
		− 86379		− 59			− 34554		
1.0	337100		13529		− 735	135292		5387	5387
		− 72850		− 794			− 29167		
1.2	264250		12735		− 456	106125		5079	5079
		− 60115		− 1250			− 24088		
1.4	204135		11485		− 229	82037		4587	4586
		− 48630		− 1479			− 19501		
1.6	155505		10006		− 61	62536		4000	4000
		− 38624		− 1540			− 15501		
1.8	116881		8466		+ 58	47035		3388	3388
		− 30158		− 1482			− 12113		
2.0	86723		6984		132	34922		2798	2798
		− 23174		− 1350			− 9315		
2.2	63549		5634		168	25607		2260	2259
		− 17540		− 1182			− 7055		
2.4	46009		4452		184	18552		1786	1787
		− 13088		− 998			− 5269		
2.6	32921		3454		177	13283		1388	1388
		− 9634		− 821			− 3881		
2.8	23287		2633		162	9402		1059	1059
		− 7001		− 659			− 2822		
3.0	16286		1974			6580			

Units of 10^{-5}	Units of 10^{-6}

The results are nearly identical with those of Example 8.3, the later values showing an increasing error.

Two further points concerning this method should be mentioned. First, if a table of G' is required simultaneously with G it is most conveniently given by the formula, derived from (5.39)

$$G'_k = F_k = (w/2)\{2\sigma f_k - (1/12)(2\delta f_k)$$
$$+ (11/720)(2\delta^3 f_k) - \ldots\} \quad (8.31)$$

in which σf_k, etc., are mean sums and differences.

Secondly, rather than incorporate $\delta^2 f$ in the integration for G, as in Example 8.9, it may be more convenient to ignore it in the first instance, and to perform a subsidiary integration analogous to the η process in the recurrence method. Thus, assume $G^{(1)}$ is the solution given by

$$G^{(1)} = w^2\{\sigma^2 f^{(1)} + (1/12)f^{(1)}\}$$

and that the more accurate solution $G^{(1)} + \eta$ satisfies

$$G^{(1)} + \eta = w^2\{\sigma^2(f^{(1)} + \Delta f) + (1/12)(f^{(1)} + \Delta f)$$
$$- (1/240)\delta^2(f^{(1)} + \Delta f)\}$$

where $f^{(1)} + \Delta f$ is calculated from $G^{(1)} + \eta$. By subtraction

$$\eta \simeq w^2\{\sigma^2(\Delta f) + (1/12)\Delta f - (1/240)\delta^2 f^{(1)}\} \qquad (8.32)$$

and hence a solution of this equation gives η. The starting conditions, if G_0 and G_1 are fixed, require that $\Delta f_0 = \Delta f_1 = 0$, $\eta_0 = \eta_1 = 0$; the rest of the calculation is straightforward and may not even require a calculating machine. Δf may be calculated directly, using $G^{(1)} + \eta$, or approximately from

$$\Delta f = \eta(\partial f/\partial G)$$

8.8. Second-order Equations Including First Derivative

When the equation contains the derivative F explicitly, it can be replaced by two first-order equations and solved by a double application of Nyström's method, along the lines of Milne's method described in § 8.5. An alternative which is probably better is to combine the use of (8.28) with two formulas for predicting and correcting F. The first of these is (5.42)

$$\overline{F}_{k+1} = F_{k-1} + 2w\{f_k + (1/6)\delta^2 f_k - (1/180)\delta^4 f_k + \ldots\} \quad (8.33)$$

and the second is (8.31).

To show their use, assume that in the table below the unbracketed quantities are known (all suffices may be increased by k), and that the terms in $\delta^2 f$, $\delta^3 f$, $\delta^4 f$ in (8.28), (8.31), (8.33) respectively are negligible.

F_{-1}	$\sigma^2 f_{-1}$		f_{-1}		$\delta^2 f_{-1}$	G_{-1}
		$\sigma f_{-1/2}$		$\delta f_{-1/2}$		
$\overline{F}_0$	$\sigma^2 f_0$		f_0		$(\delta^2 f_0)$	G_0
		$\sigma f_{1/2}$		$(\delta f_{1/2})$		
	$\sigma^2 f_1$		(f_1)			

$\overline{F}_0$ is here only approximate and has to be verified. The sequence of operations leading to G_1 is as follows—

(a) $\overline{F}_1$ is estimated using (8.33) with a guessed value of $\delta^2 f_0$.

(b) From the same value of $\delta^2 f_0$, f_1 is obtained by summation, and hence an estimate $\bar{G}_1$, using (8.28).

(c) From $\overline{F}_1$ and $\bar{G}_1$, $\bar{f}_1$ is calculated and compared with the value assumed. $\delta \bar{f}_{1/2}$ and $\delta^2 \bar{f}_0$ are derived and $\bar{F}_1$ is corrected if necessary.

(d) $\bar{F}_0$ is checked using (8.31) with the value of $\delta \bar{f}_{1/2}$; f_0 and G_0 are adjusted if necessary.

The cycle is repeated, estimating $\bar{F}_2$, $\bar{G}_2$, etc. Although apparently complicated the process usually goes smoothly if w is well chosen. For starting, only two values of G, F, f are are required. It is often simpler to record simple multiples of F and f, as the following example shows.

EXAMPLE 8.10. Begin the integration of $G'' - (1/4)F^2 + G = 0$ as in Example 8.5.

Let $M = 2KwF$, $m = 4Kw^2 f = 4Kw^2 \{ - G + (M/4Kw)^2 \}$ where K is a convenient constant between 1 and 5.

If $w = 0.2$ and $K = 1.25$, then $M = \frac{1}{2}F$, $m = 0.2(- G + M^2)$, and the integration formulas become—

$$G_1 = 0.2 \{ \sigma^2 m_1 + (1/12)m_1 - (1/240)\delta^2 m_1 + \ldots \}$$
$$\bar{M}_1 = M_{-1} + m_0 + (1/6)\delta^2 m_0 - (1/180)\delta^4 m_0 + \ldots$$
$$M_0 = (1/4) \{ 2\sigma m_0 - (1/12)(2\delta m_0) + (11/720)(2\delta^3 m_0) + \ldots \}$$

The computation appears as follows, the starting values being in heavy type as usual.

x	$\bar{M}$	M	$\sigma^2 m$	σm	m	δm	$\delta^2 m$	$m/12$	$\bar{G}$	G
0·0		**0**	501672		− 20000		1188	− 1667		100000
				− 10000		594				
0·2		− 9901	491672		− 19406		1119	− 1617		98010·0
				− 29406		1713				
0·4	(− 19208) −19220	− 19219	462266		− 17693		929	− 1474	92140	92157·5
				− 47099		2642				
0·6	− 27439	− 27438	415167		− 15051		661	− 1254	82784	82782·0
				− 62150		3303				
0·8	− 34160		353017		− 11748		369	− 979	70406	70409·2
				− 73898		3672				
1·0	− 39124		279119		− 8076			− 673	55687	

All values in units of 10^{-5}

Some remarks about the beginning of the integration are necessary. The initial value of $\delta^2 m$ is obviously about 1188 because m is an odd function of x, and this shows that a correction of 5 should be included in $\sigma^2 m_0$ and $\sigma^2 m_1$. Then, assuming $\delta^2 m$ is constant at 1188, the estimate of $\bar{M}$ at $x = 0.4$ is

$$- 19406 + (1/6)(1188) = - 19208$$

This is later altered to $- 19220$ when $\delta^2 m$ is found at $x = 0.2$. Some allowance for $\delta^3 m$ is necessary in computing M.

This integration is more accurate than that of Example 8·5, in which the $\delta^2 m$ terms are incorrectly allowed for (see Exercises 8, No. 4).

8.9. Comparison of Recurrence and Integral Methods

It is evident by now that the computer has a considerable choice of method in solving first- and second-order equations, though this choice is more limited if the equation is not linear. To some extent the choice in a particular instance depends on personal preference, and here the writer has a decided preference for the sum and difference methods just described. In these the differences provide obvious insight into the behaviour of the solution and its derivatives at each step; the higher differences act as a guide to the accuracy of the approximation and a guard on accidental errors, and also show when there is advantage to be gained by making the interval longer or shorter. These are valuable advantages when the course of the solution is not fully understood prior to the calculation. On the other hand, in more routine operations, when it is known that the formula is adequate, it may be better to dispense with differences as in Milne's methods, favouring a more automatic process. Such methods may receive considerable use with fast electronic machines.

When recurrence methods are applicable, they are also valuable for a preliminary and rapid sketching out of the solution at a fairly wide interval, after which its accuracy can be refined as desired by including the difference correction. The fact that only a few significant figures need be retained in the first approximation, and the full accuracy (for the interval chosen) reserved till later, constitutes one of the main advantages of this type of solution. When recurrence formulas are used the start of the integration, and change of interval length, can generally be made quite smoothly; the difference correction at the beginning, however, may give a little trouble when it is expressed in central differences.

Nevertheless it remains true that sum and difference methods have the widest application. To illustrate this consider the three formulas (8.8), (8.25) and (8.28), which for linear equations of the type $G'' + q(x)G = r(x)$ are formally identical. (8.8) and (8.28) are similar in that there is usually no difficulty in including correction terms, in the forms $\delta^6 G/240$ and $\delta^2 f/240$ respectively. With (8.25) this correction cannot be immediately included, and one must therefore be more cautious in opening out the interval of integration. Both (8.25) and (8.28), however, are applicable to non-linear equations, and the use of (8.28) is easily extended to equations in which the first derivative occurs explicitly.

Errors of Solution

The cumulative errors associated with step-by-step processes of integration require some comment. There is still much to be discovered about these, and we do not propose to do more than indicate the nature of the problem. Such errors arise both from the use of a curtailed formula, and from rounding errors. The former, usually called truncation errors, occur primarily because the differential equation is replaced by a finite difference equation, and are the more systematic in their effect. The errors introduced at any particular step can be estimated without much difficulty; what needs investigation is the delayed effect of this error several steps later in the integration. Some progress in this direction has been made, largely by pursuing the solution of a few simple but typical equations, for which the difference equations can be solved exactly.

The effect of truncation errors can be examined most easily for linear equations solved by means of recurrence formulas of the Fox-Goodwin type. We can follow up an example considered by Fox and Goodwin, the equation

$$G'' + 20G' + 19G = 0$$

which has the solution, $G = Ae^{-x} + Be^{-19x}$. Writing $x = nw$

$$G_n = A(0 \cdot 8187)^n + B(0 \cdot 0224)^n$$

in which the dominant term after a few steps is clearly the first. Now consider the application to this equation of the formulas (8.9), (8.10) and (8.7), neglecting all difference corrections. Each of these recurrence relations can be written in terms of the operator E, and when numerical coefficients are inserted and F is eliminated they become

(8.9): $\{(2 + 19w)E - (2 - 19w)\}\{(2 + w)E - (2 - w)\}G_k = 0$

(8.10): $\{(3 + 19w)E^2 + 76wE - (3 - 19w)\}$
$$\{(3 + w)E^2 + 4wE - (3 - w)\}G_k = 0$$

(8.7): $\{(1 + 10w)E^2 - (2 - 19w^2)E + (1 - 10w)\}G_k = 0$

Now the solution of a difference equation, $f(E)G_k = 0$, where $f(E)$ is a polynomial, takes the form

$$G_n = A_1\alpha_1{}^n + A_2\alpha_2{}^n + A_3\alpha_3{}^n + \ldots$$

where $\alpha_1, \alpha_2, \alpha_3, \ldots$ are the roots of $f(E) = 0$. Accordingly we find, for the three cases above, taking $w = 0 \cdot 2$,

(8.9): $G_n = A(0 \cdot 8182)^n + B(- 0 \cdot 3103)^n$

(8.10): $G_n = A(0 \cdot 8187)^n + B(- 0 \cdot 0539)^n$
$$+ C(- 2 \cdot 1814)^n + D(- 1 \cdot 0687)^n$$

(8.7): $G_n = A(0 \cdot 8199)^n + B(- 0 \cdot 4066)^n$

which may be compared with the solution given above for the differential equation. In each case it appears that the first term is a fairly good representation of the dominant solution e^{-x}. In no case, however, is e^{-19x} even approximately represented by a solution of the difference equation. With w as large as $0 \cdot 2$ this is not to be expected, but with (8.9) and (8.7) the fact is not serious because the secondary terms die out rapidly as n increases. In using (8.10), however, this is not so, as two of the exponents exceed unity: indeed, if even a small multiple of the C term is present in G_0 and G_1 it will be subsequently magnified and lead to quite erroneous results. This shows the importance, first of obtaining the starting values of a recurrence relation as accurately as possible and secondly, of choosing a recurrence relation in which the spurious roots of the difference equation cannot dominate the solution. This holds particularly when, as in (8.10), the order of the difference equation exceeds that of the differential equation. The danger cannot always be avoided by taking w small, because a simple analysis shows that as $w \to 0$ the roots of $f(E)$ for (8.10) behave approximately as e^{-w}, $- e^{-19w}$, $- e^{w/3}$ and $e^{19w/3}$. The unwanted roots are therefore always greater than unity. One has to rely entirely on the difference correction to remove unwanted solutions, and this is not always satisfactory.

Another treatment of this particular equation would be to solve it in its normal form. Thus if $g(x) = e^{10x}G(x)$

$$g'' = 81g$$

which can be solved by (8.8) or the equivalent formulas (8.25) and (8.30). Neglecting the difference correction in (8.8), the recurrence relation can be expressed as

$$\{(12 - h^2)E^2 - (2 + 10h^2)E + (12 - h^2)\}g_k = 0$$

where $h = 9w$. Taking $w = 0 \cdot 2$ as before, the solution is

$$g_n = a(6 \cdot 279)^n + b(0 \cdot 1593)^n$$

compared with the solution of the differential equation

$$g_n = a(6 \cdot 050)^n + b(0 \cdot 1653)^n$$

The agreement is not particularly good for this value of w, but quite good results, for both solutions, are possible if $w < 0 \cdot 05$. Improvement can also be obtained, as one should expect, by including a difference correction $- (h^2/240)\delta^6 g$.

A further point is illustrated by the equation in the normal form. The solutions then comprise one increasing and one decreasing exponential, and it is clear that if the recurrence relation is used to derive the solution e^{-9x} alone, and is applied in the direction of increasing x, there is danger of serious error through a small multiple of e^{9x} creeping in, either initially or through rounding errors. This difficulty arose earlier in Example 8.3. When the two solutions are of this kind, the increasing solution only should be derived by integrating in the direction of increasing x and the other by integrating in the reverse direction.

In this elementary analysis only exponential solutions have been considered. For equations with oscillatory solutions, cumulative errors tend to be less significant, as the introduction of an unwanted solution involves an error which remains small and does not grow without limit. Spurious solutions arising from the difference equation may likewise be oscillatory and remain small, but this cannot be relied upon.

The analysis of the cumulative effect of rounding errors is quite different, and necessarily statistical. It is usual to assume that rounding errors occur randomly. The total probable error in G_n then tends to be proportional to $n^{3/2}$, though the maximum error in unfavourable cases may increase as n^2. The error can have a dominating effect when few significant figures are used in the solution, and truncation errors are small. The assumption of randomness is usually reasonable, but if w is so small that the solution is nearly linear over a number of intervals, exceptions are possible.

Modified Taylor Series Methods

For most purposes one or other of the methods of solution already described should prove sufficient. We shall, however, consider briefly some modifications of the Taylor series by which accurate results can be obtained without using many derivatives of the solution. Some of these have been proposed by Milne,* and

* W. E. Milne, *J. Res. Nat. Bur. Stand.*, **43** (1949), 537.

resemble the methods described in § 8.4 and § 8.5 in the use of two formulas for prediction and correction. The first method, however, for solving first-order equations, is due to Hartree.*

8.10. Hartree's Method for First-order Equations

The ease with which second-order equations can be integrated, and the stability of the calculation in general, suggests that first order equations of the form $F' = f(x, F)$ might with advantage be converted to second order by differentiation, and thereafter solved by using (8.28). This has its dangers, because the second-order equation has a second solution which may behave quite differently to the one required, and the introduction of a small multiple of this may be disastrous, e.g. $F' = - F$ has the solution e^{-x}, but $F'' = F$ is also satisfied by e^x, which may come to dominate any *outward* integration. This point has already been discussed on pages 234–5. Nevertheless the device is useful for predicting purposes in combination with a suitable correcting formula, and so Hartree suggests the use of

$$\delta^2 \overline{F}_0 = w^2\{f'_0 + (1/12)\delta^2 f'_0\} \tag{8.34}$$

for prediction, and the formula

$$\delta F_{1/2} = \tfrac{1}{2}w\{f_0 + \bar{f}_1 - (w/6)(\bar{f}'_1 - f'_0)\} \tag{8.35}$$

for correction, $\bar{f}_1$ and $\bar{f}'_1$ having been calculated from $\overline{F}_1$, which is derived from $\delta^2 \overline{F}_0$. This second formula, taken from Exercises 6, No. 4(b), has an error $(w^5/720)f^{(4)}$, which is attractively small, and it has the advantage that values of f' are also used in (8.34). The calculation of the derivatives must, however, be reasonably easy. The following example indicates the procedure.

EXAMPLE 8.11. Integrate the equation $d\eta/dx = x - \eta^2$ inwards from $x = 5\cdot2$ to $x = 2\cdot0$.

This Riccati equation is also Airy's equation, $G'' = xG$, in disguise, since it is obtained by taking $\eta = G'/G$. The preliminary step, which is independent of the method of solution, is to obtain two initial values of η. This we do by writing the equation as

$$(1/2\eta)(d\eta^2/dx) = x - \eta^2$$

which, when an approximate value of $d\eta^2/dx$ is given, can be regarded as a simple cubic for η, to be solved by iteration. As a first approximation $\eta^2 \simeq x$, so $d\eta^2/dx \simeq 1$; using this value we obtain better values

---

* D. R. Hartree, *Proc. Camb. Phil. Soc.*, **46** (1950), 523.

for η^2, and so on. The following table shows how this works out at the points $x = 5\cdot2,\ 5\cdot0,\ 4\cdot8$.

x	$(\eta^2)_0$	$(\delta\eta^2/\delta x)_0$	$(\eta^2)_1$	$(\delta\eta^2/\delta x)_1$	$(\eta^2)_2$	$(\delta\eta^2/\delta x)_2$	$(\eta)_2$
4·8	4·8		5·023		5·0187		− 2·2402
		1·0		0·98		0·9795	
5·0	5·0		5·219		5·2146		− 2·2836
		1·0		0·98		0·9805	
5·2	5·2		5·415		5·4107		− 2·3262

The process converges quickly owing to the near constancy of $d\eta^2/dx$. The values of $(\eta)_2$ are in fact correct to 4D. Note that the negative root of η^2 is taken, corresponding to the solution $Ai(x)$ of Airy's equation.

The rest of the integration is carried out at an interval of 0·4, and is laid out as follows. It must be remembered that the integration is inward and all derivatives, etc., should be interpreted with respect to $- x$ as variable.

The integrating equations, with $w = 0\cdot4$, are—

$$\delta^2\bar\eta_0 \simeq 0\cdot16f'_0 = 0\cdot16(1 + 2\eta^3 - 2x\eta)_0$$

$$\delta\eta_{1/2} \simeq 0\cdot2\{(f_0 + f_1) - (1/15)\delta f'_{1/2}\}, \quad f = x - \eta^2$$

The procedure, given the starting values shown in heavy type, is first to estimate $\delta^2\bar\eta$ for $x = 4\cdot8$; this leads to $\eta(4\cdot4)$ and thence to $f(4\cdot4)$ and $f'(4\cdot4)$. These values enable $\delta\eta$ to be checked by the second formula, and $\eta(4\cdot4)$ verified. Any necessary adjustments must be made before proceeding to the next interval.

x	η	$\delta\eta$	$\delta^2\bar\eta$	f'	$\delta f'$	$f_k + f_{k+1}$	f_k	$\delta^2\eta - \delta^2\bar\eta$
5·2	− 2·3262			0·0175			0·2112	
		0·0859			0·0032	0·4298		
4·8	− 2·2402		0·0033	0·0207			0·2186	− 0·0001
		0·0891			27	0·4456		
4·4	− 2·1511		37	0·0234			0·2270	− 0·0001
		0·0927			26	0·4638		
4·0	− 2·0584		42	0·0260			0·2368	− 0·0001
		0·0968			32	0·4843		
3·6	− 1·9616		47	0·0292			0·2475	0·0000
		0·1015			36	0·5075		
3·2	− 1·8601		53	0·0328			0·2600	0·0000
		0·1068			56	0·5342		
2·8	− 1·7533		61	0·0384			0·2742	0·0000
		0·1129			71	0·5651		
2·4	− 1·6404		73	0·0455			0·2909	0·0000
		0·1202			95	0·6018		
2·0	− 1·5202			0·0550			0·3109	

If $Ai(5\cdot2)$ is known, say from asymptotic series, the above result may be used to verify $Ai(2\cdot0)$. Thus

$$\log_e\{Ai(5\cdot2)/Ai(2\cdot0)\} = \int_{2\cdot0}^{5\cdot2} \eta dx = -6\cdot23661$$

by Simpson's rule. Taking

$$\log_e Ai(5\cdot2) = -9\cdot59118, \quad Ai(2\cdot0) = 0\cdot034924$$

This may be compared with the value $0\cdot034924$ from B.A. Tables.

8.11. Milne's Method for First-order Equations

It is possible to use a more powerful formula than (8.35) if two derivatives of f are readily calculable. Thus an extension of (8.35) which has been derived in Exercises 6, No. 4, is

$$F_1 = F_0 + (1/2)w(f_1 + f_0) - (1/10)w^2(f'_1 - f'_0)$$
$$+ (1/120)w^3(f''_1 + f''_0) - (w^7/100800)f^{(6)}(\xi) \quad (8.36)$$

This is an extremely accurate checking formula and Milne has suggested its use in association with the predicting formula

$$\bar{F}_1 = 2F_0 - F_{-1} + 7w(f_0 - f_{-1}) - 3w^2(f'_0 + f'_{-1})$$
$$+ (1/12)w^3(11f''_0 - 5f''_{-1}) + (210w^7/100800)f^{(6)}(\xi') \quad (8.37)$$

which does not require any prior knowledge of f_1.

Given two starting values F_{-1}, F_0, (8.37) gives an estimate of F_1 which can be used to obtain estimates of f_1, f'_1, f''_1; these, in (8.36), give a better value of F_1 which can then be tested for consistency. The quantities to be tabulated appear as follows—

x_{-1}	$\bar{F}_{-1}$	$\bar{f}_{-1}$	$\bar{f}'_{-1}$	$\bar{f}''_{-1}$	F_{-1}	f_{-1}	f'_{-1}	f''_{-1}	$\bar{F}_{-1} - F_{-1}$
x_0	$\bar{F}_0$	$\bar{f}_0$	$\bar{f}'_0$	$\bar{f}''_0$	F_0	f_0	f'_0	f''_0	$\bar{F}_0 - F_0$
x_1	$\bar{F}_1$	$\bar{f}_1$	$\bar{f}'_1$	$\bar{f}''_1$	F_1	f_1	f'_1	f''_1	$\bar{F}_1 - F_1$

It may be unnecessary to record f and its derivatives twice. Comparison of (8.36) and (8.37) shows that the error in F_{k+1} is approximately $(\bar{F}_{k+1} - F_{k+1})/211$. It is therefore valuable to record $\bar{F}_k - F_k$ as part of the computation, and to reduce the interval of integration if this quantity approaches, say, 100 units of the final decimal in F.

Advantages of this method are that the provision of starting values usually presents no difficulty (thus, given F_0, F_1 can often be obtained by iteration from (8.36)); the coefficients are simple; the accuracy is high for functions well represented by polynomials, so that a wide interval can be used; there is no difficulty in

changing interval length; it is applicable to non-linear equations
if the calculation of f' and f'' is straightforward.

We shall not give an example of the direct use of this method
as proposed by Milne, as the reader will have no difficulty in doing
this for himself, for equations already treated. It is worth noting,
however, that for some linear equations it provides a much shorter
method of tabulation than the simple Taylor series described in
Chapter 7. We shall therefore repeat Example 7.5 along these
lines.

EXAMPLE 8.12.   Tabulate the solution of $F' = 1 - 2xF$ for
$x = 0(0\cdot5)3\cdot0$, assuming $F(0) = 0$.

Writing $F' = -2xF + 1 = f$ and $d^kF/dx^k = P_k(x)F(x) + Q_k(x)$,
it is easily seen that (8.36) is equivalent to

$$P_-(x_1)F_1 = P_+(x_0)F_0 - Q_-(x_1) + Q_+(x_0) \qquad (8.38)$$

where $P_\pm(x) = 1 + (w^2/10)P_2 \pm \{(w/2)P_1 + (w^3/120)P_3\}$
$Q_\pm(x) = (w^2/10)Q_2 \pm \{(w/2)Q_1 + (w^3/120)Q_3\}$

Since $P_\pm(x)$, $Q_\pm(x)$ can be precalculated, the recurrence relation
(8.38) provides a table of F directly. However, by itself this gives no
check on the accuracy of the solution, even of the kind afforded by
$\bar{F}_k - F_k$. Some check on the computation is possible by using the
recurrence relation in reverse, thus given F_1 to check F_0 by the
formula

$$P_+(x_0)F_0 = P_-(x_1)F_1 - Q_+(x_0) + Q_-(x_1)$$

Using the values of $P_0, \ldots, P_3, Q_0, \ldots, Q_3$ given in Example 7.5,
the following table is obtained.

x	P_+	P_-	Q_+	Q_-	Values of F		
					Calc.	Check	Exact
0·0	0·950000	0·950000	0·245833	− 0·245833	0	0·000000	0
0·5	0·730208	1·219792	0·221875	− 0·271875	0·424423	0·424424	0·424436
1·0	0·554167	1·545833	0·200000	− 0·300000	0·538087	0·538087	0·538080
1·5	0·415625	1·934375	0·180208	− 0·330208	0·428252	0·428252	0·428249
2·0	0·308333	2·391667	0·162500	− 0·362500	0·301338	0·301341	0·301340
2·5	0·226042	2·923958	0·146875	− 0·396875	0·223084	0·223081	0·223084
3·0	0·162500	3·53750	0·133333	− 0·433333	0·178271		0·178271

After an initial inaccuracy in the 5th decimal, the later values are
reasonably good. The method is most reliable when the solution is
decreasing, but the check values are then less reliable because $P_+ < 1$.
Obviously one or two guarding figures are essential in this type of
calculation. In this example the asymptotic series provides a fairly

good overall check; thus the best value for $F(3)$ obtainable from the series in Example 7.10 is $0\cdot17828$.

It is interesting to compare the recurrence relation (8.38) with that of Fox and Goodwin (8.3), which is

$$\{1 + \tfrac{1}{2}x_1\}F_1 = \{1 - \tfrac{1}{2}x_0\}F_0 + \tfrac{1}{2} - (w^3/12)f^{(2)}(\xi)$$

The one used here is

$$\left(1 + \frac{1}{2}\cdot\frac{39}{38}\,x_1 + \frac{2}{19}\,x_1{}^2 + \frac{1}{114}\,x_1{}^3\right)F_1$$

$$= \left(1 - \frac{1}{2}\cdot\frac{39}{38}\,x_0 + \frac{2}{19}\,x_0{}^2 - \frac{1}{114}\,x_0{}^3\right)F_0 + \frac{1}{2}\cdot\frac{59}{57}$$

$$+ \frac{1}{19}\,(x_1 - x_0) + \frac{x_0{}^2 + x_1{}^2}{228} - (w^7/100800)f^{(6)}(\xi)$$

8.12. Second-order Equations

The extension to second-order equations of the form

$$G'' = f(x,\,G,\,F)$$

is straightforward, with the added help of the equations

$$\bar{G}_1 = G_0 - 2G_{-1} + 7w(F_0 - F_{-1}) - 3w^2(f_0 + f_{-1})$$
$$+ (w^2/12)(11f'_0 - 5f'_{-1}) \quad (8.39)$$

$$G_1 = G_0 + (w/2)(\bar{F}_1 + F_0) - (w^2/10)(\bar{f}_1 - f_0)$$
$$+ (w^3/120)(\bar{f}'_1 - f'_0) \quad (8.40)$$

The procedure to find G_1, given G_0, G_{-1}, F_0, F_{-1}, is as follows—
(a) predict $\bar{F}_1$ by (8.37) and $\bar{G}_1$ by (8.39);
(b) calculate $\bar{f}_1$, $\bar{f}'_1$ and $\bar{f}''_1$ using the differential equation;
(c) correct F_1 by (8.36) and G_1 by (8.40);
(d) verify that f_1, f'_1 and f''_1 are not significantly altered.

It is a help to record both $G_k - \bar{G}_k$ and $F_k - \bar{F}_k$ as part of the computation, otherwise the tabulation is very like that for first order equations with columns added for $\bar{G}$ and G.

No numerical example of this method will be given here. Milne gives an application to Bessel's equation for J_0, which is obtained accurately to 6D with $w = 0\cdot5$, and to 10D with $w = 0\cdot1$; the latter result in particular shows the high accuracy of the formulas used.

Single-step Methods

There are a few methods of step-by-step integration which do not use values of the functions occurring in the differential equation except within the step being considered. Thus in advancing one step no use is made of knowledge of the solution in the previous step. All that is required of the solution is that it can be expanded as a finite Taylor series (usually with terms up to the fourth or fifth power of the increment) at the starting point of the step. If these conditions are fulfilled no special procedure is needed to start the integration or to change the step-length at any stage; nor is there any forward estimation requiring iterations. The cost of such advantages is usually much greater labour per step than is needed for methods using differences or recurrence relations; therefore, although the methods are often suitable for automatic computation, they may be uneconomic for hand computation.

We shall introduce here some methods of Runge-Kutta type and also one devised by de Vogelaere for second-order equations, although it does not quite fall into the category of single-step methods.

8.13. Runge-Kutta Methods

These methods are applicable to systems of first-order equations of the form (7.1), (7.2) or (7.10), and can be developed to various degrees of accuracy. Let us consider briefly the fourth-order formulas, which are typical and most frequently used. For the single equation (7.1), in the step beginning at (x_0, F_0), the basic process is to evaluate the function $f(x, F)$ successively at four points as follows—

$$k_0 = w f(x_0, F_0)$$
$$k_1 = w f(x_0 + qw, F_0 + qk_0)$$
$$k_2 = w f(x_0 + rw, F_0 + tk_1 + (r - t)k_0)$$
$$k_3 = w f(x_0 + sw, F_0 + uk_2 + vk_1 + (s - u - v)k_0)$$

where q, r, s, t, u, v are parameters with values not exceeding unity. Provided these parameters are suitably chosen the increment in the solution can be expressed as

$$F_1 - F_0 = ak_0 + bk_1 + ck_2 + dk_3$$

with a truncation error of order w^5. Expanding both left and right sides of this equation as Taylor series in powers of w, using partial derivatives of f with respect to x and F at (x_0, F_0), and comparing corresponding terms, leads to eight relations between the ten parameters.* Two of the three parameters q, r, s can therefore be chosen arbitrarily.

The best choice is represented by the following expressions for the k's

$$k_0 = w\, f(x_0,\, F_0)$$
$$k_1 = w\, f(x_0 + \tfrac{1}{2}w,\, F_0 + \tfrac{1}{2}k_0)$$
$$k_2 = w\, f(x_0 + \tfrac{1}{2}w,\, F_0 + \tfrac{1}{2}k_1)$$
$$k_3 = w\, f(x_0 + w,\, F_0 + k_2)$$

and

$$F_1 - F_0 = (1/6)(k_0 + 2k_1 + 2k_2 + k_3) + 0(w^5) \qquad (8.41)$$

When f is independent of F, this reduces to Simpson's rule for quadrature. An alternative, known as Gill's modification, uses the parameters

$$q = r = \tfrac{1}{2},\, s = 1,\, t = 1 - 1\sqrt{2},\, u = 1 + 1/\sqrt{2},\, v = -1\sqrt{/2},$$

and these lead to $a = d = 1/6$, $b = t/3$, $c = u/3$.

There are many other variants, and a comparison of some of them for suitability for automatic computers has been made by Martin.† An error analysis of (8.41) by Carr‡ shows that the process is reasonably stable, at least for a single equation.

The fourth order Runge-Kutta process requires four evaluations of the function $f(x,\, F)$ for each step. This fact alone makes it desirable that w should not be shorter than necessary for the accuracy needed. However the calculation itself does not give any indication of the truncation error incurred, and if (8.41) is used it is essential to perform a check at suitable stages in the integration in which the step-length is either halved or doubled, and the results over a specified range compared.

A check such as that just proposed is time-consuming, and another variation of the Runge-Kutta procedure due to Merson offers an alternative. This is to evaluate five k's as follows—

$$k_0 = (1/3)w\, f(x_0,\, F_0)$$
$$k_1 = (1/3)w\, f(x_0 + (1/3)w,\, F_0 + k_0)$$
$$k_2 = (1/3)w\, f(x_0 + (1/3)w,\, F_0 + (1/2)k_1 + (1/2)k_0)$$
$$k_3 = (1/3)w\, f(x_0 + (1/2)w,\, F_0 + (9/8)k_2 + (3/8)k_0)$$
$$k_4 = (1/3)w\, f(x_0 + w,\, F_0 + 6k_3 - (9/2)k_2 + (3/2)k_0)$$

---

* Further details are given by Levy and Baggott, *Numerical Studies in Differential Equations* (Watts, 1934), 103.
† D. W. Martin, *Computer J.*, **1** (1958), 118.
‡ J. W. Carr, *J. Assoc. Comp. Mach.*, **5** (1958), 39.

and to use the integration formula.

$$F_1 - F_0 = \tfrac{1}{2}(k_0 + 4k_3 + k_4) + 0(w^5) \qquad (8.42)$$

for which an estimate of the truncation error E is given by

$$10E = 2k_0 - 9k_2 + 8k_3 - k_4 \qquad (8.43)$$

If at any step this quantity is found to exceed 10 times the acceptable error, then the integration should be repeated with w halved; alternatively if E is less than 1/32 of the acceptable error, w may be doubled. In practice, despite the additional evaluation of f at each step, this process can lead to an overall gain of efficiency.

EXAMPLE 8.13. Use Runge-Kutta methods to begin the integration of

$$F' = - (xF - 1)^{1/2} \text{ from } x = 1 \text{ with } F(1) = 2.$$

We apply first the formula (8.41) with $w = 0 \cdot 2$

$$
\begin{aligned}
k_0 & & = - 0 \cdot 200000 \\
k_1 & - 0 \cdot 2(1 \cdot 1 \times 1 \cdot 9 - 1)^{1/2} & = - 0 \cdot 208806 \\
k_2 & - 0 \cdot 2(1 \cdot 1 \times 1 \cdot 895597 - 1)^{1/2} & = - 0 \cdot 208342 \\
k_3 & - 0 \cdot 2(1 \cdot 2 \times 1 \cdot 791658 - 1)^{1/2} & = - 0 \cdot 214475
\end{aligned}
$$

Hence $F(1 \cdot 2) = 2 - (0 \cdot 414475 + 2 \times 0 \cdot 417148)/6 = \mathbf{1 \cdot 791872}$.

A detailed check with $w = 0 \cdot 1$ leads to the following results—

Interval	$1 \cdot 0 - 1 \cdot 1$	$1 \cdot 1 - 1 \cdot 2$
k_0	$- 0 \cdot 100000$	$- 0 \cdot 104284_0$
k_1	$- 0 \cdot 102347_5$	$- 0 \cdot 105945_2$
k_2	$- 0 \cdot 102287_2$	$- 0 \cdot 105900_1$
k_3	$- 0 \cdot 104282_5$	$- 0 \cdot 107247_8$
Increment in F	$- 0 \cdot 102258_6$	$- 0 \cdot 105870_4$

Hence $\qquad F(1 \cdot 2) = 2 - 0 \cdot 208129 = \mathbf{1 \cdot 791871}$

This result using two steps is in fact correct to 6D, as may be shown using the power series given in Example 8.4. Apart from this the calculation indicates that the calculation with $w = 0 \cdot 2$ is reliable to 5D, and if this accuracy is adequate further steps can be taken at this interval. Two such steps give

$$F(1 \cdot 4) = 1 \cdot 574177 \qquad\qquad F(1 \cdot 6) = 1 \cdot 355698$$

The reader should examine the possibility of enlarging the first step to 0·4.

With the check the above calculation requires 11 evaluations of

9—(T.642)

$(xF - 1)^{1/2}$. By using (8·42) and (8·43) this number may be reduced to five. With $w = 0·2$ the results are as follows—

$$k_0 \quad -0·0666667$$
$$k_1 \quad -0·0687095$$
$$k_2 \quad -0·0686743$$
$$k_3 \quad -0·0695227$$
$$k_4 \quad -0·0715007$$

	ΔF	E	x	F
First step	$-0·208129$	$-0·000005_4$	1·2	1·791871
Second step	$-0·217695$	$-0·000003_5$	1·4	1·574176
Third step	$-0·218480$	$-0·000002_8$	1·6	1·355696

These results are accurate to 6D. In this example the values of E overestimate the actual error per step, but this need not always occur.

8.14. De Vogelaere's Method

This may be more accurately described as a "step and a half" method* as use is made of the solution at the midpoint of the previous step. However it performs much the same service for second-order equations of the form $G'' = f(x, G)$, in which the first derivative does not appear explicitly, as Runge-Kutta methods perform for first-order equations.

Three relations are used in the basic process—

$$G_{1/2} = G_0 + (1/2)wF_0 + (1/24)w^2 (4f_0 - f_{-1/2}) + 0(w^4) \quad (8.44)$$

$$G_1 = G_0 + wF_0 + (1/6)w^2(f_0 + 2f_{1/2}) + 0(w^5) \quad (8.45)$$

$$F_1 = F_0 + (1/6)w(f_0 + 4f_{1/2} + f_1) + 0(w^5) \quad (8.46)$$

The first two approximations are easily derived by symbolic methods or by the method of § 3.12; the third is Simpson's rule. The truncation errors are respectively $w^4G(\xi)/128$, $w^5G^{(5)}(\xi)/720$ and $-w^5G^{(6)}(\xi)/2880$.

For the initial integration step starting at x_0, with prescribed values of G_0 and F_0, an estimate of $G_{-1/2}$ is required to provide $f_{-1/2}$. A formula which is usually adequate for this is

$$G_{-1/2} = G_0 - (1/2)wF_0 + (1/8)w^2f_0 + 0(w^3) \quad (8.47)$$

(8.44) is then used to give $G_{1/2}$, which determines $f_{1/2}$ and thence G_1 by (8.45). F_1 is found from (8.46) in preparation for the next step. This uses the three relations in the same order, but with all suffices increased by unity.

* R. de Vogelaere, *J. Research N.B.S.*, **54** (1955), 119.

The method is well suited to automatic as well as to hand computation, and requires only two evaluations of $f(x, G)$ in each step. It should be noted that the values of G at midpoints are obtained with less precision than those at the end of each step. Doubling the interval at any stage does not involve a variation in procedure, but any other change may need a further use of (8.47). A check on the possible error introduced at each step is essential. This is partly provided by the remainder of (8.45), which is given at least approximately by

$$(w^2/720)\delta^3 f_k$$

These differences should be evaluated at each step to ensure that the truncation error is unlikely to give rise to serious accumulated error. Any undue variation in the differences will also show up possible arithmetical errors. A more drastic check, as in the Runge-Kutta methods, is to repeat some steps with half the interval.

EXAMPLE 8.14. Repeat the integration of $G'' + \sin G = 0$ from $x = 1$, using the starting values given in Example 8.8.

We have $G(1 \cdot 0) = 0 \cdot 108544_2$, and by differentiating the series for G given in Ex. 8.8, we find $F(1.0) = -0 \cdot 167625$. Thence by (8.47) an estimate of $G(0 \cdot 95)$ is $0 \cdot 11679$. In the layout of the integration it is convenient to tabulate $(1/2)wF_k$, $(1/12)w^2 f_k$, as these quantities occur with simple multiples in (8.44), (8.45) and (8.46).

x	$G_{k-1/2}$	G_k	$(1/2)wF_k$	$(1/12)w^2f_k$	$(1/3)w^2f_{k-1/2}$
	116790				$-388 \cdot 4$
$1 \cdot 0$		**108544·2**	$-$ **8381·2**	$-$ **90·3**	
	100030				$-332 \cdot 9$
$1 \cdot 1$		91268·3	$-8880 \cdot 4$	$-76 \cdot 0$	
	82277				$-274 \cdot 0$
$1 \cdot 2$		73081·5	$-9291 \cdot 2$	$-60 \cdot 8$	
	63702				$-212 \cdot 2$
$1 \cdot 3$		54165·3	$-9609 \cdot 3$	$-45 \cdot 1$	
	44492				$-148 \cdot 3$
$1 \cdot 4$		34708·2	$-9831 \cdot 6$	$-28 \cdot 9$	
	24837				$-82 \cdot 8$
$1 \cdot 5$		14904·4	$-9955 \cdot 7$	$-12 \cdot 4$	
	4934				$-16 \cdot 4$
$1 \cdot 6$		$-5048 \cdot 2$	$-9980 \cdot 3$	$+4 \cdot 2$	

All values in units of 10^{-6}

The final decimal has been retained as a guarding figure only. The values of G do not differ by more than 10^{-6} from those obtained in

Example 8.8. Inspection of $\delta^3 f$ shows that $(w^2/720)\delta^3 f$ nowhere exceeds 10^{-8}; hence it appears that the truncation error is negligible in this range, and errors in the integration are due to rounding.

Two-point Boundary Conditions

The extension of step-by-step methods to meet conditions on the solution of second-order equations at two points generally presents no difficulty when the equation is linear and homogeneous. All that is required is the tabulation of two independent solutions as will be shown shortly. There are important exceptions, however, which occur in problems involving latent roots ("eigenvalues"), when the conditions can be met only if a parameter in the equation has certain discrete values. Thus the solution of $G'' + \mu^2 G = 0$ will satisfy the conditions $G(0) = G(1) = 0$, only if μ^2 is an integral multiple of π. Consideration of such problems will be reserved until Chapter 14, where the use of interpolatory methods, such as relaxation, for two-point conditions will be fully discussed.

For non-linear equations there is no certain method of dealing with two-point conditions, though some possible lines of attack are discussed below.

8.15. Linear Equations

If we have an equation of the form (8.6) it is often possible to obtain, either numerically by one or other of the step-by-step methods already described, or in the form of series, two solutions G_a, G_b, which satisfy the conditions

$$\left. \begin{array}{l} G_a = 0, \ G_a' = 1 \\ G_b = 1, \ G_b' = 0 \end{array} \right\} \text{ when } x = x_0 \qquad (8.48)$$

The general solution is then

$$G = AG_a + BG_b$$

If boundary conditions, $G(x_0) = G_0$, $G(x_n) = G_n$, are imposed, it is obvious that

$$B = G_0, \ A = \{G_n - G_0 G_b(x_n)\}/G_a(x_n) \qquad (8.49)$$

The two conditions thus determine A and B, and the same initial pair of solutions can be used to satisfy a variety of such boundary conditions. These need not be as simple as those suggested above, as they may involve the derivatives of G at $x = x_0, x_n$;

or indeed may be relations between the values of G and G' at a number of points between x_0 and x_n. In fact any two equations which determine A and B uniquely are acceptable boundary conditions.

EXAMPLE 8.15. Obtain the solution of $G'' = xG$ which satisfies the conditions $G(0) = 0.5$, $G'(1)/G(1) = 1.0$.

It is possible here to use the series solutions given in Example 7.8, from which

$$G_a(1) = 1.085340 \qquad G_a'(1) = 1.34744$$
$$G_b(1) = 1.172300 \qquad G_b'(1) = 0.53403$$

If the required solution $G = AG_a + BG_b$

then

$$A = 0.5, \quad (1.34744A + 0.53403B)/(1.08534A + 1.17230B) = 1$$

and hence

$$B = 0.13105/0.63827 = 0.20532$$

The solution G can therefore be tabulated.

It may not always be possible to find a solution G_b which satisfies the above conditions if the equation has a singularity at x_0, e.g. the solutions of Bessel's equation, other than J_0, are either zero or infinite at $x = 0$. However, if the singularity is regular two series solutions (with perhaps a log x term in one of them) can be found in its neighbourhood, and these can be extended by numerical integration to the other boundary point.

If the equation is inhomogeneous, of form (8.6), the solutions G_a, G_b of the corresponding homogeneous equation are insufficient, and one needs also a particular solution G_c of the given equation. This is probably obtained most easily by a step-by-step method, starting at x_0 and using any convenient starting conditions; alternatively by the method given in Exercises 7, No. 2. Then if

$$G = AG_a + BG_b + G_c$$

A, B can again be found by applying the boundary conditions.

8.16. Non-linear Equations

The treatment of non-linear equations must necessarily proceed on rather less definite lines, and the boundary conditions be met by applying methods which are more or less iterative in character. Of these we shall consider briefly two, a straightforward method of successive approximation, and one based on Picard's method. For many equations relaxation is also satisfactory and this is discussed in Chapter 14.

If it is desired to meet the conditions $G(x_0) = G_0$, $G(x_n) = G_n$, and a reasonable guess can be made about the value of $G'(x_0)$ which will lead to a solution passing near the point (x_n, G_n), then it may be worth developing a series of step-by-step solutions with different initial gradients. Given two such solutions passing on opposite sides of the point (x_n, G_n), a better value of the initial gradient can usually be found by interpolation; and if the solution

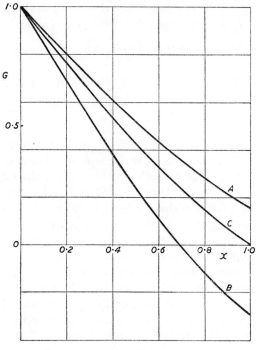

FIG. 8.1

obtained from this is not accurate enough, it can be further improved by another interpolation. The procedure is illustrated in Fig. 8.1, which refers to Example 8.16.

EXAMPLE 8.16. Find to 4D the solution of $G'' = x^2/(G + 2x - 1)$ for which $G(0) = 1$, $G(1) = 0$.

If G'' be ignored, the required initial gradient would be -1; however, the solution would then have positive values of G'', and this suggests that $G'_0 < -1$. Assuming $w = 0\cdot1$, it seems reasonable to try $0\cdot90$ and $0\cdot85$ as starting values for $G(0\cdot1)$. The solutions up to

$x = 1$ are then obtained quite rapidly by the usual summation method, and give results as follows—

$G(0\cdot1)$	$0\cdot90$	$0\cdot85$
$G(1\cdot0)$	$0\cdot1577$	$-0\cdot2935$

These suggest that a better value of $G(0\cdot1)$ is $0\cdot8825$, which gives $G(1\cdot0) = 0\cdot0125$; a further trial with $G(0\cdot1) = 0\cdot8811$ gives $G(1\cdot0) = 0\cdot0013$. To 4D the starting value at $0\cdot1$ can hardly be improved beyond $0\cdot8810$.

The general behaviour of G is shown in Fig. 8.1.

Another iterative method, applicable to equations of the type (7.3a), uses Picard's formula (see (7.26))

$$G_{k+1} = \int_{x_0}^{x} dx \int_{x_0}^{x} f(x, G_k) + A_k x + B_k \qquad (8.50)$$

where G_k is an approximate solution satisfying the boundary conditions. The double integration can be performed by a suitable formula, and A_k, B_k chosen so that the required conditions are also satisfied by G_{k+1}. This may be used to obtain a better approximation, and so on. The limitations on this method are clearly those of convergence, as we know that the Picard sequence does not normally converge to the correct solution outside a certain range from x_0. If x_n lies within this range the method should be quite satisfactory, otherwise it is doubtful.*

EXERCISES 8

1. If $F' + p(x)F + q(x)G = 0$ and $G' + P(x)G + Q(x)F = 0$, show that—

$$\{(1 + s_1)(1 + S_1) - t_1 T_1\}F_1$$
$$= \{(1 - s_0)(1 + S_1) + t_1 T_0\}F_0 + (1 + S_1)\triangle_F$$
$$- \{t_0(1 + S_1) + t_1(1 - S_0)\}G_0 - t_1 \triangle_G$$

$$\{(1 + s_1)(1 + S_1) - t_1 T_1\}G_1$$
$$= \{(1 - S_0)(1 + s_1) + T_1 t_0\}G_0 + (1 + s_1)\triangle_G$$
$$- \{T_0(1 + s_1) + T_1(1 - s_0)\}F_0 - T_1 \triangle_F$$

where $s_k = \frac{1}{2}wp_k$, $S_k = \frac{1}{2}wP_k$, $t_k = \frac{1}{2}wq_k$, $T_k = \frac{1}{2}wQ_k$, and the difference corrections have the form

$$\triangle_F = \{-(1/12)\delta^3 + (1/120)\delta^5 - \ldots\}F_{1/2}$$
$$\triangle_G = \{-(1/12)\delta^3 + (1/120)\delta^5 - \ldots\}G_{1/2}$$

* A modified method, without this immediate limitation, has been described by H. Levy; see Levy and Baggott, *Numerical Studies in Differential Equations* (Watts, 1934) p. 170.

2. From the same equations as in No. 1, show that

$$\{(1 + s_1)(1 + S_1) - t_1 T_1\}G_1$$
$$= 4\{t_0 T_1 - S_0(1 + s_1)\}G_0 + \{(1 + s_1)(1 - S_{-1}) + t_{-1}T_1\}G_{-1}$$
$$+ (1 + s_1)\triangle_G + 4\{s_0 T_1 - T_0(1 + s_1)\}F_0$$
$$- \{(1 + s_1)T_{-1} + (1 - s_{-1})T_1\}F_{-1} - T_1\triangle_F$$

where $s_k = \frac{1}{3}wp_k$, $S_k = \frac{1}{3}wP_k$, etc.

$$\triangle_F = \{-(1/90)\delta^5 + (1/315)\delta^7 - \ldots\}F_0$$

and $\triangle_G$ is similar. Obtain a similar equation for F_1.

(Fox and Goodwin, 1948)

3. If $dF/dx = f(x, F)$, show that the quartic polynomial which coincides with F at x_{k-2}, x_{k-1}, and x_k, and with F' at x_{k-1}, x_k, gives an extrapolated estimate for $\bar{F}_{k+1}$

$$\bar{F}_{k+1} = F_{k-2} + 9F_{k-1} - 9F_k + 6w(f_{k-1} + f_k)$$

the truncation error having the form

$$- (1/10)w^5 f^{(4)}(\xi), \quad \text{where} \quad x_{k-2} \leqslant \xi \leqslant x_{k+1}$$

If an improved estimate is then obtained using the quadrature formula

$$F_{k+1} = F_k + (1/24)w(f_{k-2} - 5f_{k-1} + 19f_k + 9\bar{f}_{k+1})$$

where $\bar{f} = f(x, \bar{F})$, show that in the special case $f = aF$, the truncation error is reduced to $(19/720)(aw)^5 F(\xi)$.

(W. S. Loud, *J. Math. Phys.*, 1949)

4. Show that equations (8.21), (8.22) and (8.23), used in Milne's method for solving second-order equations, are equivalent to the single formula

$$G_k = w^2\{\sigma^2 + (1/12) + (1/144)\delta^2 + \ldots\}f_k$$

and contain a truncation error of order $(w^2/90)\delta^2 f_k$.

CHAPTER 9

POLYNOMIAL AND OTHER ALGEBRAIC
EQUATIONS

AT this point the study of differential equations will be dropped, to be resumed in Chapter 14, when it will be found that techniques developed in intervening chapters are of great value. It is necessary to consider the solution of equations roughly described as algebraic, as they contain various algebraic functions, with polynomial equations as an important category. The most common problem here is the evaluation of real roots, the location of which is roughly known but for which no explicit formula is available. This is considered first. Since most numerical methods involve making successive approximations, the opportunity is taken to discuss some of the general features of iterative processes, which occur frequently in later chapters. The evaluation of complex roots has naturally been developed furthest for polynomials, and we therefore discuss in some detail the derivation and improvement of quadratic factors of a polynomial. Finally, more powerful methods are described, such as the Bernoulli-Aitken method for the roots of larger modulus, and the root-squaring method which provides all roots of algebraic equations, real and complex. Discussion of the special but important class of equations known as determinantal is deferred to Chapter 12. Graphical and nomographic methods are not discussed.

Iterative Methods of Improving Real Roots

Let the equation to be solved be written as

$$F(x) = 0 \qquad (9.1)$$

where $F(x)$ is assumed to be a continuous function of x. If a real root X of this equation has been located roughly,* by inspecting

---

* For *polynomials*, Descartes' rule of signs is often useful in indicating the nature and position of the roots. This states that the number of positive real roots cannot exceed the number of sign changes in the sequence of coefficients in the polynomials, and can differ from this only by an even number. A similar limitation on the negative real roots is obtained by changing the sign of x. A more elaborate investigation can be made using the derived Sturm functions, or by rules developed by Routh. These are described in various text-books, see e.g. Frazer, Duncan and Collar, *Elementary Matrices*, pp. 152–155.

the variation of $F(x)$, assisted perhaps by a graph, improvement
can of course be made by tabulating $F(x)$ at regular intervals over
a range of x spanning the root, which can then be evaluated by
any standard method of inverse interpolation, e.g. by successive
approximation as in Chapter 5. This is straightforward, and as a
method, not to be despised, for it is often quite rapid.

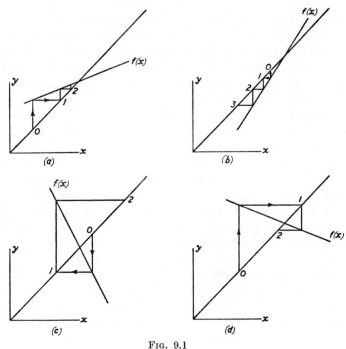

Fig. 9.1

However, we prefer to consider here methods which spring
essentially from a rewriting of (9.1) in the form

$$x = f(x) \qquad (9.2)$$

which is then replaced by an iterative formula

$$x_{n+1} = f(x_n) \qquad (9.3)$$

This yields by calculation a sequence of values $x_0, x_1, x_2, \ldots$
which in suitable cases converge rapidly to the required root X.
It can be shown analytically that convergence is not possible
unless $|f'(x)| < 1$ near X. The reason for this can be seen geo-
metrically in Fig. 9.1 where $y = f(x)$ is drawn as a straight line

making various angles with the x-axis, and the root X is the intersection with the line $y = x$. The condition just stated requires the line $y = f(x)$ to be inclined to the x-axis at an angle between $\pm 45°$. In each of the four cases illustrated a sequence x_0, x_1, x_2 is shown, obtained by starting near X and applying (9.3), and it is clear that convergence towards X can occur only in (a) and (d).

This limitation on the practical use of (9.3) makes it desirable to try some other iterative formula. The basis of several well established methods is the formula

$$x_{n+1} = x_n - F(x_n)/m \qquad (9.4)$$

where m is a suitably chosen quantity. The significance of this is again obvious geometrically, and from Fig. 9.2 (a) it is seen that

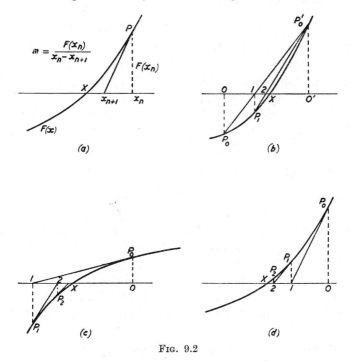

Fig. 9.2

m is the slope of a line through the point $P = (x_n, F(x_n))$ which, if the method is to succeed, must intersect the x-axis at a point nearer to X than x_n. The ideal value of m would be the slope of the line PX, but this of course is not initially known. We shall now discuss some particular methods of applying (9.4).

9.1. Method of False Position

Another description of this method would be *repeated linear interpolation*. It depends first on being able to find two values of x between which the required root (and no other) lies. If these values are x_0 and x_0', then $F(x_0)$ and $F(x_0')$ have opposite signs, and by taking

$$m = m_0 = \{F(x_0') - F(x_0)\}/(x_0' - x_0) \qquad (9.5)$$

a closer approximation to X is obtained than either x_0 or x_0'. The reason for this is clearly seen from Fig. 9.2 (*b*), in which m_0 is the slope of the line $P_0 P_0'$. A still better result is then obtained from the intersection of $P_1 P_0'$ with the x-axis, which corresponds to a second use of (9.4) with

$$m = m_1 = \{F(x_0') - F(x_1)\}/(x_0' - x_1)$$

For the success of this process it is generally desirable that $F'(x)$ should not vanish, nor $F''(x)$ change sign, near X, i.e. no maximum, minimum or point of inflexion in $F(x)$. Of course the convergence towards X can be hastened if improvements in x_0' can also be made in the direction of bringing P_0' nearer to X. This can usually be done by guesswork, or by the Newton-Raphson method described later.

EXAMPLE 9.1. Find the smallest positive root of

$$F(x) = \tan x + \tanh x = 0$$

Since $\tanh x$ tends rapidly to 1 for $x > 0$, it is obvious that the roots will be close to the points at which $\tan x = -1$, or $x = 3\pi/4, 7\pi/4, \ldots$ We therefore start near the point $x = 2 \cdot 36$, and the calculation by repeated linear interpolation proceeds as follows—

x	$F(x)$	
2·36	− 0·01009	$m_0 = 0 \cdot 02000/0 \cdot 01 = 2 \cdot 000$
2·37	+ 0·00991	$x_1 = 2 \cdot 36 - (-0 \cdot 01009/2 \cdot 000)$
		$\quad = 2 \cdot 36505$
2·36505	+ 0·000059	$m_1 = 0 \cdot 01015/0 \cdot 00505 = 2 \cdot 001$
		$x_2 = 2 \cdot 36505 - 0 \cdot 000059/2 \cdot 001$
		$\quad = 2 \cdot 365021$
2·365021	+ 0·0000001	$x_3 = 2 \cdot 365020_5$

This carries the calculation of the root to the limit possible with 6D tables of $\tan x$ and $\tanh x$. The last stage has little significance.

Alternatively we can tabulate $F(x)$ as follows—

x	$F(x)$			
2·35	− 0·030495			
		20403		
2·36	− 0·010092		− 401	
		20002		15
2·37	+ 0·009910		− 386	
		19616		
2·38	+ 0·029526			

By inverse interpolation $X = 2\cdot365021$, which is correct to 6D. A more accurate result can be obtained by solving the equivalent equation $e^{2y} \tan y = e^{-3\pi/2}$, where $x = 3\pi/4 + y$ (see Example 9.3).

9.2. Newton-Raphson Method

Instead of using the chord joining two points which span the root, we may use the tangent at the point $x = x_n$. Then

$$m = F'(x_n)$$

and the iterative formula (9.4) becomes

$$x_{n+1} = x_n - F(x_n)/F'(x_n) \qquad (9.6)$$

This is the basis of a method devised by Raphson in 1690, though it has points in common with an earlier method of Newton's. It is obvious from Fig. 9.2 that neither $F'(x)$ nor $F''(x)$ should vanish near X, and that the convergence is likely to be better if the root is approached from the side on which the curve of $F(x)$ is convex to the x-axis, as in Fig. 9.2 (d). We consider two simple examples of this method.

EXAMPLE 9.2. Solve the equation $4x - \cos x - 1 = 0$.

Cursory inspection of a cosine table shows that the root lies between 0·45 and 0·50. Since $F'(x) = 4 + \sin x$ and $F'' = \cos x$ both derivatives are positive in this range, and it is preferable to start with the larger value. The following table summarizes the calculation.

n	x_n	$F(x_n)$	$F'(x_n)$	$x_{n+1} - x_n$
0	0·5	0·1224	4·479	− 0·0273
1	0·473	0·001794	4·456	− 0·000403
2	0·472597			
	(correct to 6D)			

EXAMPLE 9.3. Find the smallest root of the equation
$$e^{2y} \tan y = e^{-3\pi/2} = 0 \cdot 008983\ 291021$$

The wanted root of this equation is clearly close to the value $e^{-3\pi/2}$, so that $0 \cdot 009$ is a suitable first approximation. If extensive tables of exponentials and tangents are not available it is preferable to use series expansions. Thus

$$F(y) = e^{2y} \tan y - e^{-3\pi/2}$$
$$= \{1 + 2y + 2y^2 + (4/3)y^3 + (2/3)y^4 + (4/15)y^5 + \ldots\}$$
$$\{y + (1/3)y^3 + (2/15)y^5 + \ldots\} - e^{-3\pi/2}$$
$$= y\{1 + 2y + (7/3)y^2 + 2y^3 + (22/15)y^4 + (44/45)y^5 + \ldots\}$$
$$- e^{-3\pi/2}$$
$$F'(y) = 1 + 4y + 7y^2 + 8y^3 + (22/3)y^4 + \ldots$$

The numerical results are as follows—

n	y_n	$F(y_n)$	$F'(y_n)$	$y_{n+1} - y_n$
0	$0 \cdot 009$	$0 \cdot 000179\ 41$	$1 \cdot 0366$	$- 0 \cdot 000173\ 1$
1	$0 \cdot 008826\ 9$	$0 \cdot 000001\ 054254$	$1 \cdot 035858$	$- 0 \cdot 000001\ 017759$
2	$0 \cdot 008825\ 882241$	$0 \cdot 000000\ 000001$	$1 \cdot 036$	$- 0 \cdot 000000\ 000001$
3	$0 \cdot 008825\ 882240$			

This is essentially the same problem as Example 9.1, since
$$X = 3\pi/4 + Y = 2 \cdot 365020\ 372432$$
This more than confirms the previous result.

Both examples bring out strikingly a feature of the Newton-Raphson method, the way in which the number of significant figures is roughly doubled at each step. The reason for this is that the iterative process is one of second order, to use a term which will be defined more exactly in the next section. It implies that the error of x_{n+1} is proportional to $(X - x_n)^2$, by contrast with a process of linear interpolation, e.g. false position, in which the error of x_{n+1} is proportional to $(X - x_n)$.

This can be seen immediately from the Taylor series for $F(X)$ in terms of $F(x_n)$ and derivatives of $F(x)$ at x_n

$$F(X) = 0 = F(x_n) - \xi_n F'(x_n) + (1/2)\xi_n^2 F''(x_n + \theta\xi_n) \quad (9.7)$$

where $0 \leqslant \theta \leqslant 1$ and ξ_n is the error of x_n defined by

$$X = x_n - \xi_n$$

By (9.6) $$\xi_{n+1} - \xi_n = - F(x_n)/F'(x_n)$$

so $$\xi_{n+1} = \xi_n^2 \{F''(x_n + \theta\xi_n)/2F'(x_n)\} \quad (9.8)$$

In many examples to which the method is applied

$$|F''/2F'| < 1$$

and since also $|\xi_{n+1}| \ll |\xi_n|$, it follows that

$$|\xi_{n+1}| < |\xi_{n+1} - \xi_n|^2 \qquad (9.9)$$

This is the basis for the statement made above about significant figures.

It would appear from (9.7) that, if F'' is not varying rapidly and F' is not too small, a better iterative formula is obtainable by including a correction for the quadratic term. Replacing ξ_n^2 by $\{F(x_n)/F'(x_n)\}^2$ we obtain

$$x_{n+1} = x_n - \frac{F(x_n)}{F'(x_n)} - \frac{F''(x_n)\{F(x_n)\}^2}{2\{F'(x_n)\}^3} \qquad (9.10)$$

as a special case of the more general iterative formula

$$x_{n+1} = x_n - \frac{F(x_n)}{m_1} - \frac{\{F(x_n)\}^2}{m_2} \qquad (9.11)$$

Applied to Example 9.2, (9.10) gives

$$x_1 = 0 \cdot 5 - 0 \cdot 027329 - 0 \cdot 000073 = 0 \cdot 472598$$

which is in error by one digit only in the last figure. It is essential for this extension that $F''(x_n)$ be readily calculable.

Many iterative formulas for simple algebraic operations are applications of (9.6). The following table contains some of the most useful of these, in which $x_{n+1} = f(x_n)$.

	$F(x)$	$f(x)$	$X = \lim x_n$	
Reciprocal	$\dfrac{1}{x} - a$	$x + x^2 \left(\dfrac{1}{x} - a\right)$ or $x(2 - ax)$	$1/a$	(9.12)
Inverse pth root	$ax^p - 1$	$x - \dfrac{x}{p}(ax^p - 1)$	$a^{-(1/p)}$	(9.13)
Square root (i)	$x^2 - a$	$x - \dfrac{1}{2x}(x^2 - a)$ or $\dfrac{1}{2}\left(x + \dfrac{a}{x}\right)$ (Newton)	$a^{1/2}$	(9.14)
(ii)	$x^2 - a$	$x - \dfrac{x(x^2 - a)}{3x^2 - a}$	$a^{1/2}$	(9.15)
(iii)	$x^2 - a$	$x - \dfrac{x(x^2 - a)}{2a}$	$a^{1/2}$	(9.16)

pth root	$x^p - a$	$x - \dfrac{x}{ap}(x^p - a)$	$a^{(1/p)}$	(9.17)
Reduced cubic	$x^3 - ax - b$	$x - \dfrac{x^3 - ax - b}{3x^2 - a}$	Real root of cubic	(9.18)

It should be observed that some of these formulas, e.g. (9.13), (9.15), (9.16), (9.17), have been simplified by replacing $x_n F'(x_n)$ with $X F'(X)$; thus in (9.13), apx^{p-1} is replaced by p/x. This is easily proved not to invalidate the second order property of the iteration, and often leads to a formula in which no division is required, a useful advantage in computing both by hand and automatic machines. In (9.15), it is the non-zero root of $xF(x) = 0$ which is sought, and the formula is a special case of (9.18). An extension to (9.17) is given in Exercises 9, No. 1.

Two final comments about the Newton-Raphson process must be made.

1. It is sometimes suggested that the Newton-Raphson method should be combined with that of false position to obtain limits between which the true root must lie, as one can see from Fig. 9.2 that the two methods converge to X from opposite sides. As an initial step to improve the location when this is known only within wide limits, the idea has some usefulness, but in later stages the fact that the iterations are of first order on one side and second order on the other renders the convergence rather one-sided.

2. The numerical examples already given suggest that in the false position method there is no need to recalculate m at each step, the value m_0 being quite adequate. This is certainly true if the curvature of $F(x)$ is not too great. Similarly in Raphson's method, the value $F'(x_0)$ can be used throughout to avoid further calculation of derivatives. This destroys to some extent the second-order character of the iteration, but, as the rapid growth of significant figures in this method is sometimes an embarrassment rather than a necessity, the loss may not matter.

9.3. Another Method for Polynomial Equations

Although the Newton-Raphson method is usually well suited to polynomial equations, it is also worth describing how these can be reduced to a form for which the simple iterative process (9.3) is applicable. The method uses the root-shifting device commonly associated with Horner (whose well-known method of solving polynomial equations is now outmoded by the advent of calculating machines), though, as pointed out by Jeffreys,* it is more akin to the process originally used by Newton. An example best illustrates the procedure.

EXAMPLE 9.4. Find the root of $x^4 - 5x^3 + x + 7 = 0$ between 1 and 2.

Let
$$x = 1 + y_1$$

Then $0 = 7 + (1 + y_1) - 5(1 + 3y_1 + 3y_1{}^2 + y_1{}^3)$
$$+ 1 + 4y_1 + 6y_1{}^2 + 4y_1{}^3 + y_1{}^4$$
$$= 4 - 10y_1 - 9y_1{}^2 - y_1{}^3 + y_1{}^4$$

From the leading terms y_1 lies between 0·3 and 0·4, so let
$$y_1 = 0\cdot3 + y_2$$

and a similar operation shows that
$$0 = 0\cdot1711 - 15\cdot562y_2 - 9\cdot36y_2{}^2 + 0\cdot2y_2{}^3 + y_2{}^4$$
or
$$15\cdot562y_2 = 0\cdot1711 - 9\cdot36y_2{}^2 + 0\cdot2y_2{}^3 + y_2{}^4$$

This equation can be solved quickly by direct iteration, approximate values being substituted on the right. Since $0\cdot1711/15\cdot562 = 0\cdot01099$, we try first 0·0109 and 0·0110.

Approximate root (y_2)	Improved root (y_2')	$y_2' - y_2$
0·0109	0·01092329	− 0·00007671
0·0110	0·01092197	+ 0·00002197

Linear interpolation can now be used to obtain a better value such that $y_2' = y_2$. The result is that $y_2 = 0\cdot01092299$, and therefore $X = 1\cdot31092299$, correct to 8D.

9.4. Treatment of Difficult Cases

The methods so far described usually give no difficulty provided $F'(x)$ is not zero near X. A lack of convergence may mean that $F'(x)$ does vanish, and that a modified approach is necessary. If so, a useful preliminary is to estimate the position of the root of $F'(x) = 0$, say X', and then to evaluate $F(X')$ and $F''(X')$. If $F''(X') \neq 0$, three cases arise—

(a) $F(X')$ and $F''(X')$ alike in sign.   No real roots near X'.
(b) $F(X') = 0$.   Double root of
$$F(x) = 0 \text{ at } X'.$$
(c) $F(X')$ and $F''(X')$ opposite in sign. Two real roots near X'.

These possibilities are illustrated in Fig. 9.3.

* Jeffreys, M.M.P., p. 275.

In case (c), a first approximation to the position of the two roots is obviously given by the Taylor series

$$F(X) = 0 = F(X') + \tfrac{1}{2}(X - X')^2 F''(X') + 0(X - X')^3$$

from which $X_1, X_2 \simeq X' \pm \{- 2F(X')/F''(X')\}^{1/2}$. Thereafter each root must be evaluated separately. If the Newton-Raphson method is used it may be preferable, since $F'(x_n)$ is likely to be

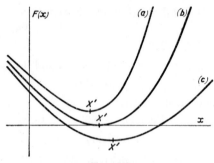

FIG. 9.3

small, to retain the quadratic term in (9.7) and to solve the equation

$$0 = F(x_n) + \Delta x_n F'(x_n) + \tfrac{1}{2}(\Delta x_n)^2 F''(x_n) \qquad (9.19)$$

or

$$\Delta x_n = x_{n+1} - x_n = - \frac{F(x_n)}{F'(x_n)} - (\Delta x_n)^2 \frac{F''(x_n)}{2F'(x_n)}$$

The smaller root of this quadratic can usually be found by simple iteration.

Bodewig has given modified forms of the Newton-Raphson formula (9.6) which are more suitable when $F(x)$ has a multiple root at X (see Exercises 9, Nos. 3 and 4).

EXAMPLE 9.5. Investigate the roots of $\cosh x = 1 \cdot 51x$.

It can be seen graphically, or from tables, that this equation has two roots near the point $x = 1 \cdot 2$.

Now if $F(x) = \cosh x - 1 \cdot 51x$

then $F'(x) = \sinh x - 1 \cdot 51$

$$F''x = \cosh x$$

Hence $F'(x) = 0$

when $x = X' = \sinh^{-1} 1 \cdot 51 = 1 \cdot 2003$

We find $F(X') = - 0 \cdot 00134, \; F''(X') = 1 \cdot 8111$

so $X_1, X_2 \simeq 1 \cdot 2003 \pm (0 \cdot 000742)^{1/2} = 1 \cdot 227, \; 1 \cdot 173$

We investigate each root in turn.

n	x_n	$F(x_n)$	$F''(x_n)$	$F'(x_n)$	$x_{n+1} - x_n$
0	1·23	− 0·000667	1·853	0·04991	0·00863 by (9.19)
1	1·23863	− 0·000001	1·857	0·05447	0·00001
2	1·23864				
0	1·17	− 0·000520	1·766	− 0·05419	− 0·00844 by (9.19)
1	1·16156	− 0·000000	1·754	− 0·06904	$\|\Delta x\| < 0\cdot00001$

Thus, to the accuracy provided by 6-figure tables,

$$X_1 = 1\cdot23864, \ X_2 = 1\cdot16156$$

9.4A. Other Iterative Methods

Although the Newton-Raphson method is often an extremely rapid and easy means of evaluating real roots, there may be occasions when the evaluation of $F'(x)$ as well as $F(x)$ adds significantly to the amount of calculation for each iteration. We shall therefore consider one or two other iterative methods which only require the evaluation of $F(x)$ at each step.

One of these is due to Wegstein* and is a modification of the simple iterative formula (9.3) which is not subject to the restrictions $|f.(x)| < 1$. Wegstein introduces a second sequence $\bar{x}_n$ and replaces (9.3) by

$$x_{n+1} = f(\bar{x}_n) \tag{9.3a}$$

The next element in the $\bar{x}$ sequence is then defined by

$$\bar{x}_{n+1} = x_{n+1} - \frac{(x_{n+1} - x_n)(x_{n+1} - \bar{x}_n)}{x_{n+1} - x_n - \bar{x}_n + \bar{x}_{n-1}} \tag{9.3b}$$

The significance of this relation can be seen geometrically by referring to one of the cases in Figure 9.1, say (c). Assume that the point 1 corresponds to $\bar{x}_1$ and the point 2 to x_2, given by $x_2 = f(\bar{x}_1)$. The divergent behaviour can be removed if α can be chosen so that $\bar{x}_2$ given by

$$\bar{x}_2 = \alpha \bar{x}_1 + (1 - \alpha)x_2$$

is as close as possible to the required root. This requires only an estimate of the slope $f'(x)$, and for the straight line approximation to $f(x)$ this is given by

$$(f(\bar{x}_1) - f(\bar{x}_0))/(\bar{x}_1 - \bar{x}_0) \text{ or } (x_2 - x_1)/(\bar{x}_1 - \bar{x}_0).$$

* J. H. Wegstein, *Comm. Assoc. Comp. Mach.* (June 1958).

This assumption leads to

$$\alpha = (x_2 - x_1)/(x_2 - x_1 - \bar{x}_1 + \bar{x}_0)$$

and, when suitably generalized, to (9.3b).

The practical starting procedure is to assume $x_1 = f(x_0)$ and that $\bar{x}_0 = x_0$, $\bar{x}_1 = x_1$. Then $\bar{x}_2$ is given by

$$\bar{x}_2 = x_2 - (x_2 - x_1)^2/(x_2 - 2x_1 + x_0)$$

which is a simple geometrical extrapolation of the kind described in § 9.5. Thereafter x_3, $\bar{x}_3$, x_4, $\bar{x}_4$ ... are derived using the above relations.

EXAMPLE 9.5A. Find the roots of $3x = e^x$.

This is a special case of the equation $Ax = e^x$ which, when $A > e$, has two roots, one less and one greater than unity. For the second root $f'(x) > 1$ and the simple iteration will fail. This is illustrated by the following sequences based on (9.3) using three different starting values.

n	Values of x_n		
0	0·5	1·5	1·6
1	0·550	1·494	1·651
2	0·5778	1·485	1·737
3	0·5940	1·472	1·893
4	0·6037	1·453	2·213
5	0·6096	1·425	3·048
6	0·6132	1·386	
7	0·6154	1·333	
8	0·6168	1·264	
9	0·6177	1·180	

The first sequence is converging leisurely to the smaller root. The second sequence will also lead to this root eventually, despite the fact that the larger root is only slightly above 1·5. The third is diverging rapidly away from the larger root.

We now give three examples of using the Wegstein procedure—

n	x_n	$\bar{x}_n$	x_n	$\bar{x}_n$	x_n	$\bar{x}_n$
0	0·5	0·5	0·5	1·5	2·0	2·0
1	0·550	0·550	1·4939	1·4939	2·4630	2·4630
2	0·5778	0·6126	1·4848	1·5124	3·9133	1·7829
3	0·615074	0·618715	1·512536	1·512128	1·9824	1·6744
4	0·618847	0·619060	1·512125	1·512134	1·77853	1·55593
5	0·619060		1·512134		1·57983	1·52064
6					1·52505	1·51265
7					1·512914	1·512141
8					1·512144	1·512135

The sequence starting with 0·5 shows greatly improved convergence to the smaller root. That starting with 1·5 now converges easily to the larger root; so does the third sequence, which shows how the Wegstein iteration overcomes the initial divergent behaviour of x_n. Although the example is not one for which the method is inherently better than Newton-Raphson it does indicate its potential usefulness.

Another iterative method, introduced by Muller,* is essentially an extension of the method of false position in which *three* values of $F(x)$ at x_{n-2}, x_{n-1}, x_n, are fitted by a quadratic polynomial. The three-point Lagrange formula is used for this purpose and one of its roots provides x_{n+1}, the next member of the sequence. The details of the method are easily worked out. It is sometimes used with a digital computer to derive the roots of a polynomial of high degree, in ascending order of magnitude. The method is not restricted to polynomials with real coefficents.

Iteration in General

Iterative methods are so important in many branches of computing that it is desirable to amplify some of the remarks made in the last section. This we shall do for the simple sequence $x_0, x_1, x_2, \ldots$ derived from a formula of the type $x_{n+1} = f(x_n)$ and converging to the desired value X. The fundamental properties of such a sequence have been summarized in papers by Hartree and Domb.†

First we define the order of an iterative process. If $x_n = X + \xi_n$ and $f(x_n)$ be expanded as a Taylor series about X, so that

$$\xi_{n+1} = a_1\xi_n + a_2\xi_n{}^2 + a_3\xi_n{}^3 + \ldots \qquad (9.20)$$

where $a_1 = f'(X)$, $a_2 = f^{(2)}(X)/2!$, $a_3 = f^{(3)}(X)/3!$, etc., then if the first non-zero coefficient is a_k, the process is one of kth order. Most processes in common use are of first or second order; thus those used incidentally in solving differential equations in Chapter 8 were first order, and the Newton-Raphson process has already been shown to be second order. The advantage of a second-order process needs no stressing.

It can be shown, however, that iterative processes for solving simple equations, whatever the order, are not unique, and given two processes of kth order, one of $(k + 1)$th order can be derived

---

* D. E. Muller, *Math. Tab., Wash.,* **10** (1956), 208.

† D. R. Hartree, *Proc. Camb. Phil. Soc.,* **45** (1949), 230; C. Domb, *ibid.,* **45** (1949), 237.

See also P. Samuelson, *J. Math. Phys.,* **24** (1945), 131. E. Bodewig, *Quart. Appl. Math.,* **7** (1949), 325. The last paper discusses an iterative formula of Laguerre which is suitable for polynomial equations with all roots real, and converges to a root whatever the starting value may be.

from them. Domb, for instance, shows that the solution of an algebraic equation, $F(x) = 0$, can be obtained by a wide class of formulas, all of second order, for which

$$f(x) = x - \frac{p(x)F(x)}{(d/dx)(pF) + s(x)F(x)} \qquad (9.21)$$

$p(x)$, $s(x)$ being arbitrary polynomials.* The Newton-Raphson formula is of course a special case, in which $p = 1$, $s = 0$. When $f(x)$ is modified by inserting X for x in the denominator, so that

$$f(x) = x - \{p(x)F(x)\}/\{p(X)F'(X)\} \qquad (9.22)$$

the second-order character is unchanged. If $p(x)$ can be chosen so that the denominator is independent of X a particularly useful formula may result. As seen earlier, (9.13), (9.16) and (9.17) are examples with $p(x) = x$.

Domb has suggested one way of constructing iterative formulas of this kind. If we assume a form

$$f(x) = x - P(x)F(x) \qquad (9.23)$$

where $P(x)$ is some polynomial, the condition for a second-order process becomes

$$f'(X) = 0 = 1 - P(X)F'(X)$$

This is certainly satisfied if we can find another polynomial $Q(x)$ such that

$$P(x)F'(x) + F(x)Q(x) = 1 \qquad (9.24)$$

The simplest polynomials satisfying (9.24), say P_1, Q_1, can in fact be obtained by the process of finding the "resultant" of the polynomials $F(x)$ and $F'(x)$ (assuming no common factor), described in algebraic text-books (e.g. Bocher, *Higher Algebra*, pp. 191–3). The method can also lead to processes of higher order, since the result so far is not affected if

$$P(x) = P_1(x) + P_2(x)F(x), \quad Q(x) = Q_1(x) - Q_2(x)F(x),$$

so that $\qquad f(x) = x - P_1(x)F - P_2(x)F^2 \qquad (9.25)$

---

* An obvious extension of (9.21) would be

$$f(x) = x - \frac{p(x)G\{F(x)\}}{(pG)' + s(x)H\{F(x)\}}$$

where G, H are arbitrary polynomials in F. If x_n then converges to any definite limit, this will be a root of $G\{F(x)\} = 0$.

It is only necessary to impose the condition, $f^{(2)}(X) = 0$, to make this a third-order formula, and this leads to an equation from which $P_2(x)$ can be derived from the resultant of two more polynomials. (9.25) may be compared with (9.10). We quote two examples making use of these ideas.

1. The three formulas for finding $a^{1/2}$, (9.14), (9.15) and (9.16), differ in the magnitude of the quadratic error, i.e. the coefficient a_2 in (9.20), which is $(1/2)a^{-1/2}$, $(3/2)a^{-1/2}$, $-(3/2)a^{-1/2}$ respectively. It follows that a suitable linear comination of two of these formulas should give one in which $a_2 = 0$, the best combination being that of (9.14) and (9.16) in the ratio $3/4 : 1/4$, and giving

$$f(x) = x - x(x^2 - a)/2a + 3(x^2 - a)^2/8ax \qquad (9.26)$$

This is a third-order formula for finding $a^{1/2}$. With $a = 10$ and $x_0 = 3$, successive approximations to $10^{1/2}$ are

$$3 \cdot 1625, \quad 3 \cdot 16227\ 76601\ 678$$

The last is correct to 12D.

2. Application of (9.23) and (9.24) to the cubic equation, $F(x) = x^3 - ax - b = 0$, leads to the iterative formula

$$f(x) = x - (1/D)\{1 + (9b/4a^2)x - (3/2a)x^2\}F(x) \qquad (9.27)$$

where $D = 3(3b/2a)^2 - a$, which is of second order and has the advantage over (9.18) that no division is required. Perhaps the simplest derivation is from (9.22), assuming $p(x) = 1 + \alpha x + \beta x^2$ and choosing α, β so that $p(X)F'(X)$ is independent of X. As an example we can take Wallis' celebrated cubic, $x^3 - 2x - 5 = 0$, for which successive values of the root are 2, $2 \cdot 090$, $2 \cdot 09454$, $2 \cdot 0945514812$ (correct to 10S).

It would appear that some of these ideas might be extended to more general types of algebraic equation (see Exercises 9, No. 6).

9.5. Extrapolation in Iterative Processes of First Order

Since most iterative processes in common use are of first order only, and the convergence often leaves much to be desired, it is useful to be able to anticipate the result of further repetitions. This is possible if quadratic higher terms in (9.20) can be ignored and the formula replaced with sufficient accuracy by

$$\xi_{n+1} = t\xi_n \quad (t \simeq a_1 < 1) \qquad (9.28)$$

The errors are then in geometrical progression, and

$$\xi_k = \xi_0 t^k$$

Hence, given x_0, x_1, x_2 as three consecutive approximations to X, we have

$$t = \xi_1/\xi_0 = \xi_2/\xi_1 = (\xi_1 - \xi_2)/(\xi_0 - \xi_1)$$

or

$$t = (X - x_1)/(X - x_0) = (X - x_2)/(X - x_1) = (x_1 - x_2)/(x_0 - x_1)$$

Solving for X leads at once to the result

$$X_1 = x_2 - (x_2 - x_1)^2/(x_2 - 2x_1 + x_0) \qquad (9.29a)$$

or

$$X_1 = x_1 + (x_1 - x_0)t/(1 - t) \qquad (9.29b)$$

Now X_1 may not coincide with X because the errors have been assumed to form a geometrical sequence, but it can provide a starting point for two further applications of the linear process, from which, by another use of (9.29a), a better value X_2 is derived, and so on. It can be shown from (9.20) that X_1, X_2, . . . correspond to a second-order iteration. The second form (9.29b) is sometimes useful if only two values x_0 and x_1 are available, and some independent knowledge of t.

EXAMPLE 9.6. Find to 6D the first zero of

$$J_0(x) = 1 - \left(\frac{x}{2}\right)^2 + \frac{1}{(2\,!)^2}\left(\frac{x}{2}\right)^4 - \frac{1}{(3\,!)^2}\left(\frac{x}{2}\right)^6 + \cdots$$

If $z = (x/2)^2$, the series can be written in the form

$$z = 1 + z^2/(2\,!)^2 - z^3/(3\,!)^2 + z^4/(4\,!)^2 - \cdots$$
$$= 1 + 0.25z^2 \qquad + 0.0017361z^4 + 0.00000193z^6$$
$$- 0.0277778z^3 - 0.0000694z^5 - 0.00000004z^7$$

which can be solved by direct iteration if z is not too large.

Beginning with $z_0 = 1$, the sequence of approximations is as follows—

z_0	1·0		1·415931		1·445619
z_1	1·223891		1·428959		1·445696
z_2	1·327264		1·436270		1·445740
Z_1	1·415931	Z_2	1·445619	Z_3	1·445799
t_1	0·46172	t_2	0·5612	t_3	0·57

Each Z value is obtained by applying (9.29 (a)) to the three values above. The last gives $X_3 = 2.404828$, showing that the final extrapolation slightly overshoots the correct value, which to 7D is 2·4048256.

The Newton-Raphson method of course obtains this root much more quickly, the first three approximations to Z being 1·0, 1·43285 and 1·44574.

In a similar way, if $\xi_{n+1} = k\xi_n{}^2$, it is possible to use the consecutive approximations to X to obtain a better value. Thus

$$\xi_2 = k\xi_1{}^2 = k^3\xi_0{}^4 = \xi_2{}^3\xi_0{}^4/\xi_1{}^6$$

and hence
$$(x_2 - X)(x_0 - X)^2 = (x_1 - X)^3 \tag{9.30}$$

This is a quadratic for X from which the correct root can easily be picked out.

9.6. Improvement of Other Types of Sequence

The idea of obtaining derived sequences which converge more rapidly to the required value can be extended to sequences in which the errors of successive terms do not satisfy the two term recurrence relation (9.28), but a more general relation, such as

$$\xi_{n+1} = c_1\xi_n + c_2\xi_{n-1} + c_3\xi_{n-2} + \ldots$$

Bernoulli's method, described later, will provide an example of this. If there are only three terms on the right, the difference equation can be written

$$(E^3 - c_1E^2 - c_2E - c_3)\xi_{n-2} = 0 \tag{9.31}$$

which gives a cubic for E. If the roots of this are t_1, t_2, t_3 then

$$x_k = X + A_1t_1{}^k + A_2t_2{}^k + A_3t_3{}^k \tag{9.32}$$

Obviously the sequence will not converge to X unless the modulus of all the roots is less than unity.

We consider three cases of practical importance.

1. Suppose all roots are real, and $|t_1| > |t_2| > |t_3|$.

A sequence converging more rapidly than x_k is then obtained as follows.

Let
$$x_k{}^{(1)} = y_k{}^{(1)}/\delta^2 x_{k+1} \tag{9.33}$$

where
$$y_k{}^{(1)} = \begin{vmatrix} x_k & x_{k+1} \\ x_{k+1} & x_{k+2} \end{vmatrix}$$

and
$$\delta^2 x_{k+1} = x_{k+2} - 2x_{k+1} + x_k$$

Then, if terms in t_3 are ignored,

$$y_k{}^{(1)} = X\{A_1(1 - t_1)^2t_1{}^k + A_2(1 - t_2)^2t_2{}^k\} + A_1A_2t_1{}^kt_2{}^k(t_1 - t_2)^2$$

$$\delta^2 x_{k+1} = A_1(1 - t_1)^2t_1{}^k + A_2(1 - t_2)^2t_2{}^k$$

so
$$x_k{}^{(1)} = X + 0(t_2{}^k)$$

Thus $x_k^{(1)}$ converges to X more rapidly than x_k unless $|t_2| = |t_1|$.

It is worth noting that formulas (9.29) and (9.33) are identical, although the errors associated with X_k and $x_k^{(1)}$ are different, and the mode of using these sequences is somewhat different.

If a sequence $x_k^{(2)}$ be formed from $x_k^{(1)}$ in the same way that $x_k^{(1)}$ is formed from x_k, it can be shown that

$$x_k^{(2)} = X + 0(t_3^k) + 0(t_2^{2k}/t_1)$$

This sequence converges still more rapidly, unless again $|t_2| = |t_1|$. It should be observed that to form one value of $x_k^{(1)}$ requires three consecutive terms of the sequence x_k, and one value of $x_k^{(2)}$ requires five terms.

2. Suppose $|t_1| \simeq |t_2| > |t_3|$ (all roots again being real). This situation is better dealt with by forming the sequence $y_k^{(1)}$ as above, and then a second derived sequence

$$x_k^{(2)} = \begin{vmatrix} y_{k+1}^{(1)} & y_{k+2}^{(1)} \\ y_{k+2}^{(1)} & y_{k+3}^{(1)} \end{vmatrix} \div x_{k+2} \begin{vmatrix} \delta^2 x_{k+1} & \delta^2 x_{k+2} \\ \delta^2 x_{k+2} & \delta^2 x_{k+3} \end{vmatrix} \quad (9.34)$$

for which it can be verified that

$$x_k^{(2)} = X + 0(t_3^k)$$

Thus terms in both t_1 and t_2 have been removed.

3. Suppose the roots are $re^{i\theta}$, $re^{-i\theta}$, t_3, where $1 > |r| > |t_3|$.

When the dominant roots are complex, the solution of (9.31) can be written as

$$x_k = X + Br^k \cos(k\theta + \delta) + A_3 t_3^k$$

Let us now consider the sequence

$$z_k^{(1)} = y_k^{(1)} - h^2 y_{k+1}^{(1)}$$

It is easily verified that

$$z_k^{(1)} = X\{\delta^2 x_{k+1} - h^2 \delta^2 x_{k+2}\} - B^2 X r^{2k+2}(1 - r^2 h^2) \sin^2 \theta + 0(r^k t_3^k)$$

and hence that

$$x_k^{(2)} = \frac{y_k^{(1)} - h^2 y_{k+1}^{(1)}}{\delta^2 x_{k+1} - h^2 \delta^2 x_{k+2}} = X + 0(t_3^k) \quad (9.35)$$

provided that h^2 is a good approximation to $1/r^2$. In many applications there is no difficulty in estimating r^2 from the original sequence, and so this method of deriving a better sequence can be followed.

This method of constructing more rapidly convergent sequences was introduced by Aitken in 1926, and is usually known as Aitken's δ^2-process. It has many applications, not only to a simple sequence such as has been considered here, but also to sequences in which each term consists of a set of numbers, representing say the solution of a set of linear simultaneous equations, or of a differential equation (see Chapter 14).

Simultaneous Equations

The real roots of a pair of equations can usually be evaluated accurately by iterative methods once their approximate position is known. For this a graphical approach is usually most helpful. If the equations are

$$F(x, y) = 0, \quad G(x, y) = 0 \tag{9.36}$$

it may be possible to use direct iteration, with a pair of equations, similar to (9.3),

$$x_{n+1} = f(x_n, y_n), \quad y_{n+1} = g(x_n, y_n) \tag{9.37}$$

or a pair of difference equations, analogous to (9.4),

$$x_{n+1} = x_n - H_1(x_n, y_n)/m_1, \quad y_{n+1} = y_n - H_2(x_n, y_n)/m_2 \tag{9.38}$$

For (9.37) to be suitable, fairly stringent convergence conditions must be satisfied. It can be shown that near the root the conditions

$$|\partial f/\partial x| + |\partial g/\partial x| < 1, \quad |\partial f/\partial y| + |\partial g/\partial y| < 1$$

must be satisfied, and before embarking on iterative calculations it is well to verify if possible that they are satisfied with a good margin, otherwise long and fruitless computations may be the result.

We shall confine this discussion to the extension of the Newton-Raphson method to two variables, this being a particular case of (9.38) with the advantage of being a second-order process.

9.7. Newton-Raphson Method for Two Unknowns

The appropriate extension of (9.6) is most easily derived if $F(x, y)$ and $G(x, y)$ are expanded in the form of Taylor series near a root (X, Y). Thus

$$F(X, Y) = 0 = F(x_n, y_n) + \xi_n(\partial F/\partial x)_n$$
$$+ \eta_n(\partial F/\partial y)_n + 0(\xi_n{}^2, \eta_n{}^2)$$

$$G(X, Y) = 0 = G(x_n, y_n) + \xi_n(\partial G/\partial x)_n$$
$$+ \eta_n(\partial G/\partial y)_n + 0(\xi_n{}^2, \eta_n{}^2)$$

where $X = x_n + \xi_n$, $Y = y_n + \eta_n$, and the derivatives are evaluated for x_n, y_n. This suggests that we assume for the differences the following values—

$$\left. \begin{aligned} \Delta x_n = x_{n+1} - x_n = -(G_y F - G F_y)_n / D \\ \Delta y_n = y_{n+1} - y_n = (G_x F - G F_x)_n / D \end{aligned} \right\} \quad (9.39)$$

where $F_x = (\partial F/\partial x)$, etc., $D = \begin{vmatrix} F_x & F_y \\ G_x & G_y \end{vmatrix} \neq 0$

Iteration is likely to be successful provided D is not small.

EXAMPLE 9.7. Find the real roots of the equations

$$y = \cosh (x - \tfrac{1}{2}y), \quad x = \sinh (y - \tfrac{1}{2}x)$$

To locate the roots it is more convenient to write the equations in the form

$$x = \cosh^{-1} y + \tfrac{1}{2}y, \quad y = \sinh^{-1} x + \tfrac{1}{2}x$$

When these two curves are plotted, it is clear that there are two roots, near the points $(0\cdot7, 1\cdot0)$ and $(4\cdot3, 4\cdot3)$ (see Fig. 9.4).

Let

$$F(x, y) = y - \cosh (x - \tfrac{1}{2}y), \quad G(x, y) = x - \sinh (y - \tfrac{1}{2}x)$$

Then

$$F_x = -\sinh (x - \tfrac{1}{2}y) \qquad F_y = 1 + \tfrac{1}{2}\sinh (x - \tfrac{1}{2}y)$$
$$G_x = 1 + \tfrac{1}{2}\cosh (y - \tfrac{1}{2}x) \qquad G_y = -\cosh (y - \tfrac{1}{2}x)$$

The computations giving the two roots to 6S can be set out as follows—

First Root

			x_0	$0\cdot7$	y_0	$1\cdot0$
F	$-0\cdot02007$		F_x	$-0\cdot20134$	F_y	$1\cdot10067$
G	$0\cdot00325$		G_x	$1\cdot60940$	G_y	$-1\cdot21879$
D	$-1\cdot5260$		$-\Delta x_0$	$-0\cdot01368$	Δy_0	$0\cdot02073$

		x_1	$0\cdot7137$	y_1	$1\cdot0207$
	$-0\cdot000047$		$-0\cdot2048$		$1\cdot1024$
	$+0\cdot000005$		$1\cdot6143$		$-1\cdot2286$
	$-1\cdot5280$	$-\Delta x_1$	$-0\cdot000034$	Δy_1	$0\cdot000049$
		x_2	$0\cdot713734$	y_2	$1\cdot020749$

These values are correct to 6D.

Second Root

		x_0	4·3	y_0	4·3
F	− 0·05067	F_x	− 4·23419	F_y	3·11709
G	0·06581	G_x	3·17534	G_y	− 4·35067
D	8·5237	− Δx_0	0·00180	Δy_0	0·01382

		x_1	4·29820	y_1	4·31382
	− 0·000136		− 4·1964		3·0982
	− 0·000490		3·2067		− 4·4135
	8·5858	− Δx_1	0·000247	Δy_1	− 0·000290
		x_2	4·297953	y_2	4·313530

A subsequent check shows that the last digit of y_2 should be reduced by one unit.

Complications necessarily arise when D is zero or small near the required root. This indication of the presence of multiple or

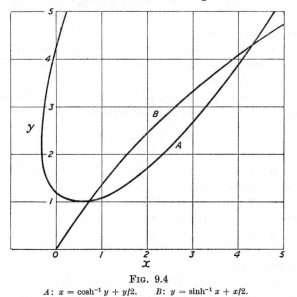

Fig. 9.4

$A: x = \cosh^{-1} y + y/2.$ $B: y = \sinh^{-1} x + x/2.$

close roots should already have been evident from the graphical investigations, and as for a single equation the difficulty cannot be resolved without including quadratic terms in the Taylor series. We shall not consider this in detail.

Cubic Equations

The evaluation of real roots of cubic equations by iteration has already been adequately discussed. Since every cubic has at least one real root, it is possible to remove the linear factor when it is known leaving only a quadratic to be solved. Alternatively, one can proceed to derive all three roots simultaneously, using an explicit solution such as the well-known one by Cardan, or that given in $M.T.C.$ [4], p. 231. Explicit solutions usually begin by transforming the cubic

$$a_0x^3 + a_1x^2 + a_2x + a_3 = 0$$

or $$x^3 + \alpha x^2 + \beta x + \gamma = 0$$

to the reduced form

$$y^3 + py + q = 0 \qquad (9.40)$$

where $\quad y = x + \alpha, \quad p = \beta - 3\alpha^2, \quad q = 2\alpha^3 - \alpha\beta + \gamma$

This equation has a pair of complex roots when $27q^2 + 4p^3 > 0$.
The object of this section, however, is to call attention to tables which exist to facilitate a complete solution of cubic equations.*
These include, in particular, tables by Emde, Zavrotsky and Salzer, Richards and Arsham, which we shall describe briefly.

1. *Emde's Tables.* These use the reduced form

$$z^3 - rz + 2 = 0$$

obtained from (9.40) if $z = (2/q)^{1/3}y$, $r = -(2p^3/q^2)^{1/3}$, and having complex roots if $r < 3$.

(a) $r \geqslant 3$. Roots z_1, z_2, z_3 all real and tabulated to 4 or 5S for $r = 3(0\cdot01)$ $3\cdot2(0\cdot02)$ $4(0\cdot05)$ $5(0\cdot1)$ $10(0\cdot5)$ 15.

(b) $r < 3$. Roots $z_1, z_2 = z' \pm iz'' = se^{\pm i\sigma}$, $z_3 = 2s \cos \sigma$.

z', z'' and s are tabulated to 4 or 5S, and σ to 4 or 5D, for $r = -9\cdot9(0\cdot1)$ $1(0\cdot05)$ $2(0\cdot02)$ $2\cdot8(0\cdot01)$ 3.

2. *Zavrotsky's Tables.* These are more comprehensive tables, and use the reduced form (9.40). Zavrotsky tabulates two roots to 5D, for $p = -100(1)100$, $q = 0(1)100$, and the third

---

* The tables described are in the following publications—
1. F. Emde, *Tables of Elementary Functions* (B. G. Teubner, 1940); see also Jahnke and Emde, *Tables of Functions* (2nd ed., 1933), for additional values.
2. A. Zavrotsky, *Tablas para la Resolucion de las Ecuacionas Cubicas* (Caracas, Venezuela, 1945).
3. H. E. Salzer, C. H. Richards and I. Arsham, *Table for the Solution of Cubic Equations* (McGraw-Hill, 1958).
These and other tables for solving cubics are described in *Math. Tab., Wash.*, **1** (1943/5) 441, **2** (1946/7), 28 and **6** (1952), 82.

root can be derived by the fact that the sum is zero. The choice of roots for tabulation depends on p and is as follows—

Roots tabulated

$p = -100(1) - 41$ Two positive real roots

$p = -40(1) - 1$ Two real roots if $27q^2 < 4(-p)^3$
or Two complex roots if $27q^2 > 4(-p)^3$

$p = 0(1)\ 100$ Two complex roots

3. *Tables by Salzer, Richards and Arsham.* These extensive tables use the form

$$a'z^3 + b'z + c' = 0$$

where $z = x + a_1/3a_0$, $a' = a_0$, and express the three roots as $(-c'/b')$ times $f_1(\theta)$, $f_2(\theta)$ and $f_3(\theta)$ respectively, where $\theta = a'c'^2/b'^3$. Tabulation is for

$$1/\theta = -0.001(-0.001) - 1;\ \theta = -1(0.001)1;$$
$$1/\theta = 1(-0.001)0.001).$$

f_1, f_2 and f_3 are nearly everywhere given to 7D. In the ranges $\theta > 0$, $\theta < -4/27$, f_2 and f_3 are chosen to represent the complex roots, and given as complex numbers. Linear interpolation is adequate throughout much of the table.

Quadratic Factors of Polynomial Equations

When we consider complex roots in general it is difficult to put forward any systematic procedure for equations which are other than polynomial. The location of complex roots of equations involving other types of algebraic function usually involves a special consideration of each equation, perhaps by representing the functions approximately by power series. The Newton-Raphson method can still be used to improve complex roots, but a good first approximation is usually important. It must be remembered that if a real starting value is assumed in this method, only a real root can be derived; hence in seeking a complex root it is essential that the initial approximation should have an imaginary part. In practice, in solving polynomial equations with real coefficients, it is usually sufficient* to assume that $x_0 = \pm i$.

For polynomial equations, however, complex roots are essentially associated with quadratic factors of the polynomial, and it is

---

* This is the experience of R. A. Brooker, "Solution of algebraic equations on the Edsac," *Proc. Camb. Phil. Soc.*, **52** (1952), 255. This paper discusses the Bernoulli-Aitken method, the root-squaring method, and methods which minimize $\{F(x)\}^2$ (of which the Newton-Raphson method is an example), in connexion with automatic computers.

important to have, first, methods of obtaining rough approximations to such factors and, secondly, methods of improving their accuracy. We shall consider both of these aspects of the problem.

9.8. Location of Quadratic Factors by Test Functions

The problem of finding quadratic factors is more important for equations of even degree. Equations of odd degree have at least one real root, which can usually be evaluated without difficulty, and the linear factor removed. The following method, particularly useful for discovering the coefficients of quadratic factors to two or three figures, though capable of greater accuracy, will be developed for quartic and sextic equations.

First we state some general relations to which frequent reference will have to be made. Let us assume that

$$Q(x) = x^2 + px + q$$

is fairly close to a factor of the polynomial

$$F(x) = a_0 x^n + a_1 x^{n+1} + \ldots + a_{n-1} x + a_n \qquad (9.41)$$

We can always divide $F(x)$ by $Q(x)$, with the result

$$F(x) = G(x)Q(x) + R(x) \qquad (9.42)$$

where $\quad G(x) = b_0 x^{n-2} + b_1 x^{n-3} + \ldots + b_{n-3} x + b_{n-2}$

$\quad R(x) = b_{n-1}(x + p) + b_n$

In general the remainder $R(x)$ will not vanish, and will do so only if $Q(x)$ is an exact factor. By comparing coefficients in (9.42) we find easily enough that—

$$
\left.
\begin{aligned}
b_0 &= a_0 \\
b_1 &= a_1 - pb_0 \\
b_2 &= a_2 - pb_1 - qb_0 \\
&\;\cdot \\
&\;\cdot \\
&\;\cdot \\
b_{n-2} &= a_{n-2} - pb_{n-3} - qb_{n-4} \\
b_{n-1} &= a_{n-1} - pb_{n-2} - qb_{n-3} \\
b_n &= a_n - pb_{n-1} - qb_{n-2}
\end{aligned}
\right\} \qquad (9.43)
$$

Now if no information about p and q is available, it is possible to assume various values for p, and to derive from (9.43) expressions for b_{n-4}, b_{n-3} and b_{n-2} which involve only q as unknown. If

p were correctly chosen these expressions substituted in the last two equations of (9.43) would lead to zero values of b_{n-1} and b_n. Usually this will not happen and it is necessary to choose a convenient function of p, called a *test function*, which vanishes only when b_{n-1} and b_n are simultaneously zero. This is the basis of the following method A, due to Porter and Mack,* which is fairly simple to apply when the equation is quartic or sextic.

METHOD A

Quartic Equations. Assume $a_0 = 1$, so that

$$F(x) = x^4 + a_1 x^3 + a_2 x^2 + a_3 x + a_4$$
$$= (x^2 + px + q)(x^2 + b_1 x + b_2) + b_3(x + p) + b_4$$

It is convenient to evaluate the following quantities which depend on p—

$$c_1 = a_1 - p \qquad d_1 = c_1 - p \qquad (9.44)$$
$$c_2 = a_2 - pc_1$$
$$c_3 = a_3 - pc_2$$

Then the last pair of equations in (9.43) become

$$b_3 = c_3 - qd_1, \qquad b_4 + pb_3 = a_4 - q(c_2 - q)$$

If we define $q = q' = c_3/d_1$, then $b_3 = 0$; b_4 will also vanish if

$$T(p) = q'(c_2 - q') - a_4 \qquad (9.45)$$

vanishes. $T(p)$ is therefore a suitable test function, and we should vary p until T vanishes to the required accuracy.

It should be observed that T is a continuous function of p except when $p = a_1/2$, when T goes to $-\infty$ from both sides. For large values of p of either sign T goes to $+\infty$. Hence if T has opposite signs for two values of p, there is certainly a value of p between them for which $T = 0$.

Sextic Equations. The scheme for quartic equations is extended as follows—

$$c_1 = a_1 - p \qquad d_1 = c_1 - p \qquad e_1 = d_1 - p \qquad (9.46)$$
$$c_2 = a_2 - pc_1 \qquad d_2 = c_2 - pd_1$$
$$c_3 = a_3 - pc_2 \qquad d_3 = c_3 - pd_2$$
$$c_4 = a_4 - pc_3$$
$$c_5 = a_5 - pc_4$$

---

* A. Porter and C. Mack, *Phil. Mag.*, **40** (1949), 578.

The last two equations of (9.43) can then be written

$$b_5 = c_5 - qd_3 + q^2 e_1$$
$$b_6 + pb_5 = a_6 - qc_4 + q^2 d_2 - q^3$$

It is possible from these two equations to find a value q' which makes b_5 and b_6 vanish simultaneously; it is in fact

$$q' = \{a_6 - (d_2 - D)C\}/\{c_4 - C - (d_2 - D)D\} \qquad (9.47)$$

where $\qquad C = c_5/e_1, \; D = d_3/e_1$

We use as test function the expression for b_5, writing

$$T(p) = b_5/e_1 = C - q'(D - q') \qquad (9.48)$$

The vanishing of T then shows that $x^2 + px + q'$ is a true factor of $F(x)$, except in one case. Although T is a continuous function of p, both e_1 and T vanish when $p = a_1/3$, but this will not normally represent a genuine factor. Porter and Mack suggest using $T_1 = T/e_1$ as test function near $p = a_1/3$.

EXAMPLE 9.8. Find quadratic factors of the equation
$$x^6 + 3x^5 + 20x^4 + 3x^3 + 2x^2 + 4x + 5 = 0$$

We consider negative values of p, beginning with 0 and -1. As $T(p)$, defined by (9.48), has opposite signs for these two values, there is a factor with an intermediate value of p, which is clearly close to -1. Further trials with $p = -0.9$, -0.91, locate it more rapidly than might be expected. The calculation is summarized below, the final stage being shown in detail—

p	C	D	q'	T
0	1·333	1	1·109	1·542
-1	5·5	9·3333	0·6446	-0.1007
-0.9	4·4507	8·6326	0·54934	0·0102
-0.91	4·5475	8·7028	0·55832	0·0002

$p = -0.91$	c_1	3·91	d_1	4·82	e_1	5·73
	c_2	23·5581	d_2	27·9443	D	8·7028
	c_3	24·4379	d_3	49·8673		
	c_4	24·2385			C	4·5475
	c_5	26·0570				

$$q' = (5 - 19.2415 \times 4.5475)/(19.6910 - 19.2415 \times 8.7028) = 0.55832$$
$$T = 4.5475 - 0.55832 \times 8.1445 = 0.0002$$

The best order of calculation is

$$c_1 \quad d_1 \quad e_1 \quad c_2 \quad d_2 \quad c_3 \quad c_4 \quad c_5 \quad D \quad C \quad q' \quad T$$

From these results the quadratic factor is approximately

$$x^2 - 0{\cdot}910x + 0{\cdot}558$$

It will be shown later, in illustrating Bairstow's method (Example 9.12) that a more accurate result is

$$x^2 - 0{\cdot}910212x + 0{\cdot}558514$$

Dividing by this factor we obtain the quartic

$$x^4 + 3{\cdot}91021x^3 + 23{\cdot}00061x^2 + 21{\cdot}75152x + 8{\cdot}95233 = 0$$

This can be resolved by the same method. If Routh's rule is applied it will be found that all roots have negative real parts, which implies that one value of p now lies between 0 and $3{\cdot}91/2$. Hence we begin with the values 0 and 1 for p. The calculation is summarized below—

p	q'	$c_2 - q'$	T
0	5·563	17·438	− 88·05
1	0·8696	19·221	− 7·76
1·1	− 0·0870	19·996	10·69
1·05	0·4167	19·581	0·794
1·046	0·45466	19·550	0·0637
1·04565	0·457966	19·5473	0·0003

The final step is satisfactory for five decimal accuracy and provides the factor

$$x^2 + 1{\cdot}04565x + 0{\cdot}45797$$

with the complementary factor $x^2 + 2{\cdot}86456x + 19{\cdot}5478$. Hence the roots of the original sextic are

$$0{\cdot}4551 \pm i\ 0{\cdot}5928,\ - 0{\cdot}5228 \pm i\ 0{\cdot}4297,\ - 1{\cdot}4323 \pm i\ 4{\cdot}1829$$

This procedure can obviously be extended to equations of higher degree though it becomes increasingly more approximate and cumbersome. The use of test functions for quartic, sextic and octic equations was considered earlier by Frazer and Duncan (from whose paper* the equation used in Example 9.8 was taken). Their method for quartics used a similar test function

$$T = (q'b_2 - a_4)(2p - a_1)^2$$

but was numerically much longer than that of Porter and Mack. The same paper describes a useful graphical method for quartic and sextic equation (see Exercises 9, Nos. 7 and 8).

Method B gives an alternative for quartic equations described by Porter and Mack.

* Frazer and Duncan, *Proc. Roy. Soc.*, **A.125** (1929), 68.

METHOD B

Quartic Equations. This involves varying q instead of p until the chosen test function vanishes. Ignoring b_3 and b_4, we can calculate

$$b_2 = a_4/q, \quad p' = (a_3 - a_1q)/(b_2 - q), \quad b_1 = a_1 - p'$$

Then for consistency, $b_2 = a_2 - p'b_1 - q$, so we can use as test function

$$T(q) = b_2 - a_2 + p'b_1 + q \qquad (9.49)$$

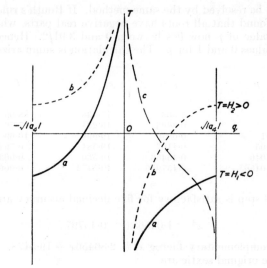

FIG. 9.5. METHOD *B*. VARIATION OF TEST FUNCTION

Some points about the variation of T with q must be noted. First, for one of the quadratic factors of the quartic q lies between $\pm \sqrt{|a_4|}$, so T vanishes for some value within these limits. When q takes either of these extreme values, T takes the value

$$H = \tfrac{1}{4}(a_1^2 + a_3^2/a_4) - a_2$$

Three cases can now be distinguished, and are shown in Fig. 9.5.

(a) $a_4 < 0,\ H > 0$　　　Then $0 < q \leqslant \sqrt{|a_4|}$.

(b) $a_4 < 0,\ H < 0$　　　Then $-\sqrt{|a_4|} \leqslant q < 0$.

(c) $a_4 > 0$　　　　　　　Then $0 < q < \sqrt{a_4}$ always, since
$$T(0) = +\infty \text{ and } T(\sqrt{a_4}) = -\infty.$$

Thus when $a_4 < 0$ the initial choice of q is eased by finding the sign of H.

EXAMPLE 9.9. Find the roots of

$$x^4 - 5x^3 + 7x^2 + 9x - 4 = 0$$

This equation is given by Porter and Mack. Since $a_4 < 0$ and $H < 0$, the range $(-2, 0)$ for q must be examined. It is natural to start with $q = -1$, and since T is then negative, to continue in the range $(-1, 0)$ (see Fig. 9.5). The calculation is summarized as follows—

q	b_2	p'	b_1	T
-1	4	0·8	$-5·8$	$-8·64$
$-0·5$	8	0·765	$-5·765$	$-3·91$
$-0·25$	16	0·477	$-5·477$	$6·135$
$-0·40$	10	0·673	$-5·673$	$-1·220$
$-0·365$	10·959	0·6336	$-5·6336$	$0·025$
$-0·36565$	10·93942	0·634385	$-5·634385$	$-0·00060$

Linear interpolation for q and p', to make T more nearly zero, suggests that the factors are

$$(x^2 + 0·634377x - 0·365635)(x^2 - 5·634377x + 10·9399)$$

from which $x = -1·00000, \quad 0·365635, \quad 2·81719 \pm i\,1·73288$.

This method can also be extended to equations of higher degree.

9.9. Improvement of Quadratic Factors: Lin's Method

The following simple procedure for improving the accuracy of quadratic factors, and in suitable cases for obtaining them without prior knowledge, was suggested by Lin.* If

$$Q_0(x) = x^2 + p_0 x + q_0$$

is an approximate factor of $F(x)$, it uses the last two equations of (9.43) to obtain improved coefficients, p_1 and q_1. Thus, ignoring b_{n-1} and b_n,

$$p_1 = (a_{n-1} - q_0 b_{n-3})/b_{n-2}, \quad q_1 = a_n/b_{n-2} \qquad (9.50)$$

It is often better to use the improved value q_1 rather than q_0 in deriving p_1. New values of b_{n-3}, b_{n-2} may be obtained from the division of $F(x)$ by the new quadratic, and these used to obtain q_2, p_2, and so on. The sequence converges most readily when the factor $Q(x)$ corresponds to a pair of roots, real or complex, with modulus much less than that of other roots of the equation. This

* Shih-Nge Lin, *J. Math. Phys.*, **20** (1941), 231; also ibid., **22** (1943). A study of the convergence of Lin's method using (9.50) has been made by Aitken, *Proc. Roy. Soc. Edin.*, **63** (1951/2), 326.

sometimes suggests starting values of p and q, as in the following example.

EXAMPLE 9.10. Find a quadratic factor of

$$5x^6 + 4x^5 + 2x^4 + 3x^3 + 20x^2 + 3x + 1 = 0$$

If x is small, the last three terms represent an approximate factor, and we can assume $p_0 = 3/20 = 0.15$, $q_0 = 1/20 = 0.05$. The following calculation represents the synthetic division by $x^2 + 0.15x + 0.05$, using the recurrence relation $b_k = a_k - pb_{k-1} - qb_{k-2}$ (cp. division by a linear factor, § 2.8).

	First improvement		Second improvement
n	a_n	b_n	b_n
0	5	5	5
1	4	3·25	3·267
2	2	1·2625	1·26506
3	3	2·6481	2·64727
4	20	19·5397	19·54714
5	3		
6	1		

$q_1 = 1/19.5397 = 0.0512$ $q_2 = 1/19.54714 = 0.0511584$

$p_1 = \{3 - 0.0512$ $p_2 = \{3 - 0.051158$

       $\times 2.6481\}/19.5397$ $\times 2.64727\}/19.54714$

$= 0.1466$ $= 0.146547$

The equation here considered is the reciprocal of that in Example 9.8, and the factor derived is the last one, which now contains the roots with least modulus. The factor thus arrived at with remarkably little effort may be written

$$19.5471x^2 + 2.86547x + 1$$

which agrees well with the result in Example 9.8. The example is of course very well suited to Lin's method.

EXAMPLE 9.11. Improve by Lin's method the factor

$$x^2 - 0.910x + 0.558$$

of the equation in Example 9.8.

A first approach by the above method, using the equations in original form, gives the following results—

q_0	0·558	p_0	-0.910
q_1	0·5582	p_1	-0.9089
q_2	0·5617	p_2	-0.9211
q_3	0·5352	p_3	-0.8338

This is clearly not converging to the desired factor, the reason being that the equation as given has another pair of complex roots with very similar modulus. One way of overcoming this difficulty is to use

Horner's root-shifting device, reducing all roots by a suitable quantity. In this case, let $x = y + 0.5$, so giving the equation

$$y^6 + 6y^5 + 31.25y^4 + 53y^3 + 41.1875y^2 + 19.375y + 9.234375 = 0$$

with an approximate factor $y^2 + 0.090y + 0.353$.
The following sequence is now obtained—

q_0	0·353	p_0	0·090
q_1	0·3534	p_1	0·0899
q_3	0·35347	p_2	0·08973
q_4	0·35340	p_3	0·08978
q_5	0·353400	p_4	0·089797

Convergence is now much better, and at this stage the improved factor of the original equation is

$$x^2 - 0.91020x + 0.55850$$

9.10. Improvement of Quadratic Factors: Bairstow's Method

Regarded as iterative processes, the methods of Porter and Mack, and Lin, are first order. It is important to have a second-order process for improving quadratic factors, similar to the Newton-Raphson process for linear factors, and this is provided by a method first devised by Bairstow.*

Returning to (9.42) we can perform a division of $G(x)$ by $Q(x)$ giving

$$G(x) = H(x)Q(x) + S(x) \qquad (9.51)$$

where $H(x) = c_0x^{n-4} + c_1x^{n-5} + \ldots + c_{n-4}$

$$S(x) = c_{n-3}(x + p) + c_{n-2}$$

and $c_k = b_k - pc_{k-1} - qc_{k-2}$ $(k = 1, 2, \ldots, n - 2)$ (9.52)

Hence $F(x) = H(x)\{Q(x)\}^2 + S(x)Q(x) + R(x)$

$Q(x)$ is a near factor, say $Q_0(x)$ as in Lin's method. We may suppose that the true factor is

$$x^2 + (p_0 + \Delta p)x + q_0 + \Delta q$$

and if X is either root of this it follows that

$$F(X) = 0 = H(X)\{Q_0(X)\}^2 + S(X)Q_0(X) + R(X) \quad (9.53)$$

Now $Q_0(X) = -(\Delta pX + \Delta q)$, so the first term is of second degree in Δp, Δq, and may justifiably be neglected. If in addition

---

* Originally given in 1914 (*Aero. Mem. No. 514*), it was published by Frazer and Duncan, *loc. cit.* Since then it has been rediscovered several times, and is presented here in the form given by Milne, *Numerical Calculus*.

X^2 is replaced by $-\{(p_0 + \Delta p)X + q_0 + \Delta q\}$ and we define $c_{n-1} = -pc_{n-2} - qc_{n-3}$ then, to first order in Δp and Δq, (9.53) becomes

$$b_n - c_{n-1}\Delta p - c_{n-2}\Delta q + (X + p_0)\{b_{n-1} - c_{n-2}\Delta p - c_{n-3}\Delta q\} = 0$$

This equation is linear in X, but must in general be satisfied by two distinct roots of the form $\alpha \pm \beta$; consequently it can be replaced by the pair of equations—

$$\left.\begin{array}{l} - b_n\ \ \ \ + c_{n-1}\Delta p + c_{n-2}\Delta q = 0 \\ - b_{n-1} + c_{n-2}\Delta p + c_{n-3}\Delta q = 0 \end{array}\right\} \tag{9.54}$$

from which

$$\left.\begin{array}{l} \Delta p = (-b_n c_{n-3} + b_{n-1}c_{n-2})/D \\ -\Delta q = (-b_n c_{n-2} + b_{n-1}c_{n-1})/D \end{array}\right\} \tag{9.55}$$

where $\qquad D = c_{n-2}{}^2 - c_{n-1}c_{n-3}$

These equations obviously form the basis of a second-order iterative formula.

EXAMPLE 9.12. Reconsider Example 9.11 by Bairstow's method.

The first stage is a double application of a quadratic division procedure, followed by use of (9.55). The essential relations are

$$\begin{aligned} b_k &= a_k - pb_{k-1} - qb_{k-2} \quad (k = 1, 2, \ldots, n) \\ c_k &= b_k - pc_{k-1} - qc_{k-2} \quad (k = 1, 2, \ldots, n-2) \\ c_{n-1} &= \qquad\quad -pc_{n-2} - qc_{n-3} \end{aligned}$$

The calculation is given below—

$$p_0 - 0\cdot910 \qquad\qquad q_0 = 0\cdot558$$

a_0	1	b_0	1·0	c_0	1·0
a_1	3	b_1	3·910	c_1	4·820
a_2	20	b_2	23·0001	c_2	26·82
a_3	3	b_3	21·7483	c_3	43·4725
a_4	2	b_4	8·9569	c_4	33·5467
a_5	4	b_5	0·01523	c_5	6·2698
a_6	5	b_6	0·01591		
b_5	0·01523	c_4	33·5467	c_3	43·4725
b_6	0·01591	c_5	6·2698	c_4	33·5467
D	852·82	Δp	$-0\cdot000212$	$-\Delta q$	$-0\cdot000514$
		p_1	$-0\cdot910212$	q_1	0·558514

Thus a single application of Bairstow's formula gives a substantial improvement. A second application, which incidentally does not alter the c_k greatly, gives $p_2 = -0 \cdot 91021175$, $q_2 = 0 \cdot 55851366$, but of course greater accuracy is attainable if enough decimals are retained.

9.11. Mechanical Methods

Numerous mechanical and other devices have been invented for solving algebraic equations. Of these we shall mention one type only, using a principle introduced by Routh and developed, in 1928, by Kempner. In this the path of the point (α, β), where α, β represent the real and imaginary parts of the function

$$F(z) - a_n = a_0 z^n + a_1 z^{n-1} + \ldots + a_{n-1} z$$

and $z = r e^{i\theta}$, is plotted as θ varies from $0°$ to $360°$, r being kept constant.

Since $\alpha = \sum_{k=1}^{n} a_{n-k} r^k \cos k\theta$ and $\beta = \sum_{k=1}^{n} a_{n-k} r^k \sin k\theta$ the mechanical problem is one of combining harmonics. By a theorem of Cauchy, the number of times the curve encircles the point at which $F(z) = 0$ is equal to the number of roots of this equation for which $|z| < r$. By increasing r in steps, the modulus and amplitude of successive roots can be determined.

Two machines using this principle are—

1. The isograph, designed by T. C. Fry in 1934 at Bell Telephone Laboratories, which can combine 10 harmonics with prescribed amplitude and plot the motion of the point (α, β) as θ varies. The roots of algebraic equation of degree up to 10, and having real coefficients, can be located quite rapidly with an accuracy of about 1 per cent; thereafter improvement can be made by one of the methods already described.

2. The harmonic synthesizer—analyser, designed by S. L. Brown. This machine can deal with polynomials of 15th degree, and, by allowing the harmonics to be introduced with arbitrary phase differences, with equations having complex coefficients. In addition to the usual problems of harmonic analysis, the analyser has been used to find real roots of pairs of non-linear simultaneous equations, of trigonometrical equations and of some transcendental equations.*

* For a brief account of these machines, see *Math. Tab., Wash.*, **1** (1943/5), 127, 128, 165 and 166; also T. C. Fry, *Q. Appl. Math.*, **3** (1945), 89. A general account of machines for solving algebraic equations, with full references, has been given by J. S. Frame, *Math. Tab., Wash.*, **1** (1943/5), 337.

Bernoulli-Aitken Method for Algebraic Equations

For many purposes the methods already described are quite sufficient. A very frequent problem, however, is that of finding the largest root, real or complex, of an algebraic equation, corresponding to the lowest natural frequency of a mechanical or electrical system. There are various methods of approximating to such a root, one of the simplest being given by Daniel Bernoulli in 1728. This method has been extended by Aitken to derive further roots of the equation, in order of decreasing modulus, and we shall give a brief description of it.[*]

9.12. Bernoulli's Method

We begin by introducing the difference equation

$$a_0 f(k + n) + a_1 f(k + n - 1) + \ldots + a_{n-1} f(k + 1) + a_n f(k) = 0 \quad (9.56)$$

where k takes different integral values. It may also be written

$$F(E)f(k) \equiv \{a_0 E^n + a_1 E^{n-1} + \ldots + a_{n-1} E + a_n\} f(k) = 0$$

and from this form it can easily be seen that the general solution of (9.56) is

$$f(k) = A_1 X_1{}^k + A_2 X_2{}^k + \ldots + A_n X_n{}^k \quad (9.57)$$

where $X_1, X_2, \ldots, X_n$ are the roots, assumed for the moment to be distinct, of the equation $F(x) = 0$, and $A_1, A_2, \ldots, A_n$ are arbitrary constants. Moreover, if these roots are in order in descending modulus, X_1 having the largest modulus, then the quantity

$$P_{1k} = f(k + 1)/f(k) = X_1 + 0(X_2/X_1)^k$$

and so

$$X_1 = \lim_{k \to \infty} P_{1k} \quad (9.58)$$

This is the result used by Bernoulli. The sequence $f(k)$ is first derived by means of (9.56), assuming n arbitrary starting values,

e.g. $\quad f(1) = 1, f(0) = f(-1) = \ldots = f(-n + 2) = 0$

From these, $f(2), f(3)$, etc., can be calculated. From the ratios of

---

* A. C. Aitken, *Proc. Roy. Soc. Edin.*, **46** (1926), 289. Modifications to deal with equations having complex coefficients and multiple roots have been given by B. Dimsdale, *Quart. Appl. Math.*, **6** (1948), 77. Some difficulties of the Aitken method, particularly with respect to loss of significant figures in solving equations of high degree, have been stressed by F. J. W. Olver, *Phil. Trans.*, **244A** (1952).

successive values the sequence P_{1k} is formed, which should tend to the largest root X_1. It should be noticed that P_{1k} is a sequence of the type (9.32) already considered.

9.13. Aitken's Extension

Aitken's generalization of (9.58), which we shall quote without proof, is as follows—

Let
$$f_m(k) = \begin{vmatrix} f(k) & f(k+1) & \ldots f(k+m-1) \\ f(k-1) & f(k) & \ldots f(k+m-2) \\ \vdots & & \\ f(k-m+1) & f(k-m+2) & \ldots f(k) \end{vmatrix}$$

Then if $\quad P_{mk} = f_m(k+1)/f_m(k)$

$$\lim_{k \to \infty} P_{mk} = X_1 X_2 \ldots X_m \tag{9.59}$$

Although this result is established most easily when the roots are all real and distinct, it does hold more generally, provided only that $|X_{m+1}| < |X_m|$. Thus if any real root is repeated, the corresponding X on the right appears to the appropriate power. The exact form for complex roots will be considered later.

Calculation of the sequences P_{mk} can be carried out as follows, the m-rowed determinants being evaluated in steps. Thus

$$f_2(k) = \begin{vmatrix} f(k) & f(k+1) \\ f(k-1) & f(k) \end{vmatrix}$$

$$f_3(k) = \begin{vmatrix} f_2(k) & f_2(k+1) \\ f_2(k-1) & f_2(k) \end{vmatrix} \div f(k)$$

and in general

$$f_{m+1}(k) = \begin{vmatrix} f_m(k) & f_m(k+1) \\ f_m(k-1) & f_m(k) \end{vmatrix} \div f_{m-1}(k)$$

We illustrate this in a simple example involving real roots.*

EXAMPLE 9.13. Find the roots of
$$x^4 - 10x^3 - 92x^2 + 234x + 315 = 0$$

* This and the four following examples have been taken from Aitken's paper.

The calculation of $f(k), f_2(k), f_3(k), f_4(k)$, with the initial conditions $f(1)$ = 1, $f(0) = f(-1) = f(-2) = 0$, leads to the table below. Because of the large magnitudes which occur, it is convenient to present all numbers as decimals, with a preceding characteristic in heavy type giving the power of 10, e.g. $\mathbf{3} \cdot 192 = 0 \cdot 192 \times 10^3$, $-\mathbf{\bar{2}} \cdot 456 = -0 \cdot 00456$. This can readily be adapted to use with calculating machines. An alternative which may be preferred, is to place the power of 10 in brackets after the number, e.g. $192 = 0 \cdot 192(3)$.

k	$f(k)$	$f_2(k)$	$f_3(k)$	$f_4(k)$
0	$0 \cdot 0$	$0 \cdot 0$	$0 \cdot 0$	$0 \cdot 0$
1	$\mathbf{1} \cdot 1$	$\mathbf{1} \cdot 1$	$\mathbf{1} \cdot 1$	$\mathbf{1} \cdot 1$
2	$\mathbf{2} \cdot 10$	$- \ \mathbf{2} \cdot 92$	$- \ \mathbf{3} \cdot 234$	$\mathbf{3} \cdot 315$
3	$\mathbf{3} \cdot 192$	$\mathbf{5} \cdot 10804$	$\mathbf{5} \cdot 83736$	
4	$\mathbf{4} \cdot 2606$	$- \ \mathbf{7} \cdot 109412$	$- \ \mathbf{8} \cdot 253833$	
5	$\mathbf{5} \cdot 41069$	$\mathbf{9} \cdot 116902177$	$\mathbf{10} \cdot 810292$	
6	$\mathbf{6} \cdot 602364$	$- \ \mathbf{11} \cdot 1218756308$	$- \ \mathbf{13} \cdot 254130$	
7	$\mathbf{7} \cdot 9131704$	$\mathbf{13} \cdot 1283701289$	$\mathbf{15} \cdot 801681$	
8	$\mathbf{9} \cdot 136303492$	$- \ \mathbf{15} \cdot 1346100347$	$- \ \mathbf{18} \cdot 252406$	
9	$\mathbf{10} \cdot 2049261777$	$\mathbf{17} \cdot 1414212595$		
10	$\mathbf{11} \cdot 3070597564$			

The values of $f(k)$ are exact. The reader will soon find, if he repeats the calculation, that to obtain many significant figures in later columns, the first must be calculated with considerable accuracy. This is because of the "differencing" nature of the process leading to $f_2(k), f_3(k)$, etc.

It should be noticed that it is not necessary to compile the above table column by column. Aitken* pointed out that it can also be completed one row at a time using the recurrence relation

$$f_m(k + 1) = \begin{vmatrix} f_m(k) & f_{m+1}(k) \\ f_m + (k) & f_m(k) \end{vmatrix} \div f_m(k - 1)$$

which is a simple transposition of the previous one.

Assume that the table is extended by adding a column of ones to the left of $f(k)$, for $k \geqslant 1$. When the first sequence $f(k)$ is formed from initial values $0, 0 \ldots, 0, 1$ the row for $k = 1$ consists of ones, and that for $k = 2$ of the coefficients $1, -a_1, a_2, -a_3, \ldots$ in the polynomial (with $a_0 = 1$). Succeeding rows can be added by using the rule that *each entry is the square of the one above minus the product of the two flanking that one, divided by the one above that again.*

This procedure has the advantage that the computation of the first Bernoulli sequence using (9.56) is avoided, and the arithmetic required for other elements is often reduced because the divisors are smaller. The derivation of all roots of the polynomials proceeds simultaneously; and all the devices described later for accelerating convergence are available when required. Only when interest is confined to the two or three roots of largest modulus does the computation by columns seem preferable.

* A. C. Aitken, Further numerical studies in algebraic equations and matrices, *Proc. Roy. Soc. Edin.*, **51** (1930–31), 80.

Returning now to the example in hand, the following values of P_{mk} are obtained from the last five values in each column of the table—

P_{1k}	P_{2k}	P_{3k}	P_{4k}
15·16	− 104·25	− 319·22	315
14·93	− 105·33	− 313·63	
15·03	− 104·86	− 315·46	
14·98	− 105·06	− 314·86	

Hence to 3S

$$X_1 = 15·0, \ X_1X_2 = -105, \ X_1X_2X_3 = -315, \ X_1X_2X_3X_4 = 315$$

and $$X_2 = -7·00, \ X_3 = 3·00, \ X_4 = -1·00$$

It is easily verified that the roots are exactly 15, − 7, 3, − 1. The full accuracy has not been used here, because the convergence does not warrant it. The derivation of more rapidly converging sequences will be considered later.

9.14. Complex and Multiple Roots

We need to examine the application of (9.59) in situations, frequently occurring, in which two or more roots have the same modulus.

1. PAIR OF COMPLEX CONJUGATE ROOTS

Suppose that X_3, $X_4 = Re^{\pm i\theta}$, X_1 and X_2 being real. Then, because (9.57) assumes the form

$$f_k = A_1 X_1{}^k + A_2 X_2{}^k + BR^k \cos(k\theta + \delta) + \dots$$

it follows that, although P_{1k}, P_{2k} and P_{4k} tend to X_1, X_1X_2 and $X_1X_2R^2$ respectively, the leading term in P_{3k} tends rather to behave like

$$X_1X_2R \cos(\overline{k+1}\theta + \alpha)/\cos(k\theta + \alpha)$$

where α is independent of k. Thus the sequence P_{3k} does not tend to X_1X_2R but shows an irregular and oscillatory behaviour as k increases which is a clear indication that a pair of complex roots is present.

There is no difficulty in such a case in finding the modulus of the complex roots, since

$$X_3X_4 = R^2 = \lim (P_{4k}/P_{2k}) \tag{9.60}$$

Moreover a simple sequence derived from P_{3k} will lead to the real part of X_3 and X_4. Thus if $d_k = P_{3k}/X_1X_2$, then

$$\lim (d_{k+1} + R^2/d_k)$$
$$= R\{\cos(\overline{k+2}\theta + \alpha) + \cos(k\theta + \alpha)\}/\cos(\overline{k+1}\theta + \alpha)$$
$$= 2R \cos\theta$$
$$= X_3 + X_4 \tag{9.61}$$

When complex roots are suspected it is therefore desirable to form the sequence d_k and thence $(d_{k+1} + R^2/d_k)$, R^2 having first been found from (9.60). This is illustrated in the following example.

EXAMPLE 9.14. Solve the equation

$$x^5 - 13x^4 - 121x^3 - 398x^2 + 386x - 520 = 0$$

Proceeding as before gives the tables—

$f(k)$	$f_2(k)$	$f_3(k)$
0·0	0·0	0·0
1·1	1·1	1·1
2·13	− 3·121	3·398
3·290	4·9467	6·205110
4·5741	6·249109	9·1070826
6·114511	− 8·58382345	11·5544106
7·2294226	11·11940422	14·2898586
8·45860507	− 13·1303023237	
9·917298089		

P_{1k}	P_{2k}	P_{3k}	d_k	$d_{k+1} + 26/d_k$
19·946	− 26·313	515·35	− 1·3156	− 8·045
20·035	234·36	522·07	11·718	− 8·007
19·990	− 204·52	520·54	− 10·226	− 7·999
20·002	− 109·13	520·01	− 5·4555	

The behaviour of P_{2k} indicates that X_2, X_3 are complex; we conclude

$$X_1 = 20 \cdot 0, \quad X_1 R^2 = 520$$

and therefore

$$R^2 = X_2 X_3 = 26$$

Then

$$d_k = P_{2k}/20$$

and the final column shows that

$$X_2 + X_3 = - 8 \cdot 00$$

Hence

$$X_2, X_3 = - 4 \cdot 00 \pm i\, 3 \cdot 16$$

Finally from the sum and product of all the roots

$$X_4 + X_5 = 1 \cdot 00, \quad X_4 X_5 = 1 \cdot 00$$

so

$$X_4, X_5 = 0 \cdot 500 \pm i\, 0 \cdot 866$$

2. REPEATED REAL ROOTS

A pair of equal real roots is equivalent to a pair of complex roots for which $\theta = 0$ or π, and one would therefore expect the above procedure still to be effective. If the root X_1 occurs twice, the solution (9.57) is modified to the extent that $A_1 X_1{}^k + A_2 X_2{}^k$ is replaced by $(A_1 + A_2 k) X_1{}^k$; if it occurs three times, the solution contains $(A_1 + A_2 k + A_3 k^2) X_1{}^k$ and so on. If the root is double, the effect is that P_{1k} converges rather slowly to X_1, although P_{2k} converges with normal rapidity to X_1^2 if $|X_3/X_1|$ is not too nearly unity. In such a case we should assume $d_k = P_{1k}$ and applying the analogous form of (9.61), verify that

$$\lim (d_{k+1} + X_1^2/d_k) = 2X_1 \qquad (9.62)$$

This will determine the sign of X_1.

It is worth remarking that this use of (9.60) and (9.61) is not restricted to roots whose modulus is exactly equal; two real roots whose modulus is nearly equal may be distinguished by deriving their product and sum in a similar way.

EXAMPLE 9.15. Examine the roots of

$$x^4 - 22x^3 + 95x^2 + 312x - 144 = 0$$

Proceeding as usual—

$f(k)$	$f_2(k)$	P_{1k}	P_{2k}	$P_{1,\,k+1} + 144/P_{1k}$
0·0	0·0			
1·1	1·1	22·0	95·0	
2·22	2·95	17·682	167·25	
3·389	5·15889	15·825	138·64	24·005
4·6156	7·220286	14·905	145·40	23·999
5·91757	9·320304	14·338	143·66	24·000
7·1315634	11·460162	13·957	144·08	24·000
8·18362377	13·662997	13·683	143·98	24·000
9·251245344	15·954595	13·476		
10·3358709653				

The convergence of P_{2k} to 144, with the steady but slow convergence of P_{1k}, suggests that $X_1 = X_2 = 12\cdot0$. This is confirmed by the final column, using (9.62). Since

$$X_3 + X_4 = -2\cdot00 \quad \text{and} \quad X_3X_4 = 1\cdot000$$

it follows that $\qquad X_3 = -2\cdot414, \; X_4 = 0\cdot414$

(The exact roots are 12, 12, $-1 \pm \sqrt{2}$.)

This procedure can be extended to triple roots, etc. For the double root the test for equality, (9.62), can be expressed in the form

$$1 - 2c_k + c_kc_{k+1} \to 0$$

where $c_k = P_{2k}/(P_{1k}X_1)$. Similarly for a triple root ($X_1 = X_2 = X_3$)

$$1 - 3c_k + 3c_kc_{k+1} - c_kc_{k+1}c_{k+2} \to 0$$

where $c_k = P_{3k}/(P_{1k}X_1^2)$. The generalization is obvious.

3. NUMERICALLY EQUAL REAL ROOTS

Two roots of equal magnitude but opposite sign are also easily recognized. Let the roots be X_2 and $X_3(= -X_2)$, then it will be found that P_{1k}, P_{3k} tend to X_1 and $-X_1X_2^2$ as expected, but P_{2k}

consists of two distinct sequences, formed from alternate terms, and tending to different limits. If these limits are L_2 and L_2', it is found that X_2, $X_3 = \pm \sqrt{(L_2 L_2'/X_1^2)}$.

EXAMPLE 9.16. Find the roots of

$$x^4 - 10x^3 - 12x^2 + 130x - 13 = 0$$

The usual calculation gives the following table.

P_{1k}	P_{2k}	P_{3k}
10·000	− 12·00	− 130·00
11·200	− 120·33	− 128·80
9·911	− 12·108	− 128·69
10·051	− 106·84	− 128·69
9·901	− 12·122	− 128·69
9·919	− 105·30	− 128·69
9·899	− 12·123	− 128·69
9·902	− 105·10	− 128·69
9·899	− 12·124	
9·899		

Clearly $X_1 = 9\cdot899$, $X_1 X_2 X_3 = -128\cdot69$

Hence $X_2 X_3 = -13\cdot00$ and X_2, $X_3 = \pm \sqrt{13} = \pm 3\cdot606$

Finally $X_4 = 0\cdot101$

(The exact roots are $5 \pm \sqrt{24}$, $\pm \sqrt{13}$.)

We shall not consider more complicated cases which can arise, e.g. pairs of complex roots with the same modulus but with the same or different amplitude. For these, Aitken's paper should be consulted.

9.15. More Rapidly Convergent Sequences

It is clear from the examples given that the limiting values of the sequences P_{mk} are not necessarily defined with great accuracy without considerable effort. We have already seen in § 9.6, however, that subsidiary sequences can be derived which converge more rapidly. Aitken's δ^2 process was in fact introduced with this application in view. It is usually preferable to form these subsidiary sequences rather than extend the primary sequences a long way.

Let us examine the case in which the roots occurring in (9.57) are distinct, and $|X_1| > |X_2| > |X_3| > |X_4|$. As in (9.33), let

$$P_{1, k}^{(1)} = P_{1, k+2} - \frac{(P_{1, k+2} - P_{1, k+1})^2}{\delta^2 P_{1, k+1}} \tag{9.63}$$

and $$P_{1, k}^{(2)} = P_{1, k+2}^{(1)} - \frac{(P_{1, k+2}^{(1)} - P_{1, k+1}^{(1)})^2}{\delta^2 P_{1, k+1}^{(1)}} \tag{9.64}$$

It is then found that, whereas $P_{1k} = X_1 + 0(X_2/X_1)^k$,

$$P_{1k}^{(1)} = X_1 + 0(X_3/X_1)^k$$

and $\qquad P_{2k}^{(2)} = X_1 + 0(X_4/X_1)^k$

under the conditions specified; hence the sequences $P_{1k}^{(1)}$, $P_{1k}^{(2)}$ converge more rapidly to the root X_1.

EXAMPLE 9.17. Apply the foregoing to the largest root in Example 9.13.

The last six values of $f(k)$ in Example 9.13 can be used to form the following sequences to 11S. The improved convergence to the exact root 15 is very remarkable.

P_1	$P_1^{(1)}$	$P_1^{(2)}$
14·667121186	15·001418373	14·999999987
15·159777145	15·000304169	
14·926402783	15·000065221	
15·034550817		
14·983920543		

It must be remembered that each value of a derived sequence requires three values of the prior sequence.

Sequences $P_{2k}^{(1)}$, $P_{2k}^{(2)}$ can of course be formed similarly to determine the product $X_1 X_2$; likewise for $X_1 X_2 X_3$, etc., provided the later roots satisfy the necessary inequalities. However, when X_1 is being evaluated, and the roots X_2, X_3 have the same modulus, different derived sequences must be used; thus in Example 9.16 it is necessary to invoke the sequence (9.34) for the improvement of X_1 and in Example 9.14 one must use (9.35). In this latter example, it should be noted that $h^2 = X_1^2/R^2$, which is known approximately from the primary sequences P_{1k}, P_{3k}.

The Root-squaring Method

We shall now describe, with some misgiving, a method which separates all roots of an algebraic equation having different moduli, in a single major operation. The misgiving arises because, although the method is a very powerful one, usually converging very rapidly and capable, if correctly performed, of great accuracy, it has several serious drawbacks.

First, we should note that the Bernoulli-Aitken method is self-checking and self-correcting in the sense that errors leading to irregularities in any sequence are soon apparent, and can often be ignored because the ultimate convergence to the desired limit is unaffected. The root-squaring method, however, has neither of these desirable properties, and often gives trouble except when used by the most impeccable computers.* The method seems to invite errors, particularly in signs and the placing of decimal points. Secondly, the accuracy of the final result can rarely be guaranteed in advance, and any failure to anticipate loss of significant figures means that the process must be repeated from the beginning. Unlike most iterative processes, the requisite number of figures must be retained throughout the calculations, thus leading sometimes to heavy work. Thirdly, the amplitude of complex roots cannot always be found without a substantial subsidiary calculation.

Nevertheless, most texts on numerical analysis quite rightly describe the method, because (1) relatively few algebraic equations cannot be completely solved by it, (2) it is the only method to give all roots in one main operation, able to separate roots with very close moduli and to deal easily with pairs of complex roots having the same modulus, and (3) it requires no initial approximations. The root-squaring operation also has subsidiary uses, e.g. Lin's iterative method may sometimes be made to converge rapidly if preceded by one or two root-squarings, when otherwise it would converge very slowly or not at all. The method is commonly known as Graeffe's method (Graeffe, 1837), though its earliest exponent seems to have been Dandelin (1826).

9.16. The Root-squaring Operation

This is very simple.

Let $\quad F_0(x) = a_0(x - X_1)(x - X_2) \ldots (x - X_n)$

Then $(-1)^n F_0(-x)$

$\qquad = (-1)^n a_0(-x - X_1)(-x - X_2) \ldots (-x - X_n)$

$\qquad = a_0(x + X_1)(x + X_2) \ldots (x + X_n)$

Hence, by forming the product,

$(-1)^n F_0(x) F_0(-x) = a_0^2(x^2 - X_1^2)(x^2 - X_2^2) \ldots (x^2 - X_n^2)$

---

* Advantages of the method have been most clearly stated by E. Bodewig, *Quart. Appl. Math.*, **4** (1946), 177. F. W. J. Olver (*loc. cit.*), whilst supporting the use of the method, has emphasized the difficulties which arise in high-degree polynomials; he also describes precautions which should be taken to avoid errors and wasted labour due to cancellation. For another critical discussion, see D. H. Lehmer, *Math. Tab.*, *Wash.*, **1** (1943/5), 377 and K. Mitchell, *ibid.*, **2** (1946/7), 57.

it becomes clear that the equation whose roots are the squares of those of $F_0(x) = 0$ is $F_1(y) = (-1)^n F_0(-x) F_0(x) = 0$ where $y = x^2$. The coefficients of powers of y in $F_1(y)$ can be found by straightforward multiplication; thus if

$$F_0(x) = a_0 x^n + a_1 x^{n-1} + \ldots + a_{n-1} x + a_n \qquad (9.65)$$

and
$$F_1(y) = b_0 y^n + b_1 y^{n-1} + \ldots + b_{n-1} y + b_n \qquad (9.66)$$

then

$$\left.\begin{aligned}
b_0 &= a_0^2 \\
b_1 &= -a_1^2 + 2a_0 a_2 \\
b_2 &= a_2^2 - 2a_1 a_3 + 2a_0 a_4 \\
b_3 &= -a_3^2 + 2a_2 a_4 - 2a_1 a_5 + 2a_0 a_6 \\
b_4 &= a_4^2 - 2a_3 a_5 + 2a_2 a_4 - 2a_1 a_7 + 2a_0 a_8, \text{ etc.}
\end{aligned}\right\} \qquad (9.67)$$

The continuation of these relations is obvious. The alternations in sign must be noted.

In the actual computation, it is very desirable to evaluate b_k not only by calculating each product separately and forming the sum, but to check the result by an independent calculation, wholly on the machine, of

$$b_k = (\tfrac{1}{2} a_k^2 - a_{k-1} a_{k+1} - a_{k-2} a_{k+2} - \ldots) \times 2$$

9.17. Factorization by Repeated Root-squaring

The result of m root-squaring operations will be to give a transformed equation, say $F_m(y) = 0$, where $y = x^p$ and $p = 2^m$. The roots of this equation are $Y_i = X_i^p$; all roots with modulus R_j in the original equation will have modulus $S_j(= R_j^p)$ in the transformed equation. If m is large enough, all roots with differing modulus will now be widely spaced, and it is possible to factorize F_m into a number of factors, those roots with modulus S_j contributing a factor L_j of degree equal to the number of roots involved.

We examine a few simple cases to show how this factorization occurs.

1. ALL ROOTS REAL AND POSITIVE

Let $\quad F_m = y^n + m_1 y^{n-1} + \ldots + m_{n-1} y + m_n = 0 \qquad (9.68)$

the roots Y_i of this equation being widely separated, so that

$$Y_1 \gg Y_2 \gg Y_3 \gg \ldots \gg Y_n$$

$$\text{Then} - m_1 = \Sigma Y_i \qquad\quad = Y_1(1 + Y_2/Y_1 + \ldots) \simeq Y_1$$
$$m_2 = \Sigma Y_i Y_j \quad\ = Y_1 Y_2(1 + Y_3/Y_2 + \ldots) \simeq Y_1 Y_2$$
$$- m_3 = \Sigma Y_i Y_j Y_k = Y_1 Y_2 Y_3(1 + Y_4/Y_3 + \ldots)$$
$$\simeq Y_1 Y_2 Y_3, \text{ etc.}$$

In each relation all products can be ignored except the largest, and consequently

$$Y_i = - m_i/m_{i-1}$$

Hence we can reduce F_m to a set of linear factors

$$F_m = L_1 L_2 \ldots L_n$$
where $$L_i = y + m_i/m_{i-1} \qquad\qquad (9.69)$$

This holds also if some of the roots are negative.

2. ONE PAIR OF COMPLEX ROOTS

Suppose $\qquad\qquad Y_{3,\,4} = Se^{\pm i\phi}$

Then as before

$$m_2 \simeq Y_1 Y_2$$
but $$- m_3 \simeq Y_1 Y_2(Y_3 + Y_4) = 2Y_1 Y_2 S \cos\phi$$
$$m_4 \simeq Y_1 Y_2 Y_3 Y_4 = Y_1 Y_2 S^2$$

Thus

$$F_m = L_1 L_2 L_{34} L_5 \ldots$$
$$= (y + m_1)(y + m_2/m_1)\{y^2 + (m_3/m_2)y + m_4/m_2\}(y + m_5/m_4) \ldots$$

The pair of complex roots satisfies the quadratic equation

$$y^2 + (m_3/m_2)y + (m_4/m_2) = 0$$
from which $\qquad S^2 = m_4/m_2, \; 2S\cos\phi = - m_3/m_2$

3. MULTIPLE ROOTS OF SAME MODULUS

It can be shown similarly that if a real root Y_i occurs k times, it leads to a factor L_i of degree k which cannot be further resolved by the root-squaring operation, and which has in fact the form $(y - Y_i)^k$. Likewise a pair of complex roots repeated k times lead to an unresolved factor of degree $2k$ and form

$$(y^2 - 2S\cos\phi \,.\, y + S^2)^k$$

A complex pair and a real root of the same modulus will lead to an unresolved cubic factor, two complex pairs of the same modulus but different amplitudes will give a quartic factor, and so on.

The manner in which separate factors can be distinguished will become clear when numerical examples are examined. The essential point, however, is that any coefficient m_j which occurs at a point of separation between two resolved factors is merely squared by any subsequent root-squaring operations. This implies that all cross products, $l_{j-1} l_{j+1}$, etc., contributing to m_j are negligible to the approximation made. The number of operations necessary to resolve two adjacent factors depends of course on the relative modulus of the roots concerned, but does not vary greatly. Thus if X_1, X_2 are real and $|X_1/X_2| = 3$, then after 4 operations, $Y_2/Y_1 \simeq 2 \cdot 3 \times 10^{-8}$, which is a measure of the error in assuming linear factorization at this stage; one further root squaring gives $Y_2/Y_1 \simeq 5 \times 10^{-16}$. However, if $|X_1/X_2| = 1 \cdot 15$, after 3 operations, $Y_2/Y_1 \simeq 3 \cdot 1$; hence three additional root-squarings give the same accuracy as before.

9.18. Determination of Root Moduli

The foregoing theory provides all the information needed to determine the modulus of all roots of the original equation, and generally their character, i.e. whether real, complex, multiple, etc. We therefore give first two examples involving the extraction of moduli, and leave the question of amplitudes till later.

EXAMPLE 9.18. Find the roots of

$$x^4 - 10x^3 - 92x^2 + 234x + 315 = 0$$

The roots of this equation (see Example 9.13) are real and well separated, and the Graeffe process works rapidly. The calculation is set out at top of next page, using the same convention as to powers of 10 as in the Bernoulli-Aitken method.

Thus in F_5 all roots are separated to 6S, and we have—

$$Y_1 = X_1{}^{32} = 0 \cdot 431439 \times 10^{38} \qquad |X_1| = 15 \cdot 00000$$
$$Y_2 = X_2{}^{32} = 0 \cdot 476469 \times 10^{27}/0 \cdot 431439 \qquad |X_2| = 6 \cdot 99999$$
$$Y_3 = X_3{}^{32} = 0 \cdot 88292 \quad \times 10^{15}/0 \cdot 476469 \qquad |X_3| = 3 \cdot 00000$$
$$Y_4 = X_4{}^{32} = 0 \cdot 882952/0 \cdot 88292 \qquad |X_4| = 1 \cdot 000001$$

Note that both $+$ and $-$ signs are written, as an indication that they have been carefully checked; this helps to avoid errors.

	x^4	x^3	x^2	x^1	x^0
F_0	1·1	− 2·1	− 2·92	+ 3·234	+ 3·315
$\pm\, a_j{}^2$ $\mp\, 2a_{j-1}a_{j+1}$ $\pm\, 2a_{j-2}a_{j+2}$	1·1	− 3·100 − 3·184	+ 4·8464 + 4·4680 + 4·0630	− 5·54756 − 5·57960	+ 5·99225
F_1 (exact)	1·1	− 3·284	+ 5·13774	− 6·112716	+ 5·99225
	1·1	− 5·80656 + 5·27548	+ 9·189723 − 9·064023 + 9·000198	− 11·127049 + 11·027335	+ 10·984560
F_2	1·1	− 5·53108	+ 9·125898	− 11·099714	+ 10·984560
	1·1	− 10·282046 + 10·025180	+ 17·158503 − 17·010591	− 21·099429 + 21·002479	+ 20·969358
F_3	1·1	− 10·256866	+ 17·147912	− 21·096950	+ 20·969358
	1·1	− 19·659801 + 19·002958	+ 33·218780 − 33·000498	− 41·093993 + 41·000029	+ 40·939655
F_4	1·1	− 19·656843	+ 33·218282	− 41·093964	+ 40·939655
	1·1	− 38·431443 + 38·000004	+ 65·476470 − 65·000001	− 81·088292 + 81·000000	+ 80·882952
F_5	1·1	− 38·431439	+ 65·476469	− 81·088292	+ 80·882952

EXAMPLE 9.19. Find the roots of
$$x^4 - 22x^3 + 95x^2 + 312x - 144 = 0$$

From Example 9.15 this is known to have two equal roots, and it is interesting to see how this appears in the root-squaring process. In F_3 the third and fourth roots, both real, are almost resolved to 6S, and the first factor is clearly quadratic. The fact that the second coefficient in F_3 is nearly half the square of the same coefficient in F_2, is clear evidence of a double real root. Proceeding on this assumption the second and third coefficients in F_4 yield almost identical values for X_1. It is worth remembering that F_5 would give both roots to 12S if these were retained through the computation.

From F_4

$$|Y_1| = 0·18488_1 \times 10^{18} \qquad\qquad |X_1| = |X_2| = 11·9999$$
$$|Y_1|^2 = 0·341817 \times 10^{35} \qquad\qquad |X_1| = |X_2| = 12·0000$$
$$Y_3 = 0·455207 \times 10^6/0·341817 \qquad\qquad |X_3| = 2·414216$$
$$Y_4 = 0·341825 \times 10^{-6}/0·455207 \qquad\qquad |X_4| = 0·414214$$

N.B. A pair of real roots $\pm X_1$ giving a factor $y^2 - Y^2$, would easily be recognized (cp. Example 9.16).

	x^4	x^3	x^2	x^1	x^0
F_0	1·1	$-$ 2·22	2·95	3·312	$-$ 3·144
	1·1	$-$ 3·484 $+$ 3·190	$+$ 5·09025 $+$ 5·13728 $-$ 5·00288	$-$ 5·97344 $-$ 5·27360	$+$ 5·20736
F_1 (exact)	1·1	$-$ 3·294	$+$ 5·22465	$-$ 6·124704	$+$ 5·20736
	1·1	$-$ 5·86436 $+$ 5·44930	$+$ 9·504676 $-$ 9·073326 $+$ 9·000041	$-$ 11·155511 $+$ 11·009317	$+$ 9·429982
F_2	1·1	$-$ 5·41506	$+$ 9·431391	$-$ 11·146194	$+$ 9·429982
	1·1	$-$ 10·172275 $+$ 10·086278	$+$ 18·186098 $-$ 18·001214	$-$ 21·213727 $+$ 21·000371	$+$ 18·184885
F_3	1·1	$-$ 10·085997	$+$ 18·184884	$-$ 21·213356	$+$ 18·184885
	1·1	$-$ 18·73953₁ $+$ 18·36976₈	$+$ 35·341821 $-$ 35·000004	$-$ 41·455208 $+$ 41·000001	$+$ 35·341825
F_4	1·1	$-$ 18·36976₃	$+$ 35·341817	$-$ 41·455207	$+$ 35·341825

9.19. Determination of Real Parts of Complex Roots

The signs of real roots can usually be found by inspecting the original equation. Pure imaginary roots occur in pairs and therefore offer no difficulty. Likewise when there is only one pair of complex roots, the correct sign and magnitude of the real part is obtainable at once from the sum of the roots of the equation, as soon as the sign of real roots is known.

At first sight the correct amplitudes of complex roots, when more than one pair of these is present, offers a serious problem. Thus from $F_m = 0$ we may obtain a quadratic factor having roots $Se^{\pm i\phi}$, when ϕ lies between 0 and π. The corresponding roots of $F_0 = 0$ will be $Re^{\pm i\theta}$, where $R = S^{1/p}$ and θ has *one* of the p values

$$(\phi + 2q\pi)/p, \quad q = 0, 1, \ldots, p - 1$$

It might be necessary to try each of these possible values in the equation satisfied by the real part of the root, i.e.

$$a_0 R^n \cos n\theta + a_1 R^{n-1} \cos(n-1)\theta + \ldots + a_{n-1} R \cos\theta + a_n = 0$$

until the correct one is found, obviously a long and tedious process. Yet, when there are only two pairs of complex roots, a much simpler expedient is possible, using the two expressions for the sum of the roots and the sum of their reciprocals. These are

$$X_1 + X_2 + \ldots + X_n = - a_1/a_0$$
$$1/X_1 + 1/X_2 + \ldots + 1/X_n = - a_{n-1}/a_n$$

Suppose $\quad X_{1,2} = R_1 e^{\pm i\theta_1}, \; X_{3,4} = R_3 e^{\pm i\theta_3}$

all other roots being real and completely determined, as well as R_1 and R_3. Then

$$2R_1 \cos \theta_1 + 2R_3 \cos \theta_3 = - a_1/a_0 - X_5 - \ldots - X_n$$
$$(2 \cos \theta_1)/R_1 + (2 \cos \theta_3)/R_3$$
$$= - a_{n-1}/a_n - 1/X_5 - \ldots - 1/X_n \quad (9.70)$$

Thus we have two equations which determine $R_1 \cos \theta_1$ and $R_3 \cos \theta_3$ unambiguously, and which hold even when one or other of the cosines has the value 0 or ± 1, or when $\theta_1 = \theta_3$. The equation already considered in Example 9.14 provides an example of this technique.

EXAMPLE 9.20.   Find the roots of
$$x^5 - 13x^4 - 121x^3 - 398x^2 + 386x - 520 = 0$$

The roots are well separated, so few root-squarings are necessary. It can be seen that F_3 is almost resolved into one linear and two quadratic factors. In F_4 the resolution is complete to 6S, and the moduli can be determined.

	x^5	x^4	x^3	x^2	x^1	x^0
F_0	1·1	− 2·13	− 3·121	− 3·398	+ 3·386	− 3·520
		− 3·169	+ 5·14641	− 6·158404	+ 6·148996	
		− 3·242	− 5·10348	− 6·093412	− 6·413920	
			+ 5·00772	− 6·013520		
F_1 (exact)	1·1	− 3·411	+ 5·05065	− 6·265336	− 6·264924	− 6·270400
		− 6·168921	+ 9·025654	− 11·704032	+ 12·070185	
		+ 6·010130	− 9·218106	− 11·026837	− 12·143494	
			− 9·000530	− 11·002223		
F_2	1·1	− 6·158791	− 9·192982	− 11·733092	− 12·073309	− 11·731162
		− 11·252146	+ 17·372421	− 22·537424	+ 23·053742	
		− 11·003860	− 17·232817	+ 22·002829	− 23·107202	
			− 17·000001	− 22·000002		
F_3	1·1	− 11·256006	+ 17·139603	− 22·534597	− 23·053460	− 22·534598
		− 21·655391	+ 33·194890	− 44·285794	− 44·285797	
		+ 21·000028	− 33·273720	− 44·000001	+ 44·571590	
F_4	1·1	− 21·655363	− 33·078830	− 44·285795	+ 44·285793	− 44·285795

From F_4

$$Y_1 = X_1{}^{16} = 6\cdot55363 \times 10^{20} \qquad |X_1| = 20\cdot00000$$
$$S_2{}^2 = R_2{}^{32} = 0\cdot285795 \times 10^{23}/0\cdot655363 \qquad R_2{}^2 = 26\cdot00004$$
$$S_4{}^2 = R_4{}^{32} = 0\cdot285795/0\cdot285795 \qquad R_4{}^2 = 1\cdot000000$$

By inspection, $X_1 = +20$. We now have the following equations for $R_2 \cos \theta_2$, $R_4 \cos \theta_4$—

$$R_2 \cos \theta_2 + R_4 \cos \theta_4 = (13 - 20)/2 = -3\cdot5$$

$$(R_2 \cos \theta_2)/26\cdot00004 + (R_4 \cos \theta_4)/1\cdot000000$$
$$= 193/520 - 1/40 = 9/26$$

Hence $\qquad R_2 \cos \theta = -4\cdot00000$, $R_4 \cos \theta = 0\cdot500000$

and the required roots, obtained correctly to 6S, are

$$+20, \quad -4\cdot00000 \pm i\,3\cdot16228, \quad 0\cdot500000 \pm i\,0\cdot866025$$

This method of determining real parts can be extended to more than two pairs of roots, though a corresponding number of simultaneous equations must be solved. Such cases are not uncommon, particularly in problems of dynamical stability, therefore Brodetsky and Smeal,* developing an idea of Runge's, considered a different approach. This involves an infinitesimal change of variable from x to $x' = x + \varepsilon$, by which the equation $F_0(x) = 0$ is transformed to $F_0(x') - \varepsilon F_0'(x') = 0$. Applying the usual root-squaring process to this equation, retaining only linear terms in ε, leads to factorization as usual, and, by combining suitably the parts of each factor which do and do not depend upon ε, the modulus and amplitude of any pair of roots can be obtained easily. This includes the sign of real roots. The labour involved is approximately twice that normally required to determine the moduli only, but this is partly compensated by the fact that the two root-squaring processes, which are carried out side-by-side, must ultimately lead to consistent results. This is perhaps the nearest approach to an overall check of this computation which has been devised. For details of this the original paper of Brodetsky and Smeal should be consulted.

An extended account of methods of finding the phases of complex roots has been given by Olver (*loc. cit.*). He concludes that for speed, accuracy and simplicity, the best way of finding a factor $(x^2 - qrx + r^2)$ of the original equation, r being known

---

* S. Brodetsky and G. Smeal, *Pro. Camb. Phil. Soc.*, **22** (1924), 83.

and q unknown, is to proceed somewhat as in § 9.8 and find the value of q which is a common zero of $J(q)$ and $K(q)$, where

$$F(x) = G(x)(x^2 - qrx + r^2) + xJ(q) + K(q)$$

The process reduces to finding the highest common factor of $J(q)$ and $K(q)$.

9.20. Zeros of Infinite Power Series

The root-squaring method can be applied to find the lower zeros, real or complex, of functions which are represented by power series of the form

$$F(x) = a_0 + a_1x + a_2x^2 + a_3x^3 + \ldots$$

When the zeros are given by real values of x, there is little difficulty provided the series converges well and there is no serious cancellation in the expressions (9.67). The amplitude of complex roots does present difficulty because the simpler methods are not applicable to an equation which may have an infinite number of roots. Brodetsky and Smeal's method, however, can be adapted to deal with this case, and this has been discussed by Lehmer (see reference on p. 285), together with the problem of cancellation in higher coefficients.

We give a simple example of real zeros.

EXAMPLE 9.21. Find the first two zeros of $J_0(x)$.

We use the series considered in Example 9.6, viz.

$$J_0 = 1 - z + 0\cdot25z^2 - 0\cdot0277778z^3$$
$$+ 0\cdot0017361z^4 - 0\cdot0000694z^5 + \ldots$$

where $z = (x/2)^2$. In forming F_1 on next page, terms up to z^{12} are used in the original equation, and it is important to notice the cancellation effects, involving two or three significant figures in the later coefficients. This restricts the accuracy of the final result for the second root. In F_3 resolution is complete enough for the roots to be evaluated.

From F_3

$$Y_1^{-1} = Z_1^{-8} = 0\cdot0523773 \qquad\qquad Z_1 = 1\cdot445796$$
$$Y_2^{-1} = Z_2^{-8} = 0\cdot46220 \times 10^{-7}/0\cdot523773 \quad Z_2 = 7\cdot6171$$

Hence $X_1 = 2Z_1^{1/2} = 2\cdot404826$ and $X_2 = 2Z_2^{1/2} = 5\cdot5198$

The first root is correct to 6D; the second should be $5\cdot520078$.

	x^0	x^1	x^2	x^3	x^4	x^5	x^6
F_0	1·1	− 1·1	+ 0·25	− $\bar{1}$·2777778	+ $\bar{2}$·173611	− $\bar{4}$·694444	+ $\bar{5}$·192901
		− 1·10	+ $\bar{1}$·625	− $\bar{3}$·7716049	+ $\bar{5}$·301408	− $\bar{8}$·482253	+ $\overline{11}$·372109
		+ 1·05	− $\bar{1}$·5555556	+ $\bar{3}$·8680556	− $\bar{5}$·385802	+ $\bar{8}$·669796	− $\overline{11}$·546772
			+ $\bar{1}$·0347222	− $\bar{3}$·1388889	+ $\bar{5}$·096450	− $\bar{8}$·218709	+ $\overline{11}$·213583
				+ $\bar{3}$·0038580	− $\bar{5}$·007873	+ $\bar{8}$·030756	− $\overline{11}$·042189
					+ $\bar{5}$·000123	− $\bar{8}$·001519	+ $\overline{11}$·003797
						+ $\bar{8}$·000015	− $\overline{11}$·000126
							+ $\overline{11}$·000001
F_1	1·1	− 0·5	+ $\bar{1}$·1041667	− $\bar{4}$·385802	+ $\bar{7}$·4306	− $\overline{10}$·1914	+ $\overline{14}$·403
		− 0·25	+ $\bar{3}$·108507	− $\bar{8}$·148844	+ $\overline{14}$·1854		
		+ 0·020833	− $\bar{3}$·038580	+ $\bar{8}$·08971	− $\overline{14}$·1477		
			+ $\bar{3}$·000086	− $\bar{8}$·001914	+ $\overline{14}$·0084		
				+ $\bar{8}$·000001			
F_2	1·1	− 0·229167	+ $\bar{4}$·70013	− $\bar{9}$·6105	+ $\overline{15}$·461		
		− $\bar{1}$·525173	+ $\bar{8}$·49018				
		+ $\bar{1}$·001400	− $\bar{8}$·02798				
			+ $\bar{8}$·00000				
F_3	1·1	− $\bar{1}$·523773	+ $\bar{8}$·46220				

Determinantal Equations

An equation of the form

$$
\begin{vmatrix}
a_{11} - \lambda & a_{12} & \cdots & a_{1n} \\
a_{21} & a_{22} - \lambda & \cdots & a_{2n} \\
\vdots & & & \\
a_{n1} & a_{n2} & \cdots & a_{nn} - \lambda
\end{vmatrix} = 0
$$

is known as a determinantal equation in λ. Such equations arise frequently in dynamical problems and their solution has great importance. If the determinant is expanded, it is obviously a polynomial equation in λ and could be solved by the methods of this chapter. However, solution can often be obtained more expeditiously with the help of matrices, and for this reason this type of equation will not be considered until Chapter 12, after matrices have been introduced. It may be remarked here that both the Bernoulli-Aitken and root-squaring methods can be given instructive expression in terms of matrices.

EXERCISES 9

1. Show that the real zero of the equation, $F(x) = a - x^p = 0$, i.e. the pth root of a, p being integral, can be conveniently obtained to many figures by the iterative formula

$$x_{n+1} = x_n(1 - r)^{-1/p} = x_n(1 + c_1 r + c_2 r^2 + c_3 r^3 + \dots)$$

where $\qquad r = 1 - x_n{}^p/a = F(x_n)/a$

(Note that this method usually avoids division by long numbers.) Verify the following coefficients—

	c_1	c_2	c_3	c_4	c_5
$p = 2$	1/2	3/8	5/16	35/128	63/256
$p = 3$	1/3	2/9	14/81	35/243	91/729

Show that an alternative expansion is provided by the formula

$$x_{n+1} = x_n + \frac{F(x_n)}{p x_n{}^{p-1}} \phi_p(r)$$

where $\qquad \phi_p(r) = \frac{p}{r}\{(1 - r)^{1-1/p} - (1 - r)\}$

(E. H. Bateman, Math. Gaz., 1953)

2. Apply the formula (9.6) to the equation, $x^4 - 6x^2 - 11 = 0$ with $x_0 = 1$. Why does the Newton-Raphson method fail in this instance?

3. If $F(x) = 0$ has a root X of multiplicity s, i.e.

$$F(x) = (x - X)^s G(x)$$

where $G(X) \neq 0$, show that Newton's iterative formula in the modified form

$$x_{n+1} = x_n - aF(x_n)/F'(x_n)$$

is of second order provided that $a = s$, and then

$$e_{n+1} = \frac{1}{s}\frac{G'(X)}{G(X)} e_n{}^2 + 0(e_n{}^3)$$

where $\qquad x_n = X + e_n$

(E. Bodewig, Quart. Appl. Math., 1949)

4. Examine the convergence of the formula $x_{n+1} = f(x_n)$ for finding a root of $F(x) = 0$, where

$$f(x) = x - F(x)/\{F'(x) - as(x)F(x)\} \quad \text{and} \quad s(x) = F''(x)/F'(x)$$

and show that

(a) the convergence is of second order if the root is simple and a is arbitrary, or if the root is multiple and $a = 1$;

(b) when the root has multiplicity s and $a = 1$, the error

$$e_{n+1} = -\frac{1}{s}\frac{G'(X)}{G(X)}\,e_n{}^2 + 0(e_n{}^3)$$

(cp. No. 3 above)

(c) when $a = 1/2$, the convergence is of third order.

(E. Bodewig, 1949)

5. Examine the convergence of the formula $x_{n+1} = f(x_n)$ for finding a simple zero of $F(x) = 0$, where

$$f(x) = x - F(x)/m - (F(x)/m)^3(s_2{}^2 - s_3)$$
$$m = F' - s_2(x)F, \quad s_2 = F''/2F', \quad s_3 = F'''/6F'$$

If $F(x) = x^3 - 4x^2 + 5$ and $x_0 = 1\cdot4$, show that the value of x_1 given by this formula represents the root correctly to 6D.

(E. H. Bateman, 1953)

6. Derive the iterative formula, of third order, in which

$$f(x) = x - (1/a)(e^x - a) + (e^{-x}/2a)(e^x - a)^2$$

for the root of $e^x = a$; and show that with $x_0 = 2$, $\log_e 10$ is obtained correctly to 6D after two iterations.

7. If $x^2 + px + q$ is a factor of

$$a_0x^4 + a_1x^3 + a_2x^2 + a_3x + a_4$$

show that $p = (a_1q^2 - a_3q)/(a_0q^2 - a_4)$
$$q = -(a_0p^3 - a_1p^2 + a_2p - a_3)/(2a_0p - a_1)$$

8. If $x^2 + px + q$ is a factor of $a_0x^6 + \ldots + a_6$, show that

$$f_1(p, q)x + f_2(p, q) = 0$$

where

$$f_1(p, q) = (3a_0p - a_1)q^2 - (4a_0p^3 - 3a_1p^2 + 2a_0p - a_3)q$$
$$+ a_0p^5 - a_1p^4 + a_2p^3 - a_3p^2 + a_4p - a_5$$
$$f_2(p, q) = a_0q^3 + (3a_0p^2 - 2a_1p + a_2)q^2$$
$$+ (a_0p^4 - a_1p^3 + a_2p^2 - a_3p + a_4)q + a_6$$

and hence that $f_1 = f_2 = 0$

Note. The intersections of $f_1 = 0$ and $pqf_1 + (p^2 - q)f_2 = 0$, excluding those on the curve $p^2 = q$, can be used to determine quadratic factors of the sextic.   (Frazer and Duncan, 1929)

9. If $X_1, X_2, \ldots, X_n, \ldots$ are roots of the equation

$$F(x) = c_0 + c_1x + \ldots + c_nx^n + \ldots = 0$$

and $|X| < |X_1| < |X_2| < \ldots < |X_n| < \ldots$

show that
$$c_0 = F(X)\{1 + P_1X + P_2X^2 + P_3X^3 + \ldots\}$$
where P_s denotes the sum of the homogeneous powers and products of the reciprocals of the roots taken s at a time, given by the recurrence relations
$$-c_0P_1 = c_1$$
$$-c_0P_2 = c_2 + c_1P_1$$
$$-c_0P_s = c_s + c_{s-1}P_1 + \ldots + c_1P_{s-1}$$
Hence show that
$$X_1 = \lim_{s \to \infty} (P_{s-1}/P_s)$$

(E. T. Whittaker, 1918)

10. If a quadratic factor $Q(x)$ of a polynomial $F(x)$ is approximated closely

by $Q_0(x) = x^2 + p_0x + q_0$ with remainder $r_0x + s_0$

by $Q_1(x) = x^2 + p_1x + q_1$ with remainder $r_1x + s_1$

and by $Q_2(x) = x^2 + p_2x + q_2$ with remainder $r_2x + s_2$

show that a better approximation is given by
$$\{A_0Q_0(x) + A_1Q_1(x) + A_2Q_2(x)\}/(A_0 + A_1 + A_2)$$
where

$$A_0 + \begin{vmatrix} r_1 & s_1 \\ r_2 & s_2 \end{vmatrix}, \quad A_1 = \begin{vmatrix} r_2 & s_2 \\ r_0 & s_0 \end{vmatrix}, \quad A_2 = \begin{vmatrix} r_0 & s_0 \\ r_1 & r_1 \end{vmatrix}$$

(Aitken's Quadratic Regula Falsi)

Apply this result to improve the factor of the polynomial in Example 9.8, using $p_0 = -0.910$, $q_0 - 0.558$; $p_1 = -0.911$, $q_1 = 0.558$; $p_2 = -0.911$, $q_2 = 0.559$.

CHAPTER 10

FITTING OF DATA BY THE METHOD
OF LEAST SQUARES

THE main object of the present chapter is to describe methods of fitting a given set of data as closely as possible by a simple function, usually a polynomial. In doing this we shall make considerable use of a well-known principle involving probability, Legendre's principle of least square error, which, though not within the scope of this book to describe fully, is readily understood, and can be followed up in any standard text-book on statistical methods.

When the data consist of values of a function for a number of *equally spaced* values of the argument, the fitting is most conveniently carried out using *orthogonal polynomials*, which will be described here in detail. Otherwise, the problem may be reduced to the solution of a set of linear simultaneous equations, called normal equations, having a symmetrical matrix of coefficients. General methods of solving such equations are reserved for the subsequent chapter.

Legendre's Principle of Least Square Error

It is first necessary to describe in general terms how a function of a single variable, say $f(x)$, may be represented approximately by a linear combination of known functions. Let us assume that there are available, possibly as the result of experiment or statistical investigation, the n values

$$f_0 \quad f_1 \quad f_2 \ldots f_{n-1}$$

corresponding to $\quad x_0 \quad x_1 \quad x_2 \ldots x_{n-1}$

These may contain various kinds of error. We decide to represent, or replace for practical purposes, the function $f(x)$ by the linear combination

$$f_m(x) = a_0 v_0(x) + a_1 v_1(x) + \ldots + a_m v_m(x) \qquad (10.1)$$

where $v_0(x)$, etc., are known linearly independent functions,* and

---

* The $(m + 1)$ functions $v_j(x)$ are linearly independent when no one of them is expressible as a linear combination of two or more of the others.

305

a_0, etc., are coefficients whose values are to be determined from the given values f_k. The object of this procedure may be to see to what extent the data are consistent with a simple empirical relationship, and it is then described as curve-fitting. Frequently, however, the intention is to derive from the given values, which are subject to random errors, a set of smoothed values having regular differences. The latter process is often called graduation, but, when based on the method of least squares, is essentially the same as curve-fitting.

As examples of functions $v_j(x)$ which are commonly used, we mention

(a) the powers, 1, x, x^2, . . ., x^m;

(b) the trigonometrical functions, $\sin x$, $\sin 2x$, . . ., $\sin mx$; 1, $\cos x$, $\cos 2x$, . . . $\cos mx$.

Other examples will arise in the following sections.

A somewhat similar situation arises if the data correspond to particular values of several variables z_1, z_2, . . . z_m, i.e. $f(x)$ is replaced by $f(z_1, z_2, . . ., z_m)$. If we then try to fit by means of the function

$$f_m(z_1, z_2, . . ., z_m) = z_1{}^{a_1} z_2{}^{a_2} . . . z_m{}^{a_m}$$

then $\quad \log f_m = a_1 \log z_1 + a_2 \log z_2 + . . . + a_m \log z_m \quad$ (10.2)

Again we have a linear combination of terms in which the coefficients a_1, etc., have to be determined.

Returning to (10.1), consider one of the given values, say f_k. The corresponding expression for $f_m(x_k)$ may be written

$$f_{km} = a_0 v_{k0} + a_1 v_{k1} + . . . + a_m v_{km} \quad (10.3)$$

where $v_{kj} = v_j(x_k)$. There are n such equations, since k may have any of the values 0, 1, 2, . . ., $n - 1$; if $n > m + 1$, and if f_{km} were exactly equal to f_k, we should have more than enough equations to determine the coefficients a_j. In practice f_{km} and f_k are usually unequal, whatever the choice of the coefficients, and the difference

$$R_k = f_k - f_{km}$$

is called the *residual* of f_k for the chosen representation.

Legendre's principle, propounded in 1806, now amounts to the statement that the sum of squares of the residuals

i.e. $\qquad\qquad\qquad S_m{}^2 = \sum_{k=0}^{n-1} R_k{}^2$

should be a minimum for small variations in the coefficients of (10.1). It should be remarked that this is not necessarily the best criterion to adopt in the fitting process, but it can be shown to follow from the assumption that the errors associated with the f_k's are distributed according to the normal law, or arise by the addition of many small random errors.*

A more general statement can be made if we attach a positive weight w_k to the residual of f_k, and decree that

$$S_m{}^2 = \sum_k w_k R_k{}^2 \tag{10.4}$$

should be a minimum.

10.1. Normal Equations

We now combine (10.3) and (10.4), and apply the usual conditions for $S_m{}^2$ to have a stationary value.

Thus if $\partial S_m{}^2/\partial a_i = 0$, it follows that $\sum_k w_k R_k(\partial R_k/\partial a_i) = 0$

or

$$\sum_k w_k \Big(f_k - \sum_{j=0}^{m} a_j v_{kj} \Big) v_{ki} = 0 \tag{10.5}$$

This is written more simply as

$$\sum_{=0}^{m} c_{ij} a_j - c_i = 0 \tag{10.6}$$

where $\qquad c_{ij} = \sum_k w_k v_{ki} v_{kj}$ and $c_i = \sum_k w_k f_k v_{ki}$

Since i may take any value from 0 to m, there are $(m + 1)$ equations of the form (10.6), which are called the *normal equations* of the system. It is worth writing them in full—

$$\tfrac{1}{2}(\partial S_m{}^2/\partial a_0) = c_{00} a_0 + c_{01} a_1 + \ldots + c_{0m} a_m - c_0 = 0$$
$$\tfrac{1}{2}(\partial S_m{}^2/\partial a_1) = c_{10} a_0 + c_{11} a_1 + \ldots + c_{1m} a_m - c_1 = 0$$
$$\cdot$$
$$\cdot$$
$$\cdot$$
$$\tfrac{1}{2}(\partial S_m{}^2/\partial a_m) = c_{m0} a_0 + c_{m1} a_1 + \ldots + c_{mm} a_m - c_m = 0$$

These equations suffice in general to determine the coefficients a_j. An important point is that $c_{ij} = c_{ji}$, so that the square matrix of these coefficients is in fact symmetrical about a diagonal.

---

* See, for example, *Whittaker and Robinson*, Ch. IX.

It is useful to derive an alternative expression for S_m^2 with the help of (10.5). Let (10.5) be multiplied by a_i and the $(m + 1)$ equations of this form be added together; the result, since the summations over k and i can be interchanged, may be written

$$\sum_k w_k(f_k - f_{km})(\sum_i a_i v_{ki}) = 0 \left.\vphantom{\sum_k}\right\}$$

or

$$\sum_k w_k(f_k - f_{km})f_{km} = 0 \left.\vphantom{\sum_k}\right\} \tag{10.7}$$

It follows that

$$S_m^2 = \sum_k w_k(f_k^2 - 2f_k f_{km} + f_{km}^2)$$

$$= \sum_k w_k(f_k^2 - f_k f_{km}) \text{ by (10.7)}$$

If f_{km} is now expanded as in (10.3), and $d = \sum_k w_k f_k^2$,

$$S_m^2 = d - c_0 a_0 - c_1 a_1 - \ldots - c_m a_m \tag{10.8}$$

This is a convenient formula for S_m^2 as soon as the a's have been evaluated.

Methods of solving the normal equations systematically will be described in Chapter 11; for the present we shall merely indicate a convenient layout for calculating the coefficients involved.*

In the table on next page the matrix $\mathbf{V}$ consists entirely of known quantities; the last column, headed (σ), contains the sums of elements in each row of $\mathbf{V}$, and is added for checking purposes. Now if the corresponding elements of any two columns in $\mathbf{V}$, say columns (i) and (j), are multiplied, and the products then added, the result may be called the *product sum* of these two columns; provided all the weights w_k are unity, it is in fact the element c_{ij} in the matrix $\mathbf{C}$ below. Thus c_{00} is the sum of squares of elements in column (0) of $\mathbf{V}$, and $c_{01} \ldots c_{0m}, c_0, \Sigma_0$ are the product-sums of

---

* In view of the extensive use made of matrices in the following chapter, it is worth remarking here that the process of forming normal equations is simply expressed in terms of matrices. If the original equations are represented by $\mathbf{Va} = \mathbf{f}$, where $\mathbf{V}$ has n rows and m columns and $\mathbf{a}$, $\mathbf{f}$ are single-column matrices with n elements, then the result of premultiplying by the transposed matrix $\mathbf{V}'$ is that

$$\mathbf{V'Va} = \mathbf{V'f} \quad \text{or} \quad \mathbf{Ca} = \mathbf{c}$$

where $\mathbf{C} = \mathbf{V'V}$ and $\mathbf{c} = \mathbf{V'f}$. This represents the normal equations.

Also, in the notation given at the beginning of Chapter 11,

$$c_{ij} = C_i(\mathbf{V}) \times C_j(\mathbf{V}), \quad c_i = C_i(\mathbf{V}) \times C(\mathbf{f})$$

$C_i(\mathbf{V})$ denoting the ith column of $\mathbf{V}$, etc. The weights w_k are here taken to be unity.

column (0) with columns (1) . . . (m), ($m + 1$) and (σ) respectively. It is obvious that

$$\Sigma_0 = c_{00} + \ldots + c_{0m} + c_0$$

and this numerical check should be applied as soon as the first row of $\mathbf{C}$ has been evaluated.

	(0)	(1)	(2)	. . . (m)	($m + 1$)	(σ)
	v_{00}	v_{01}	v_{02}	. . . v_{0m}	f_0	σ_0
	v_{10}	v_{11}	v_{12}	. . . v_{1m}	f_1	σ_1
$\mathbf{V}$.						
.						
.						
.	$v_{n-1,\,0}$	$v_{n-1,\,1}$	$v_{n-1,\,2}$	. . . $v_{n-1,\,m}$	f_{n-1}	σ_{n-1}
	c_{00}	c_{01}	c_{02}	. . . c_{0m}	c_0	Σ_0
	c_{10}	c_{11}	c_{12}	. . . c_{1m}	c_1	Σ_1
$\mathbf{C}$.						
.						
.	c_{m0}	c_{m1}	c_{m2}	. . . c_{mm}	c_m	Σ_m
	c_0	c_1	c_2	. . . c_m	d	

The same scheme is applicable when the weights differ from unity if all the elements of the kth row of $\mathbf{V}$ are first multiplied by $w_k^{1/2}$.

Owing to the symmetric property of the elements of $\mathbf{C}$ it is not necessary to calculate separately the elements in $\mathbf{C}$ below the diagonal, provided the Σ check is applied systematically to each complete row of $\mathbf{C}$. The final row in the table contains those elements required in calculating $S_m{}^2$ by (10.8), d being the product-sum of column ($m + 1$) in $\mathbf{V}$ with itself. With an ordinary calculator which accumulates products the whole computation proceeds very easily. One warning is necessary: the elements in $\mathbf{C}$ *must not be rounded* to the same number of significant figures as those in $\mathbf{V}$, as all available digits may be required in solving the normal equations.

EXAMPLE 10.1. An object is observed to move as follows—

Distance s (ft)	0	10	30	50	80	110
Time t (sec)	0	0·9	1·9	3·0	3·9	5·0

Find its initial velocity and acceleration (assumed constant).

We must fit the data as closely as possible by the relation

$$s = ut + \tfrac{1}{2} ft^2$$

giving the same weight to each observation. In the notation of (10.3)

$$f_k = s_k, \quad v_{k0} = t_k, \quad v_{k1} = t_k{}^2$$

t_k	$t_k{}^2$	s_k	σ
0·9	0·81	10	11·71
1·9	3·61	30	35·51
3·0	9·00	50	62·00
3·9	15·21	80	99·11
5·0	25·00	110	140·00
53·63	218·9070	1078·0	1350·537
218·9070	951·0324	4533·2	5703·1394
1078·0	4533·2	22000 ($= d$)	

The normal equations are

$$53 \cdot 63u + 218 \cdot 9070(f/2) = 1078 \cdot 0$$
$$218 \cdot 9070u + 951 \cdot 0324\,(f/2) = 4533 \cdot 2$$

and the solution of these gives $u = 10 \cdot 658$ ft/sec, $f = 4 \cdot 627$ ft/sec^2, though only the first three digits have much significance. From the last row of the table, $S^2 = 24$ ft^2. Note the use of the σ column in checking the normal equations.

10.2. Alternative Derivation of Normal Equations

It often happens that the original problem is stated somewhat differently, and that it is desired to find the values of quantities $r_0, r_1, \ldots, r_{n-1}$ which make

$$S^2 = \sum_{k=0}^{n-1} w_k r_k{}^2$$

a minimum, but simultaneously satisfy *exactly* several relations of the form

$$q_{i0}r_0 + q_{i1}r_1 + \ldots + q_{i,\,n-1}r_{n-1} - q_i = 0 \qquad (10.9)$$

If i takes values from 0 to m, there are $m + 1$ such conditions, and we may assume $m + 1 < n$.

It is usual, in minimizing a function subject to conditions of this kind, to consider the function

$$S'^2 = S^2 - 2 \sum_{j=0}^{m} \lambda_j \{ \sum_k q_{jk}r_k - q_j \}$$

which is identical with S^2 if the conditions (10.9) are satisfied. S', however, introduces $(m + 1)$ parameters λ_j, usually known as Lagrange multipliers, which are at first undetermined. We treat S'^2 as a function of the r_k's and λ_j's, and minimize with respect to all of these.

Then $\qquad \partial S'^2/\partial r_k = 0$ becomes $r_k = (1/w_k) \sum_{j=0}^{m} \lambda_j q_{jk} \qquad$ (10.10)

and $\qquad \partial S'^2/\partial \lambda_i = 0$ becomes equation (10.9)

The λ's are now chosen so as to ensure that the equations of condition are satisfied; thus, on substitution for r_k in (10.9),

$$\sum_k (1/w_k) q_{ik} (\sum_j \lambda_j q_{jk}) - q_i = 0$$

or, more simply,

$$\sum_j d_{ij} \lambda_j - q_i = 0 \qquad (10.11)$$

where $\qquad d_{ij} = \sum_k (1/w_k) q_{ik} q_{jk}$

The $(m + 1)$ equations (10.11), corresponding to $i = 0, 1, \ldots, m$, are formally the same as the normal equations (10.6), if $q_{ik}/w_k = v_{ki}$. Their solution provides values of λ_j, which in turn, by (10.10), give r_k.

This type of problem occurs frequently in survey work, and is illustrated by the following elementary example.

EXAMPLE 10.2. The four angles of a quadrilateral have measured values $\theta_1, \theta_2, \theta_3, \theta_4$, with respective weights w_1, w_2, w_3, w_4. Find the most probable values of the angles, $\bar{\theta}_1, \bar{\theta}_2, \bar{\theta}_3, \bar{\theta}_4$, consistent with the condition $\bar{\theta}_1 + \bar{\theta}_2 + \bar{\theta}_3 + \bar{\theta}_4 = 2\pi$.

Let $r_k = \theta_k - \bar{\theta}_k$. Then we wish to minimize $S^2 = \sum_{k=1}^{4} w_k r_k^2$, subject to the condition

$$r_1 + r_2 + r_3 + r_4 = (\theta_1 + \theta_2 + \theta_3 + \theta_4) - 2\pi = q_0 \text{ (say)}$$

According to § 10.2 we first minimize

$$S'^2 = S^2 - 2\lambda_0(\Sigma r_k - q_0)$$

with respect to r_k, and obtain

$$w_k r_k = \lambda_0$$

From the equation of condition,

$$d_{00} \lambda_0 = q_0$$

where $\qquad d_{00} = 1/w_1 + 1/w_2 + 1/w_3 + 1/w_4$

and consequently

$$\bar{\theta}_k = \theta_k + \{2\pi - (\theta_1 + \theta_2 + \theta_3 + \theta_4)\}/w_k d_{00}$$

10.3. Validity of the Least Squares Method

In considering whether the least squares procedure does in fact provide a satisfactory solution of the curve-fitting problem outlined at the beginning of this section, we should naturally ask whether the direct use of the normal equations does lead to an absolute minimum of S^2, and not a maximum or merely stationary value. We do not propose to prove this, but state that the value of S^2 so obtained is indeed a true minimum.*

The second question is whether the "smoothed" values of the function $f(x)$ yielded by least squares, i.e. the values f_{km}, are in any sense closer to the "true" values than the values f_k, which are known to be approximate. It has already been mentioned that the errors of the f_k's should be distributed in a way similar to the normal law. A partial answer to the question is, however, given by the following important theorem.

Let it be assumed that the f_k's are approximate values of a "true" function $h(x)$ having the form

$$h(x) = b_0 v_0(x) + b_1 v_1(x) + \ldots + b_m v_m(x) \qquad (10.12)$$

Then writing h_k for $h(x_k)$

$$
\begin{aligned}
(f_k - h_k)^2 &= (f_k - f_{km} + f_{km} - h_k)^2 \\
&= (f_k - f_{km})^2 + (f_{km} - h_k)^2 + 2(f_k - f_{km})(f_{km} - h_k)
\end{aligned}
$$

Since
$$f_{km} - h_k = \sum_{j=0}^{m} (a_j - b_j) v_{kj}$$

$$(f_{km} - h_k)(f_k - f_{km}) = \sum_j (a_j - b_j) v_{kj} \{ f_k - \sum_i a_i v_{ki} \}$$

and we find, after interchanging the sums for k and j, that

$$
\begin{aligned}
\sum_k w_k (f_{km} - h_k)(f_k - f_{km}) &= \sum_j (a_j - b_j) \sum_k w_k v_{kj} \{ f_k - \sum_i a_i v_{ki} \} \\
&= 0 \text{ by } (10.5)
\end{aligned}
$$

Hence

$$\sum_k w_k (f_k - h_k)^2 = \sum_k w_k (f_k - f_{km})^2 + \sum_k w_k (f_{km} - h_k)^2$$

$$\geqslant \sum_k w_k (f_{km} - h_k)^2 \qquad (10.13)$$

In other words, the weighted sum of the squared residuals

* See, for example, Milne, N.C., p. 254.

between the f_{km}'s and the true values h_k is less than the corresponding sum for the f_k's. It does not of course follow that any individual f_{km} is closer to h_k than is f_k. The method is thus justified fully when $h(x)$ can be expressed in the form (10.12), but when this expansion is approximate even for $h(x)$ the validity of the least squares procedure involves the validity of this approximation and is thereby complicated.

Use of Orthogonal Functions

A very considerable simplification in the solution of a set of normal equations can be achieved when the functions $v_j(x)$ satisfy conditions of the form

$$c_{ij} = \sum_k w_k v_{ki} v_{kj} = 0 \quad \text{when} \quad j \neq i \qquad (10.14)$$

i.e. are orthogonal when summed over the chosen values of x, with the specified weights w_k. A glance at the normal equations (10.6) then shows that

$$a_j = c_j/c_{jj} = \sum_k w_k f_k v_{kj} / \left(\sum_k w_k v_{kj}^2 \right) \qquad (10.15)$$

The coefficients a_j can therefore be evaluated directly from a knowledge of the values v_{kj}.

Formula (10.8) can, in these circumstances, be written

$$S_m^2 = \sum_k w_k f_k^2 - \sum_j c_{jj} a_j^2 \qquad (10.16)$$

This simplification is not easily achieved in practice unless the orthogonal functions $v_j(x)$ are simple in form, which implies that the basic values of x shall be spaced in a regular way. The most fruitful restriction of this sort is that the values of x shall be equally spaced, so that if $x = x_0 + rw$, the values x_k do in fact correspond to integral values of r from 0 to $n - 1$. We shall only consider orthogonal functions for which this is so, and moreover, the remainder of this section is concerned only with functions for which all w_k's are unity.

10.4. Orthogonal Polynomials

Polynomials which are orthogonal in the sense just described have an obvious importance, and we therefore begin by snowing how they may be constructed. Since the orthogonality condition involves summation, it is natural to expand a typical polynomial in terms of factorials rather than powers. Thus we shall assume that the polynomial of mth degree, denoted by $T_m(r; n)$, has the form

$$T_m(r; n) = d_{0m} + d_{1m} r/(n-1) + d_{2m} r^{(2)}/(n-1)^{(2)}$$
$$+ \ldots + d_{mm} r^{(m)}/(n-1)^{(m)} \quad (10.17)$$

which uses descending factorials; the variable r ranges from 0 to $n-1$, and the coefficients d_{jm} also depend on n although this is not explicitly denoted. These coefficients are unchanged if reduced factorials are used throughout.

Two points about (10.17) are worth notice. First, it has the form of the Gregory-Newton formula for $T_m(r; n)$, and comparison with (5.1) shows that the jth leading difference

$$\Delta^j T_m(0; n) = d_{jm}/(n-1)_{(j)} \quad (10.18)$$

Secondly, if we introduce a new variable $y = r/(n-1)$ and allow n to tend to infinity, the limiting form of (10.17) is

$$T_m(y; \infty) = d_{0m} + d_{1m}y + d_{2m}y^2 + \ldots + d_{mm}y^m \quad (10.19)$$

the range of y being $(0, 1)$.

The orthogonality condition satisfied by the polynomials is that

$$\sum_r T_j(r; n)T_m(r; n) = 0 \quad \text{when} \quad j \neq m$$

where $\sum_r$ means that r is summed over integral values from 0 to $n-1$ inclusive. It is, however, equivalent to the condition

$$\sum_r p_j(r)T_m(r; n) = 0 \quad (10.20)$$

where $p_j(r)$ is any polynomial of degree j, where $j < m$, which may be chosen at will. Similarly it follows that

$$\sum_r \{T_m(r; n)\}^2 = \sum_r p_m(r)T_m(r; n) \quad (10.21)$$

where $p_m(r)$ is any polynomial of degree m having the same coefficient of r^m as $T_m(r; n)$.

We now set out to find the coefficients d_{jm} which satisfy the condition (10.20), and for this purpose choose

$$p_j(r) = (r+j)^{(j)}$$

In the expansion of $p_j(r)T_m(r)$, the term in $d_{im}/(n-1)^{(i)}$ is multiplied by $(r+j)^{(j)}r^{(i)}$, which by the addition theorem (2.23) for descending factorials, is equal to $(r + j)^{(j+i)}$. When summed for integral values of r from 0 to $n - 1$ this becomes

$$(n + j)^{(j+i+1)}/(j + i + 1)$$

which, by a second use of the addition theorem, is equal to

$$(n + j)^{(j+1)}(n - 1)^{(i)}/(j + i + 1)$$

We thus find that

$$\sum_r (r + j)^{(j)} T_m(r)$$
$$= (n + j)^{(j+1)}\{d_{0m}/(j + 1) + d_{1m}/(j + 2) + \ldots + d_{mm}/(j + m + 1)\}$$
$$= (n + j)^{(j+1)} D(j)/(j + m + 1)^{(m+1)}, \text{ say} \tag{10.22}$$

Here $D(j)$, considered as a polynomial in j, is of degree m and by the orthogonality condition (10.20) is known to vanish when j has any of the values $0, 1, \ldots, m - 1$. $D(j)$ must therefore be proportional to the factorial $j^{(m)}$. To find the missing constant, we observe that

$$D(j) = (j + m + 1)^{(m)}$$
$$[d_{0m} + (j + 1)\{d_{1m}/(j + 2) + \ldots + d_{mm}/(j + m + 1)\}]$$
$$= m!\, d_{0m}, \text{ when } j = -1$$

Hence $$D(j) = (-1)^m d_{0m} j^{(m)} \tag{10.23}$$

To find d_{im}, which is the coefficient of the fraction $1/(j + i + 1)$, we can use the well-known rule for forming partial fractions. This states that d_{im} is the value of

$$(j + i + 1)D(j)/(j + m + 1)^{(m+1)}$$

when $$j = -(i + 1)$$

Since $(j + m + 1)^{(m+1)} = (j + m + 1)^{(m-i)}(j + i + 1)(j + i)^{(i)}$

it follows that

$$d_{im} = d_{0m} \frac{(-1)^m(-i - 1)^{(m)}}{(m - i)!\,(-1)^i\, i!} = (-1)^i d_{0m} \frac{(m + i)^{(m)}}{(m - i)!\, i!}$$

In terms of reduced factorials this may be written

$$d_{im} = (-1)^i d_{0m}(m + i)_{(m)} m_{(i)} \tag{10.24}$$

To complete the investigation we must consider (10.21), using

$$p_m(r) = d_{mm}(r + m)^{(m)}/(n - 1)^{(m)}$$

From (10.24) $$d_{mm} = (-1)^m d_{0m}(2m)_{(m)}$$
and from (10.22) and (10.23)

$$\Sigma(r + m)^{(m)} T_m(r) = (-1)^m d_{0m}(n + m)^{(m+1)}(m!)^2/(2m + 1)!$$

therefore

$$\sum_r \{T_m(r)\}^2 = \left\{\frac{(-1)^m d_{0m}}{(n - 1)_{(m)}}\right\}^2 \frac{(n + m)^{(m+1)}(n - 1)^{(m)}(2m)_{(m)}}{(2m + 1)!}$$

However,
$$(n + m)^{(m+1)}(n - 1)^{(m)} = (n + m)^{(2m+1)}$$
so finally
$$\sum_r \{T_m(r)\}^2 = \{(- 1)^m d_{0m}/(n - 1)_{(m)}\}^2(n + m)_{(2m+1)}(2m)_{(m)} \quad (10.25)$$

It is interesting to examine the first few polynomials defined by (10.17) and (10.24). To save space, we write merely the limiting forms (10.19), but obviously $T_m(r; n)$ is obtained at once by replacing y^i by $r_{(i)}/(n - 1)_{(i)}$.

$$\left.\begin{aligned}
T_0(y) &= d_{00} \\
T_1(y) &= d_{01}(1 - 2y) \\
T_2(y) &= d_{02}(1 - 6y + 6y^2) \\
T_3(y) &= d_{03}(1 - 12y + 30y^2 - 20y^3) \\
T_4(y) &= d_{04}(1 - 20y + 90y^2 - 140y^3 + 70y^4) \\
T_5(y) &= d_{05}(1 - 30y + 210y^2 - 560y^3 + 630y^4 \\
&\qquad\qquad\qquad\qquad\qquad\qquad - 252y^5)
\end{aligned}\right\} \quad (10.26)$$

The choice of d_{0m} is clearly conventional, but in this respect we shall follow Aitken (Ref. 4, below), and write
$$d_{0m} = (- 1)^m(n - 1)_{(m)}$$
The general expansion of $T_m(r; n)$ then becomes
$$\begin{aligned}
T_m(r; n) = (2m)_{(m)}r_{(m)} &- (2m - 1)_{(m)}(n - m)r_{(m-1)} \\
&+ (2m - 2)_{(m)}(n - m + 1)_{(2)}r_{(m-2)} \\
&+ \ldots + (- 1)^m(n - 1)_{(m)} \quad (10.27)
\end{aligned}$$
and
$$\sum_r \{T_m(r; n)\}^2 = (n + m)_{(2m+1)}(2m)_{(m)} \quad (10.28)$$

It is instructive to look at another form for $T_m(r; n)$, namely
$$T_m(r; n) = \Delta^m\{r_{(m)}(r - n)_{(m)}\} \quad (10.29)$$
It is not difficult to show that this is identical with (10.27), (see Exercises 10, No. 1), but it recalls Rodrigues' formula for Legendre polynomials in the range $(0, n)$—
$$P_m(r) = (d/dr)^m\{r^m(r - n)^m/(m!)^2\}$$

This emphasizes the fact that Legendre polynomials are limiting forms of the orthogonal polynomials discussed here. In particular the polynomials which in (10.26) are shown in brackets, are the Legendre polynomials for the range $(0, 1)$.

10.5. Central Form of T_m Polynomials

In the applications of these polynomials to be described later, it is more satisfactory to use a central form, in which the range of the variable is $(-\frac{1}{2}(n-1), +\frac{1}{2}(n-1))$ rather than $(0, n-1)$. The change is conveniently made by means of (10.29), in which we first replace r by ρ and then redefine r as $\rho - \frac{1}{2}(n-1)$. At the same time, forward differences are replaced by central differences. Thus

$$T_m(\rho; n) = \Delta^m\{\rho_{(m)}(\rho - n)_{(m)}\}$$

$$T_m(r; n) = \Delta^m\{(r + \tfrac{1}{2}n - \tfrac{1}{2})_{(m)}(r - \tfrac{1}{2}n - \tfrac{1}{2})_{(m)}\}$$

$$= \delta^m\{(r + \tfrac{1}{2}m + \tfrac{1}{2}n - \tfrac{1}{2})_{(m)}(r + \tfrac{1}{2}m - \tfrac{1}{2}n - \tfrac{1}{2})_{(m)}\}$$

$$\text{since } \Delta^m u(r) = \delta^m u(r + \tfrac{1}{2}m)$$

$$= \delta^m\{(r + q)_{\{m\}}(r - q)_{\{m\}}\} \qquad (10.30)$$

where

$$n = 2q$$

Incidentally this central form may be compared with Rodrigues' formula for Legendre polynomials in the range $(-q, q)$, viz.

$$P_m(r) = (d/dr)^m\{(r^2 - q^2)^m/(m!)^2\}$$

The elaboration of (10.30) is straightforward, and leads to expressions for $T_m(r)$ which involve central and mean central factorials of r alternately. The results are best presented separately for even and odd values of n, and are given below for polynomials up to T_5

n odd

$$
\begin{aligned}
T_0 &= 1 \\
T_1 &= 2r \\
T_2 &= 6r_{[2]} - (q^2 - 1/4) \\
T_3 &= 20r_{\{3\}} - 2(q^2 - 9/4)r \\
T_4 &= 70r_{[4]} - 5(q^2 - 9/4)r_{[2]} + (1/4)(q^2 - 1/4)(q^2 - 9/4) \\
T_5 &= 252r_{\{5\}} - 14(q^2 - 25/4)r_{\{3\}} + (1/2)(q^2 - 9/4)(q^2 - 25/4)r
\end{aligned}
$$

n even

$$
\begin{aligned}
T_0 &= 1 \\
T_1 &= 2r \\
T_2 &= 6r_{\{2\}} - (q^2 - 1) \\
T_3 &= 20r_{[3]} - 2(q^2 - 1)r \\
T_4 &= 70r_{\{4\}} - 5(q^2 - 4)r_{\{2\}} + (1/4)(q^2 - 1)(q^2 - 4) \\
T_5 &= 252r_{[5]} - 14(q^2 - 4)r_{[3]} + (1/2)(q^2 - 1)(q^2 - 4)r
\end{aligned}
$$

$$(10.31)$$

The reason for the alternative forms is not difficult to understand. When n is odd, the values of r with respect to which the polynomials are orthogonal are all integral; whereas when n is even, they are all half-integral. It is natural therefore, when n is odd, to use a form corresponding to the Stirling formula (5.9), and when n is even a form corresponding to the Bessel formula (5.13). Let us examine the significance of this.

Odd n. It is clear from the few examples just given that $T_m(r)$ is an even function of r if m is even, and an odd function if m is odd; accordingly alternate terms, either odd or even, in the Stirling series are always missing. If we write

$$T_m = g_{1m}r + g_{3m}r_{\{3\}} + \ldots + g_{mm}r_{\{m\}}, \quad m \text{ odd}$$
$$= h_{0m} + h_{2m}r_{[2]} + \ldots + h_{mm}r_{[m]}, \quad m \text{ even}$$

where g and h coefficients are associated with central and mean central factorials respectively, then provided $j + m$ is even,

$$g_{jm} = \delta^j T_m(0), \quad h_{jm} = \mu \delta^j T_m(0) \tag{10.32}$$

where μ is the averaging operator. The following table should make the meaning of the coefficients quite clear.

h_{00}	.	h_{02}	.	h_{04}	.			
	g_{11}	.	g_{13}	.	g_{15}			
		h_{22}	.	h_{24}	.			
			g_{33}	.	g_{35}			
				h_{44}	.			
					g_{55}			

$T_0(0)$	.	$T_2(0)$	.	$T_4(0)$	.
$\mu\delta T_1(0)$	.	$\mu\delta T_3(0)$	.	$\mu\delta T_5(0)$	
		$\delta^2 T_2(0)$	.	$\delta^2 T_4(0)$	.
		$\mu\delta^3 T_3(0)$	.	$\mu\delta^3 T_5(0)$	
				$\delta^4 T_4(0)$	.
				$\mu\delta^5 T_5(0)$	

The value of this relationship will appear in § 10.8.

Even n. We now have

$$T_m(r) = h_{1m}r + h_{3m}r_{[3]} + \ldots + h_{mm}r_{[m]}, \quad m \text{ odd}$$
$$= g_{0m} + g_{2m}r_{\{2\}} + \ldots + g_{mm}r_{\{m\}}, \quad m \text{ even}$$

The Bessel series for a function tabulated for half-integral values of the argument is

$$T(r) = \mu\{1 + r_{\{2\}}\delta^2 + r_{\{4\}}\delta^4 + \ldots\}T(0)$$
$$+ \{r\delta + r_{[3]}\delta^3 + \ldots\}T(0)$$

and therefore, when $j + m$ is even,

$$h_{jm} = \delta^j T_m(0), \quad g_{jm} = \mu\delta^j T_m(0) \tag{10.33}$$

These equalities are exemplified by the following table—

g_{00} · g_{02} · g_{04} ·	$\mu T_0(0)$ ·	$\mu T_2(0)$ ·	$\mu T_4(0)$ ·
h_{11} · h_{13} · h_{15}	$\delta T_1(0)$ ·	$\delta T_3(0)$ ·	$\delta T_5(0)$
g_{22} · g_{24} ·		$\mu\delta^2 T_2(0)$ ·	$\mu\delta^2 T_4(0)$ ·
h_{33} · h_{35}		$\delta^3 T_3(0)$ ·	$\delta^3 T_5(0)$
g_{44} ·			$\mu\delta^4 T_4(0)$ ·
h_{55}			$\delta^5 T_5(0)$

It is now possible to consider the manner of using these orthogonal polynomials, which is generally simpler than some of the preceding theory would suggest. Of the two methods to be described, the first is quite simple and direct; the second, due to Aitken, makes use of factorial moments of the data, and is at first sight rather elaborate.

REFERENCES

The literature on these polynomials, often known as Tchebycheff (or Chebyshev) polynomials, is extensive; we select the following, appending the value chosen for d_{0m}.

$$d_{0m}$$

1. Tchebycheff: *Oeuvres* (1899), Vol. **1**, 203, 541; Vol. **2**, 219. $(-1)^m m! \, (n-1)^{(m)}$

2. Ch. Jordan: *Proc. Lond. Math. Soc.*, (2) **20** (1921), 297. $(-1)^m (n-1)^{(m)}/2^m$

3. Birge and Shea: *Phys. Rev.*, **24** (1924), 206. $(-1)^m (n-1)^{(m)}$

4. Aitken: *Proc. Roy. Soc. Edin.*, **53** (1932), 54. $(-1)^m (n-1)_{(m)}$

5. Sasuly: *Trend Analysis of Statistics* (1934). $(-1)^m (n-1)^{(m)}/(2m)_{(m)}$

6. Birge: *Rev. Mod. Phys.*, **19** (1947), 298 (Appendix by J. W. Weinberg). $(-1)^m (n-1)_{(m)}$

7. Milne: *Numerical Calculus* (1949). 1

Birge's valuable review denotes by P''_B the polynomial defined by (10.27), and reserves T_m for Sasuly's form. A minor difference is that Birge uses $n = 2q + 1$, not $2q$. More references are given on p. 340.

10.6. Application of Orthogonal Polynomials: Direct Method

The use of orthogonal polynomials with the least squares method has been developed independently by many writers, notably, in the present method, by Birge and Weinberg, and by Fisher and Yates. This method uses essentially the central polynomials $T_j(r)$ defined by (10.30), with one important difference. In applying (10.15) it is an obvious advantage numerically that the numbers v_{kj} should be integers, but not larger integers than necessary. Now the values of $T_j(r)$ given by (10.30) for the pivotal values of r are certainly integers, but those with the same values of n and j sometimes have a common factor which is better removed. Denoting this factor by f

let
$$V_j(r) = T_j(r)/f \qquad (10.34)$$

Then the polynomials $V_j(r)$ are used in place of $T_j(r)$ in the fitting process.

We consider the fitting or smoothing of n values u_r, corresponding to integral or half-integral values of r from $-q + \frac{1}{2}$ to $q - \frac{1}{2}$ $(n = 2q)$, by means of the polynomial

$$u_m(r) = b_0 + b_1 V_1(r) + b_2 V_2(r) + \ldots + b_m V_m(r) \quad (10.35)$$

It follows from Legendre's principle, and the orthogonal property of the V's that

$$b_j = \sum_r V_{rj} u_r / N_j \quad \text{cp. (10.15)} \qquad (10.36)$$

$$S_m{}^2 = \sum_r \{u_r - u_m(r)\}^2 = \sum_r u_r{}^2 - \sum_{j=0}^{m} N_j b_j{}^2 \quad \text{cp. (10.16) (10.37)}$$

where $V_{rj} = V_j(r)$ and $N_j = \sum_r V_{rj}{}^2$. All that is required for the computation are the values of V_{rj} and N_j for the appropriate value of n. These have been tabulated by Birge and others for polynomials up to the fifth, and some tables for $n \leqslant 12$ are included in Appendix 5.

The complete calculation may consist of the following parts—

1. evaluation of the coefficients b_j, and of $S_m{}^2$;
2. evaluation of the fitted or smoothed values $u_m(r)$;
3. conversion of $u_m(r)$ into a polynomial of powers of r

i.e.
$$u_m(r) = \sum_{j=0}^{m} a_{jm} r^j \qquad (10.38)$$

4. estimation of the statistical weights and probable errors of the coefficients b_j and a_{jm}.

We shall discuss these briefly in order.

Evaluation of b_j. When central polynomials are used, the calculation of b_j is made easier by the fact that $V_j(r) = V_j(-r)$

when j is even, and $V_j(r) = -V_j(-r)$ when j is odd. The contribution of a pair of given values u_r, u_{-r} to $b_j N_j$ is therefore

$$(u_r + u_{-r})V_{rj} \text{ when } j \text{ is even}$$

and $\qquad (u_r - u_{-r})V_{rj}$ when j is odd

V_{rj} need be tabulated for positive values of r only, and the number of multiplications similarly reduced, if as a preliminary the values of u_r are replaced by $(u_r + u_{-r})$ and $(u_r - u_{-r})$. This is illustrated in Example 10.4, which shows also a convenient layout for the calculation.

Evaluation of $S_m{}^2$. It is very necessary as a check on the efficacy of the fitting that $S_m{}^2$ should be calculated, and formula (10.37) is particularly suitable. Each polynomial contributes independently to $S_m{}^2$, so the effect of adding, say, the mth polynomial can be seen at a glance.

Smoothed Values. These are conveniently calculated from (10.35), using tabulated values of V_{rj}. The magnitude of successive terms can be examined, or, if the number of terms has already been decided, they can be summed immediately. A subsequent calculation of $\sum_r \{u_r - u_m(r)\}^2$ provides an important check on the whole computation to this stage.

Conversion to Power Series. Birge (Ref. 6) has simplified this by providing a table of the coefficients S_{ij} such that

$$V_j = \sum_{i=0}^{j} S_{ij} r^i \qquad (10.39)$$

It follows from (10.35) and (10.38) that

$$a_{im} = \sum_{j=0}^{m} S_{ij} b_j \qquad (10.40)$$

Part of Birge's table is reproduced in Appendix 5, Table 2.

Statistical Weights and Standard Deviations. We shall not discuss the meaning of statistical terms, nor the arguments which lead to the conclusion that the b_j's act statistically like independent quantities. From (10.37) it appears that the statistical weight of b_j is N_j, and it follows from the standard formula for combining weights, that the weight $p_m(r)$ of the smoothed value $u_m(r)$ is given by

$$1/\{p_m(r)\} = \sum_{j=0}^{m} V_{rj}{}^2/N_j \qquad (10.41)$$

and the weight p_{im} of the coefficient a_{im} in (10.38) by

$$1/p_{im} = \sum_{j=0}^{m} S_{ij}^2/N_j \qquad (10.42)$$

Now from any weight p, the corresponding *variance* is given by

$$\sigma^2 = S_m^2/\{(n - m - 1)p\} \qquad (10.43)$$

when n unweighted quantities are fitted by a linear combination containing $(m + 1)$ parameters; σ is then the *standard deviation* of the quantity concerned, now commonly used in preference to the *probable error*, which is $0 \cdot 6745\sigma$. All these points are illustrated in Examples 10.4 and 10.5.

10.7. Fitting by a Straight Line

The problem of fitting a set of data by a straight line occurs so often that it is worth a separate discussion. In the notation of the previous section, we use the function

$$u_1(r) = b_0 + 2b_1 r \qquad (10.44)$$

to fit n equally-spaced values u_r, where the argument r is chosen so that $r = 0$ lies centrally, and the given values correspond to integral values of r if n is odd, and half-integral values if n is even.

Then $\qquad b_0 = (1/n)\sum_{r} u_r, \quad b_1 = \sum_{r} 2r u_r / \sum_{r} (2r)^2$

or, more conveniently,

$$2b_1 = \sum_{|r|} (u_r - u_{-r}) 2r / \sum_{|r|} (2r)^2 \qquad (10.45)$$

where each sum is over positive values of r only.

The explicit form of $2b_1$, when $n(= 2q)$ is odd, is

$$2b_1 = \frac{2(u_1 - u_{-1}) + 4(u_2 - u_{-2}) + \ldots + (n-1)(u_{q-1/2} - u_{-q+1/2})}{2^2 + 4^2 + \ldots + (n - 1)^2}$$

and when n is even

$$2b_1 = \frac{(u_{1/2} - u_{-1/2}) + 3(u_{3/2} - u_{-3/2}) + \ldots + (n-1)(u_{q-1/2} - u_{-q+1/2})}{1^2 + 3^2 + \ldots + (n - 1)^2}$$

We see that b_0 is the arithmetic mean of the u's. The significance of $2b_1$, which is the slope of the least squares straight line, is seen more easily if (10.45) is written in the form

$$2b_1 = \sum_{|r|} (2r)^2 \{(u_r - u_{-r})/2r\} / \sum_{|r|} (2r)^2$$

Now $(u_r - u_{-r})/2r$ is an estimate of the slope afforded by a single pair of values, symmetrically placed. The final slope is the weighted average of $n/2$ or $(n-1)/2$ such estimates, the weight being $(2r)^2$.

To find the standard deviations of b_0 and b_1, we first calculate

$$S_1^2 = \sum_r u_r^2 - N_0 b_0^2 - N_1 b_1^2$$

where $\qquad N_0 = n, \quad N_1 = \sum_r (2r)^2 = (1/3)n(n^2 - 1)$

Since the statistical weights of b_0, b_1 are N_0, N_1 respectively, their standard deviations, according to (10.43), are

$$\left.\begin{aligned}
\sigma_0 &= \left\{\frac{S_1^2}{n(n-2)}\right\}^{1/2} \\[2mm]
\sigma_1 &= \left\{\frac{3S_1^2}{(n+1)n(n-1)(n-2)}\right\}^{1/2}
\end{aligned}\right\} \qquad (10.46)$$

and the standard deviation of the fitted value $u_1(r)$ is

$$\sigma_1(r) = \left\{\frac{S_1^2}{n-2}\left(\frac{1}{n} + \frac{4r^2}{N_1}\right)\right\}^{1/2} \qquad (10.47)$$

EXAMPLE 10.3. Fit the following data by a straight line

x	0	0·2	0·4	0·6	0·8	1·0	1·2	1·4
$f(x)$	27	40	49	54	64	77	84	90

Here $n = 8$. We define $r = (x - 0\cdot7)/0\cdot2$, and fit by means of (10.44).

$$b_0 = 485/8 = 60\cdot625$$
$$2b_1 = (10 + 3 \times 28 + 5 \times 44 + 7 \times 63)/84 = 8\cdot988$$

Hence $\qquad S_1^2 = 32827 - 8 \times (60\cdot625)^2 - 168 \times (4\cdot494)^2$
$$= 32827 - 29403\cdot1 - 3393\cdot0 = 30\cdot9$$

and using (10.46) for the standard deviations

$$b_0 = 60\cdot625 \pm 0\cdot803, \quad b_1 = 4\cdot494 \pm 0\cdot177$$

The fitted values of $f(x)$, with standard deviations given by (10.47), are as follows—

x	$f(x)$	x	$f(x)$
0·0	29·2 $\pm$ 1·5	0·8	65·1 $\pm$ 0·8
0·2	38·2 $\pm$ 1·2	1·0	74·1 $\pm$ 1·0
0·4	47·1 $\pm$ 1·0	1·2	83·1 $\pm$ 1·2
0·6	56·1 $\pm$ 0·8	1·4	92·1 $\pm$ 1·5

An independent calculation of S_1^2 using residuals, again gives 30·9.

EXAMPLE 10.4. Fit the data of Example 2.8 by orthogonal polynomials up to the fifth degree, and derive smoothed values—

r	-5	-4	-3	-2	-1	0	1	2	3	4	5
u_r	32	67	75	79	84	102	146	150	166	155	77

The first stage of the calculation is conveniently laid out as follows—

(1) V_5	(2) V_3	(3) V_1	(4) $u_r - u_{-r}$	(5) r	(6) $u_r + u_{-r}$	(7) V_2	(8) V_4
$+3$	$+30$	$+5$	45	5	109	$+15$	$+6$
-6	-6	$+4$	88	4	222	$+6$	-6
-1	-22	$+3$	91	3	241	-1	-6
$+4$	-23	$+2$	71	2	229	-6	-1
$+4$	-14	$+1$	62	1	230	-9	$+4$
				0	102	-10	$+6$

(1) 156	4290	110		N_j	11	858	286
(2) 48	-3681	1054	$\sum_r u_r V_{rj} = N_j b_j$		1133	-1738	-821
(3) 0·3077	$-0·8580$	9·5818	b_j		103	$-2·0256$	$-2·8706$
(4) 14·8	3158·4	10099·2	$N_j b_j^2$		116699	3520·6	2356·8

$$\Sigma u_r^2 = 136165$$

$$S_m^2 = \sum_r u_r^2 - \sum_{j=0}^m N_j b_j^2$$

m	S_m^2
0	19466
1	9367
2	5846
3	2688
4	331
5	316

First the sums and differences of symmetrical pairs are formed in columns (6) and (4), *except* u_0, which is not doubled. The values of the polynomials $V_1, \ldots, V_5$ for $n = 11$ are placed in columns (3), (7), (2), (8), (1), being taken from Appendix 5 (Table 1), and the values of N_j in row (1) at the foot. Row (2) contains the product-sums of column (4) with odd polynomials, and of column (6) with even polynomials. The values of b_j in row (3) are then quotients of row (2) by row (1), and the values of $N_j b_j^2$ are products of rows (2) and (3).

The successive values of S_m^2 given below the table are obtained in an obvious manner from row (4), using the value of Σu_r^2, which must be separately summed. A feature of this example is the very gradual improvement in the fit when quadratic and cubic polynomials are added. The quartic introduces a very marked improvement, to which the quintic makes little change.

r	$b_1 V_1$	$b_2 V_2$	$b_3 V_3$	$b_4 V_4$
5	47·91	$-30·38$	$-25·74$	$-17·22$
4	38·33	$-12·15$	$+5·15$	$+17·22$
3	28·75	$+2·03$	18·88	17·22
2	19·16	12·15	19·73	$+2·87$
1	9·58	18·23	12·01	$-11·49$
0	0·0	20·26	0·0	$-17·22$

r	$u_1(r)$	$u_2(r)$	$u_3(r)$	$u_4(r)$	u_r	$u_r - u_4(r)$
-5	55·1	24·7	50·4	33·2	32	$-$ 1·2
-4	64·7	52·5	47·4	64·6	67	$+$ 2·4
-3	74·2	76·3	57·4	74·6	75	$+$ 0·4
-2	83·8	96·0	76·3	79·1	79	$-$ 0·1
-1	93·4	111·6	99·6	88·2	84	$-$ 4·2
0	103·0	123·3	123·3	106·0	102	$-$ 4·0
1	112·6	130·8	142·8	131·3	146	$+$ 14·7
2	122·2	134·3	154·0	156·9	150	$-$ 6·9
3	131·8	133·8	152·7	169·9	166	$-$ 3·9
4	141·3	129·2	134·3	151·6	155	$+$ 3·4
5	150·9	120·5	94·8	77·6	77	$-$ 0·6

$$S_4{}^2 = 331·8$$

The process of deriving the smoothed values $u_j(r)$ is straightforward. If only the sum to the 4th polynomial is wanted, the summation can usually be carried in one operation for each r. In this instance, however, the values of $b_1V_1, \ldots, b_4V_4$ are tabulated separately, and then the successive smoothed values up to $u_4(r)$. In combining the terms for negative r, the signs of odd terms are of course reversed. The superiority of the quartic representation now becomes very obvious, although a few residuals are still large. An indispensable check on the whole computation is given by the recalculation of $S_4{}^2$ from the residuals; the result is 331·8, in satisfactory agreement with the earlier value.

If the power series form of $u_4(r)$ is required, we must use the expansions, for $n = 11$, given in Appendix 5 (Table 2)—

$$V_1 = r \qquad\qquad V_3 = 0·8333r^3 - 14·83r$$
$$V_2 = r^2 - 10 \qquad V_4 = 0·0833r^4 - 2·083r^2 + 6$$

Hence, using the values of b_j

$$u_4(r) = 106·03 + 22·309r + 3·9548r^2 - 0·7150r^3 - 0·2392r^4$$

EXAMPLE 10.5. Find the standard deviations associated with the coefficients b_j and with the smoothed values of $u_4(r)$ in Example 10.4.

The standard deviation of b_j is

$$\sigma_j = \left\{ \frac{S_4{}^2}{(n-5)N_j} \right\}^{1/2} = \left(\frac{331}{6N_j} \right)^{1/2} = 7·43N_j{}^{-1/2}$$

which leads to the following results—

j	$1/(N_j)^{1/2}$	b_j	σ_j
0	0·3015	103	2·24
1	0·0953	$+$ 9·582	0·708
2	0·0341	$-$ 2·026	0·253
3	0·0153	$-$ 0·858	0·114
4	0·0591	$-$ 2·871	0·439

To obtain standard deviations of $u_4(r)$, we need

$$1/\{p_4(r)\} = \sum_{j=0}^{4} V_{rj}^2/N_j$$

These are quantities independent of the data, which once calculated will serve for any similar problem; they depend only on $|r|$. The standard deviation

$$\sigma_4(r) = 7\cdot43\{p_4(r)\}^{-1/2}$$

r	V_0^2/N_0	V_1^2/N_1	V_2^2/N_2	V_3^2/N_3	V_4^2/N_4	$1/p_4(r)$	$\sigma_4(r)$
0	0·0909	0·0	0·1166	0·0	0·1259	0·577	4·3
1	0·0909	0·0091	0·0944	0·0457	0·0559	0·544	4·0
2	0·0909	0·0364	0·0420	0·1233	0·0035	0·544	4·0
3	0·0909	0·0818	0·0012	0·1128	0·1259	0·642	4·8
4	0·0909	0·1455	0·0420	0·0084	0·1259	0·642	4·8
5	0·0909	0·2273	0·2622	0·2098	0·1259	0·957	7·1

10.8. Aitken's Method, Using Central Factorial Moments

Aitken (4), in particular, has developed an elegant method of fitting and smoothing by polynomials using reduced factorial moments of the data. The method may be used with the orthogonal polynomials expressed either in terms of descending factorials, or of central factorials. The latter is slightly more complicated, but once the method is understood, it is easily carried out and has various advantages. We shall describe only the central factorial method.

It was seen in § 10.5 that

$$T_j(r) = \sum_{\substack{i=0 \\ j+n \text{ odd}}}^{j} g_{ij}r_{\{i\}} \quad \text{or} \quad \sum_{\substack{i=0 \\ j+n \text{ even}}}^{j} h_{ij}r_{[i]}$$

where the coefficients g_{ij} and h_{ij} are always zero if $i + j$ is odd.

If $\quad u_m(r) = a_0 + a_1 T_1(r) + a_2 T_2(r) + \ldots + a_m T_m(r) \quad$ (10.48)

it follows that

$$a_j \sum_r \{T_j(r)\}^2 = \sum_r u_r T_j(r)$$

$$= \sum_{\substack{i \\ j+n \text{ odd}}} g_{ij} M_{\{i\}} \quad \text{or} \quad \sum_{\substack{i \\ j+n \text{ even}}} h_{ij} M_{[i]} \quad (10.49)$$

where $M_{\{i\}}$ and $M_{[i]}$ are reduced central and mean central factorial moments of the data, defined in Chapter 2. The evaluation of a_j

is thus reduced to the calculation of these moments, and subsequent use of a table of the g and h coefficients.

If $u_m(r)$ is required in the form of a power series, we should need expressions for $T_j(r)$ in powers of r; but if only the smoothed values of the data are required we proceed as follows. The central differences of $u_m(0)$ are given by

$$\left.\begin{aligned} \delta^i u_m(0) &= \sum_{j=0}^{m} a_j \delta^i T_j(0) = \sum_j a_j g_{ij} \quad \text{or} \quad \sum_j a_j h_{ij} \\ \text{and} \quad \mu\delta^i u_m(0) &= \sum_{j=0}^{m} a_j \mu\delta^i T_j(0) = \sum_j a_j h_{ij} \quad \text{or} \quad \sum_j a_j g_{ij} \end{aligned}\right\} \quad (10.50)$$

when we apply (10.32) and (10.33). Thus the same g and h coefficients can be used to obtain the central differences of $u_m(0)$, as were used in calculating a_j, the only change being that the sum is carried out with a constant value of i (i.e. along a row), instead of a constant value of j (down a column). With these differences as a basis, the values of $u_m(r)$ are built-up in the usual way, as Examples 10.6 and 10.7 indicate.

The sum of squared residuals is given by

$$S_m^2 = \sum_r u_r^2 - \sum_j a_j^2 M_j \tag{10.51}$$

where $M_j = \sum_r T_{rj}^2$, (not to be confused with the power moment M_j). This can again be checked by direct calculation from residuals. The estimation of standard deviations, both for the coefficients a_j and the smoothed values $u_m(r)$, is identical with the method of § 10.6.

Aitken has tabulated g_{ij}, h_{ij} and M_j for polynomials up to the 5th, and n up to 25. A part of his table ($n \leqslant 12$) is reproduced in Appendix 5 (Table 3). It is clear that the use of the polynomials V_j instead of T_j is precluded in this method by the use of differences.

EXAMPLE 10.6. Fit the data of Example 10.4, using central factorial moments.

The necessary moments have already been calculated (Example 2.8).

$$M_{[0]} = 1133 \qquad M_{[1]} = 1054$$
$$M_{[2]} = 4796 \qquad M_{[3]} = 2215$$
$$M_{[4]} = 5782 \cdot 5$$

We set out the subsequent calculation as follows, using Aitken's table of g_{ij}, h_{ij} for $n = 11$ (Appendix 4, Table 3).

$M_{[i]}$ or $M_{\{i\}}$	a_0 103	a_1 4·7909	a_2 − 0·6752	a_3 − 0·2145	a_4 − 0·08202		
1133	1	.	− 30	.	210	106·03	$u_4(0)$
1054		2	.	− 56	.	21·59	$\mu\delta u_4(0)$
4796			6	.	− 140	7·43	$\delta^2 u_4(0)$
2215				20	.	− 4·29	$\mu\delta^3 u_4(0)$
5782·5					70	− 5·74	$\delta^4 u_4(0)$
M_j	11	440	7722	68640	350350		
$M_j a_j$	1133	2108	− 5214	− 14724	− 28735	$\sum\limits_r u_r{}^2 = 136165$	
$M_j a_j{}^2$	116699	10099	3520	3158	2357		
$S_j{}^2$	19466	9367	5847	2689	332		

The values of $M_j a_j$ are obtained by forming the product-sums of the moment column with each column inside the upper rectangle in turn, in accordance with (10.49). Values of a_j (on top line) follow at once using the known values of M_j, and thence $M_j a_j{}^2$ and $S_j{}^2$. The latter values confirm the conclusions of Example 10.4. The central differences of $u_4(0)$ are now obtained, according to (10.50), as the product-sums of the row of a_j's with each row in the rectangle. The results are shown on the right of the table.

In the building-up process there is a slight advantage in decomposing $u_4(r)$ into even and odd parts

i.e. let
$$V = u_4(r) + u_4(-r)$$
$$W = u_4(r) - u_4(-r)$$

V and W can be built up separately for positive values of r only, the process being obvious from the numerical example—

$|r|$	V	δV	$\delta^2 V$	$\delta^3 V$	$\delta^4 V$	W	δW	$\delta^2 W$	$\delta^3 W$
0	106·03	(− 3·72)	7·43	+ 2·87	− 5·74	0	21·59	0	− 4·29
1	109·75	3·72	4·56	− 2·87	− 5·74	21·59	17·30	− 4·29	− 4·29
2	118·03	8·28	− 4·05	− 8·61	− 5·74	38·89	8·72	− 8·58	− 4·29
3	122·26	4·23	− 18·40	− 14·35	− 5·74	47·61	− 4·15	− 12·87	− 4·29
4	108·09	− 14·17	− 38·49	− 20·09		43·46	− 21·31	− 17·16	
5	55·43	− 52·66				22·15			

Hence, combining V and W, we obtain the smoothed values—

r	− 5	− 4	− 3	− 2	− 1	0	1	2	3	4	5
$u_4(r)$	33·3	64·6	74·6	79·1	88·2	106·0	131·3	156·9	169·9	151·6	77·6

which confirm the results of Example 10.4.

EXAMPLE 10.7. Fit the data of Example 2.10 similarly.

This example illustrates the slight differences in the Aitken method when n is even. From Example 2.10 the required moments are—

$$M_{\{0\}} = 1101 \qquad M_{[1]} = 663\cdot5$$
$$M_{\{2\}} = 3789 \qquad M_{[3]} = 960\cdot5$$
$$M_{\{4\}} = 3555$$

The first stage in the calculation is formally the same as in Example 10.6; the building-up differs a little because the tabular arguments are half-integral.

Mo-ments	a_0 110·1	a_1 4·0212	a_2 $- 0\cdot7765$	a_3 $- 0\cdot36824$	a_4 $- 0\cdot07328$		
1101	1	.	$- 24$	.	126	119 50	$\mu u_4(0)$
663·5		2	.	$- 48$	.	25·72	$\delta u_4(0)$
3789			6	.	$- 105$	3·04	$\mu\delta^2 u_4(0)$
960·5				20	.	$- 7\cdot36$	$\delta^3 u_4(0)$
3555					70	$- 5\cdot13$	$\mu\delta^4 u_4(0)$
M_j	10	330	4752	34320	140140		
$M_j a_j$	1101	1327	$- 3690$	$- 12638$	$- 10269$	$\sum_r u_r{}^2 = 135141$	
$M_j a_j{}^2$	121220	5336	2865	4654	752		
$S_j{}^2$	13921	8585	5720	1066	314		

$\lvert r \rvert$	V	δV	$\delta^2 V$	$\delta^3 V$	$\delta^4 V$	W	δW	$\delta^2 W$	$\delta^3 W$
		0		0			25·72		$- 7\cdot36$
1/2	119·50		3·04		$- 5\cdot13$	12·86		$- 3\cdot68$	
		3·04		$- 5\cdot13$			22·04		$- 7\cdot36$
3/2	122·54		$- 2\cdot09$		$- 5\cdot13$	34·90		$- 11\cdot04$	
		0·95		$- 10\cdot26$			11·00		$- 7\cdot36$
5/2	123·49		$- 12\cdot35$		$- 5\cdot13$	45·90		$- 18\cdot40$	
		$- 11\cdot40$		$- 15\cdot39$			$- 7\cdot40$		$- 7\cdot36$
7/2	112·09		$- 27\cdot74$			38·50		$- 25\cdot76$	
		$- 39\cdot14$					$- 33\cdot16$		
9/2	72·95					5·34			

Smoothed values and residuals—

r	$- 9/2$	$- 7/2$	$- 5/2$	$- 3/2$	$- 1/2$	$1/2$	$3/2$	$5/2$	$7/2$	$9/2$
u_r	67	75	79	84	102	146	150	166	155	77
$u_4(r)$	67·6	73·6	77·6	87·6	106·6	132·4	157·4	169·4	150·6	78·3
$u_r - u_4(r)$	$- 0\cdot6$	$+ 1\cdot4$	$+ 1\cdot4$	$- 3\cdot6$	$- 4\cdot6$	$+ 13\cdot6$	$- 7\cdot4$	$- 3\cdot4$	$+ 4\cdot4$	$- 1\cdot3$

The value of $S_4{}^2$ calculated from residuals is 311, which is acceptable.

10.9. Comparison of Methods

It is worth discussing briefly the relative merits of the two methods just described. This depends very much on the machines available, as the factorial moment method, which involves mainly summation, is greatly assisted by suitable printing-adding machines; the direct Birge-Fisher method, however, involves mainly multiplication for which calculating machines are essential. A detailed analysis has been made by Anderson and Houseman (for Ref., see Appendix 5), who state that if both calculating and printing-adding machines are available, the summation type of method requires on the average 30 per cent more time than the product method. Although the product method is particularly efficient for high-degree polynomials, the time difference of the two methods is largely removed if no comparison is wanted of the fit of polynomials of various degree. An advantage of the summation method is the smaller bulk of the auxiliary tables.

Many other curve-fitting procedures by least squares have been devised, and for a description of these it is best to refer to Birge's article, in which he uses the following classification—

Form of polynomials		Form of data used
(A) Power series	(α) Orthogonal	(1) Power moments
(B) Factorial series	(β) Non-orthogonal	(2) Factorial moments
		(3) Actual observations
		(4) Finite differences

In this scheme the method of § 10.6 is $A3\alpha$; Aitken's is $B2\alpha$, like similar methods of Sasuly and Jordan. Birge also describes a method of type $A4\alpha$. Methods using non-orthogonal polynomials are distinctly inferior, e.g. Davis $(A1\beta)$, Kerawala $(A3\beta)$.

Continuous Approximation by the Method of Least Squares

So far the least squares principle has been applied only to the problem of approximating to a function at a finite number of points. Its possible use, however, is much wider than this. Thus, if $f_m(x)$ has the form (10.1), it is possible to replace the condition (10.4) by the condition that the integral

$$I_m = \int_a^b w(x)\{f(x) - f_m(x)\}^2 dx \qquad (10.52)$$

where $w(x)$ is a weighting function, should be a minimum for variations in the coefficients a_j. This means that the best approximation to $f(x)$, as measured by the integral of the squared error, is obtained over the *continuous* range (a, b); hence the term "continuous approximation."

Again the evaluation of the coefficients in (10.1) is much simplified if the functions $v_j(x)$ satisfy orthogonality conditions of the form

$$\left. \begin{array}{l} \int_a^b w(x)v_i(x)v_j(x) = 0 \quad \text{when } i \neq j \\ \qquad\qquad\qquad = N_j \quad \text{when } i = j \end{array} \right\} \qquad (10.53)$$

It is then easily verified that the condition $\partial I_m / \partial a_j = 0$ leads to the result

$$N_j a_j = \int_a^b w(x)f(x)v_j(x)dx \qquad (10.54)$$

which may be compared with (10.15). Otherwise, for non-orthogonal functions, a set of linear simultaneous equations must be solved.

The general theorem (10.13), established in the case of sums to indicate the validity of the method, holds also when integrals are involved. Thus if $f(x)$ is the observed equivalent of a "true" function $h(x)$, which must be expressible in the form (10.1), then

$$\int_a^b w(x)\{f(x) - h(x)\}^2 dx \geqslant \int_a^b w(x)\{f_m(x) - h(x)\}^2 dx$$

i.e. the least squares approximation $f_m(x)$ is "closer" to $h(x)$ over the range (a, b) than is $f(x)$. The proof is similar.

Whether (10.54) is an effective formula in practice depends a great deal on the nature of $f(x)$. It may be taken as the exception rather than the rule that the integrals involved will be calculable by analytical means. A resort to numerical integration is mostly inevitable, as when $f(x)$ is known only as a tabular function. However, if the information about $f(x)$ is adequate, the integrals can be estimated as a weighted combination of the values of $f(x)$ at a finite number of points in the range (a, b), by some standard quadrature formula. Then, in effect, (10.54) takes the same form as (10.15), though the weights w_k will depend, in part at least, on the quadrature formula.

One further point of a general nature is that the integral to be minimized need not be of the form (10.52). Thus, the integral I_m might be either

$$(a) \int_a^b w(x)\{f(x) - \sum_j a_j v_j\}^2 dx \rightarrow N_j a_j = \int_a^b w(x)f(x)v_j(x)dx$$

or   (b) $\displaystyle\int_a^b \{f(x) - \sqrt{w(x)}\sum_j a_j v_j\}^2 dx \to N_j a_j = \int_a^b \sqrt{w(x)}f(x)v_j(x)dx$

or   (c) $\displaystyle\int_a^b w(x)\{f(x)/w(x) - \sum_j a_j v_j\}^2 dx \to N_j a_j = \int_a^b f(x)v_j(x)dx$

Obviously (a), which is the case considered above, emphasizes the fitting in the region where $w(x)$ is greatest; (c) places greater emphasis on regions where $w(x)$ is small, and is particularly useful when $f(x)$ and $w(x)$ have features in common; (b) is intermediate. It will be possible to enlarge on this when certain standard orthogonal polynomials are discussed in the following section.

10.10. Standard Orthogonal Polynomials

Some of the possibilities latent in the foregoing results, which are rather general, may be brought out by considering some standard orthogonal functions. We choose the Legendre, Hermite and Laguerre polynomials, of which the main properties, concerning range, weighting factor, normalization, etc., are summarized in the table below.* They are well-known for their applications in many physical problems.

Poly-nomials	Range (a, b)	$w(x)$	N_m	Formula
Legendre $P_m(x)$	$(-1, 1)$	1	$2/(2m + 1)$	$\dfrac{1}{2^m m!}\left(\dfrac{d}{dx}\right)^m (x^2 - 1)^m$
Hermite $H_m(x)$	$(-\infty, \infty)$	e^{-x^2}	$\pi^{1/2}2^m m!$	$(-1)^m e^{x^2}\left(\dfrac{d}{dx}\right)^m e^{-x^2}$
Laguerre of order $\alpha(> -1)$ $L_m^{(\alpha)}(x)$	$(0, \infty)$	$e^{-x}x^\alpha$	$\Gamma(\alpha + 1) \cdot (m + \alpha)_{(m)}$ When $\alpha = 0$, $(m!)^2$	$L_m^{(0)} = e^x\left(\dfrac{d}{dx}\right)^m (e^{-x}x^m)$ $L_m^{(\alpha)} = \left(\dfrac{d}{dx}\right)^\alpha L_m^{(0)}$

Typical Legendre Polynomials

$$P_0 = 1 \qquad\qquad P_3 = \tfrac{1}{2}(5x^3 - 3x)$$
$$P_1 = x \qquad\qquad P_4 = \tfrac{1}{8}(35x^4 - 30x^2 + 3)$$
$$P_2 = \tfrac{1}{2}(3x^2 - 1) \qquad\qquad P_5 = \tfrac{1}{8}(63x^5 - 70x^3 + 15x)$$

Recurrence relation: $(m + 1)P_{m+1} = (2m + 1)xP_m - mP_{m-1}$

* For further information about these polynomials, a standard text-book should be consulted, e.g. Margenau and Murphy, *The Mathematics of Physics and Chemistry* (van Nostrand, 1943).

Typical Hermite Polynomials

$$H_0 = 1 \qquad\qquad H_3 = 8x^3 - 12x$$
$$H_1 = 2x \qquad\qquad H_4 = 16x^4 - 48x^2 + 12$$
$$H_2 = 4x^2 - 2 \qquad H_5 = 32x^5 - 160x^3 + 120x$$

Recurrence relation: $H_m{}' = 2mH_{m-1}$, $H_{2k}(0) = (-1)^k(2k)!/k!$

Laguerre Polynomials (of Zero Order)

$$L_0 = 1 \qquad\qquad L_3 = 6 - 18x + 9x^2 - x^3$$
$$L_1 = 1 - x \qquad\quad L_4 = 24 - 96x + 72x^2 - 16x^3 + x^4$$
$$L_2 = 2 - 4x + x^2 \quad L_5 = 120 - 600x + 600x^2 - 200x^3$$
$$+ 25x^4 - x^5$$

Recurrence relation: $L_{m+1} = (1 + 2m - x)L_m - m^2 L_{m-1}$

Legendre polynomials are a simple form of Jacobi polynomials $J_m^{(\alpha,\,\beta)}(x)$, which are characterized by a weight function

$$w(x) = (1 - x)^\alpha (1 + x)^\beta,$$

where
$$\alpha, \beta > -1$$

Though the range $(-1, 1)$ is convenient for these polynomials, it is also possible to use $(0, 1)$ or $(0, n)$.

It is not possible here to deal at length with the use of these orthogonal polynomials, and the following remarks are only meant to be suggestive of possible modes of fitting. For fitting over a finite range, the first choice is Legendre polynomials, for which the cases (a), (b), (c) are equivalent; all that is required is that $f(x)$ should be finite and continuous in the range. When $f(x)$ covers an infinite range $(-\infty, \infty)$, Hermite polynomials are suggested, with the use of (a) when $f(x)$ is not finite for large x, and (b) or (c) when $f(x) \to 0$ as $|x| \to \infty$.

In particular, statistical distributions about a mean value can often be fitted by means of (c), which is sometimes called the Gram-Charlier approximation when Hermite polynomials are used. Finally, when $f(x)$ covers only a semi-infinite range $(0, \infty)$, some class of Laguerre polynomials may be suitable.

The fact that Legendre polynomials are the limiting form of the Tchebycheff polynomials $T_m(r; n)$, when the number of approximating points becomes infinite within a finite range, has already been stressed in § 10.4. In this example the weight function is unity throughout the range, but it suggests that there may be polynomials $v_m(r; n)$ which satisfy orthogonality conditions of the type

$$\sum_{r=0}^{n} w(r)v_j(r; n)v_m(r; n) = 0 \quad \text{when} \quad j \neq m$$

where $w(r)$ is a weight function. Moreover there may be polynomials which in the limit of large n become Hermite or Laguerre polynomials. For Hermite polynomials this is certainly so, and one finds, for example, a set of polynomials

$$h_m(r; n) = \sum_{j=0}^{m} (-2)^j r_{(j)} m_{(j)} / n_{(j)}$$

which satisfy the condition

$$\sum_{r=0}^{n} n_{(r)} n_{(m)} h_j(r; n) h_m(r; n) = 2^m \delta_{jm}$$

[Note that $h_m(r; n) = h_r(m; n)$.] A full description of these and other interesting polynomials,* showing how they reduce to the Hermite variety, is not possible here, but an elementary account is given by Milne, *N.C.*, with applications to the fitting of frequency distributions.

10.11. Trigonometrical Functions: Harmonic Analysis

The use of the trigonometrical functions for interpolation, etc., has, by design, been regarded as outside the scope of this book. However, it seems appropriate here to refer to their rather exceptional orthogonal properties. First, if we consider a full period $(0, 2\pi)$, the functions $\sin mx$, $\cos mx$ satisfy conditions of the form

$$\left.\begin{aligned}
\int_0^{2\pi} \sin jx \sin mx \, dx = \int_0^{2\pi} \cos jx \cos mx \, dx = \pi\delta_{jm} \\
\int_0^{2\pi} \sin jx \cos mx \, dx = 0
\end{aligned}\right\} \tag{10.55}$$

But if the range be divided into n equal parts of length $\alpha(= 2\pi/n)$, it is also true that

$$\left.\begin{aligned}
\alpha \sum_{r=0}^{n-1} \sin rj\alpha \sin rm\alpha = \alpha \sum_{r=0}^{n-1} \cos rj\alpha \cos rm\alpha = \pi\delta_{jm} \\
\sum_{r=0}^{n-1} \sin rj\alpha \cos rm\alpha = 0
\end{aligned}\right\} \tag{10.56}$$

* Reference may be made to the standard treatise by Szegö, *Orthogonal Polynomials*.

In other words, these functions are orthogonal not only for *continuous* approximation over a finite range, but also for approximation at a number of regularly spaced *points*. The first property is used in the development of Fourier series, and the Fourier coefficients are in fact exactly those which Legendre's principle predicts; the second forms the basis of harmonic analysis.

We can easily summarize the formulas both for Fourier and harmonic analysis.

Fourier Analysis in Range $(0, 2\pi)$. Assume

$$f(x) = \tfrac{1}{2}a_0 + \sum_j (a_j \cos jx + b_j \sin jx) \qquad (10.57)$$

Then

$$a_j = (1/\pi) \int_0^{2\pi} f(x) \cos jx \, dx, \quad b_j = (1/\pi) \int_0^{2\pi} f(x) \sin jx \, dx \qquad (10.58)$$

These are valid for all values of j provided the integrals are convergent.

Harmonic Analysis in Range $(0, 2\pi)$. We write $x = r\alpha$, and replace (10.57) by

$$
\left.
\begin{aligned}
u_r &= f(r\alpha) \\
&= \tfrac{1}{2}a_0 + \sum_{j=1}^{(n-1)/2} (a_j \cos rj\alpha + b_j \sin rj\alpha), \quad n \text{ odd} \\
&= \tfrac{1}{2}\{a_0 + (-1)^r a_{n/2}\} \\
&\quad + \sum_{j=1}^{n/2-1} (a_j \cos rj\alpha + b_j \sin rj\alpha), \quad n \text{ even}
\end{aligned}
\right\}
\qquad (10.59)
$$

It may not be necessary to include all the higher harmonics, but of course not more than n coefficients can be determined from n values of $f(x)$. Then

$$a_j = (2/n) \sum_{r=0}^{n-1} u_r \cos rj\alpha, \quad b_j = (2/n) \sum_{r=0}^{n-1} u_r \sin rj\alpha \qquad (10.60)$$

When n is even and equal to $2q$, the summations are conveniently confined to the range $(0, \pi)$. This can be done if we define

$$v_r = (u_r + u_{n-r})/2$$

except

$$v_0 = u_0/2, \quad v_q = u_q/2$$

and

$$w_r = (u_r - u_{n-r})/2$$

Then (10.60) can be replaced by

$$a_j = (2/q) \sum_{r=0}^{q} v_r \cos rj\alpha, \quad b_j = (2/q) \sum_{r=1}^{q-1} w_r \sin rj\alpha \quad (10.61)$$

A similar modification is possible when n is odd.

The matter of tables and schedules for harmonic analysis is dealt with extensively in many books, to which further reference should be made.

The following works deal with the theory and practice of harmonic analysis.

1. *Whittaker and Robinson*; Chap. X.
2. Brunt; *Combination of Observations* (Cambridge, 2nd ed., 1931).
3. K. Stumpff; *Grundlagen und Methoden der Periodenforschung* (Berlin, 1937) and *Tafeln und Aufgaben zur Harmonischen Analyse und Periodogrammrechnung* (Berlin, 1939). (Both lithoprinted by Edwards, Ann Arbor, 1944.)
4. Lowan and Laderman, *J. Math Phys.*, **22** (1943), 136. Contains a table enabling a polynomial representation of a function to be transformed to a Fourier representation.
5. L. W. Pollak; *Geophysical Publications* (Dublin, Stat. Office). Vol. 1 (1947), Harmonic analysis and synthesis schedules for 3 to 100 equidistant values of empiric functions. Vol. 2 (1949), All term guide for harmonic analysis and synthesis.
6. *Index*, Section 24.

An article by C. Lanczos, *J. Math. Phys.*, **17** (1938), 123, dealing with trigonometric interpolation, has particular interest, and also a book by the same author, *Applied Analysis* (Pitman, 1957).

Fitting by Sums of Exponentials

There are many occasions when the fitting of a tabular function $f(x)$ by a linear combination of exponentials is desirable. This may be important when the values of $f(x)$ arise

(a) from a simple decay process, e.g. radioactive decay;

(b) from a decay process with damped oscillations, e.g. electric discharges;

(c) from superposition of periodic processes with unrelated periods, e.g. tidal variations, stellar fluctuations.

If we assume that $f(x)$ can be represented by

$$f_m(x) = a_1 e^{\alpha_1 x} + a_2 e^{\alpha_2 x} + \ldots + a_m e^{\alpha_m x} \quad (10.62)$$

it follows that in (a) the exponents α_j are all real, in (b) they may be complex, and in (c) they are pure imaginary.

We shall describe a method due to Prony, which is applicable when the given values of $f(x)$ correspond to $x = x_0 + kw$, where

$k = 0, 1, 2, \ldots, n$. This is directed first to determining the α's, and then the values of the a's. It is convenient to write

$$c_j = a_j e^{\alpha_j x_0}, \quad v_j = e^{\alpha_j w} \qquad (10.63)$$

so that (10.62) takes the form

$$f_{km} = c_1 v_1{}^k + c_2 v_2{}^k + \ldots + c_m v_m{}^k \qquad (10.64)$$

Consider the first $(m + 1)$ equations of this kind, corresponding to $k = 0, 1, \ldots, m$, and let $v_1 \ldots v_m$ be the roots of the equation

$$v^m + s_1 v^{m-1} + s_2 v^{m-2} + \ldots + s_m = 0 \qquad (10.65)$$

Then if we form the sum

$$f_0 s_m + f_1 s_{m-1} + \ldots + f_m$$

the term in c_j will be

$$s_m + s_{m-1} v_j + \ldots + s_1 v_j{}^{m-1} + v_j{}^m$$

which is identically zero since v_j is a root of (10.65). It follows that the above sum is identically zero; indeed a similar result holds for any $(m + 1)$ *consecutive* values of f_k, so that in general

$$f_k s_m + f_{k+1} s_{m-1} + \ldots + f_{k+m-1} s_1 + f_{k+m} = 0 \qquad (10.66)$$

where $k = 0, 1, \ldots, n - m$. There are $(n - m + 1)$ such equations, which, if $n \geqslant 2m - 1$, can be solved for the m quantities $s_1, \ldots, s_m$, using the method of least squares, if necessary.

A possible difficulty at the outset may be mentioned. This arises if the ultimate zero of the function, say in a decay process, is not exactly known; so that the known values should rather be represented by the function

$$g_m(x) = a_0 + a_1 e^{\alpha_1 x} + \ldots + a_m e^{\alpha_m x} \qquad (10.67)$$

where a_0 is unknown. However, if we define

$$f_{km} = g_{k+1, m} - g_{km}$$

then (10.64) is replaced by

$$f_{km} = c_1 v_1{}^k (v_1 - 1) + c_2 v_2{}^k (v_2 - 1) + \ldots + c_m v_m{}^k (v_m - 1)$$

This, however, leads to the same relations (10.66) between the f's, so that any subsequent working is unchanged. The only disadvantage is loss of accuracy due to taking differences of the g's.

The next stage is the solution of the algebraic equation (10.65), the roots of which lead, by (10.63), to the values of α_j. The nature of these roots will be determined by their physical origin, which may be of type (a), (b) or (c). The final stage, which need not always be carried through to the end, is the evaluation of the amplitudes $a_1, \ldots, a_m$. This is done by means of the $(n + 1)$ equations (10.64), in which the known values of $v_j{}^k$ can now be substituted. If each f_{km} is replaced by the observed value f_k, we have a set of equations for the c's which can be solved, again using the least squares method if necessary. The a's follow from (10.63). The procedure is easily modified to include c_0 when necessary.

We conclude with an example involving damped oscillations.*

EXAMPLE 10.8.   Analyse the following data, using a 3-term exponential function

$$a_1 e^{\alpha_1 x} + a_2 e^{\alpha_2 x} + a_3 e^{\alpha_3 x}$$

x	0	2	4	6	8	10	12	14	16	18	20
$f(x)$	3000	2695	1995	1332	845	531	341	230	163	121	92

We first derive the equation

$$v^3 + s_1 v^2 + s_2 v + s_3 = 0$$

whose roots are $v_1 = e^{2\alpha_1}$, $v_2 = e^{2\alpha_2}$, $v_3 = e^{2\alpha_3}$.

There are 8 linear equations of the form (10.66), from which we obtain normal equations for s_1, s_2, s_3, using the scheme described in § 10.1.

s_3	s_2	s_1	s_0	σ
3000	2695	1995	1332	9022
2695	1995	1332	845	6867
1995	1332	845	531	4703
1332	845	531	341	3049
845	531	341	230	1947
531	341	230	163	1265
341	230	163	121	855
230	163	121	92	606
23182441	17990091	12461495	8130156	61764183
	14209010	9924814	6491491	48615406
		6960626	4559421	33906356
8130156	6491491	4559421	2989065	22170133

* No example of purely periodic processes has been included. For those interested, however, an analysis of the light from a variable star is given by Whittaker and Robinson, Ch. 13, using a systematic method of searching for periods, and the same problem is discussed by Willers, *Practical Analysis* (p. 360, 1947 edition) on the lines of Prony's method.

The normal equations can be solved by any of the methods described in Chapter 11, with the result that

$$s_1 = -1{\cdot}6838, \quad s_2 = 0{\cdot}9911, \quad s_3 = -0{\cdot}2147$$

It should be remarked that considerable cancellation occurs in the course of solving these normal equations, which are "ill-conditioned" in the sense described on p. 362. To obtain the above results correct to 4D, ten significant figures should be introduced at the start; thus it is essential *not* to round the coefficients in the normal equations.

The equation $v^3 - 1{\cdot}6838v^2 + 0{\cdot}9911v - 0{\cdot}2147 = 0$ has a real root, $v_1 = 0{\cdot}72604$, which is easily found by the Newton-Raphson method. On removing the linear factor, the remaining quadratic is found to have complex roots

$$w \exp(\pm 2i\gamma) = 0{\cdot}54377 \exp(\pm i0{\cdot}49348)$$

We now write

$$f_k = av_1{}^k + w^k(b \cos 2\gamma k + c \sin 2\gamma k)$$

where v_1, w and 2γ have the above values, and proceed to find a, b and c by the method of least squares. The table leading to the new set of normal equations appears as follows, the coefficients of a, b and c being multiplied by 10^4—

k	$a \cdot 10^{-4}$	$b \cdot 10^{-4}$	$c \cdot 10^{-4}$	f_k	σ
0	10000	10000	0	3000	23000
1	7260	4789	2576	2695	17320
2	5271	1630	2467	1995	11363
3	3827	+ 146	1601	1332	6906
4	2778	− 343	804	845	4084
5	2017	− 371	297	531	2474
6	1464	− 254	+ 46	341	1597
7	1063	− 134	− 43	230	1116
8	772	− 53	− 55	163	827
9	560	− 11	− 40	121	630
10	406	+ 5	− 22	92	481
	21127 0228	14165 8107	4061 2748	6957 2008	46311 3091
		12595 3454	1620 2784	4573 8897	32955 3242
			1602 8765	1482 3571	8766 7868

These normal equations do not involve much loss of significant figures in solution, and with 6–7 digits throughout the working, one obtains easily

$$a = 2360{\cdot}2, \quad b = 639{\cdot}7, \quad c = 2621{\cdot}3$$

For the final check, we assume

$$f_{km} = 2360v_1{}^k + w^k(640 \cos 2\gamma k + 2621 \sin 2\gamma k)$$

and obtain the values in the following table.

k	0	1	2	3	4	5	6	7	8	9	10
f_k	3000	2695	1995	1332	845	531	341	230	163	121	92
f_{km}	3000	2695	1995	1332	844	530	341	231	164	121	90
$f_k - f_{km}$	0	0	0	0	$+1$	$+1$	0	-1	-1	0	$+2$
$f_k{}^*$	3000	2692	1993	1333	847	531	341	230	163	121	92

It will be seen that only in the last value is there a discrepancy of more than one unit.

A final word of caution is necessary, to the effect that when fitting by exponentials not too much importance should be ascribed to the actual values of the constants obtained. This is shown very clearly by comparing the values of f_{km} and $f_k{}^*$ in the table above, where

$$f_k{}^* = 2000v_1{}^k + w^k(1000 \cos 2\gamma k + 3000 \sin 2\gamma k)$$

and $v_1 = 0 \cdot 7408$, $w = 0 \cdot 5488$, $2\gamma = 0 \cdot 45$. Although the values of f_{km} and $f_k{}^*$ differ at most by 3 units, the values of b, for instance, in the expression for f_{km} is over 30 per cent less than in that for $f_k{}^*$.

ADDITIONAL REFERENCES ON ORTHOGONAL POLYNOMIALS

The properties and uses of Chebyshev polynomials are well described in the introductions to two books of tables.

1. "Tables of Chebyshev polynomials," Ed. C. Lanczos, *Nat. Bur. Stand. Appl. Math. Ser.*, **9** (1952).

2. C. W. Clenshaw, "Chebyshev series for mathematical functions," *Math. Tab. Nat. Phys. Lab.*, **5** (1962).

Orthogonal polynomials can also be used for fitting data which are unequally spaced. The following papers describe suitable numerical methods, the first having special relevance to hand computation.

1. J. G. Hayes and T. Vickers, "The fitting of polynomials to unequally spaced data," *Phil. Mag.*, **42** (1951), 1387.

2. G. E. Forsythe, "Generation and use of orthogonal polynomials for data-fitting with a digital computer," *J. Soc. Ind. Appl. Math.*, **5** (1957), 74.

3. M. Ascher and G. E. Forsythe, "SWAC experiments on the use of orthogonal polynomials for data fitting," *J. Ass. Comp. Mach.*, **5** (1958), 9.

4. C. W. Clenshaw, "Curve-fitting with a digital computer," *Computer J.*, **2** (1960), 170.

EXERCISES 10

1. Verify the expansion of $\Delta^m\{r_{(m)}(r-n)_{(m)}\}$ used in (10.27). Examine also, for integral and half-integral values of q, the expansion of $\delta^m\{(r+q)_{\{m\}}(r-q)_{\{m\}}\}$, arising in (10.30).

2. Expand Stirling's formula (5.9), up to terms in δ^8, as a power series

$$u_r = u_0 + a_1r + a_2r^2 + a_3r^3 + \ldots + a_8r^8,$$

in which the coefficients contain central differences of u_0. Show that this gives a convenient method of fitting an odd number $(n+1)$ of tabular values at equal intervals by a polynomial of degree n in r or x.

Treat Bessel's formula (5.13) in the same way.

3. Show that the least squares fitting of the values u_{-1}, u_0, u_1 by a straight line, $\bar{u}(r) = b_0 + 2b_1r$, leads to the result

$$\bar{u}_0 = (1/3)\,(u_{-1} + u_0 + u_1)$$

Show that a similar fitting of five values, $u_{-2}, \ldots, u_2$, by a quadratic or cubic polynomial gives

$$\bar{u}_0 = (1/35)\{-3u_{-2} + 12u_{-1} + 17u_0 + 12u_1 - 3u_2\} = u_0 - (3/35)\delta^4u_0$$

Compare, wherever possible, the results of Examples 10.3 and 10.4 with the values of $\bar{u}_k$ given by these formulas.

Note. These are simple examples of graduation formulas, based on least squares, used for smoothing data for which 2nd or 4th differences respectively are expected to be small and regular.

4. By using a quadratic polynomial obtain the graduation formula

$$\bar{u}_0 = (1/21)\{-2u_{-3} + 3u_{-2} + 6u_{-1} + 7u_0 + 6u_1 + 3u_2 - 2u_3\}$$
$$= u_0 - (3/7)\delta^4u_0 - (2/21)\delta^6u_0$$

5. Show that when n values of a periodic function are fitted by harmonic analysis, as in (10.59),

$$\sum_0^{n-1} f_r^2 = \tfrac{1}{4}n(a_0^2 + a_m^2) + \tfrac{1}{2}n(a_1^2 + b_1^2 + \ldots + a_{m-1}^2 + b_{m-1}^2)$$
$$\text{when} \quad n = 2m$$
$$= \tfrac{1}{4}na_0^2 + \tfrac{1}{2}n(a_1^2 + b_1^2 + \ldots + a_m^2 + b_m^2)$$
$$\text{when} \quad n = 2m + 1.$$

If harmonics beyond the mth are ignored $(2m < n)$, show that the least square error is given by

$$S_{2m+1}^2 = \sum_0^{n-1} f_r^2 - \tfrac{1}{2}n\{\tfrac{1}{2}a_0^2 + a_1^2 + b_1^2 + \ldots + a_m^2 + b_m^2\}$$

CHAPTER 11

DIRECT SOLUTION OF SIMULTANEOUS LINEAR EQUATIONS

WE return now to a problem which was encountered in the last chapter but not solved, the systematic solution of a set of simultaneous linear algebraic equations. Direct methods of doing this tend to involve one of the following processes—
1. Solution in terms of determinants.
2. Progressive elimination of the unknowns.
3. Transformation or inversion of matrices.

In addition there are various indirect methods involving iteration. Of these (1), though well known, has not much computational interest. Elimination, moreover, usually means a lightly disguised manipulation of matrices, so, although one well established elimination method will be introduced and described as such, most of this chapter is concerned with the application of matrix algebra. Little more is involved, however, than the rules for multiplication of matrices. Indirect methods will be considered in Chapter 13.

Introduction

The given set of equations involving n unknowns will usually be written in the form

$$\left.\begin{aligned}
a_{11}x_1 + a_{12}x_2 + \ldots + a_{1n}x_n &= b_1 \\
a_{21}x_1 + a_{22}x_2 + \ldots + a_{2n}x_n &= b_2 \\
&\;\;\vdots \\
a_{n1}x_1 + a_{n2}x_2 + \ldots + a_{nn}x_n &= b_n
\end{aligned}\right\} \qquad (11.1)$$

Two subsidiary sets of equations are also important. These are

$$\left.\begin{aligned}
l_{11}x_1 &\phantom{+ l_{22}x_2 + \ldots + l_{nn}x_n} = c_1 \\
l_{21}x_1 + l_{22}x_2 &\phantom{+ \ldots + l_{nn}x_n} = c_2 \\
&\;\;\vdots \\
l_{n1}x_1 + l_{n2}x_2 + \ldots + l_{nn}x_n &= c_n
\end{aligned}\right\} \qquad (11.2)$$

and

$$
\left.\begin{aligned}
u_{11}x_1 + u_{12}x_2 + \ldots + u_{1n}x_n &= d_1 \\
u_{22}x_2 + \ldots + u_{2n}x_n &= d_2 \\
\cdot \\
\cdot \\
u_{nn}x_n &= d_n
\end{aligned}\right\} \qquad (11.3)
$$

In matrix notation (11.1) can be written

$$
\begin{bmatrix} a_{11} \cdots a_{1n} \\ \cdot \\ \cdot \\ \cdot \\ a_{n1} \cdots a_{nn} \end{bmatrix} \begin{bmatrix} x_1 \\ \cdot \\ \cdot \\ \cdot \\ x_n \end{bmatrix} = \begin{bmatrix} b_1 \\ \cdot \\ \cdot \\ \cdot \\ b_n \end{bmatrix} \quad \text{or} \quad \mathbf{Ax} = \mathbf{b} \qquad (11.4)
$$

where $\mathbf{A}$ is a square matrix of order n (i.e. with n rows and columns), and $\mathbf{x}$, $\mathbf{b}$ are single column matrices. Similarly (11.2) and (11.3) become

$$
\mathbf{Lx} = \mathbf{c}, \quad \mathbf{Ux} = \mathbf{d}
$$

where $\mathbf{L}$ and $\mathbf{U}$ are called lower and upper triangular matrices respectively.

Before proceeding it may be advisable to state briefly conditions under which equations of form (11.1) possess a solution. We first define the rank $r(\mathbf{A})$ of a matrix $\mathbf{A}$ as the order of the largest submatrix, having r rows and columns selected from those of $\mathbf{A}$, having a non-zero determinant. If $r < n$, then this obviously implies that the determinant $|\mathbf{A}| = 0$, and that the rows and columns of $\mathbf{A}$ are not independent; in fact, writing a_i for the ith row of $\mathbf{A}$, there are normally $n - r(\mathbf{A}) = q(\mathbf{A})$ linear relations of the form

$$
c_{k1}a_1 + c_{k2}a_2 + \ldots + c_{kn}a_n = 0 \quad (k = 1, 2, \ldots, q)
$$

between the rows, and similarly for the columns. The number $q(\mathbf{A})$ is sometimes called the degeneracy of $\mathbf{A}$.

Let us denote by $\mathbf{B}$ the augmented matrix obtained by appending to $\mathbf{A}$, as the $(n + 1)$th column, the column $\mathbf{b}$. Then if

(i) $r(\mathbf{A}) = n$, the solution of (11.1) is unique;
(ii) $r(\mathbf{A}) < r(\mathbf{B}) \leqslant n$, there is no solution;
(iii) $r(\mathbf{A}) = r(\mathbf{B}) = n - q(\mathbf{A})$ there is an infinity of solutions, but the general solution can be expressed as an arbitrary linear combination of q independent solutions.

We shall be concerned here only with case (i), in which the matrix **A** has a non-zero determinant, i.e. is not a singular matrix.

A general point should be made here about numerical processes involving the multiplication of matrices. In the conventional definition the element p_{ij} of a product matrix $\mathbf{P} = \mathbf{AB}$ is given by the product $R_i(\mathbf{A}) \times C_j(\mathbf{B})$, where $R_i(\mathbf{A})$ stands for the ith row of **A** and $C_j(\mathbf{B})$ for the jth column of **B**. In practice it is important that in forming a sum of products such as p_{ij} the numbers involved should be recorded in parallel lines, either horizontal or vertical, any pair of numbers to be multiplied being as nearly as possible adjacent. In forming the product **AB** it is therefore advisable to record either **A** and **B**′, where **B**′ stands for the matrix with rows and columns of **B** transposed, or **A**′ and **B**. The conventional rule is then replaced by one of the following—

(a) **A**, **B**′ recorded　　　$p_{ij} = R_i(\mathbf{A}) \times R_j(\mathbf{B}')$
(b) **A**′, **B** recorded　　　$p_{ij} = C_i(\mathbf{A}') \times C_j(\mathbf{B})$

Whether row × row products or column × column products are used will depend on personal preference, or perhaps on the complete layout of the calculation; likewise the question of whether **P** or **P**′ is recorded. These arguments apply equally when **B**, say, is a single-column matrix.

11.1. Triangular Sets of Equations

The methods to be described for solving the general set of equations (11.1) have one feature in common, that they aim to reduce the problem to the solution of equations with a triangular matrix of coefficients, as (11.2) or (11.3). It is therefore desirable to begin by considering such equations.

The method of solving (11.2) is obvious enough. The first equation gives x_1; the second, using this value of x_1, gives x_2, and so on. The process may be called *forward substitution*. What is important, however, is the layout of the calculation and the method of checking the result. This can be illustrated as follows in the case of 3 equations.

$$
\begin{bmatrix} l_{11} & 0 & 0 \\ l_{21} & l_{22} & 0 \\ l_{31} & l_{32} & l_{33} \end{bmatrix} \quad \begin{matrix} b_1 \\ b_2 \\ b_3 \end{matrix}
$$

$$s_1 \quad s_2 \quad s_3 \qquad d$$

$$x_1 \quad x_2 \quad x_3$$

Here s_1, s_2, s_3 and d are the sums of the quantities in the columns above each. The unknowns are evaluated in the order x_1, x_2, x_3 and placed under s_1, s_2, s_3. Finally the sum $s_1x_1 + s_2x_2 + s_3x_3$ is calculated, and should obviously be equal to d. This is the check.

It will be observed that the single-column matrix **x** is recorded in transposed form, in agreement with the working principle laid down above.

One further point concerns the method of calculating the x's. For instance, x_3 is given by

$$l_{31}x_1 + l_{32}x_2 + l_{33}x_3 = b_3$$

When using an electric calculating machine $b_3 - l_{31}x_1 - l_{32}x_2$ can be accumulated in the product register, and immediately divided by l_{33} to give x_3. No writing of intermediate results is necessary or desirable. It may be convenient, if there are many equations to solve, to write $-x_1$, $-x_3$, etc., as obtained, on the bottom edge of a separate sheet of paper, which can then be placed above each row of l's in turn as the necessary product sums are formed.

The solution of (11.3) is exactly similar, except that it proceeds by *back substitution*, beginning with the final equation. The procedure is illustrated by two simple examples.

EXAMPLE 11.1. Solve
$$4x_1 \quad\quad\quad = 36$$
$$7x_1 + 5x_2 \quad\quad = 23$$
$$9x_1 + 4x_2 + x_3 = 52$$

The calculation, which can be done mentally, appears as follows—

				b
L	4	0	0	36
	7	5	0	23
	9	4	1	52
S	20	9	1	**111**
x'	9	-8	3	

From the solution $x_1 = 9$, $x_2 = -8$, $x_3 = 3$, the value of d (in heavy type) is satisfactorily checked.

EXAMPLE 11.2. Solve
$$2x_1 + 3x_2 + x_3 = 32$$
$$- x_2 + 5x_3 = 14$$
$$4x_3 = 20$$

The solution can be presented in the same layout as Example 11.1, or it may be convenient to transpose rows and columns so that the coefficients of each equation appear in a vertical line. It is then necessary to obtain product sums of columns instead of rows. Sometimes one presentation is convenient, sometimes the other, so both are given here by way of illustration. The order of the calculation, starting with x_3, should be self-evident.

$$(a) \qquad \mathbf{U} \begin{bmatrix} 2 & 3 & 1 \\ 0 & -1 & 5 \\ 0 & 0 & 4 \end{bmatrix} \begin{matrix} \mathbf{b} \\ 32 \\ 14 \\ 20 \end{matrix}$$

$$\begin{matrix} \mathbf{S} & 2 & 2 & 10 & \mathbf{66} \\ \mathbf{x'} & -3 & 11 & 5 \end{matrix}$$

$$\begin{matrix} (b) & \mathbf{b'} & 32 & 14 & 20 & \mathbf{66} \end{matrix}$$

$$\mathbf{U'} \begin{bmatrix} 2 & 0 & 0 \\ 3 & -1 & 0 \\ 1 & 5 & 4 \end{bmatrix} \begin{matrix} 2 & -3 \\ 2 & 11 \\ 10 & 5 \\ \mathbf{s'} & \mathbf{x} \end{matrix}$$

Of course the calculation in Example 11.1 can be similarly transposed.

Symmetrical Equations

It was clear from the previous chapter that in the application of the method of least squares the solution of *normal* equations, in which the coefficients form a symmetrical matrix, is particularly important. We therefore consider such equations as a stage towards the solution of a general set of equations. Two methods will be described.

1. The Gauss-Doolittle method.
2. The Choleski or square-root method.

In principle, however, both of these are only special forms of the method of solving equations with an unsymmetrical matrix, to be described in § 11.9.

11.2. The Gauss-Doolittle Method

This is based on the method of elimination proposed by Gauss, though subsequently modified in various ways.* Though usually explained as a process of elimination of the unknowns, the method has also a simple explanation in terms of matrices, as will be seen later.

---

* See e.g. P. S. Dwyer; *Ann. Math. Stat.*, **12** (1941), 449, "The Doolittle technique." A. N. Black; *Quart. J. Mech. Appl. Math.*, **2** (1949), 321.

The object of the elimination is to produce a set of equations of the form (11.3), with an upper triangular matrix of coefficients u_{ij} and b_i replaced by y_i. In the process use is also made of the coefficients defined by

$$l_{ji} = u_{ij}/u_{ii} \qquad (11.5)$$

These of course form a lower triangular matrix with unit diagonal elements. Since the method mainly involves taking linear combinations of the equations in the original set (11.1) and the final set (11.3), it is useful to denote the ith equation in each of these sets by A_i and U_i respectively.

To demonstrate how the elimination is carried out, let us assume a set of four equations of form (11.1), with the condition that $a_{ij} = a_{ji}$. Then there are four steps, which define the equations U_1, U_2, U_3, U_4.

(1) $U_1 = A_1$. Accordingly $l_{j1} = a_{1j}/a_{11}$ ($j = 2, 3, 4$).

(2) $U_2 = A_2 - l_{21}U_1$. It can easily be seen that, if $a_{21} = a_{12}$, equation U_2 contains no term in x_1.

(3) $U_3 = A_3 - l_{31}U_1 - l_{32}U_2$. This contains no term in either x_1 or x_2.

(4) $U_4 = A_4 - l_{41}U_1 - l_{42}U_2 - l_{43}U_3$. This contains only x_4.

The calculation can be seen in greater detail in the following table. Only the coefficients of each x are given.

	u_{11}	u_{12}	u_{13}	u_{14}	y_1	
U_1						
A_2	a_{21}	a_{22}	a_{23}	a_{24}	b_2	Elimination
$- l_{21}U_1$	$- l_{21}u_{11}$	$- l_{21}u_{12}$	$- l_{21}u_{13}$	$- l_{21}u_{14}$	$- l_{21}y_1$	of x_1
U_2	0	u_{22}	u_{23}	u_{24}	y_2	
A_3	a_{31}	a_{32}	a_{33}	a_{34}	b_3	
$- l_{31}U_1$	$- l_{31}u_{11}$	$- l_{31}u_{12}$	$- l_{31}u_{13}$	$- l_{31}u_{14}$	$- l_{31}y_1$	Elimination
$- l_{32}U_2$	0	$- l_{32}u_{22}$	$- l_{32}u_{23}$	$- l_{32}u_{24}$	$- l_{32}y_2$	of x_2
U_3	0	0	u_{33}	u_{34}	y_3	
A_4	a_{41}	a_{42}	a_{43}	a_{44}	b_4	
$- l_{41}U_1$	$- l_{41}u_{11}$	$- l_{41}u_{12}$	$- l_{41}u_{13}$	$- l_{41}u_{14}$	$- l_{41}y_1$	Elimination
$- l_{42}U_2$	0	$- l_{42}u_{22}$	$- l_{42}u_{23}$	$- l_{42}u_{24}$	$- l_{42}y_2$	of x_3
$- l_{43}U_3$	0	0	$- l_{43}u_{33}$	$- l_{43}u_{34}$	$- l_{43}y_3$	
U_4	0	0	0	u_{44}	y_4	

The unknown x's can now be derived from the equations $U_1, \ldots, U_4$ by back-substitution, as described in § 11.1.

It now remains to convert this process into a satisfactory computation. It is clearly not essential to write down all the separate products formed during the elimination, if machine facilities are at hand to accumulate products; indeed, accumulation on the machine helps to reduce rounding errors. Anyone new to the method may at first prefer to lay out the calculation as in the above table, but experience soon shows that the only quantities which must be written are—

(a) The elements of **A** and **b**.

(b) The elements of **U** and **y**.

(c) The elements of the triangular matrix **L**, preferably transposed about the diagonal (and reversed in sign if an electric calculator is used).

(d) The solution **x**, also transposed to a horizontal line.

(e) Certain sums used in checking, including the sums of the coefficients of each equation A_i and U_i (Σ_i and σ_i respectively), and the sums of the columns of **U** and **y**.

The calculation may now appear like this—

	a_{11}	a_{12}	a_{13}	a_{14}	b_1	Σ_1
A		a_{22}	a_{23}	a_{24}	b_2	Σ_2
			a_{33}	a_{34}	b_3	Σ_3
				a_{44}	b_4	Σ_4
	u_{11}	u_{12}	u_{13}	u_{14}	y_1	σ_1
		u_{22}	u_{23}	u_{24}	y_2	σ_2
U			u_{33}	u_{34}	y_3	σ_3
				u_{44}	y_4	σ_4
s	s_1	s_2	s_3	s_4	d	
x'	x_1	x_2	x_3	x_4		

	$\leftarrow$	$-l_{21}$	$-l_{31}$	$-l_{41}$
$-\mathbf{L'}$		$\leftarrow$	$-l_{32}$	$-l_{42}$
			$\leftarrow$	$-l_{43}$
				$\leftarrow$

The order of the calculation, after the necessary quantities in **A**, **b** and the sums Σ have been written, is as follows—

1. The first row of **U** is copied from the first row of **A**, and leads to the first row of $-\mathbf{L'}$.

2. The second row of **U** is derived by the rule already laid down, σ_2 being given similarly by $\Sigma_2 - l_{21}\sigma_1$. It is immediately verified

that σ_2 equals the sum of other quantities in the same row. It should be noticed too that if u_{23} is formed in the product register of the machine, it can be divided at once by u_{22} to give l_{32}, and so on.

3. Successive rows of $\mathbf{U}$ and $-\mathbf{L}'$ are formed in a similar way, each row of $\mathbf{U}$ being checked by the appropriate σ.

4. The x's are derived by back-substitution of the equations $\mathbf{Ux} = \mathbf{y}$ (cp. the scheme in Example 11.2 (a)).

5. The final check is applied using the identity

$$s_1 x_1 + s_2 x_2 + s_3 x_3 + s_4 x_4 = d$$

Three further points should be noticed.

(a) The matrix $-\mathbf{L}'$ can be written on a separate sheet which can be folded between the columns as indicated by the dotted lines. This enables numbers which have to be multiplied to be placed side by side; thus in deriving u_{33}, u_{34}, y_3 and σ_3, the fold is made so that $-l_{31}$, $-l_{32}$ appear on the left edge of the sheet, which is then placed in turn against the columns headed by u_{13}, u_{14}, y_1 and σ_1. The arrow in the diagonal space always indicates where the result of each product sum should be set. The advantage of writing $-l_{ji}$ is that it reduces the mental effort required to keep track of signs.

(b) Since the elimination process is well checked by the σ's, it is usually sufficient to check the back-substitution in the manner shown above. This final check can, if preferred, be transferred to the original equations by forming sums of the columns of $\mathbf{A}$ and $\mathbf{b}$, instead of $\mathbf{U}$ and $\mathbf{y}$. Moreover, a separate substitution into each original equation is very desirable, to obtain the residual errors of the solution.

(c) It is a matter of choice whether $\mathbf{U}$, $\mathbf{L}'$ and $\mathbf{x}'$ are written, as in the above scheme, or $\mathbf{U}'$, $\mathbf{L}$ and $\mathbf{x}$, in which case the product sums of rows are formed, instead of columns. It is also possible to solve the equations represented by $\mathbf{L}'\mathbf{x} = \mathbf{z}$, where $z_i = y_i/u_{ii}$, instead of $\mathbf{Ux} = \mathbf{y}$. The reader should have no difficulty in making the necessary changes.

EXAMPLE 11.3. Solve the equations
$$
\begin{aligned}
62x_1 - 20x_2 + 20x_3 + \quad 5x_4 &= \quad 23{\cdot}0 \\
-20x_1 + 59x_2 + 22x_3 + \quad 3x_4 &= -36{\cdot}8 \\
20x_1 + 22x_2 + 63x_3 - \quad 15x_4 &= -22{\cdot}3 \\
5x_1 + \quad 3x_2 - 15x_3 + 206x_4 &= -14{\cdot}0
\end{aligned}
$$

We divide all coefficients by 100, and retain 4 decimals in the computation

					b	Σ		
	0·6200	− 0·2000	0·2000	0·0500	0·2300	0·9000		
A		0·5900	0·2200	0·0300	− 0·3680	0·2720		
			0·6300	− 0·1500	− 0·2230	0·6770		
				2·0600	− 0·1400	1·8500		

					y	σ		
	0·6200	− 0·2000	0·2000	0·0500	0·2300	0·9000	√	
U		0·5255	0·2845	0·0461	− 0·2938	0·5623	√	
			0·4115	− 0·1911	− 0·1381	0·0822		0·0823
				1·9632	− 0·1969	1·7663	√	

s	0·6200	0·3255	0·8960	1·8682	− **0·3988** √
x′	0·3916	− 0·3434	− 0·3822	− 0·1003	

	− 1	0·3226	− 0·3226	− 0·0806
− L′		− 1	− 0·5414	− 0·0877
			− 1	0·4644
				− 1

Thus $x_1 = 0·392$, $x_2 = − 0·343$, $x_3 = − 0·382$, $x_4 = − 0·100$

Substituting these values in the left side of the first equation and subtracting 23·0 gives the residual error

$$r_1 = 0·024$$

Similarly, from the other equations

$$r_2 = 0·019, \quad r_3 = 0·028, \quad r_4 = 0·061$$

11.3. Matrix Interpretation

Although the Doolittle method has been described in terms of elimination, which may appeal more strongly to anyone not familiar with matrices, it is not at all heavily disguised that in fact the equations used in forming the coefficients u_{ij} and l_{ij} are precisely those which must be satisfied if the matrix product $\mathbf{LU} = \mathbf{A}$. Thus the typical relation is

$$a_{ij} = l_{i1}u_{1j} + l_{i2}u_{2j} + \ldots + l_{i,\,j-1}u_{j-1,\,j}$$
$$+ u_{ij} = R_i(\mathbf{L}) \times C_j(\mathbf{U})$$

and remembering that $l_{ii} = 1$, and $l_{ij} = 0$ when $j > i$, this is just the rule for multiplying an upper by a lower triangular matrix. In other words the elimination process has effectively resolved the matrix $\mathbf{A}$ into the product of two triangular matrices, $\mathbf{L}$ and $\mathbf{U}$, and the solution of the equations represented by

$$\mathbf{LUx} = \mathbf{b}$$

is then achieved by one process of forward substitution, i.e. the solution of

$$\mathbf{Ly} = \mathbf{b} \qquad (11.6)$$

and one of back substitution, i.e. the solution of

$$\mathbf{Ux} = \mathbf{y} \qquad (11.7)$$

Actually in the Doolittle process the solution of (11.6) is carried out in a slightly disguised way during the resolution of $\mathbf{A}$ into $\mathbf{LU}$.

This resolution of $\mathbf{A}$ indeed provides the clue to the method to adopt in the case of unsymmetrical equations, but this will be discussed later. Meanwhile the special property of symmetrical equations must be noted, i.e. $\mathbf{U}$ differs from the transposed matrix $\mathbf{L}'$ only in containing a diagonal matrix as an extra factor. Thus if

$$\mathbf{D} = \begin{bmatrix} u_{11} & 0 & \ldots & 0 \\ 0 & u_{22} & \ldots & 0 \\ \cdot & & & \\ \cdot & & & \\ \cdot & & & \\ 0 & 0 & \ldots & u_{nn} \end{bmatrix}$$

then $\mathbf{U} = \mathbf{DL}'$

Conversely, if $\mathbf{A}$ can be resolved into the form $\mathbf{LDL}'$, it follows that $\mathbf{A}' = \mathbf{A}$, since the transpose of $\mathbf{U}$ is $\mathbf{LD}$ and that of $\mathbf{LU}$ is $\mathbf{U}'\mathbf{L}'$; thus $\mathbf{A}$ is symmetrical.

This result suggests at once another method of solving the equations $\mathbf{Ax} = \mathbf{b}$. If we define

$$\mathbf{L}_1 = \mathbf{LD}^{1/2} \quad \text{and} \quad \mathbf{U}_1 = \mathbf{D}^{1/2}\mathbf{L}' \qquad (11.8)$$

then $\mathbf{U}_1 = \mathbf{L}_1'$

and $\mathbf{A} = \mathbf{L}_1\mathbf{L}_1'$

The elements of $\mathbf{D}^{1/2}$ are just the square-roots of the elements of $\mathbf{D}$. If this resolution can be performed from the beginning it should clearly be sufficient to write down the matrix $\mathbf{L}_1$, instead of both $\mathbf{L}$ and $\mathbf{U}$, and to complete the solution by the back substitution of $\mathbf{L}_1'\mathbf{x} = \mathbf{y}$ where $\mathbf{L}_1\mathbf{y} = \mathbf{b}$. This is in fact the basis of the method now to be described, which is variously known as the square-root method or the Choleski method.*

* The origin of the square-root method is rather uncertain; it was described by Banachiewicz in 1938, but it is commonly ascribed to Choleski at an earlier date. References to articles describing it in detail, and also the Doolittle method, are given by P. S. Dwyer, *Linear Computations*, p. 117.

11.4. The Square-root Method

The task of deriving the elements of a matrix $\mathbf{L}_1$, such that $\mathbf{L}_1\mathbf{L}_1' = \mathbf{A}$, and of the single-column matrix defined by $\mathbf{L}_1\mathbf{y} = \mathbf{b}$ presents no difficulty. First $\mathbf{A}$, $\mathbf{b}$ and the row sums ($\boldsymbol{\Sigma}$) are written as in the Doolittle method. The complete calculation, for four unknowns, can be displayed as follows—

a_{11}	a_{12}	a_{13}	a_{14}	b_1	Σ_1
$\mathbf{A}$	a_{22}	a_{23}	a_{24}	b_2	Σ_2
		a_{33}	a_{34}	b_3	Σ_3
			a_{44}	b_4	Σ_4
l_{11}	l_{21}	l_{31}	l_{41}	y_1	σ_1
$\mathbf{L}_1'$	l_{22}	l_{32}	l_{42}	y_2	σ_2
		l_{33}	l_{43}	y_3	σ_3
			l_{44}	y_4	σ_4
$\mathbf{x}'$ s_1	s_2	s_3	s_4	d	
x_1	x_2	x_3	x_4		

Here s_j are the column sums of $\mathbf{L}_1'$, and σ_1 are the row sums, including the y's; d is the column sum of $\mathbf{y}$.

From the matrix multiplication rule it follows that

$$a_{ij} = C_i(\mathbf{L}_1') \times C_j(\mathbf{L}_1')$$
$$b_i = C_i(\mathbf{L}_1') \times C(\mathbf{y})$$

Also $$\Sigma_i = C_i(\mathbf{L}_1') \times C(\boldsymbol{\sigma})$$

The order of the calculation using these relations is as follows—

1. The elements of the first row of $\mathbf{L}_1'$ are derived from the relations

$$l_{11}{}^2 = a_{11}, \quad l_{11}l_{i1} = a_{i1} \quad (i = 2, 3, 4)$$

With a hand calculator it is possible to set l_{11} and successively find the multipliers which give a_{21}, a_{31}, etc., and similarly y_1 and σ_1 are given by $l_{11}y_1 = b_1$, $l_{11}\sigma_1 = \Sigma_1$. It can be checked immediately that σ_1 equals the sum of the first row.

2. The elements of $R_2(\mathbf{L}_1')$ are derived, using the relations

$$l_{22}{}^2 = a_{22} - l_{21}{}^2, \quad l_{22}l_{i2} = a_{i2} - l_{21}l_{i1} \quad (i = 3, 4)$$

Similarly y_2 and σ_2 are evaluated, and σ_2 is checked. For elements of $R_3(\mathbf{L}_1')$,

$$l_{33}l_{i3} = a_{i3} - l_{31}l_{i1} - l_{32}l_{i2}$$

and so on; each row is checked before proceeding to the next.

3. The elements of **x** are obtained by back-substitution of the equations $\mathbf{L_1'x} = \mathbf{y}$, the process being similar to that in Example 11.2 (*a*). The final check is that

$$s_1 x_1 + s_2 x_2 + s_3 x_3 + s_4 x_4 = d$$

Example 11.4 gives a numerical example following this scheme. One disadvantage of the method is the need for square-rooting; on the other hand it is generally claimed to be very accurate,* and it is of course extremely compact. It matters little whether positive or negative roots are taken; sometimes $\mathbf{L_1'}$ may contain pure imaginary elements (when **A** has negative diagonal elements), but this does not impede the solution in any way.

EXAMPLE 11.4. Solve the equations of Example 11.3 by the square-root method.

The following table should not need further explanation; quantities used for checking are as usual given in heavy type, and there is only one minor discrepancy (in s_4).

					b	**Σ**
A	0·6200	− 0·2000	0·2000	0·0500	0·2300	0·9000
		0·5900	0·2200	0·0300	− 0·3680	0·2720
			0·6300	− 0·1500	− 0·2230	0·6770
				2·0600	− 0·1400	1·8500
					y	**σ**
$\mathbf{U_1 = L_1'}$	0·7874	− 0·2540	0·2540	0·0635	0·2921	1·1430
		0·7249	0·3925	0·0636	− 0·4053	0·7757
			0·6414	− 0·2979	− 0·2153	0·1282
				1·4011	− 0·1405	1·2606
s	0·7874	0·4709	1·2879	1·2303	− **0·4690** (= *d*)	
				(1·2302)		
x'	0·3916	− 0·3433	− 0·3823	− 0·1003		

The solution is in satisfactory agreement with that of Example 11.3.

11.5. Inversion of a Symmetrical Matrix

In solving equations of the form (11.1) it has so far been assumed that the quantities b_i are specific numbers. It may be, however, that the solution is required in an algebraic form in which the elements of **b** remain unspecified. Thus if several sets of equations are to be solved with the same matrix **A**, but different **b**, it may be more economical to derive the inverse of **A**, i.e. the matrix $\mathbf{A^{-1}}$ such that

$$\mathbf{A^{-1}A = AA^{-1} = I} \qquad (11.9)$$

---

* However, according to Black (*loc. cit.*), the Doolittle method involves fewer numerical operations than the square-root method, particularly for large numbers of equations, and is little inferior in accuracy.

where the matrix $\mathbf{I}$ is a diagonal matrix of the same order as $\mathbf{A}$, with unit elements on the diagonal. The solution of (11.5) thus takes the form

$$\mathbf{x} = \mathbf{A}^{-1}\mathbf{b} \tag{11.10}$$

which can be evaluated with each $\mathbf{b}$ in turn.

The Doolittle method can easily be modified to provide $\mathbf{A}^{-1}$, the procedure being describable most briefly in terms of matrices. Thus, assuming that $\mathbf{A}$ be resolved into the product $\mathbf{LU}$, it follows by premultiplying $\mathbf{AA}^{-1}$ by $\mathbf{L}^{-1}$, that

$$\mathbf{UA}^{-1} = \mathbf{L}^{-1} \tag{11.11}$$

Similarly, postmultiplying $\mathbf{A}^{-1}\mathbf{A}$ by $\mathbf{U}^{-1}$,

$$\mathbf{A}^{-1}\mathbf{L} = \mathbf{U}^{-1} \tag{11.12}$$

Either (11.11) or (11.12) can be used to determine the elements of $\mathbf{A}^{-1}$, the number of independent elements being $\frac{1}{2}n(n+1)$ when $\mathbf{A}$ (and therefore $\mathbf{A}^{-1}$) is symmetrical. At first sight it might seem that all the elements of $\mathbf{L}^{-1}$ or $\mathbf{U}^{-1}$ are required for this purpose. In fact this is not so, because the reciprocal of $\mathbf{L}$, for instance, has the form

$$\mathbf{L}^{-1} = \begin{bmatrix} 1 & 0 & .\ .\ . & 0 \\ k_{21} & 1 & .\ .\ . & 0 \\ . & & & \\ . & & & \\ . & & & \\ k_{n1} & k_{n2} & .\ .\ . & 1 \end{bmatrix}$$

The diagonal and zero elements of $\mathbf{L}^{-1}$ are $\frac{1}{2}n(n+1)$ in number and therefore provide just enough equations to determine all the elements of $\mathbf{A}^{-1}$. From the multiplication rule for $\mathbf{UA}^{-1}$ it follows that

$$R_i(\mathbf{U}) \times R_i(\mathbf{A}^{-1})' = 1$$
$$R_i(\mathbf{U}) \times R_j(\mathbf{A}^{-1})' = 0 \quad \text{when} \quad j > i \tag{11.13}$$

A further relation which is useful for checking is that, if $\mathbf{s}$ denotes the row obtained by summing the columns (or rows) of $\mathbf{A}$, then

$$R(\mathbf{s}) \times \text{any row of } (\mathbf{A}^{-1})' = 1 \tag{11.14}$$

Let us therefore summarize the calculation for a matrix $\mathbf{A}$ of order 4, using (11.11). First, the derivation and checking of $\mathbf{U}$ proceeds exactly as in Example 11.3, except that the columns $\mathbf{b}$

and $\mathbf{y}$, and the row $\mathbf{s}$, can be omitted. The elements of $\mathbf{A}^{-1}$, denoted by a_{ij}^{-1}, are then derived in the following order—

1. The final row of $(\mathbf{A}^{-1})'$ is derived from products of this row with rows of $\mathbf{U}$ in reverse order, using the equations

$$u_{44}a_{44}^{-1} = 1$$
$$u_{33}a_{34}^{-1} + u_{34}a_{44}^{-1} = 0$$
$$u_{22}a_{24}^{-1} + u_{23}a_{34}^{-1} + u_{24}a_{44}^{-1} = 0$$
$$u_{11}a_{14}^{-1} + u_{12}a_{24}^{-1} + u_{13}a_{34}^{-1} + u_{14}a_{44}^{-1} = 0$$

This row is checked immediately by using (11.14).

2. The third row of $(\mathbf{A}^{-1})'$, or rather the elements a_{33}^{-1}, a_{23}^{-1}, a_{13}^{-1}, since a_{43}^{-1} is known by symmetry, is obtained from the equations

$$u_{33}a_{33}^{-1} + u_{34}a_{43}^{-1} = 1$$
$$u_{22}a_{23}^{-1} + u_{23}a_{33}^{-1} + u_{24}a_{43}^{-1} = 0$$
$$u_{11}a_{13}^{-1} + u_{12}a_{23}^{-1} + u_{13}a_{33}^{-1} + u_{14}a_{43}^{-1} = 0$$

3. Similarly the products of $R_2(\mathbf{A}^{-1})'$ with $R_2(\mathbf{U})$ and $R_1(\mathbf{U})$ give a_{22}^{-1} and a_{12}^{-1}, and that of $R_1(\mathbf{A}^{-1})'$ and $R_1(\mathbf{U})$ gives a_{11}^{-1}. Each row of $\mathbf{A}^{-1}$ is checked as soon as completed.

Example 11.5 illustrates the complete process.

EXAMPLE 11.5. Invert the matrix used in Example 11.3.

					Σ	
A	0·6200	− 0·2000	0·2000	0·0500	0·6700	
		0·5900	0·2200	0·0300	0·6400	
			0·6300	− 0·1500	0·9000	
				2·0600	1·9900	
					σ	
U	0·6200	− 0·2000	0·2000	0·0500	0·6700	√
		0·5255	0·2845	0·0461	0·8561	√
			0·4115	− 0·1911	0·2203	(0·2204)
				1·9632	1·9632	√
− L′	− 1	0·3226	− 0·3226	− 0·0806	May be on a separate	
		− 1	− 0·5414	− 0·0877	sheet as suggested	
			− 1	0·4644	previously.	
				− 1		
					Check	
A⁻¹	2·4705	1·3267	− 1·2887	− 0·1731	1·0000	
	1·3267	2·6738	− 1·3959	− 0·1728	0·9997	
	− 1·2887	− 1·3959	2·5400	0·2366	0·9998	
	− 0·1731	− 0·1728	0·2366	0·5094	1·0001	

Calculation of the product $\mathbf{A}^{-1}\mathbf{b}$, with $\mathbf{b}$ as in Example 11.3, gives $x_1 = 0·3916$, $x_2 = − 0·3433$, $x_3 = − 0·3823$, $x_4 = − 0·1003$ in agreement with previous results.

The procedure using (11.12) is very similar, the principal difference being that the diagonal elements of U^{-1} are not unity. This also occurs in the following section.

11.6. Inversion by the Square-root Method

When a symmetrical matrix A is resolved as in (11.8), its inverse can be derived from the equation

$$L_1'A^{-1} = L_1^{-1} \qquad (11.15)$$

using the diagonal and zero elements of L_1^{-1} to determine those of A^{-1}. The diagonal elements of L_1^{-1} are simply the reciprocals of the diagonal elements of L_1; hence the required relations are

$$\left.\begin{array}{l} R_i(L_1') \times R_i(A^{-1})' = 1/l_{ii} \\ R_i(L_1') \times R_j(A^{-1})' = 0, \; j > i \end{array}\right\} \qquad (11.16)$$

with the same check formula (11.14) as before.

It is hardly necessary to examine the procedure again in detail, and the layout of the calculation is shown in the following example.

EXAMPLE 11.6. Invert the matrix of Example 11.5 by the square-root method.

					Σ	
A	0·6200	− 0·2000	0·2000	0·0500	0·6700	
		0·5900	0·2200	0·0300	0·6400	
			0·6300	− 0·1500	0·9000	
				2·0600	1·9900	
					σ	
L_1'	0·7874	− 0·2540	0·2540	0·0635	0·8509	√
		0·7249	0·3925	0·0636	1·1810	√
			0·6414	− 0·2979	0·3435	√
				1·4011	1·4012	(1·4011)
$1/l_{ii}$	1·2700	1·3795	1·5591	0·7137	Check	
A^{-1}	2·4708	1·3271	− 1·2891	− 0·1732	0·9999	
	1·3271	2·6743	− 1·3964	− 0·1729	0·9999	
	− 1·2891	− 1·3964	2·5407	0·2366	1·0003	
	− 0·1732	− 0·1729	0·2366	0·5094	1·0006	

Since the elements of A^{-1} are considerably larger than those of A, the differences between the results of Examples 11.5 and 11.6 are not unreasonable. It may be considered an advantage to place the column Σ by the side of A^{-1}, for ease of checking.

11.7. Comparison of Methods of Inversion

Two methods of completing the inversion of a symmetrical matrix A following the resolution into LU or L_1L_1' have been described. Other methods require the inversion of one or both of the triangular matrices **L** and **U** (a process to be described in § 11.8), or of **L**$_1$, and involve rather more machine settings and readings. This is clearly undesirable as it is a point at which human errors are apt to occur. However, since a quantitative comparison of effort is of interest, an analysis has been made of the number of basic numerical operations, using a hand calculator, arising in the following three processes for obtaining **A**$^{-1}$—

    (i) from **UA**$^{-1}$ = **L**$^{-1}$, using zero elements of **L**$^{-1}$ as in § 11.5;
    (ii) from **LA**$^{-1}$ = **L**$_1$$^{-1}$, as in § 11.6;
    (iii) from **A**$^{-1}$ = **U**$^{-1}$**L**$^{-1}$, having first derived both **L**$^{-1}$ and **U**$^{-1}$.

The table below shows the number of machine settings, and operations of addition, multiplication, division and square-rooting required for a matrix of order n; except in the last two columns multiples of n have been omitted. All essential checks are included.

Method	Settings	+ or −	×	÷	√
(i)	$(n^3 + 9n^2)/2$	$2n^2$	$(n^3 + 3n^2)/2$	$n^2 - n$	—
(ii)	$(n^3 + 7n^2)/2$	$2n^2$	$(n^3 + 3n^2)/2$	n^2	n
(iii)	$(n^3 + 13n^2)/2$	$9n^2/2$	$(n^3 + 3n^2)/2$	$(n^2 - n)/2$	—

The table shows that differences between the methods are only secondary, particularly when the various operations are suitably weighted. For moderate values of n the square-root method (ii) actually involves slightly more effort than (i), with a little compensation in the way of less recording and possibly greater accuracy. The fact that (i) avoids square-rooting is in its favour, however, as such operations tend to slow down any hand computing process. For large values of n, comparisons like these are apt to be vitiated in practice because many of the non-diagonal elements of **A** are zero.

Unsymmetrical Equations

The principle underlying the solution of unsymmetrical equations has already been indicated in § 11.3. The matrix **A** is first resolved into a product **LU**, one of the triangular matrices having unit diagonal elements; the subsequent procedure depends on whether a single set of equations needs solution, or whether it is desirable to find the inverse of **A**.

    1. *Inversion of* **A**. As for symmetrical matrices, several methods are feasible, but because n^2 equations are now required to

determine all the elements of A^{-1} it is desirable to invert at least one of the matrices L and U. We can obtain A^{-1} by means of—

(i) $UA^{-1} = L^{-1}$, having first inverted L completely, or $A^{-1}L = U^{-1}$, having inverted U;

(ii) $A^{-1} = U^{-1}L^{-1}$, having inverted both L and U;

(iii) $UA^{-1} = L^{-1}$ combined with $A^{-1}L = U^{-1}$, without inverting either L or U.

The alternatives in (i) differ only trivially. For most purposes this is probably the most convenient method, and it is described in § 11.9; (ii) is somewhat longer, and (iii) is rather complicated for desk computing, though it might be suitable for automatic computers. There is no advantage in adapting the square-root method to unsymmetrical matrices.

2. *Solution of* $Ax = b$. This requires the solution of the triangular equations $Ly = b$ and $Ux = y$. The procedure is described in § 11.10.

11.8. Inversion of Triangular Matrices

As the following section uses the inverse of a triangular matrix, this aspect of the computation will be briefly considered first. For a typical case, let us take the inversion of a matrix L, assuming that L' and L^{-1} are to be recorded. It is possible to arrange either for row × row or column × column multiplication by choosing the appropriate equation as follows—

$$L^{-1}L = I, \quad R_i(L^{-1}) \times R_j(L') = \delta_{ij} \tag{11.17}$$

$$LL^{-1} = I, \quad C_i(L') \times C_j(L^{-1}) = \delta_{ij} \tag{11.18}$$

where $\delta_{ij} = 1$ if $i = j$; $= 0$ if $i \neq j$. With the first of these alternatives the scheme appears as follows when $n = 4$.

$$L' \quad \begin{bmatrix} l_{11} & l_{21} & l_{31} & l_{41} \\ & l_{22} & l_{32} & l_{42} \\ & & l_{33} & l_{43} \\ & & & l_{44} \end{bmatrix}$$

$$L^{-1} \quad \begin{bmatrix} k_{11} & & & \\ k_{21} & k_{22} & & \\ k_{31} & k_{32} & k_{33} & \\ k_{41} & k_{42} & k_{43} & k_{44} \end{bmatrix}$$

$$s \quad\quad s_1 \quad\quad s_2 \quad\quad s_3 \quad\quad s_4$$

The final row contains the column sums of $\mathbf{L}^{-1}$, which are used for checking through the relation

$$R(\mathbf{s}) \times \text{any row of } \mathbf{L}' = 1 \qquad (11.19)$$

The elements of $\mathbf{L}^{-1}$ can now be derived in the following order—
1. From (11.17), with $i = j$, it is obvious that $k_{ii} = 1/l_{ii}$. This gives the diagonal elements; reciprocal tables or build-up division on a calculator may be used.
2. Using $R_3(\mathbf{L}')$, k_{43} is given by the equation

$$k_{43}l_{33} + k_{44}l_{43} = 0$$

Division by l_{33} can be avoided if preferred by using k_{33} as a multiplier. A check is obtained by forming s_3 and $R(\mathbf{s}) \times R_3(\mathbf{L}')$.
3. Using $R_2(\mathbf{L}')$, k_{32}, k_{42} are given by

$$k_{32}l_{22} + k_{33}l_{32} \qquad\qquad = 0$$
$$k_{42}l_{22} + k_{43}l_{32} + k_{44}l_{42} = 0$$

The sum $\mathbf{s}_2$ can be formed and checked by means of

$$R(\mathbf{s}) \times R_2(\mathbf{L}')$$

before the remaining column of $\mathbf{L}^{-1}$ is derived and checked with the help of $R_1(\mathbf{L}')$.

The application of (11.18) is exactly similar, except that for convenience the matrices $\mathbf{L}'$ and $\mathbf{L}^{-1}$ should be placed side by side, and the row sums of $\mathbf{L}^{-1}$ used for checking.

11.9. Resolution and Inversion of A

The process of inverting an unsymmetrical matrix by method (i) consists of, first the resolution of $\mathbf{A}$, secondly the inversion of $\mathbf{L}^{-1}$, and finally the evaluation of $\mathbf{A}^{-1}$ using the equation $\mathbf{UA}^{-1} = \mathbf{L}$. We consider these stages in turn.

Resolution of $\mathbf{A}$. Let the scheme be one in which $\mathbf{A}$, $\mathbf{U}$ and $\mathbf{L}'$ are recorded, as in § 11.2, and column $\times$ column products are used; also let diagonal elements of $\mathbf{L}$ be unity.

The working equations are

$$C_i(\mathbf{L}') \times C_j(\mathbf{U}) = a_{ij} \qquad (11.20)$$

and $\qquad\qquad C_i(\mathbf{L}') \times C(\boldsymbol{\sigma}) = \Sigma_i \qquad (11.21)$

where $C(\boldsymbol{\sigma})$ represents the column of row sums of $\mathbf{U}$, and Σ_i is the sum of the ith row of $\mathbf{A}$.

$$\mathbf{L'} \qquad\qquad\qquad \mathbf{U}$$

$$\begin{bmatrix} 1 & l_{21} & l_{31} & l_{41} \\ & 1 & l_{32} & l_{42} \\ & & 1 & l_{43} \\ & & & 1 \end{bmatrix} \quad \begin{bmatrix} u_{11} & u_{12} & u_{13} & u_{14} \\ & u_{22} & u_{23} & u_{24} \\ & & u_{33} & u_{34} \\ & & & u_{44} \end{bmatrix} \begin{matrix} \sigma_1 \\ \sigma_2 \\ \sigma_3 \\ \sigma_4 \end{matrix}$$

The elements of $\mathbf{L'}$ and $\mathbf{U}$ are derived in the following order—

(1) $R_1(\mathbf{U}) = R_1(\mathbf{A})$

(2) l_{21}, using $l_{21}u_{11} = a_{21}$

(3) $R_2(\mathbf{U})$ using $C_2(\mathbf{L'})$

(4) $C_3(\mathbf{L'})$, using $C_1(\mathbf{U})$ and $C_2(\mathbf{U})$, etc.

As each row of $\mathbf{U}$ is completed it is checked by using (11.21) with the appropriate column of $\mathbf{L'}$.

Inversion of $\mathbf{L'}$. This follows exactly the scheme described in § 11.8, the calculation being slightly simplified by the fact that $\mathbf{L'}$ and $\mathbf{L}^{-1}$ have unit diagonal elements. If the computer prefers to record the non-diagonal elements of $\mathbf{L'}$ with $-$ signs, as in the Gauss-Doolittle method, there is no harm in doing so, and the inversion is even easier once the process has become familiar.

Evaluation of $\mathbf{A}^{-1}$. The elements of $(\mathbf{A}^{-1})'$ are computed column by column, starting with that on the right, using the relations

$$R_i(\mathbf{U}) \times R_j(\mathbf{A}^{-1})' = (\mathbf{L}^{-1})_{ij} \qquad (11.22)$$

Each column of $(\mathbf{A}^{-1})'$ involves one row of $\mathbf{U}$ and one row of $\mathbf{L}^{-1}$; as soon as completed it is checked by using the relation

$$C_i(\mathbf{A}^{-1})' \times C(\mathbf{\Sigma}) = 1$$

where $C(\mathbf{\Sigma})$ represents the column of row sums of $\mathbf{A}$, already used. For greater convenience $\mathbf{\Sigma}$ may be recorded by the side of $(\mathbf{A}^{-1})'$. There is also some advantage in recording the reciprocals of u_{ii}.

The layout of the complete calculation is shown in the following example.

EXAMPLE 11.7. Solve the following equations by inverting the matrix.

$$
\begin{aligned}
855x_1 + 308x_2 + 184x_3 + 31x_4 &= 9{\cdot}1 \\
300x_1 + 895x_2 + 218x_3 + 52x_4 &= 6{\cdot}4 \\
104x_1 + 136x_2 + 860x_3 + 107x_4 &= 11{\cdot}0 \\
29x_1 + 63x_2 + 122x_3 + 909x_4 &= 21{\cdot}7
\end{aligned}
$$

All coefficients are divided by 1000 in the following calculation.

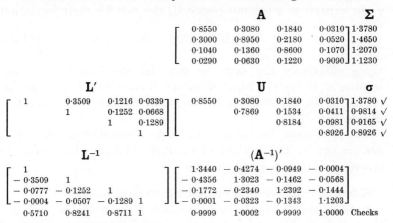

		A		**Σ**
0·8550	0·3080	0·1840	0·0310	1·3780
0·3000	0·8950	0·2180	0·0520	1·4650
0·1040	0·1360	0·8600	0·1070	1·2070
0·0290	0·0630	0·1220	0·9090	1·1230

	L′				**U**			**σ**	
1	0·3509	0·1216	0·0339	0·8550	0·3080	0·1840	0·0310	1·3780	√
	1	0·1252	0·0668		0·7869	0·1534	0·0411	0·9814	√
		1	0·1289			0·8184	0·0981	0·9165	√
			1				0·8926	0·8926	√

	L⁻¹				**(A⁻¹)′**			
1				1·3440	− 0·4274	− 0·0949	− 0·0004	
− 0·3509	1			− 0·4356	1·3023	− 0·1462	− 0·0568	
− 0·0777	− 0·1252	1		− 0·1772	− 0·2340	1·2392	− 0·1444	
− 0·0004	− 0·0507	− 0·1289	1	− 0·0001	− 0·0323	− 0·1343	1·1203	
0·5710	0·8241	0·8711	1	0·9999	1·0002	0·9999	1·0000	Checks

Finally, multiplication of each column of $(\mathbf{A}^{-1})'$ by the column

$$\begin{bmatrix} 0·0091 \\ 0·0064 \\ 0·0110 \\ 0·0217 \end{bmatrix} \text{gives} \quad \begin{aligned} x_1 &= 0·00749 \\ x_2 &= 0·00117 \\ x_3 &= 0·00892 \\ x_4 &= 0·02235 \end{aligned}$$

One modification of the process of inversion described above is to give unit diagonal elements to **U** instead of **L**. This simplifies the final stage at the expense of slightly more arithmetic in the inversion of **L**. The change involves various alterations in the order of computation and checking which the reader should have little difficulty in following out in detail.* There is little to choose between the two procedures, however, and the above form of resolution has been chosen here because it is used again in the following section in the direct solution of simultaneous equations.

11.10. Solution of Equations

For the solution of a particular set of equations, $\mathbf{Ax} = \mathbf{b}$, the resolution of **A** into **LU** proceeds as in § 11.9, except that the elements of **b** are included in the row sums of **A**. The forward substitution to obtain **y** from the equation $\mathbf{Ly} = \mathbf{b}$ can be carried

* It is described by L. Fox and J. G. Hayes, *J. Roy. Stat. Soc.* (B), **13** (1951), 83. To a large extent the computing schemes suggested in this chapter follow those given by Fox and Hayes, and in an earlier paper by Fox, *J. Roy. Stat. Soc.* (B), **12** (1950), 120.

through concurrently with the resolution; thus the elements of **y** are written as a column beside **U**, the rule for their formation

$$C_i(\mathbf{L}') \times C(\mathbf{y}) = b_i \qquad (11.23)$$

being effectively the same as that for the formation of any column of **U** (see (11.20)). Moreover, if the elements of **y** are included in the row sums of **U**, the current check (11.21) remains unchanged.

The final stage, the solution by back substitution of $\mathbf{Ux} = \mathbf{y}$, is carried out by the method of Example 11.2 (*a*). The complete scheme is shown in Example 11.8.

EXAMPLE 11.8. Solve directly the equations of Example 11.7.

In the following solution the elements of **A** are divided by 1000 and those of **b** by 100, and 4 decimals retained throughout. The final results then correspond to $10x$.

	A			**b**	**Σ**
0·8550	0·3080	0·1840	0·0310	0·0910	1·4690
0·3000	0·8950	0·2180	0·0520	0·0640	1·5290
0·1040	0·1360	0·8600	0·1070	0·1100	1·3170
0·0290	0·0630	0·1220	0·9090	0·2170	1·3400

	L′				**U**			**y**	**σ**
1	0·3509	0·1216	0·0339	0·8550	0·3080	0·1840	0·0310	0·0910	1·4690
	1	0·1252	0·0668		0·7869	0·1534	0·0411	0·0321	1·0135
		1	0·1289			0·8184	0·0981	0·0949	1·0114
			1				0·8926	0·1995	1·0921

s	0·8550	1·0949	1·1558	1·0628	0·4175 (=10**sx**)
10**x**	0·0749	0·0117	0·0892	0·2235	

The final check obtained by substituting these values in the original equations yields the following residual errors—

$$\{r_1,\ r_2,\ r_3,\ r_4\} = \{-\,0\cdot00156,\ 0\cdot00091,\ 0\cdot00073,\ -\,0\cdot00469\}$$

11.11. Other Methods

There are of course many other established methods of solving linear equations, and if emphasis has been given here to those based on resolution of the matrix, this is largely because the amount of recording is about as low as it can be, and the possible effects of rounding errors arising from the computation thereby kept to a minimum. Once the process of matrix resolution has been mastered, such methods are not difficult to follow.

However, we shall make some brief comments about other methods.*

1. ELIMINATION WITHOUT DIVISION

In applying the Doolittle method, it is customary to reduce each diagonal element to unity by division before eliminating the unknown associated with it. This is clearly not an essential step, and if omitted the elimination can still be carried out by forming the necessary cross-products. The coefficients in the triangular equations are then obtained exactly from those in the original set. Occasionally such a course may be desirable when the original matrix is also exact, but after several stages of elimination the coefficients tend to become very large.

2. PIVOTAL CONDENSATION

This is a method of elimination, applicable to unsymmetrical equations, in which a particular coefficient is chosen at each stage to serve as "pivot" for the elimination of the variable which it multiplies from all the other equations. Division by this pivotal coefficient is carried out as in the Doolittle method. However, each stage leaves a square matrix of coefficients of order one less than the previous matrix, and in hand computation each successive matrix must be recorded. In its usual form the method leaves behind a triangular set of equations which can be solved by back substitution, but there is a modification due to Jordan in which the original matrix is effectively transformed to a diagonal matrix leading directly to the solution.

For automatic computers, particularly those having rather limited storage, pivotal condensation has been found very convenient because the sequence of operations is essentially the same at each stage of elimination. Also the largest coefficient remaining

---

* A very extensive bibliography is given in a publication by the National Bureau of Standards, "Simultaneous Linear Equations and the Determination of Eigenvalues" (Eds. L. J. Paige and O. Taussky, *Applied Maths. Series* No. 29) and a detailed account of various procedures in "Contributions to the Solution of Linear Equations and the Determination of Eigenvalues" (Ed. O. Taussky, ibid. No. 39).

The following useful references include papers mentioned in the text.

P. S. Dwyer, *Linear Computations*, (Wiley, 1951).

L. Fox, H. D. Huskey and J. H. Wilkinson, *Quart. J. Mech. Appl. Math.*, **1** (1948), 149.

J. Morris, *Phil. Mag.*, **37** (1946), 106.

A. M. Turing, *Quart. J. Mech. Appl. Math.*, **1** (1948), 287.

C. Lanczos, *J. Research N.B.S.*, **49** (1952) 33.

M. R. Hestenes and E. Stiefel, *J. Research N.B.S.*, **49** (1952), 409.

at each stage can be picked out and used as pivot; this ensures that the magnitude of coefficients is kept within reasonable limits so that the machine capacity is less likely to be exceeded.

3. METHODS USING ORTHOGONAL VECTORS

In these the required solution is expressed as a linear combination of n column matrices or vectors which satisfy certain conditions of orthogonality. As a result the matrix $\mathbf{A}$ is transformed to a diagonal or nearly diagonal matrix which rapidly yields the solution of $\mathbf{Ax} = \mathbf{b}$. One such method, for symmetric matrices, has been described by Fox, Huskey and Wilkinson; the *escalator method* of Morris is practically equivalent to this. In the same category is the *method of minimized iterations* devised by Lanczos, the basis of which is described in Chapter 12, and a rather similar process due to Hestenes and Stiefel. The significance of these later developments, particularly for systems of many equations, is that an accurate solution may be obtained by a set of iterations appreciably fewer than the number of unknowns involved.

Some of these methods, mainly pivotal condensation (with and without Jordan's modification), the orthogonal vector method mentioned above, and also the square-root method, have been compared for accuracy and convenience by Fox, Huskey and Wilkinson. A detailed survey has also been given by Dwyer, and in several publications of the National Bureau of Standards. The effect of rounding errors arising during the computation has been discussed by Turing; his investigation suggests that, although such errors might theoretically accumulate to a serious level for large sets of equations, this is in practice unlikely even if only moderate use is made of guarding figures. Practical experience tends to confirm this.

11.12. Determinants and Cofactors

There is a well-known process for evaluating a determinant by expanding it into products of the elements of a chosen row and their cofactors. Thus if one omits from $\mathbf{A}$ the ith row and jth column which intersect at the element a_{ij}, there remains a matrix whose determinant D_{ij} is known as the first minor of a_{ij}. The cofactor of a_{ij} is then $A_{ji} = (-1)^{i+j} D_{ij}$, and then the expansion in terms of the ith row of $\mathbf{A}$ is

$$|\mathbf{A}| = a_{i1}A_{1i} + a_{i2}A_{2i} + \ldots + a_{in}A_{ni} \qquad (11.24)$$

This is Chio's expansion, which reduces $|\mathbf{A}|$ to a sum of n determinants of order $n - 1$. However, for determinants with n greater than 3 or 4 this does not lead to a suitable numerical process, and it is much more convenient to resolve the matrix into triangular factors as in § 11.9. The determinant of a triangular matrix is simply the product of its diagonal elements; hence

$$|\mathbf{A}| = |\mathbf{U}| \quad \text{or} \quad |\mathbf{L}_1|^2$$

according to whether $\mathbf{A}$ is resolved into $\mathbf{LU}$ (with unit elements on diagonal of $\mathbf{L}$) or $\mathbf{L}_1\mathbf{L}_1'$.

In Example 11.3
$$|\mathbf{A}| = 0 \cdot 6200 \times 0 \cdot 5255 \times 0 \cdot 4115 \times 1 \cdot 9632$$
$$= 0 \cdot 2632$$

Alternatively, using the results of Example 11.4
$$|\mathbf{A}| = (0 \cdot 7874 \times 0 \cdot 7249 \times 0 \cdot 6414 \times 1 \cdot 4011)^2 = 0 \cdot 2631$$

The cofactors A_{ji} are obtained conveniently by a slight extension of the inversion procedure. If $\hat{\mathbf{A}}$ denotes the matrix composed of the elements A_{ji} (the cofactor of a_{ij} being placed in the (ji) position), then (11.24) can be restated in the form

$$R_i(\mathbf{A}) \times C_i(\hat{\mathbf{A}}) = |\mathbf{A}|$$

It can also be shown that, when $i \neq j$,

$$R_i(\mathbf{A}) \times C_j(\hat{\mathbf{A}}) = R_i(\hat{\mathbf{A}}) \times C_j(\mathbf{A}) = 0$$

These facts are summarized in the matrix equations

$$\mathbf{A}\hat{\mathbf{A}} = \hat{\mathbf{A}}\mathbf{A} = |\mathbf{A}|\mathbf{I} \qquad (11.25)$$

from which it follows that $\hat{\mathbf{A}} = \mathbf{A}^{-1}/|\mathbf{A}|$. Consequently the cofactor of a_{ij} is obtained at once by dividing the element a_{ji}^{-1} of $\mathbf{A}^{-1}$ by $|\mathbf{A}|$.

Mistakes and Errors

We have so far been concerned more with the technique for solving linear equations or inverting a matrix than with the accuracy or significance of the results obtained. Emphasis has of course been put on the necessity for keeping adequate running checks on the computation to ensure that mistakes in intermediate results are unlikely. It should be realized, however, that the sum checks which are a feature of the methods described are not

wholly watertight, and that two compensating mistakes can sometimes be missed. This is not so improbable an event as it may
seem; thus, if any equation contains two equal coefficients with
opposite signs, then a similar miscopying of both coefficients is
liable not to be detected by a sum check. For such reasons it is
always advisable to insert any alleged solution $\mathbf{x}_0$ into the original
equations, and derive the residuals defined by the equation

$$\mathbf{r} = \mathbf{A}\mathbf{x}_0 - \mathbf{b} \qquad (11.26)$$

These residuals, with important exceptions which are discussed
later, often give a good indication of the accuracy of the solution,
and also provide a starting point for improving the solution by
iteration, if this is necessary.

Apart from computational errors we are faced with two distinct
questions relating to the accuracy of the solution $\mathbf{x}_0$—

1. Assuming that all quantities used in the original equations
are exact, how many significant figures do the elements of $\mathbf{x}_0$
contain, and how can these be increased.

2. If the elements of $\mathbf{A}$ and $\mathbf{b}$ are approximate, what accuracy is
in fact attainable?

We shall briefly consider these two aspects.

11.13. Improvement of the Solution

As already suggested, the first test to apply to any solution to
determine how reliable it is, is to calculate the residuals given by
(11.26). This in itself does not determine which digits are significant, but provided the elements of $\mathbf{A}$ and $\mathbf{b}$ can justifiably be
treated as exact, one can go on to estimate the correction to $\mathbf{x}_0$
which would eliminate $\mathbf{r}$. Thus if $\mathbf{x} = \mathbf{x}_0 + \delta\mathbf{x}$, then

$$\mathbf{A}\delta\mathbf{x} = -\mathbf{r} \qquad (11.27)$$

which represents a set of equations similar to the original set
except for a different column on the right. If the inverse $\mathbf{A}^{-1}$ has
already been found, the elements of $\delta\mathbf{x}$ are given by $-\mathbf{A}^{-1}\delta\mathbf{x}$.
The results not only show at once which figures in the earlier
solution were significant, but improve the accuracy by adding
further digits, the number of these depending on the number of
reliable figures in the inverse $\mathbf{A}^{-1}$. Repetitions of the process
increase the accuracy still further in the way one would expect of
a first-order iterative process.

In Example 11.8 the residuals of the first approximation have already been found. Using the inverse matrix evaluated in Example 11.7, one obtains

$$\delta x_1 = -0\cdot00000262 \qquad x_1 = 0\cdot00748738$$
$$\delta x_2 = +0\cdot00000183 \qquad x_2 = 0\cdot00117183$$
$$\delta x_3 = +0\cdot00000155 \qquad x_3 = 0\cdot00892155$$
$$\delta x_4 = -0\cdot00000541 \qquad x_4 = 0\cdot02234459$$

It is reasonable to assume that the improved values do not contain errors exceeding one unit in the 8th decimal.

When $\mathbf{A}^{-1}$ is not available, (11.27) must be solved in direct fashion, though this does not entail much extra labour because the resolution of $\mathbf{A}$ has already been carried out.

An approximate inverse $\mathbf{A}_0^{-1}$ can similarly be improved by an iterative process using the equation

$$\delta\mathbf{A}_0^{-1} = \mathbf{A}_0^{-1}(\mathbf{I}_n - \mathbf{A}\mathbf{A}_0^{-1})$$

This is a second-order process, and is described in detail in § 13.3.

11.14. Attainable Accuracy of Solution

A rather more frequent type of problem is that in which the elements of $\mathbf{A}$ and $\mathbf{b}$ are not exact numbers, but are subject to rounding errors and perhaps other uncertainties. If this is so there is no point in carrying the computational accuracy far beyond the stage to which it has any significance, and it becomes important to find out which figures in the solution are likely to be affected by uncertainties in the initial data. Of course it is the usual practice to treat the elements of $\mathbf{A}$ and $\mathbf{b}$ as though they were exact numbers, whether true or not, and to add one or two guarding figures throughout the calculation; the purpose of this is to reduce the effect of rounding errors which arise during the computation itself. Thus in Examples 11.5 and 11.6, four figures were used although the coefficients in the original equations were given only to two or three figures. If this practice is properly adhered to, the effects of the initial errors themselves are not obscured.

If we wish to examine the effect on an approximate solution $\mathbf{x}_0$ of making small changes in the initial data, say δb_i in b_i and δa_{ij} in a_{ij}, this can be done by means of the first-order variational equation

$$\mathbf{A}\delta\mathbf{x} = \delta\mathbf{b} - \delta\mathbf{A}\cdot\mathbf{x}_0 \qquad (11.28)$$

where $\delta\mathbf{b}$ is a column matrix with elements δb_i, and $\delta\mathbf{A}$ a square matrix with elements δa_{ij}. If $\mathbf{A}^{-1}$ has been evaluated the effect of any particular modification is given by

$$\delta\mathbf{x} = \mathbf{A}^{-1}(\delta\mathbf{b}) - \mathbf{A}^{-1}(\delta\mathbf{A} \cdot \mathbf{x}_0) \qquad (11.29)$$

The size of the elements of $\delta\mathbf{x}$ clearly depend very much on those of $\mathbf{A}^{-1}$, and much can be learned merely by examining the rows of $\mathbf{A}^{-1}$.

It is easy to place upper limits on the elements of $\delta\mathbf{x}$. Thus in Example 11.7, let all the given coefficients be subject to the usual random rounding errors, i.e. $|\delta b_i| \leqslant 0{\cdot}05$, $|\delta a_{ij}| \leqslant 0{\cdot}5$. Then no elements of $\delta\mathbf{b} - \delta\mathbf{A} \cdot \mathbf{x}_0$ can exceed in magnitude

$$0{\cdot}05 + 0{\cdot}5B$$

where $\qquad\qquad B = \sum_{i=1}^{4} |x_i|_0 \simeq 0{\cdot}040$

It follows that $|\delta x_i| < 0{\cdot}07 s_i$, where s_i is the sum of the ith row of $\mathbf{A}^{-1}$. In Example 11.7, bearing in mind the factor 1000 which was introduced, we find

$$\{s_1, s_2, s_3, s_4\} \simeq \{0{\cdot}0020, 0{\cdot}0020, 0{\cdot}0016, 0{\cdot}0013\}$$
and hence

$$\{|\delta x_1|, |\delta x_2|, |\delta x_3|, |\delta x_4|\} < \{0{\cdot}00014, 0{\cdot}00014, 0{\cdot}00011, 0{\cdot}00009\}$$

As usual when the combined effect of random errors is being considered, these limits are much in excess of any uncertainties which are at all likely to occur (see § 11.13). However, it appears that the limits of uncertainty attached to the x's do not vary greatly.

When $\mathbf{A}^{-1}$ is unavailable it is less simple to assess the importance of initial errors. For a valuable discussion of the subject of errors, and further references, see *Modern Computing Methods*, Chapter 5.

Quite apart from any assessment of this kind, however, it is sometimes obvious in the course of solving a particular set of equations, either by elimination or by triangular resolution of the matrix, that the solution contains a large inherent error which arises from the properties of the matrix concerned. Thus it may happen during the elimination that a progressive (or perhaps sudden) loss of significant figures occurs, so that when the back-substitution process is reached few if any figures remain on which reliance can be placed. This unfortunate conclusion is certain to be reached if the matrix is singular, i.e. the determinant $|\mathbf{A}| = 0$, and any solution derived in such a case has no significance whatever, being simply a combination of rounding errors. The rows of a singular matrix are not all linearly independent, and this suggests that in less extreme cases of cancellation, one or more rows of the matrix are very nearly linear combinations of the others.

Equations derived from a nearly singular matrix are often vaguely described as "ill-conditioned." A trivial example is provided by the equations

$$x_1 + x_2 \qquad = b_1$$
$$x_1 + (1 + \varepsilon)x_2 = b_2$$

which are satisfied if

$$x_1 = b_1 - (b_2 - b_1)/\varepsilon, \ x_2 = (b_2 - b_1)/\varepsilon$$

It is clear that a change in ε from one small value to another, corresponding to a small relative change in the coefficient $(1 + \varepsilon)$, can produce large changes in both x_1 and x_2 which become more extreme as ε tends to zero. This is an indication of the important effect which rounding or other errors in the coefficients of ill-conditioned equations may have on the solution. Another feature is that a very inaccurate solution may give quite small residuals of the kind defined in (11.26). Thus in the above example, if x_2 differs from its correct value by δx and x_1 by $- (1 + \alpha\varepsilon)\delta x$, then both residuals are multiples of $\varepsilon \delta x$ and can be much smaller than δx. It follows that significant reduction of both residuals requires relatively large changes in the solution. Another example of this is given in Chapter 13.

It was remarked above that the ill-conditioning property belongs essentially to the matrix **A**. Although badly conditioned matrices are often easy to recognize, it is difficult to give a simple quantitative measure of the condition. It certainly depends on the "spread" of the latent roots of the matrix, which are defined in the following chapter, and becomes most marked when the largest root is a big multiple of the smallest. Alternatively, if the determinant of **A** is evaluated by expanding in terms of the cofactors in any row, as in (11.24), then a considerable cancellation is found to occur among the terms of this expression, so that $|\mathbf{A}|$ is much less than some of the individual contributions.

Volterra Integral Equations

There are various types of integral equation the solution of which can be effectively reduced to that of a set of linear simultaneous equations. We shall discuss here the particular class known as

Volterra equations; there are two linear varieties of these, which may be written as follows—

First kind $\qquad \int_{x_0}^{x} K(x, \xi)\phi(\xi)d\xi + f(x) = 0 \qquad$ (11.30)

Second kind $\qquad \int_{x_0}^{x} K(x, \xi)\phi(\xi)d\xi + f(x) = \phi(x) \qquad$ (11.31)

Here $\phi(x)$ is the unknown function; $f(x)$ is known and so is $K(x, \xi)$. The latter is called the "kernel" of the equation, and is commonly symmetrical in x and ξ. We shall assume that $K(x, \xi)$ is a continuous function of these variables, and always finite. Equations of the second kind, in which $\phi(x)$ appears on the right, are usually easier to deal with numerically, and it is worth noting that the first kind can often be converted to the second by differentiation; thus a single differentiation gives

$$\int_{x_0}^{x} (\partial/\partial x)(K(x, \xi))\phi(\xi)d\xi + f'(x) = - K(x, x)\phi(x)$$

If $K(x, \xi)$ should happen to vanish when $\xi = x$, further differentiation may be necessary to complete the conversion to (11.31). We describe here a simple method of approximating to the solution of (11.31), and in Chapter 14 the corresponding Fredholm equations (in which both limits of the integral are fixed) are discussed.

11.15. Finite Difference Approximation

An obvious method of dealing with (11.31) is to replace the integral by a finite sum, using a suitable quadrature formula involving the values

$$\phi_j = \phi(x_j)$$

where $\qquad x_j = x_0 + jw \quad$ and $\quad j = 0, 1, 2, \ldots$

A Lagrangian type of formula is most convenient; then, for instance

$$\int_{x_0}^{x_j} K(x_j, \xi)\phi(\xi)d\xi$$
$$= w[t_{j0}K_{j0}\phi_0 + t_{j1}K_{j1}\phi_1 + \ldots + t_{jj}K_{jj}\phi_j + \triangle_j] \qquad (11.32)$$

where $K_{jk} = K(x_j, \xi_k)$. The t's are weighting factors associated with the quadrature formula, and are usually centro-symmetric, i.e. $t_{j0} = t_{jj}$, $t_{j1} = t_{j, j-1}$, etc. If the trapezoidal approximation is used throughout

$$t_{j0} = t_{jj} = 1/2, \quad t_{jk} = 1 \quad \text{when } k \neq 0 \text{ or } j.$$

The quantity $\triangle_j$ represents a correction to the closed quadrature formula.

The integral equation can now be replaced by the following set of linear equations—

$$\left.\begin{aligned}
\phi_0 &= f_0 \\
-l_{10}\phi_0 + (1 - l_{11})\phi_1 &= f_1 + w\triangle_1 \\
-l_{20}\phi_0 - l_{21}\phi_1 + (1 - l_{22})\phi_2 &= f_2 + w\triangle_2 \\
-l_{30}\phi_0 - l_{31}\phi_1 - l_{32}\phi_2 + (1 - l_{33})\phi_3 &= f_3 + w\triangle_3 \\
&\quad \ldots \text{etc.}
\end{aligned}\right\} \quad (11.33)$$

where $$l_{jk} = wt_{jk}K_{jk}$$

When the $\triangle$'s are neglected this set of triangular equations can obviously be solved in the usual way by forward substitution. However, this procedure is rather unsatisfactory because the quadrature approximation is likely to be poor in the first few equations, and the initial errors introduced thereby will be carried through the whole solution. Two possible methods of improving the starting values of the solution are worth considering—

1. A Taylor series approximation may be used to obtain the first few ϕ_j values. Thus, if $K(x, \xi)$ is an analytical function possessing the necessary derivatives, it follows from (11.31) that

$$\left(\frac{d^m\phi}{dx^m}\right)_{x_0} = \phi_0^{(m)} = f_0^{(m)} + \left\{\frac{d^{m-1}}{dx^{m-1}}(K(x, x)\phi(x))\right\}_{x_0}$$

$$+ \left\{\frac{d^{m-2}}{dx^{m-2}}(K^{(1)}(x, x)\phi(x))\right\}_{x_0} + \ldots + \{K^{(m-1)}(x, x)\phi(x)\}_{x_0} \quad (11.34)$$

where $$K^{(s)}(x, x) = \{(\partial^s/\partial x^s)(K(x, \xi))\}_{\xi=x}$$

If the Taylor series based on these derivatives converges well enough for $\phi_1, \ldots, \phi_4$, say, to be evaluated, then the solution can be continued from (11.33), starting with the equation which first contains ϕ_5. The quadrature formula used in these later equations might well be one which neglects differences of the integrand values beyond the fourth. Gregory's formula (in Lagrangian form) is often suitable, as this is of closed type.

When the terms of the Taylor series alternate in sign, its convergence may sometimes be improved by using the Euler transformation (see § 6.6).

2. If a simple quadrature formula such as the trapezoidal rule is used in (11.33), the consequent error may be estimated by carrying out a preliminary calculation with a larger interval than

that at which the solution is required to be tabulated. Thus if $\phi_{(1)}(x)$ represents the approximate solution obtained using an interval $2w$, and $\phi_{(2)}(x)$ the solution using an interval w, then since the error of the trapezoidal rule varies as the square of the interval, we can apply (3.41) at each value of x and write

$$\phi(x) = \phi_{(2)}(x) + (1/3)(\phi_{(2)}(x) - \phi_{(1)}(x)) \qquad (11.35)$$

This should improve the accuracy of the solution considerably. This process of *extrapolation to zero interval*, which is possible when the dependence of the error on the interval is known, will be used frequently in later chapters. There is of course a more general result corresponding to (3.39).

Improvement of the solution by (11.35) can be continued as long as the correction to $\phi_{(2)}(x)$ remains relatively small, and the method is often easy to apply when the Taylor series method is inconvenient. However, once the accuracy of the first few values of ϕ has been brought to the desired level, it may be better to continue the solution using a more accurate quadrature formula. This is illustrated in Example 11.9.

EXAMPLE 11.9. Develop the solution of the equation

$$1 + x^2 - \frac{1}{2} \int_0^x \frac{\phi(\xi)d\xi}{1 + x + \xi} = \phi(x)$$

The Taylor series for $\phi(x)$ converges rather poorly even for values of $x \ll 1$. From the first few derivatives at $x = 0$

$$\phi(x) = 1 - (1/2)x + (15/8)x^2 - (27/16)x^3$$
$$+ (1151/384)x^4 - (20581/3840)x^5 + \ldots$$

and from these terms $\phi(0 \cdot 1) = 0 \cdot 9673$, $\phi(0 \cdot 2) = 0 \cdot 9646$. The second of these values, however, is inaccurate in the 4th decimal.

We therefore proceed by using a trapezoidal approximation to the integral when $x \leqslant 1$, first with an interval of $0 \cdot 2$ in x and then with an interval of $0 \cdot 1$. The first stage leads to the following set of equations, in which $\phi_k = \phi(0 \cdot 1k)$—

$$
\begin{array}{l}
x \\
\begin{array}{c}
0 \\
0 \cdot 2 \\
0 \cdot 4 \\
0 \cdot 6 \\
0 \cdot 8 \\
1 \cdot 0
\end{array}
\begin{bmatrix}
1 \cdot 0 & & & & & \\
0 \cdot 04167 & 1 \cdot 03571 & & & & \\
0 \cdot 03571 & 0 \cdot 0625 & 1 \cdot 02778 & & & \\
0 \cdot 03125 & 0 \cdot 05556 & 0 \cdot 05 & 1 \cdot 02273 & & \\
0 \cdot 02778 & 0 \cdot 05 & 0 \cdot 04545 & 0 \cdot 04167 & 1 \cdot 01923 & \\
0 \cdot 025 & 0 \cdot 04545 & 0 \cdot 04167 & 0 \cdot 03846 & 0 \cdot 03571 & 1 \cdot 01667
\end{bmatrix}
\begin{bmatrix}
\phi_0 \\
\phi_2 \\
\phi_4 \\
\phi_6 \\
\phi_8 \\
\phi_{10}
\end{bmatrix}
=
\begin{bmatrix}
1 \\
1 \cdot 04 \\
1 \cdot 16 \\
1 \cdot 36 \\
1 \cdot 64 \\
2 \cdot 0
\end{bmatrix}
\end{array}
$$

These are easily solved, following the scheme of Example 11.1. Details of the corresponding calculation for $w = 0 \cdot 1$ need not be given; the results are summarized at top of next page.

x	Values of $\phi(x)$			
	$w = 0\cdot2$	$w = 0\cdot1$	$w = 0$	Gregory
0	1·0	1·0	1·0	
0·1		0·9671	0·9673	
0·2	0·9639	0·9647	0·9650	
0·3		0·9886	0·9889	
0·4	1·0353	1·0363	1·0366	1·0366
0·5		1·1062	1·1065	1·1065
0·6	1·1962	1·1972	1·1975	1·1976
0·7		1·3088	1·3091	1·3092
0·8	1·4394	1·4404	1·4407	1·4408
0·9		1·5917	1·5920	1·5920
1·0	1·7613	1·7622	1·7625	1·7626

The column for $w = 0$ is obtained by making a uniform correction of $0\cdot0003$ (except at $x = 0\cdot1$, where the Taylor series value is almost certainly correct), based on (11.35). The correction is small enough to suggest that the values in this column are nearly correct to 4D. This has been further checked by a calculation assuming the values of $x < 0\cdot4$ to be correct and using Gregory's formula for integrals in which $x \geqslant 0\cdot4$, neglecting 5th and higher differences of the integrand. For this purpose a table of the coefficients t_{jk} is essential, and can easily be built up from the Gregory weight coefficients given, for example, in *Chambers* [6], p. 549. Denoting these coefficients by t_k we have the rule that

$$t_{jk} = t_k + t_{j-k} - 1$$

with the added fact that, if differences beyond the mth are ignored, $t_k = 1$ when $k > m$. In particular, when $m = 4$, we have the following values, with a factor 1440 included to avoid decimals—

k	0	1	2	3	4	5	6	...
$1440t_k$	475	1902	1104	1586	1413	1440	1440	...

These lead at once to the following table—

VALUES OF $1440t_{jk}$ (GREGORY, NEGLECTING Δ^5)

k j	0	1	2	3	4	5	6	7	8	9	10
4	448	2048	768	2048	448						
5	475	1875	1250	1250	1875	475					
6	,,	1902	1077	1732	1077	1902	475				
7	,,	,,	1104	1559	1559	1104	1902	475			
8	,,	,,	,,	1586	1386	1586	1104	1902	475		
9	,,	,,	,,	,,	1413	1413	1586	1104	1902	475	
10	,,	,,	,,	,,	,,	1440	1413	1586	1104	1902	475

Further rows are formed merely by inserting an extra 1440 in the centre of the row.

The rest of the calculation involves the tabulation of $l_{jk} = wt_{jk}K_{jk}$, and the solution of equations (11.33), for $x \geqslant 0\cdot4$, by forward substitution as before. We omit the details of this, but the resulting solution is given in the table above and shows no discrepancy with the previous values exceeding 0·0001.

Examination of the differences of $K_{jk}\phi_k$ shows that it is quite feasible to extend the solution at intervals of 0·2 in x, using the same table of Gregory coefficients, with an accuracy not far short of 4D. It should be unnecessary to stress how important it is to verify in any particular case that the Δ terms which have been ignored in (11.33) do not in fact impair the presumed accuracy of the solution.

The foregoing method is numerically simpler to apply when the kernel is a function of $(x - \xi)$ only. There is then no need to write down a two-dimensional array for K_{jk}, since these elements depend only on the parameter $j - k$. Writing $K_{jk} = K_{j-k}$, we need only tabulate K_0, K_1, K_2, . . . Although the starting procedure is much the same as in the general case, the continuation giving ϕ_j when $j \geqslant 2m$ (m being the order of the last difference retained in the quadrature formula) is very simple. The equation in (11.33) which gives ϕ_j then becomes

$$(1 - wt_0K_0)\phi_j = f_j$$
$$+ w\{t_0K_j\phi_0 + t_1K_{j-1}\phi_1 + \ldots + t_2K_2\phi_{j-2} + t_1K_1\phi_{j-1} + \triangle_j\}$$

where t_k has the same meaning as in Example 11.9, and $t_k = 1$ when $k > m$. The products on the right are conveniently summed by having two columns as shown below which can be moved relative to each other. When ϕ_j has been found, its value is added to the left column, and the column on the right shifted down one row. All is then ready for the calculation of ϕ_{j+1}, and so on.

	(K_{j+1})
$t_0\phi_0$	K_j
$t_1\phi_1$	K_{j-1}
.	.
.	.
$t_m\phi_m$	K_{j-m}
ϕ_{m+1}	K_{j-m-1}
.	.
.	.
ϕ_{j-m-1}	K_{m+1}
ϕ_{j-m}	t_mK_m
.	.
.	.
ϕ_{j-1}	t_1K_1

The danger that rounding errors may build up is one to be taken seriously in the solution of Volterra equations as it is for differential equations. Each rounding error as it occurs effectively adds to the particular solution required a small multiple of the complementary function, i.e. the solution of the homogeneous equation in which $f(x)$ is absent. If this solution increases markedly with x, then even a random selection of rounding errors is likely to result in an overall error which increases in a similar way. This is not so in Example 11.9, where the complementary function is a well-behaved oscillatory function. A brief discussion of such errors in the solution of Volterra equations, and possible methods of eliminating them, has been given by Fox and Goodwin.*

EXERCISES 11

1. When **A** is symmetrical, plan the layout for the calculation of the reciprocal matrix $\mathbf{A}^{-1}$ by means of the equation $\mathbf{A}^{-1}\mathbf{L} = \mathbf{U}^{-1}$, using only the diagonal and zero elements of $\mathbf{U}^{-1}$.

2. Verify the resolution, $\mathbf{A} = \mathbf{LU}$, for the following case—

$$
\begin{bmatrix}
a_1 & 1 & 0 & 0 & 0 \\
1 & a_2 & 1 & 0 & 0 \\
0 & 1 & a_3 & 1 & 0 \\
0 & 0 & 1 & a_4 & 1 \\
0 & 0 & 0 & 1 & a_5
\end{bmatrix}
=
\begin{bmatrix}
1 & 0 & 0 & 0 & 0 \\
l_2 & 1 & 0 & 0 & 0 \\
0 & l_3 & 1 & 0 & 0 \\
0 & 0 & l_4 & 1 & 0 \\
0 & 0 & 0 & l_5 & 1
\end{bmatrix}
\begin{bmatrix}
u_1 & 1 & 0 & 0 & 0 \\
0 & u_2 & 1 & 0 & 0 \\
0 & 0 & u_3 & 1 & 0 \\
0 & 0 & 0 & u_4 & 1 \\
0 & 0 & 0 & 0 & u_5
\end{bmatrix}
$$

where
$$u_1 = a_1, \quad l_{j+1} = 1/u_j$$
and
$$u_{j+1} = a_{j+1} - l_{j+1}$$

Show also that

$$
\mathbf{L}^{-1} =
\begin{bmatrix}
1 & 0 & 0 & 0 & 0 \\
-l_2 & 1 & 0 & 0 & 0 \\
l_3 l_2 & -l_3 & 1 & 0 & 0 \\
-l_4 l_3 l_2 & l_4 l_3 & -l_4 & 1 & 0 \\
l_5 l_4 l_3 l_2 & -l_5 l_4 l_3 & l_5 l_4 & -l_5 & 1
\end{bmatrix}
$$

and that the solution of the equations $\mathbf{Ax} = \mathbf{b}$ can be completed by a single process of back substitution, represented by the equation

$$\mathbf{Ux} = \mathbf{L}^{-1}\mathbf{b}$$

---

* L. Fox and E. T. Goodwin, *Phil. Trans.*, **245** (1953), 501. This paper provides a useful introduction to the numerical solution of linear integral equations, of both Volterra and Fredholm types.

3. Examine similarly the resolution of the matrix

$$\begin{bmatrix} a_1 & b_2 & 0 & 0 & 0 \\ b_1 & a_2 & b_3 & 0 & 0 \\ 0 & b_2 & a_3 & b_4 & 0 \\ 0 & 0 & b_3 & a_4 & b_5 \\ 0 & 0 & 0 & b_4 & a_5 \end{bmatrix}$$

4. Show that equations of the form, $(\mathbf{A} - \lambda\mathbf{B})\mathbf{x} = 0$, where λ is a parameter, can be reduced to $(\mathbf{C} - \lambda\mathbf{I})y = 0$, by resolving $\mathbf{B}$ into triangular matrices. In particular (a) if $\mathbf{B} = \mathbf{LU}$, then $\mathbf{C} = \mathbf{L}^{-1}\mathbf{A}\mathbf{U}^{-1}$ and $\mathbf{y} = \mathbf{Ux}$, (b) if $\mathbf{B} = \mathbf{L_1L_1}'$, then $\mathbf{C} = \mathbf{L_1}^{-1}\mathbf{A}(\mathbf{L_1}')^{-1}$ and $\mathbf{y} = \mathbf{L_1}'\mathbf{x}$.

CHAPTER 12

MATRICES AND DETERMINANTAL EQUATIONS

DETERMINANTAL equations were dismissed at the end of Chapter 9 with the remark that they are most easily solved with the help of matrices. Some introduction to matrices has since been made in the course of solving simultaneous linear equations, but many more of their properties will now be required. Though it is not possible here to establish these in detail, and several important theorems will only be quoted, it is hoped to include sufficient to enable those unfamiliar with matrices to appreciate methods of computation based on their use.

Summary of Matrix Properties

The general problem to be considered is the solution of the homogeneous set of linear equations

$$\left.\begin{array}{l} a_{11}x_1 + a_{12}x_2 + \ldots + a_{1n}x_n = \lambda x_1 \\ a_{21}x_1 + a_{22}x_2 + \ldots + a_{2n}x_n = \lambda x_2 \\ \\ \\ \\ a_{n1}x_1 + a_{n2}x_2 + \ldots + a_{nn}x_n = \lambda x_n \end{array}\right\} \quad (12.1)$$

which has a non-vanishing solution only if the determinant

$$D(\lambda) = \begin{vmatrix} a_{11} - \lambda & a_{12} & \ldots & a_{1n} \\ a_{21} & a_{22} - \lambda & & a_{2n} \\ \cdot & & & \\ \cdot & & & \\ \cdot & & & \\ a_{n1} & a_{n2} & \ldots a_{nn} - \lambda \end{vmatrix} = 0 \quad (12.2)$$

In general this is a polynomial equation of nth degree in λ, with roots $\lambda_1, \lambda_2, \ldots, \lambda_n$. Corresponding to each λ_i there is a solution of (12.1) which may be denoted by $\{x_{1i}, x_{2i}, \ldots, x_{ni}\}$; the $\{ \ \}$

type of brackets are used here and subsequently to mean that the quantities contained should be written as a column.*

LATENT ROOTS AND VECTORS

In matrix notation we can write (12.1) as

$$\mathbf{Ax} = \lambda\mathbf{x} \quad \text{or} \quad f(\lambda)\mathbf{x} = (\mathbf{A} - \lambda\mathbf{I}_n)\mathbf{x} = 0 \qquad (12.3)$$

where $\mathbf{x}$ is a single-*column* matrix, and $\mathbf{I}_n$ is the unit matrix of order n. (12.2) then becomes

$$|f(\lambda)| = 0 \qquad (12.4)$$

The values λ_i are then called the latent roots of the matrix $\mathbf{A}$, $D(\lambda)$ the characteristic function, and the single-column matrix

$$\mathbf{u}_i = \{x_{1i}, x_{2i}, \ . \ . \ ., \ x_{ni}\}$$

the latent column vector or modal column associated with λ_i. Other terms are often used, characteristic values, proper values or eigenvalues for λ_i, and similar expressions for $\mathbf{u}_i$.

It is also possible to introduce the set of equations represented by

$$\mathbf{yA} = \lambda\mathbf{y} \qquad (12.5)$$

where $\mathbf{y}$ is a single-*row* matrix with n elements. The latent roots associated with (12.5) are the same as before, since (12.4) is unchanged, but to λ_i there corresponds a latent row vector

$$\mathbf{v}_i = [y_{i1}, y_{i2}, \ . \ . \ ., \ y_{in}]$$

the elements of which are not in general the same as those of $\mathbf{u}_i$. However, if $\mathbf{A}$ is symmetric, $\mathbf{u}_i$ and $\mathbf{v}_i$ do contain the same elements, each being the transpose of the other, i.e. $\mathbf{u}_i = \mathbf{v}_i'$.

In the greater part of this chapter it will be assumed either that $\mathbf{A}$ has n distinct latent roots, or that if any root occurs with multiplicity q, then to this root there corresponds q independent latent vectors of each type. If the definitions of order, rank and degeneracy are recalled from the beginning of Chapter 11, then, if the roots are distinct, the matrix $\mathbf{f}(\lambda_i)$, obtained from (12.3) by

---

* This is a useful convention in presenting matrices. Normally the array is contained in square brackets, but when for ease of printing it is convenient to transpose columns into rows, curly brackets are used instead. This often happens for single column matrices. Thus

$$\{a, b, c\} \equiv \begin{bmatrix} a \\ b \\ c \end{bmatrix}$$

substituting λ_i for λ, has order n, rank $n - 1$ and degeneracy 1 for every latent root; or if λ_s occurs q times, $\mathbf{f}(\lambda_s)$ has order n, rank $n - q$ and degeneracy q. Not all matrices are like this. It may happen that to a multiple root there correspond only $p(< q)$ independent vectors of each type, and the degeneracy of $\mathbf{f}(\lambda_s)$ is p instead of q. If $p = 1$, $\mathbf{f}(\lambda_s)$ is again simply degenerate. The matrix $\mathbf{A}$ is then said to be defective, the deficiency arising from λ_s being $q - p$. Not much stress will be given here to defective matrices, however, as they arise rarely if ever in physical problems.

ORTHOGONAL PROPERTIES OF LATENT VECTORS

A most important property of the two sets of latent vectors is their orthogonality. The product $\mathbf{yx}$, in this order, of a single-row matrix $\mathbf{y}$ with a single-column matrix $\mathbf{x}$ each with n elements, is a single element known as their inner or scalar product. Now

$$\lambda_j \mathbf{v}_j \mathbf{u}_i = \mathbf{v}_j \mathbf{A} \mathbf{u}_i = \lambda_i \mathbf{v}_j \mathbf{u}_i$$

so

$$(\lambda_i - \lambda_j)\mathbf{v}_j \mathbf{u}_i = 0$$

Hence if $\lambda_i \neq \lambda_j$, the scalar product $\mathbf{v}_j \mathbf{u}_i$ vanishes, and the vectors $\mathbf{v}_j$ and $\mathbf{u}_i$ are said to be orthogonal. This orthogonality property obviously does not necessarily extend to the vectors associated with a multiple latent root, but it is possible to choose p linear combinations of these vectors which do satisfy orthogonality conditions among themselves as well as with the vectors belonging to other roots.

The special case of a symmetric matrix has already been mentioned. An important consequence of the orthogonality property is that all latent roots of a symmetric matrix must be real. Thus, suppose there is a complex root pair $\lambda_j = \mu_j \pm i\sigma_j$, with vectors $\mathbf{u}_j = \mathbf{c}_j \pm i\mathbf{d}_j$, $\mathbf{v}_j = \mathbf{c}_j' \pm i\mathbf{d}_j'$. Then the scalar product $(\mathbf{c}_j' + i\mathbf{d}_j')(\mathbf{c}_j + i\mathbf{d}_j) = \mathbf{c}_j'\mathbf{c}_j + \mathbf{d}_j'\mathbf{d}_j$, which cannot vanish, since both $\mathbf{c}_j'\mathbf{c}_j$ and $\mathbf{d}_j'\mathbf{d}_j$ are sums of squares. Hence all the roots must be real.

EXPANSIONS IN TERMS OF LATENT VECTORS

We should now mention some results of expanding an arbitrary column matrix $\mathbf{b}_0$ in terms of the latent column vectors of a non-defective matrix $\mathbf{A}$. Thus if $\mathbf{b}_0$ has n elements, we can write

$$\mathbf{b}_0 = a_1\mathbf{u}_1 + a_2\mathbf{u}_2 + \ldots + a_n\mathbf{u}_n \qquad (12.6)$$

which is equivalent to a set of simultaneous equations determining the coefficients a_i uniquely. It should be noticed that if $\mathbf{v}_j\mathbf{b}_0 = 0$, then $a_j = 0$. Since $\mathbf{Au}_i = \lambda_i\mathbf{u}_i$, repeated premultiplication by the matrix $\mathbf{A}$ gives the result

$$\mathbf{b}_k = \mathbf{A}^k\mathbf{b}_0 = a_1\lambda_1{}^k\mathbf{u}_1 + a_2\lambda_2{}^k\mathbf{u}_2 + \ldots + a_n\lambda_n{}^k\mathbf{u}_n \quad (12.7)$$

in which it may be assumed for the moment that the λ's are distinct. Further if $P(\mathbf{A})$ is any polynomial in $\mathbf{A}$

$$P(\mathbf{A})\mathbf{b}_0 = a_1P(\lambda_1)\mathbf{u}_1 + a_2P(\lambda_2)\mathbf{u}_2 + \ldots + a_nP(\lambda_n)\mathbf{u}_n \quad (12.8)$$

Similarly, if $\mathbf{d}_0$ is an arbitrary row matrix with n elements, such that

$$\mathbf{d}_0 = c_1\mathbf{v}_1 + c_2\mathbf{v}_2 + \ldots + c_n\mathbf{v}_n$$

then $\quad \mathbf{d}_k = \mathbf{d}_0\mathbf{A}^k = c_1\lambda_1{}^k\mathbf{v}_1 + c_2\lambda_2{}^k\mathbf{v}_2 + \ldots + c_n\lambda_n{}^k\mathbf{v}_n \quad (12.9)$

Again, if $\mathbf{d}_0\mathbf{u}_i = 0$, then $c_i = 0$. Much use of (12.7) and (12.9) will be made in § 12.10–§ 12.13.

Adjoint Matrix

Finally, we introduce the matrix $\mathbf{F}(\lambda)$ which is adjoint to the λ-matrix $\mathbf{f}(\lambda)$. The elements of $\mathbf{F}(\lambda)$ are the cofactors of the similar elements, in $\mathbf{f}(\lambda)$, and the whole matrix satisfies the important relations

$$\mathbf{f}(\lambda)\mathbf{F}(\lambda) = \mathbf{F}(\lambda)\mathbf{f}(\lambda) = D(\lambda)\mathbf{I}_n \quad (12.10)$$

$\mathbf{F}(\lambda)$ can be expanded as a polynomial of degree $(n-1)$ in λ, and the coefficients, which are square matrices, found from (12.10) (see Exercises 12, No. 12). Its importance arises because the rows and columns of $\mathbf{F}(\lambda_i)$ determine the latent vectors $\mathbf{u}_i$ and $\mathbf{v}_i$, and some methods of finding latent vectors, though not those described later in detail, use this fact. If λ_i is a simple root, $\mathbf{F}(\lambda_i)$ has only one independent column (and row), i.e. rank 1; it then factorizes into a multiple of the outer product $\mathbf{u}_i\mathbf{v}_i$.

We can now revert to the computational problem involved in finding latent roots and vectors, picking out three lines of approach—

1. Numerical solution of (12.1), usually iterative, without using matrix properties.

2. Expansion of the determinant (12.2) into polynomial form,

which is then solved by the methods of Chapter 9; the latent vectors, if required, being usually found by a separate process.

3. Iterative processes, mainly using convergent vector sequences, by which latent roots and vectors are obtained together, without explicitly deriving the characteristic function $D(\lambda)$.

Since this chapter is intended to exhibit the power of matrix methods, we shall ignore (1), which is adequately covered by a later chapter dealing with allied problems in differential and integral equations. The choice between (2) and (3) often depends on whether both latent roots and vectors, or latent roots only, are required. If only the roots are wanted, then (2) may be the more expeditious and certain. On the other hand (3) has definite advantages if a complete solution is not required, but only the dominant roots and their vectors. Some methods combine features of (2) and (3), e.g. Lanczos' method, which is described in § 12.14–§ 12.16. We shall endeavour to cover adequately each line of attack, beginning with direct expansion of the determinant (12.2).

Expansion of Determinantal Equations

If we write

$$D(\lambda) = (-1)^n \{\lambda^n - p_1 \lambda^{n-1} - p_2 \lambda^{n-2} - \ldots - p_{n-1}\lambda - p_n\} \quad (12.11)$$

the problem is to find the coefficients $p_1, \ldots, p_n$ from the elements of the matrix $\mathbf{A}$. One useful fact, which can be seen by inspecting the determinant (12.2), is that

$$p_1 = \lambda_1 + \lambda_2 + \ldots + \lambda_n = a_{11} + a_{22} + \ldots + a_{nn} \quad (12.12)$$

This sum of the diagonal elements of $\mathbf{A}$ is known as the trace or spur of the matrix and has useful invariant properties.

It is important to notice that (12.11) can be expressed directly as a determinant, known as Frobenius' standard form, thus—

$$D(\lambda) = \begin{vmatrix} p_1 - \lambda & p_2 & p_3 & \ldots & p_n \\ 1 & -\lambda & 0 & \ldots & 0 \\ 0 & 1 & -\lambda & \ldots & 0 \\ . & & & & \\ . & & & & \\ . & & & & \\ 0 & 0 & 0 & & -\lambda \end{vmatrix} \quad (12.13)$$

The corresponding matrix, to which we shall sometimes refer,

$$\mathbf{C} = \begin{bmatrix} p_1 & p_2 \cdots p_{n-1} & p_n \\ 1 & 0 \ldots 0 & 0 \\ 0 & 1 \ldots 0 & 0 \\ \cdot & & \\ \cdot & & \\ \cdot & & \\ 0 & 0 \ldots 1 & 0 \end{bmatrix} \tag{12.14}$$

is called the companion matrix, and it must be noted that if $\mathbf{E}$ is a suitable non-singular matrix with real elements

$$\mathbf{C} = \mathbf{E}^{-1}\mathbf{A}\mathbf{E}$$

In fact the first method to be described, due to Danielewsky,* reduces $D(\lambda)$ to the standard form (12.13) by just such a transformation. This type of transformation, known as collineatory, does of course leave the latent roots unchanged, and we notice that the trace of $\mathbf{C}$ is equal to that of $\mathbf{A}$.

12.1. Danielewsky's Method

The transformation of $\mathbf{A}$ to the form of the companion matrix is carried out by Danielewsky one row at a time. The procedure can be readily demonstrated on a 4×4 matrix.

$$\mathbf{A} = \begin{bmatrix} a_{11} & a_{12} & a_{13} & a_{14} \\ a_{21} & a_{22} & a_{23} & a_{24} \\ a_{31} & a_{32} & a_{33} & a_{34} \\ a_{41} & a_{42} & a_{43} & a_{44} \end{bmatrix}$$

The first stage uses the matrix $\mathbf{E}_1$ below, and its inverse $\mathbf{E}_1^{-1}$—

$$\mathbf{E}_1 = \begin{bmatrix} 1 & 0 & 0 & 0 \\ 0 & 1 & 0 & 0 \\ e_{31} & e_{32} & e_{33} & e_{34} \\ 0 & 0 & 0 & 1 \end{bmatrix} \qquad \mathbf{E}_1^{-1} = \begin{bmatrix} 1 & 0 & 0 & 0 \\ 0 & 1 & 0 & 0 \\ a_{41} & a_{42} & a_{43} & a_{44} \\ 0 & 0 & 0 & 1 \end{bmatrix}$$

where $e_{33} = 1/a_{43}$ and $e_{3j} = -a_{4j}/a_{43}$ $(j = 1, 2, 4)$

Notice that the elements involved are those in the last row of $\mathbf{A}$, a_{43} being used as a pivotal element.

* A. Danielewsky, *Trans. Mosc. Math. Soc.*, **44** (1937), 169. As described in § 12.1, the method is slightly modified from the original, and follows the lines suggested by H. Wayland, *Quart. Appl. Math.*, **2** (1945/6), 277. This paper is a valuable summary of methods of expanding determinantal equations.

Then

$$\mathbf{C}_1 = \mathbf{A}\mathbf{E}_1 = \begin{bmatrix} c_{11} & c_{12} & c_{13} & c_{14} \\ c_{21} & c_{22} & c_{23} & c_{24} \\ c_{31} & c_{32} & c_{33} & c_{34} \\ 0 & 0 & 1 & 0 \end{bmatrix}$$

where $\quad c_{i3} = a_{i3}e_{33}; \; c_{ij} = a_{ij} + a_{i3}e_{3j} \quad (j = 1, 2, 4)$

Premultiplication by $\mathbf{E}_1^{-1}$ now affects only the third row, thus—

$$\mathbf{D}_1 = \mathbf{E}_i^{-1}\mathbf{A}\mathbf{E}_1 = \begin{bmatrix} c_{11} & c_{12} & c_{13} & c_{14} \\ c_{21} & c_{22} & c_{23} & c_{24} \\ d_{31} & d_{32} & d_{33} & d_{34} \\ 0 & 0 & 1 & 0 \end{bmatrix}$$

where $\quad d_{3j} = a_{41}c_{1j} + a_{42}c_{2j} + a_{43}c_{3j} \quad (j = 1, 2, 4)$

$$d_{33} = a_{41}c_{13} + a_{42}c_{23} + a_{43}c_{33} + a_{44}$$

The next stage is performed with the matrices

$$\mathbf{E}_2 = \begin{bmatrix} 1 & 0 & 0 & 0 \\ e_{21} & e_{22} & e_{23} & e_{24} \\ 0 & 0 & 1 & 0 \\ 0 & 0 & 0 & 1 \end{bmatrix} \qquad \mathbf{E}_2^{-1} = \begin{bmatrix} 1 & 0 & 0 & 0 \\ d_{31} & d_{32} & d_{33} & d_{34} \\ 0 & 0 & 1 & 0 \\ 0 & 0 & 0 & 1 \end{bmatrix}$$

where $\quad e_{22} = 1/d_{32}; \; e_{2j} = - d_{3j}/d_{32} \quad (j = 1, 3, 4)$

and leads to

$$\mathbf{D}_2 = \mathbf{E}_2^{-1}\mathbf{D}_1\mathbf{E}_2 = \begin{bmatrix} c_{11}' & c_{12}' & c_{13}' & c_{14}' \\ d_{21} & d_{22} & d_{23} & d_{24} \\ 0 & 1 & 0 & 0 \\ 0 & 0 & 1 & 0 \end{bmatrix}$$

Now the elements $d_{21}, d_{22}, d_{23}, d_{24}$ are used in a similar way with d_{21} as pivot, to give the final result

$$\mathbf{D}_3 = \mathbf{E}_3^{-1}\mathbf{D}_2\mathbf{E}_3 = \begin{bmatrix} d_{11} & d_{12} & d_{13} & d_{14} \\ 1 & 0 & 0 & 0 \\ 0 & 1 & 0 & 0 \\ 0 & 0 & 1 & 0 \end{bmatrix}$$

which is in the standard form. The first row gives the coefficients of $D(\lambda)$.

In practice it is unnecessary to write out the matrices $\mathbf{D}_1, \mathbf{D}_2, \mathbf{D}_3$

fully, but only those rows which differ from $\mathbf{C}_1$, $\mathbf{C}_2$, $\mathbf{C}_3$. It is a convenience to write the elements used to form e_{ij} as a column beside the next $\mathbf{C}$ matrix; this assists in forming d_{ij}. The first stage appears as follows—

$$
\begin{array}{c}
\\
\mathbf{A}
\end{array}
\begin{bmatrix}
a_{11} & a_{12} & a_{13} & a_{14} \\
a_{21} & a_{22} & a_{23} & a_{24} \\
a_{31} & a_{32} & a_{33} & a_{34} \\
a_{41} & a_{42} & a_{43} & a_{44}
\end{bmatrix}
\begin{array}{c}
\Sigma \\
a_{15} \\
a_{25} \\
a_{35} \\
a_{45}
\end{array}
\quad \Sigma'
$$

$$\mathbf{e}_3 \qquad -e_{31} \quad -e_{32} \quad 1 \quad -e_{34} \quad -e_{35} \qquad\qquad -e_{3j} = a_{4j}/a_{43}$$
$$(j \neq 3)$$

$$
\mathbf{C}_1
\begin{bmatrix}
a_{41} \\
a_{42} \\
a_{43} \\
a_{44}
\end{bmatrix}
\begin{bmatrix}
c_{11} & c_{12} & c_{13} & c_{14} \\
c_{21} & c_{22} & c_{23} & c_{24} \\
c_{31} & c_{32} & c_{33} & c_{34} \\
0 & 0 & 1 & 0
\end{bmatrix}
\begin{array}{c}
c_{15} \\
c_{25} \\
c_{35} \\
1
\end{array}
\begin{array}{c}
c_{15}{}' \\
c_{25}{}' \\
c_{35}{}' \\
\end{array}
\begin{array}{l}
\\
c_{i3} = a_{i3}/a_{43} \\
c_{ij} = a_{ij} + a_{i3}e_{3j} \\
(j \neq 3)
\end{array}
$$

$$\mathbf{d}_3 \qquad d_{31} \quad d_{32} \quad d_{33} \quad d_{34} \quad d_{35}$$
$$\mathbf{e}_2 \qquad -e_{21} \quad 1 \quad -e_{23} \quad -e_{24} \quad -e_{25} \qquad\qquad -e_{2j} = d_{3j}/d_{32}$$
$$(j \neq 2)$$

The element e_{33} need not be written (it is here replaced by 1) as the elements e_{31}, e_{32}, e_{34}, c_{13}, c_{23}, c_{33} can all be formed as multiples of $1/a_{43}$. The remaining elements in $\mathbf{C}_1$ are best formed row by row, the first row with a_{13} as a constant multiplier, and so on. The row $\mathbf{d}_3$ is obtained by taking products of the column on the left of $\mathbf{C}_1$ with columns of $\mathbf{C}_1$ in turn, and all is then ready for the next stage of reduction.

The extra columns on the right are used for checking; each element in the Σ column is the sum of 4 elements in the same row, those in the Σ' column omit the elements in the pivotal column. If the Σ column is treated like any other column in $\mathbf{A}$ (the pivotal column excepted), the results should equal the quantities in the Σ' column at the following stage; thus it is obvious that

$$a_{15} - a_{13}(1 - e_{31} - e_{32} - e_{34}) = c_{11} + c_{12} + c_{14} = c_{15}{}'$$

There are occasional difficulties in this method which arise when the element next required for a pivot turns out to be zero. The procedure in such an event is described in the second of the following examples.

EXAMPLE 12.1. Find the characteristic function for the matrix

$$\begin{bmatrix} 7 & 4 & 3 & 2 \\ -4 & 2 & 1 & 0 \\ 5 & 3 & 0 & 6 \\ 7 & -2 & 2 & 3 \end{bmatrix}$$

We set out the calculation as outlined above

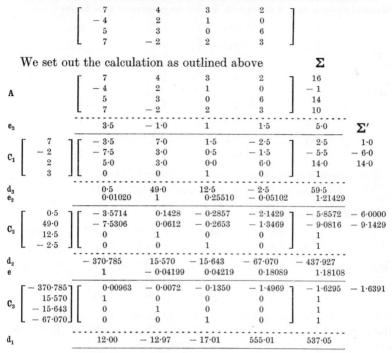

The coefficients of $D(\lambda)$ must be integers, therefore we round off the last row and write

$$D(\lambda) = \lambda^4 - 12\lambda^3 + 13\lambda^2 + 17\lambda - 555$$

EXAMPLE 12.2. Find the characteristic functions of the matrices

(a)
$$\begin{bmatrix} 7 & -3 & 3 & 2 \\ -4 & 2 & 1 & 0 \\ 5 & 3 & 0 & 6 \\ 7 & -2 & 2 & 3 \end{bmatrix}$$
(b)
$$\begin{bmatrix} -2 & -11 & 2 & 5 & 3 \\ 0 & -3 & 0 & -1 & -2 \\ -1 & -4 & 2 & 1 & 0 \\ -1 & 5 & 3 & 0 & 6 \\ 1 & 7 & -2 & 2 & 3 \end{bmatrix}$$

(a) This differs from the previous matrix only in the element a_{12}, which is now -3. The result is that the pivotal element in $\mathbf{D}_1$ vanishes, the determinant $D(\lambda)$ at this stage being

$$\begin{vmatrix} -3\cdot5 - \lambda & 0 & 1\cdot5 & -2\cdot5 \\ -7\cdot5 & 3 - \lambda & 0\cdot5 & -1\cdot5 \\ 0\cdot5 & 0 & 12\cdot5 - \lambda & -2\cdot5 \\ 0 & 0 & 1 & -\lambda \end{vmatrix}$$

The situation can be retrieved by (i) adding column 1 to column 2, (ii) subtracting row 2 from row 1, the successive stages being

$$\begin{vmatrix} -3\cdot5 - \lambda & -3\cdot5 - \lambda & 1\cdot5 & -2\cdot5 \\ -7\cdot5 & -4\cdot5 - \lambda & 0\cdot5 & -1\cdot5 \\ 0\cdot5 & 0\cdot5 & 12\cdot5 - \lambda & -2\cdot5 \\ 0 & 0 & 1 & -\lambda \end{vmatrix}$$

and

$$\begin{vmatrix} 4 - \lambda & 1 & 1 & -1 \\ -7\cdot5 & -4\cdot5 - \lambda & 0\cdot5 & -1\cdot5 \\ 0\cdot5 & 0\cdot5 & 12\cdot5 - \lambda & -2\cdot5 \\ 0 & 0 & 1 & -\lambda \end{vmatrix}$$

The course of reduction can now be resumed. The result is that

$$D(\lambda) = \lambda^4 - 12\lambda^3 - 15\lambda^2 + 136\lambda - 330$$

(b) After one stage of reduction

$$|\mathbf{D}_1| = D(\lambda) = \begin{vmatrix} -4\cdot5 - \lambda & -28\cdot5 & 7\cdot0 & 2\cdot5 & -4\cdot5 \\ 0\cdot5 & 0\cdot5 - \lambda & -1\cdot0 & -0\cdot5 & -0\cdot5 \\ -1\cdot5 & -7\cdot5 & 3 - \lambda & 0\cdot5 & -1\cdot5 \\ 0 & 0 & 0 & 1 - \lambda & 7 \\ 0 & 0 & 0 & 1 & -\lambda \end{vmatrix}$$

Here not only does the pivotal element in row 4 vanish, but so do the elements to its left, and the device used in (a) is useless. However, in such a case the determinant factorizes, thus

$$D(\lambda) = \begin{vmatrix} -4\cdot5 - \lambda & -28\cdot5 & 7\cdot0 \\ 0\cdot5 & 0\cdot5 - \lambda & -1\cdot0 \\ -1\cdot5 & -7\cdot5 & 3 - \lambda \end{vmatrix} \times \begin{vmatrix} 1 - \lambda & 7 \\ 1 & -\lambda \end{vmatrix}.$$

When this happens the determinant on the right will always be found to be in the standard form, and that on the left can be expanded directly or reduced by the general method.

Finally $D(\lambda) = -(\lambda^3 + \lambda^2 + 3\lambda - 6)(\lambda^2 - \lambda - 7)$

A more extreme instance of this kind would arise if the fourth row of $D(\lambda)$ were $(0, 0, 0, -\lambda, 0)$. This means that $(-\lambda)^2$ is a factor of $D(\lambda)$, which becomes $-(\lambda^3 + \lambda^2 + 3\lambda - 6)\lambda^2$.

12.2. Samuelson's Method

An ingenious method which involves about the same amount of computation as Danielewsky's, was devised by Samuelson.* The approach is quite different, however, and we shall first describe the computation before indicating briefly the basis of it.

The matrix **A** is first partitioned as shown on next page, **R** and **S**

* P. Samuelson, *Ann. Math. Stat.*, **13** (1942), 424.

being single-row and column matrices with $(n-1)$ elements, and **M** a square matrix of order $(n-1)$.

$$\mathbf{A} = \begin{bmatrix} a_{11} & a_{12} \ldots a_{1n} \\ a_{21} & a_{22} \ldots a_{2n} \\ \cdot & \cdot \\ \cdot & \cdot \\ \cdot & \\ a_{n1} & a_{n2} \ldots a_{nn} \end{bmatrix} = \begin{bmatrix} a_{11} & \mathbf{R} \\ \mathbf{S} & \mathbf{M} \end{bmatrix}$$

The following matrix, possessing n rows and $2n$ columns, is then set up. This is done by forming the row matrices $\mathbf{RM}, \ldots, \mathbf{RM}^{n-1}$ first, and then the products $\mathbf{RMS}, \ldots, \mathbf{RM}^{n-2}\mathbf{S}$.

$$\mathbf{B} = \begin{bmatrix} \mathbf{R} & 0 & 0 & 0 & 0 & \ldots 0 & 0 & 1 & -a_{11} \\ \mathbf{RM} & 0 & 0 & 0 & 0 & \ldots 0 & 1 & -a_{11} & -\mathbf{RS} \\ \mathbf{RM}^2 & 0 & 0 & 0 & 0 & \ldots 1 & -a_{11} & -\mathbf{RS} & -\mathbf{RMS} \\ \cdot & & & & & & & & \\ \mathbf{RM}^{n-1} & 1 & -a_{11} & -\mathbf{RS} & -\mathbf{RMS} & \ldots & & & -\mathbf{RM}^{n-2}\mathbf{S} \end{bmatrix}$$ (12.15

This matrix arises from a set of n homogeneous linear equations, $\mathbf{By} = 0$. These must be reduced by eliminating $(n-1)$ unwanted variables, corresponding to the columns on the left of the vertical line, to a single equation of $(n+1)$ terms. The coefficients of this ultimate equation are in fact the coefficients of the polynomial $D(\lambda)$.

The elimination is best carried out by a simple modification of the method of matrix resolution described in Chapter 11 for square matrices. In this instance we can resolve **B** into a product of the form **LU**, where

$$\mathbf{L} = \begin{bmatrix} l_{11} & 0 & \ldots & 0 \\ l_{21} & l_{22} & & 0 \\ \cdot & & & \\ \cdot & & & \\ \cdot & & & \\ l_{n1} & l_{n2} & & l_{nn} \end{bmatrix} \quad \mathbf{U} = \begin{bmatrix} 1 & u_{12} & \ldots u_{1n} & \ldots u_{1m} \\ 0 & 1 & u_{2n} & u_{2m} \\ \cdot & & & \\ \cdot & & & \\ 0 & 0 & \ldots 1 & \ldots u_{nm} \end{bmatrix}$$

with the usual rule that $b_{ij} = R_i(\mathbf{L}) \times R_j(\mathbf{U'})$. It is probably most convenient to set out the calculation for row $\times$ row products of **L** and **U'**; though column $\times$ column products of **L'** and **U** may also be used. With the first alternative, the order of calculation is as follows—

1. First column of $\mathbf{L}$ = first column of $\mathbf{B}$.
2. First column of $\mathbf{U'}$, given by
$$u_1 = b_{1j}/l_{11} = b_{1j}/b_{11} \quad (j = 2, \ldots, m)$$

3. Second column of **L**, given by

$$l_{i2} = - l_{i1}u_{12} + b_{i2} \quad (i = 2, \ldots, n)$$

4. Second column of **U'**, given by

$$l_{22}u_{2j} = b_{2j} - l_{21}u_{1j} \quad (j = 3, \ldots, m)$$

and so on. Column sums of **B'**, **L** and **U'** are used for checking as shown in the following example. The calculation is complete when the final column of **U'** is obtained, as this contains the coefficients of $D(\lambda)$.

EXAMPLE 12.3. Find $D(\lambda)$ for the matrix in Example 12.2 (b).

Using the notation given above, we have

R $= [- 11, \quad 2, \quad 5, \quad 3]$	**S** $= \{0, \quad -1, \quad -1, \quad 1\}$
RM $= [71, \quad 13, \quad 19, \quad 61]$	**RS** $= - 4$
RM^2 $= [257, \quad - 39, \quad 64, \quad 155]$	**RMS** $= 29$
RM^3 $= [790, \quad - 196, \quad 14, \quad 335]$	**RM^{2}S** $= 130$
RM^4 $= [829, \quad - 1020, \quad - 316, \quad - 491]$	**RM^{3}S** $= 517$

The matrix **B**, shown transposed, and the subsequent resolution into **LU**, appears as follows—

						Sum	
B'	-11	71	257	790	829	$1936 = \sigma_1$	
	2	13	-39	-196	-1020	$-1240 = \sigma_2$	
	5	19	64	14	-316	$-214 = \sigma_3$	
	3	61	155	335	-491	$63 = \sigma$	
	0	0	0	0	1		
	0	0	0	1	2		
	0	0	1	2	4		
	0	1	2	4	-29		
	1	2	4	-29	-130		
	2	4	-29	-130	-517		

	s_1	s_2	s_3	s_4	s_5
Sum	2	171	415	791	-1667

L	-11				
	71	25·9091			
	257	7·7273	165·526		
	790	$- 52·3636$	476·715	133·641	
	829	$- 869·2727$	1781·065	267·274	1

Sum check	1936	$- 888·0000$	2423·307	400·915	1

U'	1				
	$- 0·181818$	1			
	$- 0·454545$	1·97895	1		
	$- 0·272727$	3·10175	1·21505	1	
	0	0	0	0	1
	0	0	0	0·00748	0·00
	0	0	0·00604	$- 0·00658$	$- 5·00$
	0	0·03860	0·01028	0·00838	$- 16·00$
	$- 0·090909$	0·32632	0·15008	$- 0·08710$	$- 15·00$
	$- 0·181818$	0·65263	0·07663	0·08441	42·00

Sum check	$- 0·181818$	7·09824	2·45808	1·00659	7·02

The following checks are applied—
1. When $C_j(\mathbf{L})$ is complete, $R_j(\mathbf{U}') \times$ sum row $(\mathbf{L}) = \sigma_j$.
2. When $C_j(\mathbf{U}')$ is complete, $R_j(\mathbf{L}) \times$ sum row $(\mathbf{U}') = s_j$.
From the final column of $\mathbf{U}'$,

$$D(\lambda) = \lambda^5 - 5\lambda^3 - 16\lambda^2 - 15\lambda + 42$$

The detailed theory of Samuelson's method is rather long, and the following summary must suffice. Samuelson replaces λ in (12.11) by the differential operator d/dt, and so obtains the differential equation of nth order

$$D(d/dt)x_1(t) = (-1)^n\{x_1^{(n)}(t) - p_1x_1^{(n-1)}(t) - \ldots - p_nx_1(t)\} \quad (12.16)$$

where $x_1(t)$ is a function of t, which forms the first element in a single-column vector function

$$\mathbf{x}(t) = \{x_1(t),\ x_2(t),\ \ldots,\ x_n(t)\}$$

The n equations in (12.1) then become

$$\mathbf{A}\mathbf{x}(t) = \mathbf{x}'(t)$$

and by adding the sets of equations denoted by

$$\mathbf{A}\mathbf{x}'(t) = \mathbf{x}^{(2)}(t)$$
$$\mathbf{A}\mathbf{x}^{(2)}(t) = \mathbf{x}^{(3)}(t)$$
$$\cdot$$
$$\cdot$$
$$\mathbf{A}\mathbf{x}^{(n-1)}(t) = \mathbf{x}^{(n)}(t)$$

he obtains in all n^2 homogeneous equations in the $n(n+1)$ variables $x_i(t)$, $x_i'(t)$, $\ldots$, $x_i^{(n)}(t)$ $(i = 1,\ 2,\ \ldots,\ n)$. From these equations one can eliminate all $(n^2 - 1)$ variables which do not involve the suffix 1; the remaining equation is identical with the differential equation (12.16). In the reduction, $n(n-1)$ variables can be removed analytically and this leads to the matrix $\mathbf{B}$; the further removal of $(n-1)$ variables must be done numerically, as shown above.

12.3. Lanczos' Method

Further variety is provided by a method described by Lanczos in 1950, which is attractive both for the essential simplicity of the idea and the ease with which it can be applied. When the matrix is symmetric the number of elementary numerical operations involved is comparable with the previous two methods, but for unsymmetric matrices it may be about twice as great.

When the matrix $\mathbf{A}$ is unsymmetrical, the first and major step is to choose arbitrary column and row matrices, $\mathbf{b}_0$ and $\mathbf{d}_0$ respectively, and to form from them the sequences

$$\mathbf{b}_k = \mathbf{A}^k\mathbf{b}_0, \quad \mathbf{d}_k = \mathbf{d}_0\mathbf{A}^k \quad (k = 1, \ldots, n)$$

by repeated pre- or post-multiplication by $\mathbf{A}$; $\mathbf{b}_0$ and $\mathbf{d}_0$ may be quite independent, but it is often convenient to make $\mathbf{d}_0$ the transpose of $\mathbf{b}_0$. It is then possible to form a sequence of numbers by taking scalar products of pairs of row and column matrices, thus

$$c_{i+j} = \mathbf{d}_i\mathbf{b}_j = \mathbf{d}_0\mathbf{A}^{i+j}\mathbf{b}_0 \qquad (12.17)$$

It should be noticed that $\mathbf{d}_i\mathbf{b}_j = \mathbf{d}_{i+s}\mathbf{b}_{j-s}$, as this enables useful numerical checks to be made. When $\mathbf{A}$ is symmetrical of course only one sequence of matrices need be calculated if $\mathbf{d}_0 = \mathbf{b}_0'$.

Now, because $\mathbf{A}$ has only a limited number of latent vectors, the sequences $\mathbf{b}_k$ and $\mathbf{d}_k$ also have the property that only a certain number of them can be independent. If this number be m, which cannot exceed n, then $\mathbf{b}_m$ is not independent of $\mathbf{b}_0, \ldots, \mathbf{b}_{m-1}$, and can be expressed as a linear combination of them; similarly for $\mathbf{d}_m$ and $\mathbf{d}_0, \ldots, \mathbf{d}_{m-1}$. Likewise only m of the numbers c_k are independent, $c_s(s \geqslant m)$ being expressible as a combination of preceding members of the sequence. These facts can be used to derive the characteristic function of $\mathbf{A}$.

First, if we assume a relation of the form

$$s_0\mathbf{b}_0 + s_1\mathbf{b}_1 + \ldots + s_{m-1}\mathbf{b}_{m-1} + s_m\mathbf{b}_m = 0$$

then by forming scalar products with $\mathbf{d}_0, \ldots, \mathbf{d}_m$ in turn, we obtain a set of $(m + 1)$ equations homogeneous and linear in the coefficients s_j

$$\left.\begin{array}{l} c_0s_0 + c_1s_1 + \ldots + c_ms_m = 0 \\ c_1s_0 + c_2s_1 + \ldots + c_{m+1}s_m = 0 \\ \qquad \cdot \\ \qquad \cdot \\ c_ms_0 + c_{m+1}s_1 + \ldots + c_{2m}s_m = 0 \end{array}\right\} \qquad (12.18)$$

This consistent set of equations we shall designate L_m. They suffice to determine the coefficients s_j, if for convenience we assume $s_m = 1$. The determinant of the symmetrical array formed by the c's is of course zero. The solution is important because it can be shown that the polynomial

$$G_m(\lambda) = s_0 + s_1\lambda + s_2\lambda^2 + \ldots + s_m\lambda^m \qquad (12.19)$$

vanishes only if λ is equal to one of the latent roots of **A**, i.e. factors of $G_m(\lambda) = 0$ are also factors of $D(\lambda) = 0$. Clearly if $m = n$, as often happens, then $G_m(\lambda)$ must be identical with $D(\lambda)$, but we shall not in general assume this, as it will appear later that there are various circumstances in which $m < n$. We quote the above theorem without proof, though Nos. 3 and 4 of Exercises 12 are interesting in this connexion.

The solution of (12.18) is derived by Lanczos by an elegant process using very simple recurrence relations, rather than by one of the standard methods. The basis of it can be understood by considering the following two sets of equations, $\mathbf{L}_k$ and $\mathbf{L}_{k+1/2}$, which differ from (12.18) in that the number of equations and unknowns is $k + 1$, and the last equation in each set is in-homogeneous.

$$\mathbf{L}_k: \qquad \left.\begin{aligned} \sum_{j=0}^{k} c_{i+j}s_j^{(k)} &= 0, \quad i = 0, \ldots, k - 1 \\ &= h_k, \; i = k \end{aligned}\right\} \qquad (12.20)$$

with
$$s_k^{(k)} = 1$$

$$\mathbf{L}_{k+1/2}: \qquad \left.\begin{aligned} \sum_{j=1}^{k+1} c_{i+j}s_j^{(k+1/2)} &= 0, \quad i = 0, \ldots, k - 1 \\ &= h_{k+1/2}, \; i = k \end{aligned}\right\} \qquad (12.21)$$

with
$$s_k^{(k+1/2)} = 1$$

The quantities h_k and $h_{k+1/2}$ may be regarded temporarily as arbitrary. Now by combining corresponding equations in each set in the ratio $-(h_{k+1/2}/h_k):1$, we can define a new set $\mathbf{L}_{k+1}$, containing $(k + 2)$ equations, having the form

$$\mathbf{L}_{k+1}: \qquad \left.\begin{aligned} \sum_{j=0}^{k+1} c_{i+j}s_j^{(k+1)} &= 0, \quad i = 0, 1, \ldots, k \\ &= h_{k+1}, \; i = k + 1 \end{aligned}\right\} \qquad (12.22)$$

The final equation is in effect a definition of h_{k+1}, the values of $s_j^{(k+1)}$ being determined by the remainder, or given by the following recurrence relations—

$$\left.\begin{aligned} s_0^{(k+1)} &= \rho_k s_0^{(k)} && \text{where} \quad \rho_k = -h_{k+1/2}/h_k \\ s_1^{(k+1)} &= \rho_k s_1^{(k)} + s_1^{(k+1/2)} \\ &\;\;\cdot \\ &\;\;\cdot \\ s_k^{(k+1)} &= \rho_k s_k^{(k)} + s_k^{(k+1/2)} \quad \text{and} \; s_{k+1}^{(k+1)} = 1 \end{aligned}\right\} \qquad (12.23)$$

Similarly the combination of $\mathbf{L}_{k+1/2}$ and $\mathbf{L}_{k+1}$ in the ratio $- (h_{k+1}/h_{k+1/2}) : 1$, but excluding the first equation of $\mathbf{L}_{k+1}$, yields the set

$$\mathbf{L}_{k+3/2}: \quad \left. \begin{aligned} \sum_{j=1}^{k+2} c_{i+j} s_j^{(k+3/2)} &= 0, \qquad i = 0, 1, \ldots, k \\ &= h_{k+3/2}, \; i = k + 1 \end{aligned} \right\} \quad (12.24)$$

in which

$$\left. \begin{aligned} s_j^{(k+3/2)} &= \rho_{k+1/2} s_j^{(k+1/2)} + s_{j-1}^{(k+1)} \\ \rho_{k+1/2} &= - h_{k+1}/h_{k+1/2} \quad \text{and} \quad s_{k+2}^{(k+3/2)} = 1 \end{aligned} \right\} \quad (12.25)$$

The final equation in (12.24) again acts as a definition of $h_{k+3/2}$.

Thus by the two similar processes

$$\rho_k \mathbf{L}_k + \mathbf{L}_{k+1/2} \to \mathbf{L}_{k+1}$$
$$\rho_{k+1/2} \mathbf{L}_{k+1/2} + \mathbf{L}_{k+1} \to \mathbf{L}_{k+3/2}$$

two further sets of equations, $\mathbf{L}_{k+1}$ and $\mathbf{L}_{k+3/2}$, have been built up, exactly similar to $\mathbf{L}_k$ and $\mathbf{L}_{k+1/2}$ but each containing one more equation and one more unknown. The building up could be continued indefinitely but for the fact that only a limited number of the c_{i+j} are independent. This implies that eventually some h_m vanishes automatically, because c_{2m} is a linear combination of $c_m, \ldots, c_{2m-1}$. The process then comes to a full stop with the set of equations $\mathbf{L}_m$ which has precisely the form (12.18). Accordingly

$$G_m(\lambda) = s_0^{(m)} + s_1^{(m)} \lambda + s_2^{(m)} \lambda^2 + \ldots + \lambda^m = 0$$

is the equation of which the roots are also roots of $D(\lambda) = 0$.

Before considering the problem of missing roots associated with cases in which $m < n$, we shall give a simple example which shows how the computation can conveniently be laid out and in which the reader can easily verify the various steps.

EXAMPLE 12.4. Find the characteristic function of the matrix

$$\mathbf{A} = \begin{bmatrix} 2 & -2 & 3 \\ 1 & 1 & 1 \\ 1 & 3 & -1 \end{bmatrix}$$

Assume $\quad \mathbf{b}_0 = \{ \; 0, 1, \quad 0\}$ and $\quad \mathbf{d}_0 = [\; 0, 1, \; 0]$

Then $\quad \mathbf{b}_1 = \{- 2, 1, \quad 3\} \qquad \mathbf{d}_1 = [\; 1, 1, \; 1]$

$\qquad\quad \mathbf{b}_2 = \{ \quad 3, 2, - 2\} \qquad \mathbf{d}_2 = [\; 4, 2, \; 3]$

$\qquad\quad \mathbf{b}_3 = \{- 4, 3, \quad 11\} \qquad \mathbf{d}_3 = [13, 3, 11]$

$\qquad\quad c_k = 1, 1, 2, 3, 10, 23, 78$

The subsequent calculation is laid out as follows—

	h_0 ρ_0	$h_{1/2}$ $\rho_{1/2}$	h_1 ρ_1	$h_{3/2}$ $\rho_{3/2}$	h_2 ρ_2	$h_{5/2}$	h_3
c_0	1						
c_1		1	$s_0^{(1)}$				
c_2			1	$s_1^{(3/2)}$	$s_0^{(2)}$		
c_3				1	$s_1^{(2)}$	$s_1^{(5/2)}$	$s_0^{(3)}$
c_4					1	$s_2^{(5/2)}$	$s_1^{(3)}$
c_5						1	$s_2^{(3)}$
c_6							1

σ_0	$\sigma_{1/2}$	σ_1	$\sigma_{3/2}$	σ_2	$\sigma_{5/2}$	σ_3
1	1	1	-1	5	30	0
-1	-1	1	5	-6	0	

1	1				Note $h_3 = \rho_{5/2} = 0$		
1		1	-1				
2			1	-2	-1		
3				1	-1	-11	6
10					1	4	-5
23						1	-2
78							1

1	1	0	-1	-1	-6	0

The calculation is begun by assuming $h_0 = 1$. Then

$$h_{1/2} = c_1 = -\rho_0 = -s_0^{(1)}$$

Thereafter the quantities in the table are calculated in the following order—

$$h_1, \rho_{1/2}, s_1^{(3/2)}; \quad h_{3/2}, \rho_1, s_1^{(2)}, s_0^{(2)};$$
$$h_2, \rho_{3/2}, s_2^{(5/2)}, s_1^{(5/2)}; \quad h_{5/2}, \rho_2, s_2^{(3)}, s_1^{(3)}, s_0^{(3)}$$

The following points should be noticed—

1. Any head number h_k or $h_{k+1/2}$ is formed by the product-sum of the column below with the c_k column.

2. ρ_k, $\rho_{k+1/2}$ are defined by (12.23) and (12.25).

3. The recurrence relations (12.23) and (12.25) operate in the following way; to obtain quantities in the column $k + 1$, each element in the column below ρ_k is multiplied by ρ_k, the number on the same level in column $k + 1/2$ is added, and the result is placed in column $k + 1$, *but shifted down one row.* Column $k + 3/2$ is formed similarly from columns $k + 1/2$ and $k + 1$.

4. Column sums are formed, and a similar recurrence relation applied to test each column as it is completed.

The result of the calculation, from the final column, is that
$$G_3(\lambda) = D(\lambda) = \lambda^3 - 2\lambda^2 - 5\lambda + 6$$
$$= (\lambda - 1)(\lambda - 3)(\lambda + 2)$$

It is now necessary to discuss the occasions on which m falls short of n, so giving a polynomial $G_m(\lambda)$ of degree less than that of $D(\lambda)$.

1. If $\mathbf{b}_0$ should happen to be orthogonal to one of the latent row vectors of $\mathbf{A}$ say $\mathbf{v}_i$, then the factor $(\lambda - \lambda_i)$ is overlooked and omitted from $G_m(\lambda)$; similarly if $\mathbf{d}_0$ is orthogonal to the latent column vector $\mathbf{u}_i$.

The reader will soon find an example of this by repeating Example 12.4 with $\mathbf{b}_0 = \{1, 0, 0\}$, when the factor $(\lambda + 2)$ is lost. When only one root is lost, the trace of $\mathbf{A}$ will immediately reveal what its value is; otherwise missing factors may be recovered by repeating the calculation with a different $\mathbf{b}_0$ or $\mathbf{d}_0$.

2. When $\mathbf{A}$ is not defective but $D(\lambda)$ has a multiple factor $(\lambda - \lambda_s)^q$ Lanczos' method treats λ_s as a simple root and $G_m(\lambda)$ contains only the factor $(\lambda - \lambda_s)$. This result is unaffected by altering $\mathbf{d}_0$ or $\mathbf{b}_0$ but the sum of the roots may show which root is multiple.

3. When $\mathbf{A}$ is defective, and λ_s is a root with multiplicity q and degeneracy p, Lanczos method will leave a factor $(\lambda - \lambda_s)^{q-p+1}$ in $G_m(\lambda)$, in contrast to (2). The degree of such a factor is an indication of the degree of deficiency in $\mathbf{A}$.

Exercises 12, No. 5 provides examples of both (2) and (3).

12.4. Simplification of More General Determinants

The presence of λ need not be confined to the diagonal terms of the determinant, as hitherto assumed. A more complex problem is presented by a determinant in which the general element is $(a_1 + \lambda a_0)_{ij}$, so that (12.4) is replaced by the equation

$$|\mathbf{A}_1 + \lambda \mathbf{A}_0| = 0 \qquad (12.26)$$

where $\mathbf{A}_1$ and $\mathbf{A}_0$ are both square matrices of order n. This is the condition of consistency of a set of equations, which in matrix notation may be written as $(\mathbf{A}_1 + \lambda \mathbf{A}_0)\mathbf{x} = 0$. Usually the most rapid approach of solving these is to premultiply by the reciprocal matrix $\mathbf{A}_0^{-1}$, thus transforming them to the simpler form

$$(\mathbf{A}_0^{-1}\mathbf{A}_1 + \lambda \mathbf{I}_n)\mathbf{x} = 0 \qquad (12.27)$$

which is similar to (12.3). The operation of forming $\mathbf{A}_0^{-1}\mathbf{A}_1$ can be carried out by one of the methods described in Chapter 11, provided $|\mathbf{A}_0| \neq 0$. If $\mathbf{A}_0$ is singular, however, the determinant

(12.26) must be expanded by some such method as that given in § 12.5 below.

The equation $|\mathbf{A}_2 + \mathbf{A}_1\lambda + \mathbf{A}_0\lambda^2| = 0$, where $\mathbf{A}_0$, $\mathbf{A}_1$ and $\mathbf{A}_2$ are all square matrices of order n, requires a more elaborate transformation. We consider the set of n differential equations represented by

$$(\mathbf{A}_0 D^2 + \mathbf{A}_1 D + \mathbf{A}_2)\mathbf{x}(t) = 0 \tag{12.28}$$

where $\lambda = D = d/dt$ and $\mathbf{x}(t) = \{x_1(t),\ x_2(t),\ \ldots,\ x_n(t)\}$

If $|\mathbf{A}_0| \neq 0$, it is possible to premultiply by $\mathbf{A}_0^{-1}$, giving

$$(\mathbf{I}_n D^2 + \mathbf{A}_0^{-1}\mathbf{A}_1 D + \mathbf{A}_0^{-1}\mathbf{A}_2)\mathbf{x}(t) = 0$$

This may be written

$$(\mathbf{I}_n D + \mathbf{A}_0^{-1}\mathbf{A}_1)\mathbf{x}'(t) + \mathbf{A}_0^{-1}\mathbf{A}_2\mathbf{x}(t) = 0$$

and regarded as a set of n simultaneous equations in the $2n$ unknowns $x_i(t)$, $x_i'(t)$. To these may be added the n equations $\mathbf{x}' = D\mathbf{x}$, and the $2n$ equations are compatible only if

$$\begin{vmatrix} -\mathbf{A}_0^{-1}\mathbf{A}_1 - \mathbf{I}_n\lambda & -\mathbf{A}_0^{-1}\mathbf{A}_2 \\ \mathbf{I}_n & -\mathbf{I}_n\lambda \end{vmatrix} = 0 \tag{12.29}$$

D being replaced by λ. Thus we have a determinantal equation similar to (12.4) but of degree $2n$, and this can be expanded by methods already described. Again another method must be used if $\mathbf{A}_0$ is singular.

EXAMPLE 12.5. Consider the expansion of the determinantal equation

$$\begin{vmatrix} 2 & +3\lambda^2 & -2 + 3\lambda + 2\lambda^2 & 3 + 2\lambda + \lambda^2 \\ 1 + \lambda + 6\lambda^2 & 1 + \lambda + 3\lambda^2 & 1 + \lambda + \lambda^2 \\ 1 + 2\lambda + 3\lambda^2 & 3 + 2\lambda + \lambda^2 & -1 + \lambda + \lambda^2 \end{vmatrix} = 0$$

Here

$$\mathbf{A}_0^{-1} = \begin{bmatrix} -2/3 & 1/3 & 1/3 \\ 1 & 0 & -1 \\ 1 & -1 & 1 \end{bmatrix} \qquad \mathbf{A}_0 = \begin{bmatrix} 3 & 2 & 1 \\ 6 & 3 & 1 \\ 3 & 1 & 1 \end{bmatrix}$$

$$\mathbf{A}_1 = \begin{bmatrix} 0 & 3 & 2 \\ 1 & 1 & 1 \\ 2 & 2 & 1 \end{bmatrix} \qquad \mathbf{A}_0^{-1}\mathbf{A}_1 = \begin{bmatrix} 1 & -1 & -2/3 \\ -2 & 1 & 1 \\ 1 & 4 & 2 \end{bmatrix}$$

$$\mathbf{A}_2 = \begin{bmatrix} 2 & -2 & 3 \\ 1 & 1 & 1 \\ 1 & 3 & -1 \end{bmatrix} \qquad \mathbf{A}_0^{-1}\mathbf{A}_2 = \begin{bmatrix} -2/3 & 8/3 & -2 \\ 1 & -5 & 4 \\ 2 & 0 & 1 \end{bmatrix}$$

It follows from (12.29) that

$$
\begin{vmatrix}
-1-\lambda & 1 & 2/3 & 2/3 & -8/3 & 2 \\
2 & -1-\lambda & -1 & -1 & 5 & -4 \\
-1 & -4 & -2-\lambda & -2 & 0 & -1 \\
1 & 0 & 0 & -\lambda & 0 & 0 \\
0 & 1 & 0 & 0 & -\lambda & 0 \\
0 & 0 & 1 & 0 & 0 & -\lambda
\end{vmatrix} = 0
$$

When expanded, say by Danielewsky's method, this becomes

$$3\lambda^6 + 12\lambda^5 - 15\lambda^4 - 67\lambda^3 - 12\lambda^2 + 6 = 0$$

Wayland has extended this method of transformation to the general type of equation, $|\mathbf{A}_0\lambda^m + \mathbf{A}_1\lambda^{m-1} + \ldots + \mathbf{A}_m| = 0$, though if such equations arise it is usually preferable to expand them by fitting a polynomial directly as described below.

12.5. Direct Fitting by Polynomials

An entirely different approach to the expansion of λ-determinants is possible if one gives to λ a series of evenly spaced values and evaluates the resultant determinants, either directly or by resolving into a product of triangular determinants as in § 11.12. The problem is then one of fitting a given set of data by a polynomial, the degree of which does not exceed a known value n. It is clearly desirable to calculate $(n+2)$ values of $D(\lambda)$, $(n+1)$ to be used in deriving the polynomial and the extra value as a check.

The fitting may be made by means of a Lagrange polynomial, the extra value of λ being inserted finally as an overall check. Alternatively a difference table of $D(\lambda)$ may be prepared, and its accuracy checked by the fact that the nth differences must be constant. The coefficients of the polynomial can then be derived by any standard interpolation formula using differences, e.g. Newton, Bessel, Stirling.

This fitting does not require the full rigour of the least-squares fittings of Chapter 10, since the data can be fitted exactly by the polynomials; nevertheless the techniques developed by Birge and Aitken are applicable here too. Usually it is convenient to compute $D(\lambda)$ for $\lambda = 0$, ± 1, ± 2, etc., so that the central Lagrange polynomial, or interpolation formulas using central differences, are most suitable.

This course has several advantages over the more analytical methods of expansion. First, it is equally applicable to the simple type of equation (12.2) and to the more complex types, though it will be seen later to be relatively more economical as the complexity of the elements of the determinant increases. Secondly, it can be used when the matrix $\mathbf{A}_0$ in (12.26) and (12.28) is singular; and moreover, should the degree of $D(\lambda)$ fall short of n, this is clearly shown by the difference table. Thirdly, the calculation of specific values of $D(\lambda)$ may provide a guide to the position of real roots of $D(\lambda) = 0$.

EXAMPLE 12.6. Expand the determinantal equation of Example 12.5 by fitting a polynomial.

Direct algebraic expansion would here be quicker, though less easily checked, but the example serves to illustrate the method. By taking integral values of λ and evaluating the 3-rowed determinants, the following table is obtained—

λ	$D(\lambda)$						
-4	-262						
		499					
-3	$+237$		-798				
		-299		1122			
-2	-62		324		-1440		
		25		-318		1800	
-1	-37		6		360		-2160
		31		42		-360	
0	-6		48		0		-2160
		79		42		-2520	
1	$+73$		90		-2520		
		169		-2478			
2	$+242$		-2388				
		-2219					
3	-1977						

The value for $\lambda = -4$ is included to check the constancy of the 6th difference.

To determine $D(\lambda)$ we use Stirling's formula (5.9), from which, using the differences in heavy type,

$$D(\lambda) = -6 + 55\lambda + 48\lambda_{[2]} + 42\lambda_{\{3\}} - 1440\lambda_{\{5\}} - 2160\lambda_{[6]}$$
$$= -6 + 55\lambda + 24\lambda^{[2]} + 7\lambda^{\{3\}} - 12\lambda^{\{5\}} - 3\lambda^{[6]}$$

The factorials can be expanded by using the coefficients $T_m{}^j$ in Appendix 1, and finally

$$D(\lambda) = -6 + 12\lambda^2 + 67\lambda^3 + 15\lambda^4 - 12\lambda^5 - 3\lambda^6$$

Incidentally the position of four roots is shown by the above table.

If for some reason the values of λ are not equally spaced, it is necessary to solve a set of $(n+1)$ equations of the form

$$s_0 + s_1\lambda_k + s_2\lambda_k{}^2 + \ldots + s_n\lambda_k{}^n = D(\lambda_k), \quad k = 1, 2, \ldots, n+1$$

This can be done by any suitable method.

12.6. Comparison of Different Methods of Expansion

The most comprehensive analysis of different methods of expanding λ-determinants, including methods not described here,* has been given by Wayland. We can make a comparison most easily by quoting some of his figures for the number of elementary operations of multiplication and divisions required by equations of various orders. Wayland gives estimates of addition and subtraction operations also, but these lie fairly consistently between 75 per cent and 90 per cent of the multiplications and divisions, and are mostly carried out automatically by the calculating machine.

MULTIPLICATION AND DIVISION OPERATIONS

I. Type $|\mathbf{A} - \lambda \mathbf{I}_n| = 0$

n	3	4	5	7	9	Large n
Direct expansion	12	60	320	13692	$\sim 10^6$	$n!e$
Fitting by inter-						
polation formula	46	125	279	972	2525	$n^4/3$
Lanczos { Unsymm.	76	169	316	820	1684	$2n^3$
$(m = n)$ { Symm.	51	108	195	483	963	n^3
Samuelson	21	62	127	369	795	n^3
Danielewsky	22	57	116	330	712	n^3

II. Type $|\mathbf{A}_1 + \mathbf{A}_0 \lambda| = 0$

n	3	4	5	7	9	Large n
Direct expansion	42	200	1050	44702	$\sim 3 . 10^6$	$(4e-2)n!$
Interpolation formula	73	189	404	1315	3254	$n^4/3$
Reciprocation of $\mathbf{A}_0$	58	145	291	820	1765	$5n^3/2$

III. Type $|\mathbf{A}_2 + \mathbf{A}_1 \lambda + \mathbf{A}_0 \lambda^2| = 0$

n	3	4	5	6	7	Large n
Direct expansion	99	480	2535	15408	$\sim 10^5$	$(9e-3)n!$
Interpolation formula	199	499	1039	1917	3247	$2n^4/3$
Transformation (9.29)	209	522	1047	1834	2949	$9n^3$

* In particular, a method ascribed to Reiersol, *Ann. Math. Stat.*, **11** (1941), 193, should be mentioned. This is very rapid for equations of type (12.2), with $n = 3$, 4, 5.

Estimates for Lanczos' method (for unsymmetric and symmetric matrices) have been added to Wayland's table. All figures of this kind are apt to be misleading if the matrices concerned contain a number of zero elements. One must also bear in mind the relative difficulty of the calculation and the liability to make mistakes. However, some general conclusions can be drawn. For type I, both the Danielewsky and Samuelson methods commend themselves for all values of $n > 3$; the labour is much the same, though it may be (in the author's opinion, at least) that Samuelson's calculation is a little more difficult to carry through successfully. For symmetrical matrices, particularly of the larger sort, Lanczos' method is excellent because the simple layout of the final stage removes all the strain of forming cross-products. Unlike Danielewsky's method it cannot break down prematurely for fortuitous reasons, though there is the risk that some factors may be lost. Direct expansion of the λ-determinant is prohibitive for large n; and direct fitting by polynomials is also rather uneconomical.

For type II, the formation of $\mathbf{A}_0^{-1}\mathbf{A}_1$ is most economical and satisfactory for $n \geqslant 4$, though if $\mathbf{A}_0$ is singular, direct fitting by a polynomial becomes necessary. This fitting process becomes relatively less laborious for type III, and has the associated advantages already described. This conclusion becomes even truer for more complicated determinants.

General Principles of Iterative Methods

We intend now to focus attention directly on the problem of finding latent roots, particularly those of largest modulus, and their associated vectors, without the intermediary of the characteristic function. The processes to be described owe much of their development to Hotelling, Aitken, and to Collar.* All are based essentially on the formation of a vector sequence $\mathbf{b}_k$ by repeated premultiplication of an arbitrary column vector $\mathbf{b}_0$ by the matrix $\mathbf{A}$, and the expansion of $\mathbf{b}_k$, as in (12.7), in the form

$$\mathbf{b}_k = \mathbf{A}^k\mathbf{b}_0 = a_1\lambda_1{}^k\mathbf{u}_1 + a_2\lambda_2{}^k\mathbf{u}_2 + \ldots + a_n\lambda_n{}^k\mathbf{u}_n \qquad (12.7)$$

We assume, at least temporarily, that all the latent roots are distinct, and that $|\lambda_1| > |\lambda_2| > \ldots > |\lambda_n|$. Now each term in

---

* H. Hotelling, *Psychometrika*, **1** (1936), 27 and *Ann. Math. Stat.*, **14** (1943), 1; A. C. Aitken, *Proc. Roy. Soc. Edin.*, **57** (1937), 269; W. J. Duncan and A. R. Collar, *Phil. Mag.*, **17** (1934), 865 and **19** (1935), 197.

(12.7) is a column matrix with n elements, and there is an equation of the same form as (12.7) relating elements in these matrices which occupy similar positions. We need not specify this position, but if f_k is an element chosen from $\mathbf{b}_k$ and e_i the corresponding element in $a_i\mathbf{u}_i$, then

$$f_k = e_1\lambda_1{}^k + e_2\lambda_2{}^k + \ldots + e_n\lambda_n{}^k \qquad (12.30)$$

The numbers $f_0, f_1, \ldots$ therefore provide a sequence of exactly the type already considered in connexion with the Bernoulli-Aitken method, Chapter 9. The results of that analysis can therefore be applied immediately, in particular the limiting expression (9.58) for the dominant root λ_1, (9.59) for $\lambda_1\lambda_2$, $\lambda_1\lambda_2\lambda_3$, etc., with the appropriate modifications when there are two or more equal real roots, or pairs of complex roots. Also, if the primary sequences do not converge sufficiently well, Aitken's δ^2 device can be used to obtain more rapidly converging sequences. However, it will be seen shortly that there are other and sometimes better ways of improving estimates, particularly of latent roots.

There is another important result which applies more particularly to the present problem. When k is large

$$\mathbf{b}_k \simeq a_1\lambda_1{}^k\mathbf{u}_1 \qquad (12.31)$$

so that the column $\mathbf{b}_k$ provides an approximation to the latent vector $\mathbf{u}_1$ associated with λ_1, apart from an arbitrary constant multiplying all its elements. The convergence towards $\mathbf{u}_1$ can be better appreciated if the elements of each $\mathbf{b}_k$ are divided by a chosen element, which then becomes unity.

All these arguments apply equally to the sequence of row vectors $\mathbf{d}_k$ given by (12.9), from which λ_1 and $\mathbf{v}_1$ can be derived.

A trivial example will make clear the process.

Let $$\mathbf{A} = \begin{bmatrix} 4 & 3 \\ 1 & 2 \end{bmatrix}, \quad \mathbf{b}_0 = \begin{bmatrix} 1 \\ 0 \end{bmatrix}$$

Then

$$\mathbf{b}_1 = \begin{bmatrix} 4 \\ 1 \end{bmatrix}, \quad \mathbf{b}_2 = \begin{bmatrix} 19 \\ 6 \end{bmatrix}, \quad \mathbf{b}_3 = \begin{bmatrix} 94 \\ 31 \end{bmatrix}, \quad \mathbf{b}_4 = \begin{bmatrix} 469 \\ 156 \end{bmatrix}, \quad \mathbf{b}_5 = \begin{bmatrix} 2344 \\ 781 \end{bmatrix}$$

From the ratios of successive upper elements we get the sequence

$$4 \cdot 75, \ 4 \cdot 95, \ 4 \cdot 989, \ 4 \cdot 9978$$

and from the lower elements

$$6 \cdot 0, \ 5 \cdot 17, \ 5 \cdot 032, \ 5 \cdot 0064$$

Both sequences are converging, from opposite sides, to the value 5, which is easily seen to be the dominant latent root, since

$$D(\lambda) = \lambda^2 - 6\lambda + 5 = (\lambda - 5)(\lambda - 1)$$

Also, by reducing the lower element of $\mathbf{b}_3$, $\mathbf{b}_4$, $\mathbf{b}_5$ to unity we get the following approximations to $\mathbf{u}_1$—

$$\begin{bmatrix} 3\cdot03 \\ 1 \end{bmatrix}, \begin{bmatrix} 3\cdot006 \\ 1 \end{bmatrix}, \begin{bmatrix} 3\cdot0013 \\ 1 \end{bmatrix} \rightarrow \begin{bmatrix} 3 \\ 1 \end{bmatrix}$$

By assuming $\mathbf{d}_0 = [1, \ 0]$ it is easily shown again that $\lambda_1 = 5$, and $\mathbf{v}_0 = [1, \ 1]$.

12.7. Relation to Bernoulli's Method

The expression (12.30) suggests at once that a recurrence relation with $(n + 1)$ terms exists between successive members of the sequence f_k, and in this connexion it is worth showing how the Bernoulli process for finding the dominant root of an algebraic equation can itself be interpreted as the formation of a sequence of column vectors. The appropriate matrix is the companion matrix (12.14), since the method proceeds directly from the known form of $D(\lambda)$.

Let $\qquad \mathbf{b}_0 = \{f_0, f_1, \ . \ . \ ., f_{n-1}\}$

where the elements are arbitrary. Then by forming $\mathbf{Cb}_0$

$$\mathbf{b}_1 = \{f_1, f_2, \ . \ . \ ., f_n\}$$

where $\qquad f_n = p_1 f_{n-1} + p_2 f_{n-2} + \ . \ . \ . + p_n f_0$

and in general $\qquad \mathbf{b}_k = \{f_k, f_{k+1}, \ . \ . \ ., f_{k+n}\}$

where $\qquad f_{n+k} = p_1 f_{n+k-1} + p_2 f_{n+k-2} + \ . \ . \ . + p_n f_{k-1}$

This is just the recurrence relation (9.56) on which Bernoulli's method is based.

This approach suggests immediately a variant of the Bernoulli method, which has in fact been proposed by Dietzold, using the row matrix sequence $\mathbf{d}_k$ instead of $\mathbf{b}_k$.

Thus let $\qquad \mathbf{d}_0 = [g_1, g_2, \ . \ . \ ., g_n]$

Then $\qquad \mathbf{d}_1 = [g_1^{(1)}, g_2^{(1)}, \ . \ . \ ., g_n^{(1)}]$

where $\qquad g_j^{(1)} = p_j g_1 + g_{j+1} \quad (j = 1, \ . \ . \ ., n - 1)$
$$= p_n g_1 \qquad (j = n)$$

and in general $\quad \mathbf{d}_k = [g_1^{(k)}, g_2^{(k)}, \ldots, g_n^{(k)}]$

where $\quad g_j^{(k)} = p_j g_1^{(k-1)} + g_{j+1}^{(k-1)} \quad (j = 1, \ldots, n-1)$

$\qquad\qquad = p_n g_1^{(k-1)} \qquad\qquad (j = n)$

The ratio $g_j^{(k+1)}/g_j^{(k)}$ tends to λ_1 as before, and subsidiary sequences giving $\lambda_1 \lambda_2$, etc., can be derived. It may be considered an advantage of Dietzold's method that it replaces the lengthy recurrence relation (9.56) by a set of simple relations, but the disadvantage necessarily follows that more numbers must be recorded and the chance that rounding errors may accumulate is greater.

12.8. Powers of Matrices

The derivation of latent roots and vectors from a sequence $\mathbf{b}_k$ or $\mathbf{d}_k$ implies in effect the calculation of high powers of the matrix $\mathbf{A}$. Since the sequence may sometimes converge rather slowly, any device which gives high powers rapidly is valuable. Now, if $p = 2^m$, it is obvious that the calculation of $\mathbf{A}^p \mathbf{b}_0$ might be reached by forming any one of the sequences—

$$\mathbf{b}_1, \ \mathbf{b}_2, \ \mathbf{b}_3, \ \ldots, \ \mathbf{b}_p$$
$$\mathbf{A}^2, \ \mathbf{b}_2, \ \mathbf{b}_4, \ \ldots, \ \mathbf{b}_p$$
$$\mathbf{A}^2, \ \mathbf{A}^4, \ \mathbf{b}_4, \ \mathbf{b}_8, \ \ldots, \ \mathbf{b}_p$$
$$\mathbf{A}^2, \ \mathbf{A}^4, \ \mathbf{A}^8, \ \mathbf{b}_8, \ \mathbf{b}_{16}, \ \ldots, \ \mathbf{b}_p, \ \text{etc.}$$

To compare the labour involved, etc., on the assumption that none of the elements of $\mathbf{A}$ is zero, we find that these different paths require the calculation of

$$(n+1)p, \ (n+1)(n+p/2), \ (n+1)(2n+p/4), \ (n+1)(3n+p/8), \ \text{etc.}$$

sums of products of n terms, including suitable check calculations. From this it appears that the use of $\mathbf{A}^2$ is not advantageous unless $p > 2n$, that of $\mathbf{A}^4$ only if $p > 4n$, and so on. Unfortunately the requisite value of p is not often known in advance; moreover it often happens that $\mathbf{A}$ has many zero elements, whereas this need not be true of $\mathbf{A}^2$, $\mathbf{A}^4$, etc.; consequently continued multiplication by $\mathbf{A}$ may be preferable. However, there are other reasons why it is often worthwhile to compute $\mathbf{A}^2$ at least.

12.9. Use of Scalar Products in Finding Latent Roots

We must mention an alternative to Aitken's δ^2 process by which we can obtain a sequence converging to λ_1 more rapidly than any based on a single element of $\mathbf{b}_k$. This makes use of the scalar products c_{i+j} or $\mathbf{d}_i\mathbf{b}_j$ already introduced in discussing Lanczos' method. From (12.7), (12.9) and the orthogonality property of the latent vectors, we see that

$$c_s = l_1\lambda_1{}^s + l_2\lambda_2{}^s + \ldots + l_n\lambda_n{}^s \qquad (12.32)$$

and hence $\quad c_{s+1}/c_s = \lambda_1 + 0\{(\lambda_1 - \lambda_2)(\lambda_2/\lambda_1)^s\}$

Compared with the approximation to λ_1 given by f_{k+1}/f_k from (12.30), this has the merit that the error term is much smaller, since $s \simeq 2k$.

When $\mathbf{A}$ is not symmetric, the calculation of c_{2k} requires that $\mathbf{b}_1, \ldots, \mathbf{b}_k$ and $\mathbf{d}_1, \ldots, \mathbf{d}_k$ be formed, giving λ_1 with an accuracy comparable with that from the sequence $\mathbf{b}_1, \ldots, \mathbf{b}_{2k}$. There is not much gain in time, except that the numbers may be smaller, and an approximation to both $\mathbf{u}_1$ and $\mathbf{v}_1$ has been obtained. The most notable gain occurs when $\mathbf{A}$ is symmetric, for then the elements of $\mathbf{b}_k$ and $\mathbf{d}_k$ may be taken to be identical, and the additional accuracy in λ_1 is available from only k members of the sequence.

Again a simple example makes this clear.

Let $\quad \mathbf{A} = \begin{bmatrix} 3 & 1 \\ 1 & 3 \end{bmatrix} \quad \mathbf{b}_0 = \begin{bmatrix} 1 \\ 0 \end{bmatrix}$

Then $\quad \mathbf{b}_1 = \{\ 3, \quad 1\} \quad \mathbf{b}_4 = \{\ 136, \quad 120\}$
$\quad\quad\quad \mathbf{b}_2 = \{10, \quad 6\} \quad \mathbf{b}_5 = \{\ 528, \quad 496\}$
$\quad\quad\quad \mathbf{b}_3 = \{36, \quad 28\} \quad \mathbf{b}_6 = \{2080, \quad 2016\}$

From the elements of $\mathbf{b}_5$ and $\mathbf{b}_6$, we find that

$$3\cdot939 < \lambda_1 < 4\cdot065$$

Also, from $\mathbf{b}_4$, $\mathbf{b}_5$ and $\mathbf{b}_6$,

$$c_8 = 32896$$
$$c_9 = 131328 \quad c_9/c_8 = 3\cdot9922$$
$$c_{10} = 524800 \quad c_{10}/c_9 = 3\cdot9961$$
$$c_{11} = 2098176 \quad c_{11}/c_{10} = 3\cdot9981$$
$$c_{12} = 8390656 \quad c_{12}/c_{11} = 3\cdot9990$$

The improved convergence of the last sequence is obvious. The latent roots of $\mathbf{A}$ are easily seen to be 4 and 2.

Numerical Application of Iterative Methods

We shall now put into practice the ideas outlined in the previous section. Symmetric matrices will be considered first, partly

14—(T.642)

because their roots are necessarily real, but their common occurrence also makes it desirable to give them special prominence. Some devices will be described which enable the smaller latent roots and their vectors to be evaluated. Finally the treatment of repeated real roots, and of complex roots of unsymmetric matrices, when these are dominant, will be discussed.

12.10. Simple Procedure for Symmetric Matrices

The first example to be examined in detail is a highly symmetrical matrix, not wholly typical but one which does emphasize some features of the solution which are usually present in a greater or lesser degree. It brings out clearly some difficulties in finding lesser roots, and shows also how physical arguments can sometimes assist the calculations.

EXAMPLE 12.7. Find the latent roots and vectors of the matrix

$$\mathbf{A} = \begin{bmatrix} 2 & -1 & 0 & 0 \\ -1 & 2 & -1 & 0 \\ 0 & -1 & 2 & -1 \\ 0 & 0 & -1 & 2 \end{bmatrix}$$

This type of matrix is associated with a simple physical problem, the harmonic vibrations of 4 similar particles equally spaced on a taut

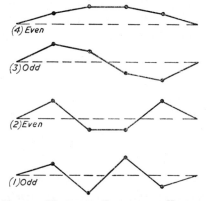

FIG. 12.1. NORMAL MODES OF TRANSVERSE VIBRATION OF FOUR PARTICLES ON LIGHT STRING

string. For physical reasons one would expect four basic modes of vibration to occur in which the particles are displaced transversely as shown in Fig. 12.1, and are always in phase with each other. These are called normal modes, and are shown in order of increasing frequency, the last corresponding to the largest latent root of **A**. The latent vectors have as their elements the relative displacements of the four particles from the straight line.

We therefore expect λ_1 to be associated with a vector having the symmetry of $\{1, -1, 1, -1\}$, so it is reasonable to assume this form for $\mathbf{b_0}$. The development of the sequence $\mathbf{b}$ is hastened slightly by first squaring the matrix $\mathbf{A}$.

Thus

$$\mathbf{A^2} = \begin{bmatrix} 5 & -4 & 1 & 0 \\ -4 & 6 & -4 & 1 \\ 1 & -4 & 6 & -4 \\ 0 & 1 & -4 & 5 \end{bmatrix}$$

$$\begin{array}{cccc} 2 & -1 & -1 & 2 \end{array}$$

This is, of course, also symmetrical. The column sums in the last row are often useful for checking. We readily obtain the following sequence, in which $\mathbf{b_7}$ has been inserted to obtain direct estimates of λ_1, though ratios of corresponding elements in $\mathbf{b_6}$ and $\mathbf{b_8}$ also give an estimate of $\lambda_1{}^2$.

$\mathbf{b_0}$	$\{1,$	$-1,$	$1,$	$-1\}$
$\mathbf{b_2}$	$\{10,$	$-15,$	$15,$	$-10\}$
$\mathbf{b_4}$	$\{125,$	$-200,$	$200,$	$-125\}$
$\mathbf{b_6}$	$\{1625,$	$-2625,$	$2625,$	$-1625\}$
$\mathbf{b_7}$	$\{5875,$	$-9500,$	$9500,$	$-5875\}$
$\mathbf{b_8}$	$\{21250,$	$-34375,$	$34375,$	$-21250\}$

We observe that each matrix has two independent elements.

From
$$\mathbf{b_6} \text{ and } \mathbf{b_7}, \quad 3\cdot61538 < \lambda_1 < 3\cdot61905$$
$$\mathbf{b_7} \text{ and } \mathbf{b_8}, \quad 3\cdot61702 < \lambda_1 < 3\cdot61842$$

Greater accuracy is obtained by forming scalar products—

thus
$$64c_{14} = 1597 \times 10^7$$
$$64c_{15} = 5778 \times 10^7 \qquad c_{15}/c_{14} = 3\cdot6180338$$
$$64c_{16} = 20905 \times 10^7 \qquad c_{16}/c_{15} = 3\cdot6180339$$

showing that to 6D, $\lambda_1 = 3\cdot618034$. Alternatively the δ^2 process can be applied to a particular element sequence from $\mathbf{b_k}$. This increased precision can of course be justified only if the elements in $\mathbf{A}$ can be treated as exact numbers, which in a physical problem may be unlikely. Also, from $\mathbf{b_8}$ we have a good approximation to the latent vector.

$$\mathbf{u_1} = \{1\cdot0, -1\cdot6176, 1\cdot6176, -1\cdot0\}$$

It is an important feature of this problem that the second latent root λ_2 can be derived by a similar process, assuming

$$\mathbf{b_0} = \{1, -1, -1, 1\}$$

as suggested by Fig. 12.1. This possibility arises because any vector of the form $\{1, \ -a, \ -a, \ 1\}$ is orthogonal to $\mathbf{v}_1(=\mathbf{u}_1')$, and is to be expected in any problem in which the latent vectors (normal modes) can be divided into two sets having even and odd symmetries.

We obtain the following sequence showing very rapid convergence

$$
\begin{array}{lll}
\mathbf{b}_0 & \{1, \quad -1, \quad -1, \quad 1\} & \\
\mathbf{b}_2 & \{8, \quad -5, \quad -5, \quad 8\} & 6 \\
\mathbf{b}_4 & \{55, \ -34, \ -34, \ 55\} & 42 \\
\mathbf{b}_5 & \{144, \ -89, \ -89, \ 144\} & 110 \\
\mathbf{b}_6 & \{377, \ -233, \ -233, \ 377\} & 288
\end{array}
$$

Note. The final numbers outside the brackets are sums of the elements, derived by multiplying the sum row of $\mathbf{A}^2$ or $\mathbf{A}$ by the previous vector. This is a check on each stage.

$$
\begin{array}{llll}
\text{From} & \mathbf{b}_4 \text{ and } \mathbf{b}_5 & 2{\cdot}61818 > \lambda_2 > 2{\cdot}61765 \\
 & \mathbf{b}_5 \text{ and } \mathbf{b}_6 & 2{\cdot}61806 > \lambda_2 > 2{\cdot}61798
\end{array}
$$

$$
\begin{array}{lll}
\text{Also} & c_{10} = & 57314 \\
 & c_{11} = 150050 & c_{11}/c_{10} = 2{\cdot}61803401 \\
 & c_{12} = 392836 & c_{12}/c_{11} = 2{\cdot}61803401
\end{array}
$$

This establishes λ_2 to 8D, and from $\mathbf{b}_6$

$$
\mathbf{u}_2 = \{1{\cdot}0, \ -0{\cdot}618037, \ -0{\cdot}618037, \ 1{\cdot}0\}
$$

The latent roots λ_3, λ_4 and their vectors remain to be found. It might be thought that by assuming, say $\mathbf{b}_0 = \{1, 1, -1, -1\}$, λ_3 and $\mathbf{u}_3$ could be derived in a similar way. However, one soon finds that

$$
\begin{array}{l}
\mathbf{b}_2 = \{ \quad 0, \ 5, \ -5, \ 0\} \\
\mathbf{b}_4 = \{-25, 50, -50, 25\}
\end{array}
$$

so the process merely leads rapidly to a rediscovery of λ_1. Similarly, the choice $\mathbf{b}_0 = \{1, 1, 1, 1\}$, leads not to λ_4 but again to λ_2.

Help with the latent roots is given by Aitken's derived sequence $c_{2, k}$, formed from c_k (see (9.60)), though it is in a rather unexpected shape. From the sequence c_k used in estimating λ_1, one obtains the following results—

$$
\begin{array}{lll}
64c_{10} = & 932 \times 10^5 & \\
64c_{11} = & 3372 & c_{2,\,11} \propto \quad 16 \\
64c_{12} = & 12200 & c_{2,\,12} \propto \quad 80 \\
64c_{13} = & 44140 & c_{2,\,13} \propto \quad 400 \\
64c_{14} = & 159700 & c_{2,\,14} \propto 2000 \\
64c_{15} = & 578800 &
\end{array}
$$

Ratios of successive values of $c_{2,\,k}$ give absolutely the value 5 for the product of two roots, but this product is $\lambda_1\lambda_3$, not $\lambda_1\lambda_2$. Likewise the c_k values used to obtain λ_2 give $\lambda_2\lambda_4 = 1$.

Hence $\qquad \lambda_3 = 1\cdot 381966, \ \lambda_4 = 0\cdot 381966$

(The exact roots are $(1/2)(5 \pm \sqrt 5), \ (1/2)(3 \pm \sqrt 5)$.)

These results again arise because $\mathbf{b}_0$ for λ_1 is orthogonal to $\mathbf{v}_2$ and therefore cannot give any information about λ_2. The reader can soon verify that if the calculation for λ_1 is repeated with an unsymmetrical matrix for $\mathbf{b}_0$, say $\{1, 1, 0, 1\}$, then Aitken's sequences give $\lambda_1, \ \lambda_1\lambda_2,$ $\lambda_1\lambda_2\lambda_3$ quite normally. The convergence is much slower, however, because $\lambda_2/\lambda_1 \simeq 0\cdot 7$, whereas $\lambda_3/\lambda_1 \simeq 0\cdot 4$.

A much simpler expedient to find λ_3 and λ_4 which can be applied here because there are only 4 roots, is to use the traces of $\mathbf{A}$ and $\mathbf{A}^2$. These give $\Sigma\lambda_i = 8$, $\Sigma\lambda_i{}^2 = 22$, and hence $\lambda_3 + \lambda_4 = 1\cdot 763932$, $\lambda_3{}^2 + \lambda_4{}^2 = 2\cdot 055728$. This leads to the same values of λ_3 and λ_4.

The remaining vectors can be obtained by the simple device of shifting the roots of the matrix by a constant. Thus the matrix $\mathbf{A} - 3\mathbf{I}$ has roots

$$0\cdot 618, \ -0\cdot 382, \ -1\cdot 618, \ -2\cdot 618$$

so the dominant roots now correspond to λ_4 and λ_3. By choosing suitable starting vectors, $\mathbf{u}_4$ and $\mathbf{u}_3$, which are unaffected by the shift, are soon found.

$$\text{Now } \mathbf{A}_1 = \mathbf{A} - 3\mathbf{I} = \begin{bmatrix} -1 & -1 & 0 & 0 \\ -1 & -1 & -1 & 0 \\ 0 & -1 & -1 & -1 \\ 0 & 0 & -1 & -1 \end{bmatrix} \quad \mathbf{A}_1{}^2 = \begin{bmatrix} 2 & 2 & 1 & 0 \\ 2 & 3 & 2 & 1 \\ 1 & 2 & 3 & 2 \\ 0 & 1 & 2 & 2 \end{bmatrix}$$

$$\cdots\cdots\cdots\cdots\cdots\cdots \qquad\qquad \cdots\cdots\cdots\cdots$$
$$-2 \ -3 \ -3 \ -2 \qquad\qquad\qquad 5 \ \ 8 \ \ 8 \ \ 5$$

The sum rows of $\mathbf{A}_1$ and $\mathbf{A}_1{}^2$ are strongly suggestive of $\mathbf{u}_4$, so we let

$$\mathbf{b}_0 = \{5, 8, 8, 5\}$$

Repeated multiplication by $\mathbf{A}_1$ is very simple and we soon find

$$\mathbf{b}_4 = \{\ \ \ \ 233, \quad\ \ 377, \quad\ \ 377, \quad\ \ 233\}$$
$$\mathbf{b}_5 = \{-610, \ -987, \ -987, \ -610\}$$
$$\mathbf{b}_6 = \{\ 1597, \quad 2584, \quad 2584, \quad 1597\}$$

From $\mathbf{b}_4$ and $\mathbf{b}_5 \qquad -2\cdot 618026 \ > \lambda_4 - 3 > \ -2\cdot 618037$
$$\mathbf{b}_5 \text{ and } \mathbf{b}_6 \qquad -2\cdot 6180328 > \lambda_4 - 3 > \ -2\cdot 6180344$$

and $\qquad \mathbf{u}_4 = \{1, \ 1\cdot 618034, \ 1\cdot 618034, \ 1\}$, correct to 6D

Similarly from $\quad \mathbf{b}_0 = \{\ \ \ \ \ \ 1, \qquad\ \ 1, \qquad -1, \qquad -1\}$
we obtain rapidly, $\mathbf{b}_{10} = \{\ \ \ 144, \qquad\ \ 89, \quad -89, \ -144\}$
$$\mathbf{b}_{11} = \{-233, \ -144, \qquad 144, \qquad 233\}$$
$$\mathbf{b}_{12} = \{\ \ \ 377, \qquad 233, \ -233, \ -377\}$$

Convergence is slower here, but from these three vectors

$$-1 \cdot 618026 > \lambda_3 - 3 > -1 \cdot 61806$$

and $$\mathbf{u}_3 = \{1, \ 0 \cdot 618037, \ -0 \cdot 618037, \ -1\}$$

the last decimal being unreliable.

The solution is thus complete.

The above example brings out several important points.

1. The dominant root and its vector, if distinct, can be derived easily by using suitable sequences. Smaller roots may be given by derived sequences, with help from the values of $\Sigma \lambda_i$, $\Sigma \lambda_i^2$.

2. The convergence is generally hastened by choosing $\mathbf{b}_0$ as close as possible to the desired latent vector. This is a matter of experience, though knowledge of the physical problem leading to the matrix may be very valuable; the column and row sums of the matrix are also a useful guide.

3. The remaining vectors may generally be found in one of two ways—

(*a*) By choosing starting vectors $\mathbf{b}_0$ which are orthogonal to all preceding vectors belonging to larger roots (this may sometimes occur naturally as for $\mathbf{u}_2$ in Example 12.7, but it can be arranged deliberately).

(*b*) By modifying the matrix $\mathbf{A}$ so as to alter the order of the roots, e.g. by considering

$$\mathbf{A}_1 = \mathbf{A} + \lambda_0 \mathbf{I} \quad \text{or} \quad \mathbf{A}_2 = (\mathbf{A} + \lambda_0 \mathbf{I})^2 + \mu_0 \mathbf{I}$$

These simple devices often suffice to solve completely any matrix having simple roots, particularly if the order does not exceed 5. Sometimes, however, more elaborate methods are required, or at least desired, to determine the vectors associated with smaller roots, and we therefore describe briefly two such aids, the first known as deflation, and the second using matrix polynomials.

12.11. Deflation

The object of deflation, introduced by Hotelling and Aitken, is to set up a symmetric matrix $\mathbf{A}_1$ having the same latent roots and vectors as $\mathbf{A}$, except that λ_1 is replaced by zero. Forming an iterative sequence with $\mathbf{A}_1$ will then yield λ_2 and $\mathbf{u}_2$; after further deflation and so on.

Let $$\mathbf{A}_1 = \mathbf{A} - (\lambda_1/\mathbf{u}_1'\mathbf{u}_1)(\mathbf{u}_1\mathbf{u}_1') \qquad (12.33)$$

where $\mathbf{u_1'u_1}$ is the scalar product of $\mathbf{u_1}$ with its transpose, and $\mathbf{u_1u_1'}$ is a square symmetric matrix of order n. $\mathbf{A_1}$ has the desired properties, since

$$\mathbf{A_1u_1} = \mathbf{Au_1} - (\lambda_1/\mathbf{u_1'u_1})\mathbf{u_1u_1'u_1} = (\mathbf{A} - \lambda_1)\mathbf{u_1} = 0$$
$$\mathbf{A_1u_i} = \mathbf{Au_i} - (\lambda_1/\mathbf{u_1'u_1})\mathbf{u_1u_1'u_i} = \lambda\mathbf{u_i}$$

The latter result uses the orthogonal property of the $\mathbf{u}$'s. We give an example of the use of (12.33).

EXAMPLE 12.8. Calculate λ_3 and $\mathbf{u_3}$ for the matrix of Example 12.7 by deflation.

From Example 12.7, $\lambda_1 = 3\cdot618034$
and $\mathbf{u_1} = \{1, -1\cdot618, 1\cdot618, -1\}$
giving

$$\lambda_1/\mathbf{u_1'u_1} = 0\cdot500 \text{ and } \mathbf{u_1u_1'} = \begin{bmatrix} 1\cdot0 & -1\cdot618 & 1\cdot618 & -1\cdot0 \\ -1\cdot618 & 2\cdot618 & -2\cdot618 & 1\cdot618 \\ 1\cdot618 & -2\cdot618 & 2\cdot618 & -1\cdot618 \\ -1\cdot0 & 1\cdot618 & -1\cdot618 & 1\cdot0 \end{bmatrix}$$

Hence, to 3D, $\mathbf{A_1} = \begin{bmatrix} 1\cdot5 & -0\cdot191 & -0\cdot809 & 0\cdot5 \\ -0\cdot191 & 0\cdot691 & 0\cdot309 & -0\cdot809 \\ -0\cdot809 & 0\cdot309 & 0\cdot691 & -0\cdot191 \\ 0\cdot5 & -0\cdot809 & -0\cdot191 & 1\cdot5 \end{bmatrix}$

$$\cdots\cdots\cdots\cdots\cdots\cdots\cdots\cdots\cdots\cdots\cdots\cdots$$

$$1 \qquad 0 \qquad 0 \qquad 1$$

We now assume $\mathbf{b_0} = \{1, 1, -1, -1\}$; successive approximations are

$$\mathbf{b_1} = 1\cdot618\ \{1,\ 0\cdot6180,\ -0\cdot6180,\ -1\}$$
$$\mathbf{b_2} = 1\cdot3819\{1,\ 0\cdot61806,\ -0\cdot61806,\ -1\}$$
$$\mathbf{b_3} = 1\cdot3820\{1,\ 0\cdot61802,\ -0\cdot61802,\ -1\}$$

Note that it is convenient in this calculation, as usual when working to a fixed number of significant figures, to reduce the leading element in each matrix to unity by abstracting the factor shown on the left. This factor tends to λ_3, and is ignored in deriving the next approximation. The convergence to $\mathbf{u_3}$ shows up clearly, being very rapid in this example.

A study of more general methods of reducing matrices, for the purpose of finding subsidiary roots and their vectors, has been made by Feller and Forsythe.* Exercises 12, Nos. 10–13 are concerned with some alternatives to deflation.

* W. Feller and G. E. Forsythe, *Quart. Appl. Math.*, **8** (1951), 325. See also J. H. Wilkinson, "The calculation of the latent roots and vectors of matrices on the pilot model of the ACE," *Proc. Camb. Phil. Soc.*, **50** (1954), 536.

12.12. The Use of Matrix Polynomials

The following method, which has been elaborated by Kincaid, depends on a prior knowledge of all the latent roots, though this knowledge need only be quite rough.* It was noted earlier that a matrix polynomial $P(\mathbf{A})$ has latent roots $P(\lambda_i)$, where λ_i is a latent root of $\mathbf{A}$. We now consider in particular the polynomial

$$P_2(\lambda) = (\lambda - \lambda_1')(\lambda - \lambda_3') \ldots (\lambda - \lambda_n') \qquad (12.34)$$

where λ_1', λ_3', etc., are approximations to λ_1, λ_3, etc., together with the corresponding matrix polynomial

$$P_2(\mathbf{A}) = (\mathbf{A} - \lambda_1')(\mathbf{A} - \lambda_3') \ldots (\mathbf{A} - \lambda_n') \qquad (12.35)$$

Because $P_2(\lambda_i')$ is exactly zero when $i \neq 2$, it is probable that $P_2(\lambda_i)$ is small, and so all the latent roots of $P_2(\mathbf{A})$ are small except $P_2(\lambda_2)$, which will not in general be small if the roots λ_i are distinct. Consequently, if $\mathbf{b}_0$ is given by (12.6)

$$P_2(\mathbf{A})\mathbf{b}_0 = a_1 P_2(\lambda_1)\mathbf{u}_1 + a_2 P_2(\lambda_2)\mathbf{u}_2 + \ldots + a_n P_2(\lambda_n)\mathbf{u}_n \quad (12.36)$$

in which the second term is dominant, and will become increasingly so as multiplication by $P_2(\mathbf{A})$ is repeated. There should therefore be no difficulty in deriving $\mathbf{u}_2$ rapidly by iteration, using $P_2(\mathbf{A})$. It is of course arbitrary to pick out $\mathbf{u}_2$ in this way, and any other latent vector can be obtained similarly.

Now suppose in addition that $\mathbf{u}_1$ is known, and $\mathbf{b}_0$ is made orthogonal to $\mathbf{u}_1'$ by choosing its elements suitably. This means that $a_1 = 0$, and the term in $\mathbf{u}_1$ falls out. It is then no longer essential that $P_2(\lambda_1) \ll P_2(\lambda_2)$, and one may be allowed to simplify $P_2(\mathbf{A})$ by omitting the factor $(\mathbf{A} - \lambda_1)$, i.e. to use instead

$$Q_2(\mathbf{A}) = (\mathbf{A} - \lambda_3') \ldots (\mathbf{A} - \lambda_n') \qquad (12.37)$$

The reduced labour in forming the matrix polynomial is often worth while.

We give another complete example to illustrate the use of such matrix polynomials.

EXAMPLE 12.9. Find latent roots and vectors for the matrix

$$\mathbf{A} = \begin{bmatrix} 2 & 1 & -1 & 0 \\ 1 & -2 & 3 & 2 \\ -1 & 3 & 4 & -1 \\ 0 & 2 & -1 & 3 \end{bmatrix}$$

---

* Kincaid, *Quart. Appl. Math.*, **5** (1947/8), 320. A similar method of "purification" has been given by L. F. Richardson *Phil. Trans. Roy. Soc.*, **242** (1950), 439; see Hartree, *Numerical Analysis*, p. 201.

The solution of this problem can be divided into five stages.

1. *Preliminary Estimation of λ_1 and $\mathbf{u}_1$.* $\mathbf{A}^2$ is useful and is therefore evaluated first.

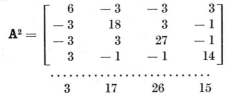

$$\mathbf{A}^2 = \begin{bmatrix} 6 & -3 & -3 & 3 \\ -3 & 18 & 3 & -1 \\ -3 & 3 & 27 & -1 \\ 3 & -1 & -1 & 14 \end{bmatrix}$$

$$\cdots\cdots\cdots\cdots\cdots\cdots\cdots$$

$$3 \qquad 17 \qquad 26 \qquad 15$$

We observe that $\Sigma \lambda_i = 7,\ \Sigma \lambda_i^2 = 65$

Assuming $\mathbf{b}_0 = \{0,\ 0,\ 1,\ 0\}$, successive multiplications by $\mathbf{A}^2$ give the following sequence—

$$27\cdot00 \quad \{-0\cdot1111,\ 0\cdot1111,\ 1,\ -0\cdot0370\}$$
$$27\cdot7027\{-0\cdot1484,\ 0\cdot1939,\ 1,\ -0\cdot0708\}$$
$$28\cdot0977\{-0\cdot1667,\ 0\cdot2494,\ 1,\ -0\cdot0936\}$$
$$28\cdot3419\{-0\cdot1774,\ 0\cdot2852,\ 1,\ -0\cdot1080\}$$
$$28\cdot4958\{-0\cdot1840,\ 0\cdot3079,\ 1,\ -0\cdot1168\}$$
$$28\cdot5925\{-0\cdot1881,\ 0\cdot3221,\ 1,\ -0\cdot1222\}$$

The numbers on the left are approximations to λ_1^2. Convergence is distinctly slow, and indicates strongly that λ_2 is comparable with λ_1. This can be verified from the sequence for λ_1^2 by deriving the sequence giving $\lambda_1^2\lambda_2^2$. It follows easily from (9.58) and (9.59) that if $M_k \sim \lambda_1^2$ and $M_{2,\,k} \sim \lambda_1^2\lambda_2^2$ then

$$M_{2,\,k}/M_k = M_{k-1}(M_{k+1} - M_k)/(M_k - M_{k-1}) \sim \lambda_2^2$$

M_k	ΔM_k	$M_{2,\,k}/M_k$
28·0977		
	0·2442	
28·3419		17·7
	0·1539	
28·4958		17·8
	0·0967	
28·5925		

This shows that $\lambda_2^2 \simeq 17\cdot8$, $\lambda_2 \simeq \pm 4\cdot21$. Further progress is considerably helped by finding all the latent roots roughly.

2. *Approximate Values of Latent Roots.* It is easily found, by multiplying any of the above column matrices by $\mathbf{A}$, that $\lambda_1 > 0$, i.e. $\lambda_1 \simeq 5\cdot35$. The sign of λ_2 needs investigation. Now

$$\lambda_2 + \lambda_3 + \lambda_4 \simeq 1\cdot65$$

so if $\lambda_2 = -4\cdot2$, both λ_3 and λ_4 must be positive, remembering that neither can exceed 4·2 in magnitude. For the matrix $\mathbf{A} - 5\mathbf{I}$, λ_2 then becomes the dominant root by far. We therefore examine $\mathbf{A} - 5\mathbf{I}$.

$$\mathbf{A}_1 = \mathbf{A} - 5\mathbf{I} = \begin{bmatrix} -3 & 1 & -1 & 0 \\ 1 & -7 & 3 & 2 \\ -1 & 3 & -1 & -1 \\ 0 & 2 & -1 & -2 \end{bmatrix}$$

$$\begin{array}{cccc} -3 & -1 & 0 & -1 \end{array}$$

Both the second and third columns suggest trying

$$\mathbf{b}_0 = \{0,\ 1,\ 0,\ 0\}$$

Multiplying by $\mathbf{A}_1$ gives the sequence

$$-7 \cdot 0\{-0 \cdot 14,\ 1,\ -0 \cdot 43,\ -0 \cdot 29\}$$
$$-9 \cdot 0\{-0 \cdot 21,\ 1,\ -0 \cdot 43,\ -0 \cdot 33\}$$
$$-9 \cdot 2\{-0 \cdot 22,\ 1,\ -0 \cdot 43,\ -0 \cdot 34\}$$

Thus $\lambda_2 - 5 \simeq -9 \cdot 2$, which clearly establishes that $\lambda_2 \simeq -4 \cdot 2$. Now using the values for $\Sigma\lambda_i$, $\Sigma\lambda_i^2$ it follows that

$$\lambda_3 + \lambda_4 = 5 \cdot 85,\ \lambda_3^2 + \lambda_4^2 = 18 \cdot 45$$

and finally that the complete set of roots is roughly $5 \cdot 35,\ -4 \cdot 2,\ 3 \cdot 7,\ 2 \cdot 1$.

3. *Improvement of λ_1 and $\mathbf{u}_1$.* This could be done by means of the polynomial

$$P_1(\mathbf{A}) = (\mathbf{A} + 4 \cdot 2)(\mathbf{A} - 3 \cdot 7)(\mathbf{A} - 2 \cdot 1) = \mathbf{A}^3 - 1 \cdot 6\mathbf{A}^2 - 16 \cdot 5\mathbf{A} - 32 \cdot 5\mathbf{I}$$

or more simply $\quad P_1(\mathbf{A}) = \mathbf{A}^3 - 2\mathbf{A}^2 - 16\mathbf{A} - 32\mathbf{I}$

A simpler expedient, avoiding the calculation of $\mathbf{A}^3$, is to use

$$P_1(\mathbf{A}) = \mathbf{A}^2 - 11\mathbf{I}$$

This has approximate roots $17, 7, 3, -7$, which are fairly well separated.

$$\mathbf{A}^2 - 11\mathbf{I} = \begin{bmatrix} -5 & -3 & -3 & 3 \\ -3 & 7 & 3 & -1 \\ -3 & 3 & 16 & -1 \\ 3 & -1 & -1 & 3 \end{bmatrix}$$

$$\begin{array}{cccc} -8 & 6 & 15 & 4 \end{array}$$

Starting with $\mathbf{b}_0 = \{-0 \cdot 17,\quad 0 \cdot 25,\quad 1,\ -0 \cdot 10\}$

we obtain
$$17 \cdot 36\ \{-0 \cdot 1843,\ 0 \cdot 3088,\ 1,\ -0 \cdot 1187\}1 \cdot 0058$$
$$17 \cdot 5980\{-0 \cdot 1910,\ 0 \cdot 3315,\ 1,\ -0 \cdot 1260\}1 \cdot 0045$$
$$17 \cdot 6935\{-0 \cdot 1932,\ 0 \cdot 3402,\ 1,\ -0 \cdot 1290\}1 \cdot 0181$$
$$17 \cdot 7292\{-0 \cdot 1941,\ 0 \cdot 3435,\ 1,\ -0 \cdot 1301\}1 \cdot 0193$$

By a rough extrapolation, using (9.29a) for each element, we obtain the vector

$$\{- 0 \cdot 1947,\ 0 \cdot 3455,\ 1,\ - 0 \cdot 1305\}$$

and by one more multiplication

$$17 \cdot 7511\{- 0 \cdot 1946,\ 0 \cdot 3455,\ 1,\ - 0 \cdot 1306\}$$

Hence $\lambda_1^2 = 17 \cdot 7511 + 11$, $\lambda_1 = 5 \cdot 36200$, and the last estimate of $\mathbf{u}_1$ is probably nearly accurate to 4D.

4. *Calculation of* λ_2, $\mathbf{u}_2$; λ_3, $\mathbf{u}_3$. Precise results for λ_2 are obtained most easily by continuing the sequence with $\mathbf{A} - 5\mathbf{I}$, as follows—

$$
\begin{aligned}
&\{- 0 \cdot 22,\quad 1,\quad - 0 \cdot 43,\quad - 0 \cdot 34\ \ \}\\
&- 9 \cdot 19\ \ \{- 0 \cdot 2274,\ 1,\ - 0 \cdot 4342,\ - 0 \cdot 3384\}\\
&- 9 \cdot 2068\{- 0 \cdot 2299,\ 1,\ - 0 \cdot 4345,\ - 0 \cdot 3379\}\\
&- 9 \cdot 2092\{- 0 \cdot 2307,\ 1,\ - 0 \cdot 4346,\ - 0 \cdot 3377\}\\
&- 9 \cdot 2099\{- 0 \cdot 2309,\ 1,\ - 0 \cdot 4346,\ - 0 \cdot 3377\}\\
&- 9 \cdot 2101\{- 0 \cdot 2310,\ 1,\ - 0 \cdot 4346,\ - 0 \cdot 3377\}\\
&- 9 \cdot 2102\{- 0 \cdot 2310,\ 1,\ - 0 \cdot 4346,\ - 0 \cdot 3377\}
\end{aligned}
$$

Thus $\lambda_2 = 5 - 9 \cdot 2102 = - 4 \cdot 2102$, and $\mathbf{u}_2$ is well established. To obtain λ_3 it is advisable to use a matrix polynomial,

$$Q_3(\mathbf{A}) = (\mathbf{A} + 4 \cdot 2)(\mathbf{A} - 2 \cdot 1) = \mathbf{A}^2 + 2 \cdot 1\mathbf{A} - 8 \cdot 82\mathbf{I}$$

or more simply $\qquad Q_3(\mathbf{A}) = \mathbf{A}^2 + 2\mathbf{A} - 9\mathbf{I}$

This assumes that the sequence leading to $\mathbf{u}_3$ is kept orthogonal to $\mathbf{u}_1'$, which may be done as follows. Suppose we require $\mathbf{u}_1' \cdot \mathbf{b}_k = 0$, where

$$\mathbf{b}_k = \{b_{1k},\ b_{2k},\ \ldots,\ b_{nk}\}$$
$$\mathbf{u}_1 = \{u_{11},\ u_{21},\ \ldots,\ u_{n1}\}$$

We can leave all the elements of $\mathbf{b}_k$ arbitrary except one, say b_{ik}; this is set equal to

$$- (u_{11}b_{1k} + \ldots + u_{i-1,\,1}b_{i-1,\,k} + u_{i+1,\,1}b_{i+1,\,k} + \ldots + u_{n1}b_{nk})/u_{i1}$$

and the condition is satisfied. b_{ik} is best chosen to correspond to the largest element u_{i1} of $\mathbf{u}_1$, which may conveniently be made unity.

Now $\qquad \mathbf{u}_1 = \{- 0 \cdot 1946,\ 0 \cdot 3455,\ 1,\qquad - 0 \cdot 1306\}$

Let $\qquad \mathbf{b}_0 = \{\quad 0,\qquad 0,\qquad 0 \cdot 1306,\quad 1\quad$

Then by repeatedly multiplying by the matrix

$$\mathbf{A}^2 + 2\mathbf{A} - 9\mathbf{I} = \begin{bmatrix} 1 & -1 & -5 & 3 \\ -1 & 5 & 9 & 3 \\ -5 & 9 & 26 & -3 \\ 3 & 3 & -3 & 11 \end{bmatrix}$$

$$\ldots\ldots\ldots\ldots\ldots\ldots\ldots\ldots\ldots$$

$$\phantom{\mathbf{A}^2 + 2\mathbf{A} - 9\mathbf{I} = \ }- 2 \qquad 16 \qquad 27 \qquad 14$$

we obtain the sequence

$$10\cdot6082 \quad \{0\cdot2213, \ 0\cdot3936, \ 0\cdot0377, \ 1\}$$
$$12\cdot7316 \quad \{0\cdot2073, \ 0\cdot3994, \ 0\cdot0329, \ 1\}$$
$$12\cdot7217 \quad \{0\cdot2078, \ 0\cdot3998, \ 0\cdot0329, \ 1\}$$
$$12\cdot7241 \quad \{0\cdot2078, \ 0\cdot3998, \ 0\cdot0329, \ 1\}$$

At each multiplication, only the 4th, 1st and 2nd elements are found in the usual way; the 3rd is chosen to maintain the orthogonality. The vector $\mathbf{u}_3$ is thus obtained, and λ_3 is obtained from the equation

$$Q_3(\lambda_3) = \lambda_3{}^2 + 2\lambda_3 - 9 = 12\cdot7241$$

The correct root, easily distinguished, is $\lambda_3 = 3\cdot7670$.

5. *Derivation of* $\mathbf{u}_4$. Using $\Sigma\lambda_i$ we find $\lambda_4 = 2\cdot0812$. The final latent vector may be best obtained by making it orthogonal to $\mathbf{u}_1'$, $\mathbf{u}_2'$, $\mathbf{u}_3'$. Thus assuming

$$\mathbf{u}_4 = \{1, \ a, \ b, \ c\}$$

there are three orthogonality conditions which give linear simultaneous equations to determine a, b, and c. By this procedure, we find

$$\mathbf{u}_4 = \{1, \ 0\cdot1777, \ 0\cdot0964, \ -0\cdot2820\}$$

12.13. Repeated Real Roots and Complex Roots

When a matrix is such that λ_1 and λ_2 are of comparable magnitude, this fact will become apparent early in the search for λ_1 as the convergence of any sequence used to find λ_1 will be very slow. We may recall the procedure in the Bernoulli-Aitken method when two roots of an algebraic equation have the same modulus; thus, corresponding to the formulas (9.60) and (9.61) we now have

$$\lambda_1\lambda_2 = \lim \frac{f_{2,\,k+1}}{f_{2,\,k}} = M_{2,\,k}$$

$$\lambda_1 + \lambda_2 = \lim (M_k + \lambda_1\lambda_2/M_{k-1}) = \lim (f_{k+1} + \lambda_1\lambda_2 f_{k-1})/f_k$$

Provided the modulus of λ_3 is not too close to that of the first two roots, the sequence $M_{2,\,k}$ will converge reasonably well to $\lambda_1\lambda_2$ and the estimated limit can be used in the second formula for $\lambda_1 + \lambda_2$. These results hold of course whether λ_1 and λ_2 are nearly equal or exactly equal, and are easily applied in either case.

When $\lambda_1 = \lambda_2$ the convergence of $\mathbf{b}_k$ to its limit may also be slow. If this is so, it may be hastened by a process called by Aitken λ-*differencing* which is appropriate when the matrix is defective in the root $\lambda_1{}^*$. The correct form of the expansion (12.7) is then

$$\mathbf{b}_k = (a_1\lambda_1{}^k + a_2 k\lambda_1{}^{k-1})\mathbf{u}_1 + a_3\lambda_3{}^k\mathbf{u}_3 + \ldots \qquad (12.38)$$

* In general, when λ_1 has multiplicity q and degeneracy p, $\mathbf{b}_k$ contains the term $(a_1\lambda_1{}^k + a_2 k\lambda_1{}^{k-1} + a_3 k_{(2)}\lambda_1{}^{k-2} + \ldots + a_{q-p+1}k_{(q-p)}\lambda_1{}^{k-q+p})\mathbf{u}_1$.

so $\Delta_\lambda \mathbf{b}_k = \mathbf{b}_{k+1} - \lambda_1 \mathbf{b}_k = a_2 \lambda_1{}^k \mathbf{u}_1 + a_3 \lambda_3{}^k (\lambda_3 - \lambda_1) \mathbf{u}_3 + \ldots$ (12.39)

Accordingly the sequence $\Delta_\lambda \mathbf{b}_k$, which can be formed when λ_1 is known, converges to a multiple of $\mathbf{u}_1$ apart from the power of λ_1. A second λ_1-*differencing* would eliminate the term in $\mathbf{u}_1$ entirely.

However, if the matrix $\mathbf{A}$ is degenerate with respect to λ_1 there are two independent vectors associated with λ_1. The term in $\mathbf{b}_k$ may be written $\lambda_1{}^k (a_1 \mathbf{u}_1 + a_2 \mathbf{u}_2)$, although neither $\mathbf{u}_1$ nor $\mathbf{u}_2$ is uniquely defined, nor can they be defined by a sequence derived from a single vector $\mathbf{b}_0$. To do this two separate calculations must be performed, using starting vectors which contain different proportions of $\mathbf{u}_1$ and $\mathbf{u}_2$.

The following example is one in which $\lambda_1 = \lambda_2$, but there is only one independent vector associated with these roots.

EXAMPLE 12.10. Examine the dominant latent root and vector of the matrix

$$\mathbf{A} = \begin{bmatrix} 4 & -4 & -3 & 1 \\ -1 & 5 & 1 & 0 \\ 1 & -5 & 0 & 1 \\ -1 & 6 & -1 & -3 \end{bmatrix}$$

We first form

$$\mathbf{A}^2 = \begin{bmatrix} 16 & -15 & -17 & -2 \\ -8 & 24 & 8 & 0 \\ 8 & -23 & -9 & -2 \\ -8 & 21 & 12 & 7 \end{bmatrix}$$

$$\begin{array}{cccc} 8 & 7 & -6 & 3 \end{array}$$

The first three columns suggest trying

$$\mathbf{b}_0 = \{1, -1, 1, -1\}$$

However, a few multiplications by $\mathbf{A}^2$ show that convergence is slow and suggest two roots close in modulus. We perform four more exact multiplications by $\mathbf{A}$, and estimate $\lambda_1 \lambda_2$ and $\lambda_1 + \lambda_2$ from the second element sequence.

24	$\{-0.6250,$	1,	$-0.9583,$	$-0.8750\}$	0.2917
21.3333	$\{-0.4903,$	1,	$-0.9902,$	$0.9668\}$	0.4863
20.0008	$\{-0.3972,$	1,	$-0.9972,$	$0.9903\}$	0.5959
19.2000	$\{-0.3325,$	1,	$-0.9991,$	$0.9970\}$	0.6654
	$\{-1.3357,$	4.3334,	$-4.3355,$	$4.3406\}$	3.0028
	$\{-5.3293,$	18.6672,	$-18.6621,$	$18.6498\}$	13.3256
	$\{-21.3499,$	80.0032,	$-80.0155,$	$80.0452\}$	58.6830
	$\{-85.3207,$	341.3504,	$-341.3207,$	$341.2490\}$	255.9580

f_k	M_k	$f_{2, k}$	$M_{2, k}$	$(16f_{k-1} + f_{k+1})/f_k$
1				
4·3334	4·3334	− 0·11115556		8·000
18·6672	4·3078	− 1·77848896	16·000000	8·000
80·0032	4·2858	− 28·45582336	16·000000	8·000
341·3504	4·2667			

From the column $M_{2, k}$ it is evident that $\lambda_1\lambda_2 = 16$, and the final column, giving $\lambda_1 + \lambda_2$, confirms that $\lambda_1 = \lambda_2 = 4$. The remaining roots are easily shown to be $- 1 \pm \sqrt{2}$.

The latent vector corresponding to $\lambda = 4$ can be found more precisely by λ-differencing, or rather, if we take alternate vectors, by λ^2-differencing. Thus taking

$$\mathbf{b}_k = \quad \{- 0\cdot3325, \quad 1, \quad - 0\cdot9991, \quad 0\cdot9970 \}$$
$$\mathbf{b}_{k+2} - \lambda_1{}^2\mathbf{b}_k = \quad \{- 0\cdot0093, \quad 2\cdot6672, \quad - 2\cdot6765, \quad 2\cdot6978 \}$$
$$= \quad 2\cdot6672 \{- 0\cdot0035, \quad 1, \quad - 1\cdot0035, \quad 1\cdot0115 \}$$
$$\mathbf{b}_{k+4} - \lambda_1{}^2\mathbf{b}_{k+2} = \quad \{- 0\cdot0519, \quad 42\cdot6752, \quad - 42\cdot7271, \quad 42\cdot8522 \}$$
$$= \quad 42\cdot6752 \{- 0\cdot00122, \quad 1, \quad - 1\cdot00122, \quad 1\cdot00415\}$$

The main effect is here to reduce the first element in the latent vector, which is clearly tending to the limit $\{0, 1, - 1, 1\}$. A more careful inspection of $\mathbf{A}$ would have suggested this in the first place.

It may have been observed that the matrix considered in the last example was unsymmetric. Of course many of the devices already applied to symmetric matrices, such as the use of matrix polynomials, serve equally to find real roots of unsymmetric matrices. We shall conclude this description of iterative methods by showing how the procedure just used to find equal real roots must be modified when the dominant roots are a complex pair. This can only arise when the matrix is unsymmetric.

If the roots are $\rho e^{\pm i\theta}$, then by analogy with (9.60) and (9.61)

$$\rho^2 = \lim M_{2, k}, \quad 2\rho \cos \theta = \lim (f_{k+1} + \rho^2 f_{k-1})/f_k$$

From any suitable sequence f_k, therefore, both ρ and $\rho \cos \theta$ can be derived. The latent vectors, however, necessarily have complex elements, and cannot be obtained directly from the sequence $\mathbf{b}_k$ in which the elements are all real. However, if

$$\mathbf{b}_k = a_1\lambda_1{}^k\mathbf{u}_1 + a_2\lambda_2{}^k\mathbf{u}_2 + a_3\lambda_3{}^k\mathbf{u}_3 + \ldots$$

we observe that

$$(\lambda_1 - \lambda_2)\mathbf{b}_k - \lambda_1\lambda_2\mathbf{b}_{k-1} + \mathbf{b}_{k+1} = 2a_1(\lambda_1 - \lambda_2)\lambda_1{}^k\mathbf{u}_1 + 0(\lambda_3{}^k\mathbf{u}_3)$$

and   (12.40)

$$(\lambda_2 - \lambda_1)\mathbf{b}_k - \lambda_1\lambda_2\mathbf{b}_{k-1} + \mathbf{b}_{k+1} = 2a_1(\lambda_2 - \lambda_1)\lambda_2{}^k\mathbf{u}_2 + 0(\lambda_3{}^k\mathbf{u}_3)$$

Hence when λ_1 and λ_2 are known, $\mathbf{u}_1$ and $\mathbf{u}_2$ can be found.

EXAMPLE 12.11. Find the dominant latent roots and vectors of the matrix

$$\mathbf{A} = \begin{bmatrix} -2 & 1 & 1 & 1 \\ -7 & -5 & -2 & -4 \\ 0 & -1 & -3 & -2 \\ -1 & 0 & -1 & 0 \end{bmatrix}$$

We examine the sequence provided by the starting vector

$$
\begin{array}{lrrrrr}
\{ & -1, & 1, & 0, & 0\} & \\
\{ & 3, & 2, & -1, & 1\} & 5 \\
\{ & -4, & -33, & -1, & -2\} & -40 \\
\{ & -28, & 203, & 40, & 5\} & 220 \\
\{ & 304, & -919, & -333, & -12\} & -960 \\
\{ & -1872, & 3181, & 1942, & 29\} & 3280 \\
\{ & 8896, & -6801, & -9065, & -70\} & \\
\{ & -33728, & -9857, & 34136, & 169\} & \\
\end{array}
$$

There is little sign of convergence here, and the behaviour of the second element indicates strongly a pair of complex roots.

The sequence formed by the first elements reveals at once that $\lambda_1\lambda_2 = 20$, $\lambda_1 + \lambda_2 = -8$, in the following table—

f_k	$f_{2,k}$	$M_{2,k}$	$(20f_{k-1} + f_{k+1})/f_k$
$-$ 4			
$-$ 28	$-$ 2000	20	$-$ 8
304	$-$ 40000	20	$-$ 8
$-$ 1872	$-$ 800000	20	$-$ 8
8896	$-$ 1600000		

The fact that these results are exact is a lucky chance, arising because the vectors $\mathbf{u}_3$ and $\mathbf{u}_4$ have zero elements in the first position. The sequence $M_{2,k}$ from the second elements converges rather slowly. Since $\Sigma\lambda_i = -10$, and from $\mathbf{A}^2$, $\Sigma\lambda_i^2 = 30$, we find that

$$\lambda_{1,2} = -4 \pm 2i, \quad \lambda_3 = -1 - \sqrt{2}, \quad \lambda_4 = -1 + \sqrt{2}$$

From the last 4 vectors in the sequence first obtained, two approximations to $\mathbf{u}_1$ and $\mathbf{u}_2$ can be found, using the formula

$$\mathbf{u}_{1,2} \sim \mathbf{b}_{k+1} - 20\mathbf{b}_{k-1} \pm 4i\mathbf{b}_k$$

These are

$$\{2816 \mp i \ 7488, 11579 \pm i \ 12724, \ - 2405 \pm i \ 7768, 170 \pm \quad 116\}$$
$$\{3712 \pm i \ 35584, \ -73477 \mp i \ 27204, \ -4704 \mp i \ 36260, \ -411 \mp \quad 280\}$$

or, if the first element is reduced to unity,

$$\{1, \ - 0{\cdot}979 \pm i \ 1{\cdot}915, \ - 1{\cdot}016 \pm i \ 0{\cdot}060, \ - 0{\cdot}006 \pm i \ 0{\cdot}025\}$$
$$\{1, \ - 0{\cdot}969 \pm i \ 1{\cdot}964, \ - 1{\cdot}022 \pm i \ 0{\cdot}026, \ - 0{\cdot}008 \pm i \ 0{\cdot}011\}$$

These are in fact two steps in the convergence to the exact latent vectors $\{1, \ - 1 \pm 2i, \ - 1, \ 0\}$. The convergence is slow, and can best be hastened by using the matrix polynomial

$$P(\mathbf{A}) = \mathbf{A}^2 + 2\mathbf{A} - \mathbf{I} = (\mathbf{A} - \lambda_3)(\mathbf{A} - \lambda_4)$$

for iteration.

Lanczos' Method

We now return to consider a more direct approach to the latent vector problem. Iterative methods, as we have seen, are most effective when only one or two dominant roots and vectors of the matrix are required, and when the unwanted roots are appreciably smaller in modulus. If the smallest roots are required they can be obtained by similar methods if the reciprocal matrix is first derived. The simple iterative procedure may, however, involve quite a long sequence, corresponding to the calculation of high powers of the matrix.

The following method of Lanczos, which is an extension of that already described in § 12.3, has the advantage that the highest power of the matrix which must be evaluated cannot exceed the number of rows and columns which it contains. There is no basic difficulty in treating matrices which have multiple roots, roots with the same modulus or roots which are widely dispersed; neither does it matter if the matrix is defective. The roots are determined from the characteristic function $D(\lambda)$, or a simplified form of it, which is the first product of the calculation and is obtained by a process which also yields information necessary to the calculation of latent vectors. All roots and vectors can be derived, or just as many as may be needed.

The first stage, which must be carried through irrespective of the number of roots to be discovered, requires for an unsymmetric matrix the calculation of two sets of vectors which are mutually orthogonal. For a symmetric matrix one set suffices. We begin by describing how these are obtained.

12.14. Derivation of Orthogonal Vectors

Let us assume that $\mathbf{A}$ is not symmetric. The aim is to derive, from arbitrary column and row matrices $\mathbf{b}_0$ and $\mathbf{d}_0$, a set of column matrices

$$\mathbf{p}_0 (= \mathbf{b}_0), \ \mathbf{p}_1, \ \mathbf{p}_2 \ . \ . \ ., \ \mathbf{p}_m$$

and a set of row matrices

$$\mathbf{r}_0 (= \mathbf{d}_0), \ \mathbf{r}_1, \ \mathbf{r}_2, \ . \ . \ ., \ \mathbf{r}_m$$

which satisfy the orthogonality conditions

$$\mathbf{r}_i \mathbf{p}_j = 0 \quad \text{when} \quad i \neq j$$

These replace the sequences $\mathbf{b}_k$ and $\mathbf{d}_k$ used earlier.

The procedure is as follows—

Let

$$\alpha_0 = \mathbf{d}_0 \ . \ \mathbf{A}\mathbf{b}_0/\mathbf{d}_0\mathbf{b}_0 = \mathbf{d}_0\mathbf{A} \ . \ \mathbf{b}_0/\mathbf{d}_0\mathbf{b}_0$$

Then

$$\mathbf{p}_1 = (\mathbf{A} - \alpha_0)\mathbf{b}_0 \quad \text{and} \quad \mathbf{r}_1 = \mathbf{d}_0(\mathbf{A} - \alpha_0)$$

are orthogonal to $\mathbf{d}_0$ and $\mathbf{b}_0$ respectively. Likewise

$$\mathbf{p}_2 = (\mathbf{A} - \alpha_1)\mathbf{p}_1 - \beta_0\mathbf{b}_0$$

is orthogonal to $\mathbf{r}_1$ and $\mathbf{r}_0$, and

$$\mathbf{r}_2 = \mathbf{r}_1(\mathbf{A} - \alpha_1) - \beta_0\mathbf{d}_0$$

is orthogonal to $\mathbf{p}_1$ and $\mathbf{p}_0$, provided

$$\alpha_1 = \mathbf{r}_1 \ . \ \mathbf{A}\mathbf{p}_1/\mathbf{r}_1\mathbf{p}_1 = \mathbf{r}_1\mathbf{A} \ . \ \mathbf{p}_1/\mathbf{r}_1\mathbf{p}_1, \quad \beta_0 = \mathbf{r}_1\mathbf{p}_1/\mathbf{r}_0\mathbf{p}_0$$

In general

$$\mathbf{p}_{s+1} = (\mathbf{A} - \alpha_s)\mathbf{p}_s - \beta_{s-1}\mathbf{p}_{s-1} \qquad (12.41)$$

is orthogonal to $\mathbf{r}_s$, $\mathbf{r}_{s-1}$ and automatically to all preceding $\mathbf{r}$ vectors, and

$$\mathbf{r}_{s+1} = \mathbf{r}_s(\mathbf{A} - \alpha_s) - \beta_{s-1}\mathbf{r}_{s-1} \qquad (12.42)$$

is orthogonal to $\mathbf{p}_s$, $\mathbf{p}_{s-1}$ and all preceding $\mathbf{p}$ vectors, provided

$$\alpha_s = \mathbf{r}_s \ . \ \mathbf{A}\mathbf{p}_s/\mathbf{r}_s\mathbf{p}_s, \quad \beta_{s-1} = \mathbf{r}_s\mathbf{p}_s/\mathbf{r}_{s-1}\mathbf{p}_{s-1} \qquad (12.43)$$

These three-term recurrence relations are very easily applied in practice, and the identities

$$\mathbf{r}_s \ . \ \mathbf{A}\mathbf{p}_s = \mathbf{r}_s\mathbf{A} \ . \ \mathbf{p}_s, \quad \mathbf{r}_s\mathbf{p}_s = \mathbf{r}_{s-1}\mathbf{A} \ . \ \mathbf{p}_s = \mathbf{r}_s \ . \ \mathbf{A}\mathbf{p}_{s-1}$$

provide valuable checks on each stage of calculation. The fact that the orthogonality is imposed step by step is also a constant safeguard against accumulation of rounding errors.

It is interesting to note that the values of the constants $\alpha_0, \ldots, \alpha_s$ and $\beta_0, \ldots, \beta_{s-1}$ are such as to make $\mathbf{r}_s \mathbf{p}_s$ a minimum. This is easily proved. For this reason, Lanczos has described the method as one of *minimized iterations*. It should also be noticed that in forming the sequence $\mathbf{p}_s$ or $\mathbf{r}_s$ we have in fact formed a sequence of matrix polynomials.

Thus if $\qquad\qquad p_0 = 1, \quad p_1(\lambda) = \lambda - \alpha_0 \qquad\qquad$ (12.44)

and in general $\quad p_{s+1}(\lambda) = (\lambda - \alpha_s)p_s(\lambda) - \beta_{s-1}p_{s-1}(\lambda)$

then $\qquad\qquad\qquad\qquad \mathbf{p}_s = p_s(\mathbf{A})\mathbf{b}_0$

i.e. $\mathbf{p}_s$ is the vector obtained by modifying $\mathbf{b}_0$ by multiplications with the matrix polynomial $p_s(\mathbf{A})$; similarly for $\mathbf{r}_s$. The relation to the procedure described in § 12.3 is that

$$p_k(\lambda) = s_0^{(k)} + s_1^{(k)}\lambda + \ldots + s_k^{(k)}\lambda^k$$

where $s_j^{(k)}$ are the coefficients, for integral values of k, obtained by the recurrence scheme there used.* These coefficients are not explicitly calculated in the present scheme.

When $\mathbf{A}$ is symmetric, $\mathbf{r}_s$ and $\mathbf{p}_s$ contain the same elements if $\mathbf{r}_0 = \mathbf{p}_0'$. The computation is therefore much simpler.

12.15. Derivation of the Characteristic Function and Latent Vectors

We now show how the foregoing sequence of vectors leads to the characteristic function of the matrix $\mathbf{A}$. First, because $\mathbf{A}$ has only m independent latent vectors of each kind, where $m \leqslant n$, not more than m mutually orthogonal vectors can be constructed from them. It is inevitable therefore that all the elements of both $\mathbf{p}_m$ and $\mathbf{r}_m$ should vanish, otherwise the conditions,

$$\mathbf{r}_m \mathbf{p}_k = \mathbf{r}_k \mathbf{p}_m = 0 \quad (k < m)$$

could not be satisfied.

Let us now consider the solution of the matrix equation

$$(1 - \mathbf{A}/\lambda)\mathbf{y} = \mathbf{b}_0 \qquad\qquad (12.45)$$

---

* In a second paper, *J. Res. Nat. Bur. Stand.*, **49** (1952), 33, Lanczos has developed the method of minimized iterations by including the intermediate polynomials $p_{k+1/2}(\lambda)$. The expansion of an arbitrary column vector in terms of the vectors $\mathbf{q}_k = p_{k+1/2}(\mathbf{A})\mathbf{b}_0$ is found to have advantages over an expansion in terms of $\mathbf{p}_k$, and Lanczos shows how this can be used in solving a linear set of equations of the form $\mathbf{A}\mathbf{x} = \mathbf{b}_0$ or in forming $\mathbf{A}^{-1}$.

expanding the solution in terms of the vectors $\mathbf{p}_k$,

i.e. $$\mathbf{y} = y_0\mathbf{p}_0 + y_1\mathbf{p}_1 + \ldots + y_{m-1}\mathbf{p}_{m-1}$$

where the coefficients y_k have to be found. On substituting in (12.45), and replacing $\mathbf{A}\mathbf{p}_k$ by $\mathbf{p}_{k+1} + \alpha\mathbf{p}_k + \beta_{k-1}\mathbf{p}_{k-1}$ in accordance with (12.41), we obtain the equations shown below when the coefficient of each vector is set equal to zero. These are shown side by side with a set of polynomials $\bar{p}_k(\lambda)$, which satisfy similar recurrence relations.

$$
\begin{aligned}
&& \bar{p}_0 &= 1 & \\
y_{m-2} &= (\lambda - \alpha_{m-1})y_{m-1} & \bar{p}_1 &= (\lambda - \alpha_{m-1})\bar{p}_0 & \\
y_{m-3} &= (\lambda - \alpha_{m-2})y_{m-2} - \beta_{m-2}y_{m-1} & \bar{p}_2 &= (\lambda - \alpha_{m-2})\bar{p}_1 - \beta_{m-2}\bar{p}_0 & \\
\cdot && \cdot & & \\
\cdot && \cdot & & (12.46) \\
y_0 &= (\lambda - \alpha_1)y_1 - \beta_1 y_2 & \bar{p}_{m-1} &= (\lambda - \alpha_1)\bar{p}_{m-2} - \beta_1\bar{p}_{m-3} & \\
\lambda &= (\lambda - \alpha_0)y_0 - \beta_0 y_1 & \bar{p}_m &= (\lambda - \alpha_0)\bar{p}_{m-1} - \beta_0\bar{p}_{m-2} &
\end{aligned}
$$

The two sets of equations are clearly identical if

$$y_k = \lambda\bar{p}_{m-k-1}(\lambda)/\bar{p}_m(\lambda)$$

Hence $$y = \{\lambda/\bar{p}_m(\lambda)\}\mathbf{u}(\lambda) \qquad (12.47)$$

where $\mathbf{u}(\lambda) = \bar{p}_{m-1}\mathbf{p}_0 + \bar{p}_{m-2}\mathbf{p}_1 + \ldots + \bar{p}_1\mathbf{p}_{m-2} + \mathbf{p}_{m-1}$ (12.48)

Equation (12.45) may now be written

$$(\lambda - \mathbf{A})\mathbf{u}(\lambda) = \bar{p}_m(\lambda)\mathbf{b}_0 \qquad (12.49)$$

and two important conclusions can be drawn from this. First, if λ is such that $\bar{p}_m(\lambda) \neq 0$, then (12.49) is satisfied by (12.48); secondly, if $\bar{p}_m(\lambda) = 0$, which will in general occur if λ has one of m values $\lambda_1, \ldots, \lambda_m$, then

$$(\mathbf{A} - \lambda_i)\mathbf{u}_i = 0$$

where $$\mathbf{u}_i = \bar{p}_{i0}\mathbf{p}_0 + \bar{p}_{i1}\mathbf{p}_1 + \ldots + \bar{p}_{i,\,m-2}\mathbf{p}_{m-2} + \mathbf{p}_{m-1} \quad (12.50)$$

and $$\bar{p}_{ik} = \bar{p}_{m-k-1}(\lambda_i)$$

Thus the values λ_i are latent roots of the matrix $\mathbf{A}$, and $\mathbf{u}_i$ is the latent column vector of $\mathbf{A}$ corresponding to λ_1.

Similarly the latent row vector $\mathbf{v}_i$ which satisfies $\mathbf{v}_i(\mathbf{A} - \lambda_i) = 0$ is given by

$$\mathbf{v}_i = \bar{p}_{i0}\mathbf{r}_0 + \bar{p}_{i1}\mathbf{r}_1 + \ldots + \bar{p}_{i,\,m-2}\mathbf{r}_{m-2} + \mathbf{r}_{m-1} \quad (12.51)$$

Equations (12.50) and (12.51) can be concisely expressed in matrix form. Thus if we introduce the following matrices,

$$\mathbf{X} = [\mathbf{u}_1, \mathbf{u}_2, \ldots, \mathbf{u}_m] \qquad \mathbf{P} = [\mathbf{p}_0\,\mathbf{p}_1 \cdots \mathbf{p}_{m-1}]$$

$$\mathbf{Y} = \begin{bmatrix} \mathbf{v}_1 \\ \mathbf{v}_2 \\ \cdot \\ \cdot \\ \cdot \\ \mathbf{v}_m \end{bmatrix} \quad \mathbf{R} = \begin{bmatrix} \mathbf{r}_0 \\ \mathbf{r}_1 \\ \cdot \\ \cdot \\ \cdot \\ \mathbf{r}_{m-1} \end{bmatrix} \quad \bar{\mathbf{P}} = \begin{bmatrix} \bar{p}_{00} & \cdots & \bar{p}_{0,\,m-2} & 1 \\ \bar{p}_{10} & \cdots & \bar{p}_{1,\,m-2} & 1 \\ \cdot \\ \cdot \\ \cdot \\ \bar{p}_{m-1,\,0} & \cdots & \bar{p}_{m-1,\,m-2} & 1 \end{bmatrix}$$

then (12.50) and (12.51) become respectively

$$\mathbf{X} = \mathbf{P}\bar{\mathbf{P}}' \quad \text{and} \quad \mathbf{Y} = \bar{\mathbf{P}}\mathbf{R}$$

We are thus led to identify $\bar{p}_m(\lambda)$ with the polynomial $G_m(\lambda)$ which was derived in § 12.3 and which is identical with the characteristic function $D(\lambda)$ when $m = n$. The remarks at the end of § 12.3 on the circumstances in which $m < n$ again apply here; this may happen either because $\mathbf{p}_0$ or $\mathbf{r}_0$ is accidentally orthogonal to certain latent vectors, or because the matrix $\mathbf{A}$ is degenerate with respect to multiple latent roots. It should be emphasized again that Lanczos' method is not invalidated if the matrix is defective.

12.16. Numerical Procedure

It is clear that the computation consists of the following parts—

1. Derivation of the vectors $\mathbf{p}_k$, $\mathbf{r}_k$ (or $\mathbf{p}_k$ alone if the matrix is symmetric), together with α_k and β_k using (12.41), (12.42) and (12.43).

2. Derivation of the polynomials $\bar{p}_k(\lambda)$ and in particular of $p_m(\lambda) = G_m(\lambda)$, by the recurrence relations (12.46).

3. Calculation of such roots of $G_m(\lambda) = 0$ as are required.

4. Calculation of the corresponding latent vectors by (12.50) and (12.51).

The layout of the calculation, or at least parts (1), (2) and (4), will be clear from the following examples. The first of these is a repetition of Example 12.4 with the addition of the latent vectors; the second treats a symmetrical matrix of order 4, and the calculation may be fruitfully compared with that in Example 12.9.

EXAMPLE 12.12. Find the latent roots and vectors of the matrix

$$\mathbf{A} = \begin{bmatrix} 2 & -2 & 3 \\ 1 & 1 & 1 \\ 1 & 3 & -1 \end{bmatrix}$$

For convenience, both the $\mathbf{p}$ and $\mathbf{r}$ vectors are written as rows.

				$r_k \mathbf{A} p_k$	$r_k p_k$				
$\mathbf{p}_0$	0	1	0	1	1	$\mathbf{r}_0$	0	1	0
$\mathbf{A}\mathbf{p}_0$	-2	1	3	$\alpha_0 = 1$		$\mathbf{r}_0\mathbf{A}$	1	1	1
$\mathbf{p}_1$	-2	0	3	0	1	$\mathbf{r}_1$	1	0	1
$\mathbf{A}\mathbf{p}_1$	5	1	-5	$\alpha_1 = 0$	$\beta_0 = 1$	$\mathbf{r}_1\mathbf{A}$	3	1	2
$\mathbf{p}_2$	5	0	-5	5	5	$\mathbf{r}_2$	3	0	2
$\mathbf{A}\mathbf{p}_2$	-5	0	10	$\alpha_2 = 1$	$\beta_1 = 5$	$\mathbf{r}_2\mathbf{A}$	8	0	7
$\mathbf{p}_3$	0	0	0			$\mathbf{r}_3$	0	0	0

The order of calculation is as follows—

(i) $\mathbf{A}\mathbf{p}_0$, $\mathbf{r}_0\mathbf{A}$, $\mathbf{r}_0\mathbf{A}.\mathbf{p}_0$ (checked by $\mathbf{r}_0 . \mathbf{A}\mathbf{p}_0$), α_0;

(ii) $\mathbf{p}_1$, $\mathbf{r}_1$, (by (12.41) and (12.42)); $\mathbf{r}_1\mathbf{p}_1$ (checked by $\mathbf{r}_0\mathbf{A}.\mathbf{p}_1$ and $\mathbf{r}_1 . \mathbf{A}\mathbf{p}_0$);

(iii) $\mathbf{A}\mathbf{p}_1$, $\mathbf{r}_1\mathbf{A}$, $\mathbf{r}_1\mathbf{A}.\mathbf{p}_1$ (checked by $\mathbf{r}_1 . \mathbf{A}\mathbf{p}_1$), α_1, β_0;

(iv) $\mathbf{p}_2$, $\mathbf{r}_2$; $\mathbf{r}_2\mathbf{p}_2$ (checked by $\mathbf{r}_1\mathbf{A} . \mathbf{p}_2$ and $\mathbf{r}_2 . \mathbf{A}\mathbf{p}_1$) and so on. Finally $\mathbf{p}_3$ and $\mathbf{r}_3$ must vanish identically, otherwise a mistake has been made.

Now
$$\bar{p}_0 = 1$$
$$\bar{p}_1 = \lambda - 1$$
$$\bar{p}_2 = \lambda\bar{p}_1 - 5 = \lambda^2 - \lambda - 5$$
$$\bar{p}_3 = (\lambda - 1)\bar{p}_2 - \bar{p}_1 = (\lambda - 1)(\lambda^2 - \lambda - 6)$$
$$= (\lambda - 3)(\lambda + 2)(\lambda - 1)$$

so the latent roots are 3, -2, 1.

The latent vector calculations are here arranged for row by row multiplication, using $\mathbf{X}' = \bar{\mathbf{P}}\mathbf{P}'$ and $\mathbf{Y} = \bar{\mathbf{P}}\mathbf{R}$.

$$\bar{\mathbf{P}} \begin{bmatrix} 1 & 2 & 1 \\ 1 & -3 & 1 \\ -5 & 0 & 1 \end{bmatrix} \begin{matrix} \lambda = 3 \\ \lambda = -2 \\ \lambda = 1 \end{matrix} \qquad \bar{\mathbf{P}} \begin{bmatrix} 1 & 2 & 1 \\ 1 & -3 & 1 \\ -5 & 0 & 1 \end{bmatrix}$$

$$\mathbf{P} \begin{bmatrix} 0 & -2 & 5 \\ 1 & 0 & 0 \\ 0 & 3 & -5 \end{bmatrix} \qquad \mathbf{R}' \begin{bmatrix} 0 & 1 & 3 \\ 1 & 0 & 0 \\ 0 & 1 & 2 \end{bmatrix}$$

$$\mathbf{X}' \begin{bmatrix} 1 & 1 & 1 \\ 11 & 1 & -14 \\ 5 & -5 & -5 \end{bmatrix} \begin{matrix} \mathbf{u}'(3) \\ \mathbf{u}'(-2) \\ \mathbf{u}'(1) \end{matrix} \qquad \mathbf{Y} \begin{bmatrix} 5 & 1 & 4 \\ 0 & 1 & -1 \\ 3 & -5 & 2 \end{bmatrix} \begin{matrix} \mathbf{v}(3) \\ \mathbf{v}(-2) \\ \mathbf{v}(1) \end{matrix}$$

A final check is obtained by testing the latent vectors for orthogonality.

EXAMPLE 12.13. Find the characteristic function and latent vectors of the matrix

$$\mathbf{A} = \begin{bmatrix} 2 & 2 & 0 & 4 \\ 2 & -1 & -1 & 3 \\ 0 & -1 & 0 & -2 \\ 4 & 3 & -2 & 0 \end{bmatrix}$$

This matrix is symmetrical, and the first stage of the calculation is therefore simplified. As the chief aim is to display the operations, the numbers are left as fractions.

					$\mathbf{p}_k'\mathbf{Ap}_k$	$\mathbf{p}_k'\mathbf{p}_k$	α_0	
$\mathbf{p}_0$	1	0	0	0	2	1	2	
$\mathbf{Ap}_0$	2	2	0	4				
$\mathbf{p}_1$	0	2	0	4			α_1	β_0
$\mathbf{Ap}_1$	18	10	-10	6	44	20	$11/5$	20
$\mathbf{p}_2$	$\frac{2}{5}\{0$	14	-25	$-14\}$			α_2	β_1
$\mathbf{Ap}_2$	$\frac{2}{5}\{0$	-10	0	$92\}$	$-3136/25$	$696/5$	$-392/435$	$174/25$
$\mathbf{p}_3$	$\frac{112}{87}\{0$	-10	-7	$5\}$			α_3	β_2
$\mathbf{Ap}_3$	$\frac{112}{87}\{0$	32	0	$-16\}$	$-\left(\frac{2240}{87}\right)^2$	$\frac{2(112)^2}{87}$	$-\frac{200}{87}$	$\frac{5}{4}\left(\frac{112}{87}\right)^2$
$\mathbf{p}_4$	0	0	0	0				

Hence
$$\bar{p}_0 = 1$$
$$\bar{p}_1 = \lambda + 200/87$$
$$\bar{p}_2 = (\lambda + 392/435)\bar{p}_1 - (5/4)(112/87)^2 = \lambda^2 + (16/5)\lambda$$
$$\bar{p}_3 = (\lambda - 11/5)\bar{p}_2 - (174/25)\bar{p}_1 = \lambda^3 + \lambda^2 - 14\lambda - 16$$
$$D(\lambda) = \bar{p}_4 = (\lambda - 2)\bar{p}_3 - 20\bar{p}_2 = \lambda^4 - \lambda^3 - 36\lambda^2 - 52\lambda + 32$$

The roots of $D(\lambda) = 0$ are found to be

$$\lambda_1 = 7 \cdot 056, \quad \lambda_2 = -4 \cdot 194, \quad \lambda_3 = -2 \cdot 327, \quad \lambda_4 = 0 \cdot 4648$$

We omit the detail of this not inconsiderable piece of work, and of the derivation of the elements of $\bar{\mathbf{P}}$, and show only the final stage giving the latent vectors.

$$\bar{\mathbf{P}} \qquad \begin{bmatrix} 286 \cdot 25 & 72 \cdot 36 & 9 \cdot 355 & 1 \\ -13 \cdot 456 & 4 \cdot 167 & -1 \cdot 895 & 1 \\ 9 \cdot 392 & -2 \cdot 032 & -0 \cdot 028 & 1 \\ -22 \cdot 191 & 1 \cdot 703 & 2 \cdot 764 & 1 \end{bmatrix}$$

$$\mathbf{P}' \qquad \begin{bmatrix} 1 & 0 & 0 & 0 \\ 0 & 2 & 5 \cdot 6 & -12 \cdot 874 \\ 0 & 0 & -10 \cdot 0 & -9 \cdot 012 \\ 0 & 4 & -2 \cdot 8 & 6 \cdot 437 \end{bmatrix}$$

$$\mathbf{Y} = \mathbf{X}' \begin{bmatrix} 286{\cdot}25 & 184{\cdot}23 & -102{\cdot}56 & 269{\cdot}68 \\ -13{\cdot}456 & -15{\cdot}152 & 9{\cdot}938 & 28{\cdot}411 \\ 9{\cdot}392 & -17{\cdot}095 & -8{\cdot}732 & -1{\cdot}613 \\ -22{\cdot}191 & 6{\cdot}010 & -36{\cdot}652 & 5{\cdot}510 \end{bmatrix}$$

On reducing the largest element in each vector to unity, we obtain

$$\mathbf{u}_1 = \{\quad 1{\cdot}0 \quad, \quad 0{\cdot}6436, \quad -0{\cdot}3583, \quad 0{\cdot}9421\}$$
$$\mathbf{u}_2 = \{-0{\cdot}4736, \quad -0{\cdot}5333, \quad 0{\cdot}3498, \quad 1{\cdot}0 \quad\}$$
$$\mathbf{u}_3 = \{-0{\cdot}5494, \quad 1{\cdot}0 \quad, \quad 0{\cdot}5108, \quad 0{\cdot}0944\}$$
$$\mathbf{u}_4 = \{\quad 0{\cdot}6055, \quad -0{\cdot}1640, \quad 1{\cdot}0 \quad, \quad -0{\cdot}1503\}$$

The orthogonality check is satisfactory.

More Recent Developments

The increasing use of automatic computers to solve large systems of equations has led to several powerful methods being developed, especially for roots and vectors of symmetric matrices. These aim to reduce the matrix by a series of simple transformations either to diagonal form (as in an old method due to Jacobi), or to a triple-diagonal (codiagonal) form from which the roots and vectors can be derived by a special process. In the latter class are two valuable methods due to Givens and to Householder. Lanczos' method can also be described more simply as a transformation of the matrix to triple-diagonal form, and has considerable merit for unsymmetric matrices. Wilkinson has made important contributions to all of these methods by developing stable numerical procedures.

A brief introduction to the newer methods is given in *Modern Computing Methods*, and further references will be found there.

EXERCISES 12

1. Show that if $a_{jj}^{(k)}$ are the diagonal elements of $\mathbf{A}^k$, then

$$s_k = a_{11}^{(k)} + \ldots + a_{nn}^{(k)} = \lambda_1^k + \lambda_2^k + \ldots + \lambda_n^k$$

Hence show that the coefficients p_k of

$$D(\lambda) = (-1)^n\{\lambda^n - p_1\lambda^{n-1} - \ldots - p_n\} = 0$$

are given by the recurrence relations

$$p_1 = s_1$$
$$p_2 = (s_2 - s_1 p_1)/2$$
$$p_k = (s_k - s_{k-1}p_1 - s_{k-2}p_2 - \ldots - s_1 p_{k-1})/k$$

(Leverrier)

2. If $\mathbf{b}_k = \mathbf{A}^k\mathbf{b}_0 = (b_{1,k}, b_{2,k}, \ldots, b_{n,k})$, where $\mathbf{b}_0$ is an arbitrary column matrix, show that the coefficients p_k satisfy the linear simultaneous equations—

$$\begin{bmatrix} b_{1,0} & b_{1,1} & \cdots & b_{1,n-1} \\ b_{2,0} & b_{2,1} & \cdots & b_{2,n-1} \\ \cdot & & & \\ \cdot & & & \\ \cdot & & & \\ b_{n,0} & b_{n,1} & \cdots & b_{n,n-1} \end{bmatrix} \begin{bmatrix} p_n \\ p_{n-1} \\ \\ \\ p_1 \end{bmatrix} = \begin{bmatrix} b_{1,n} \\ b_{2,n} \\ \\ \\ b_{n,n} \end{bmatrix}$$

Note. Use the Hamilton-Cayley theorem, $D(\mathbf{A})\mathbf{b}_0 = 0$.

3. If $\mathbf{b}_k = \mathbf{A}^k\mathbf{b}_0$ and $\mathbf{d}_k = \mathbf{d}_0\mathbf{A}^k$, where $\mathbf{b}_0$ and $\mathbf{d}_0$ are arbitrary column and row matrices respectively, and

$$c_k = \mathbf{d}_0\mathbf{A}^k\mathbf{b}_0 = \mathbf{d}_i \cdot \mathbf{b}_j$$

where $$i + j = k$$

show that

$$\begin{bmatrix} c_0 & c_1 & \cdots & c_{n-1} \\ c_1 & c_2 & \cdots & c_n \\ \cdot & & & \\ \cdot & & & \\ c_{n-1} & c_n & & c_{2n-2} \\ c_n & c_{n+1} & \cdots & c_{2n-1} \end{bmatrix} \begin{bmatrix} p_n \\ p_{n-1} \\ \\ p_1 \end{bmatrix} = \begin{bmatrix} c_n \\ c_{n+1} \\ \\ c_{2n-1} \\ c_{2n} \end{bmatrix}$$ (Lanczos)

Note. Use the results of No. 2 above.

4. If λ_i is a root of the polynomial $G_m(\lambda) = 0$ given by Lanczos' method, and

$$G_m(\lambda) = (\lambda - \lambda_i)H_i(\lambda) = (\lambda - \lambda_i)(\lambda^{m-1} + g_1{}^i\lambda^{m-2} + \ldots + g_{m-1}{}^i)$$

show that the corresponding latent vectors $\mathbf{u}_i$ and $\mathbf{v}_i$ are given by

$$\mathbf{u}_i = \mathbf{B}g_i, \quad \mathbf{v}_i = g_i'\mathbf{D}$$

where $\mathbf{g}_i$ is the column matrix $\{1, g_1{}^i, g_2{}^i, \ldots, g_{m-1}{}^i\}$ and $\mathbf{B}, \mathbf{D}$ are the square matrices $[\mathbf{b}_0, \mathbf{b}_1, \ldots, \mathbf{b}_{m-1}]$ and $\{\mathbf{d}_0, \mathbf{d}_1, \ldots, \mathbf{d}_{m-1}\}$ respectively.
Note. Start from the equation $G_m(\mathbf{A})\mathbf{b}_0 = (\mathbf{A} - \lambda_i)H_i(\mathbf{A})\mathbf{b}_0$.

5. Examine by Lanczos' method the latent roots of the matrix

$$\begin{bmatrix} 1 & 2 & 3 & 0 & 0 & 0 \\ 0 & 1 & 4 & 0 & 0 & 0 \\ 0 & 0 & 1 & 0 & 0 & 0 \\ 0 & 0 & 0 & 2 & 0 & 0 \\ 0 & 0 & 0 & 0 & 0 & 0 \\ 0 & 0 & 0 & 0 & 0 & 0 \end{bmatrix}$$

Starting with $\quad \mathbf{b}_0 = \mathbf{d}_0' = \{1, 1, 1, 1, 1, 1\}$

show that $\quad G_m(\lambda) = \lambda(\lambda - 2)(\lambda - 1)^3$

Which root of $D(\lambda)$ is multiple?

6. Show that the determinantal equation

$$|\mathbf{A}_0\lambda^3 + \mathbf{A}_1\lambda^2 + \mathbf{A}_2\lambda + \mathbf{A}_3| = 0$$

is equivalent to

$$\begin{vmatrix} \mathbf{A}_0^{-1}\mathbf{A}_1 + \mathbf{I}_n\lambda & \mathbf{A}_0^{-1}\mathbf{A}_2 & \mathbf{A}_0^{-1}\mathbf{A}_3 \\ -\mathbf{I}_n & \mathbf{I}_n\lambda & 0 \\ 0 & -\mathbf{I}_n & \mathbf{I}_n\lambda \end{vmatrix} = 0$$

provided
$$|\mathbf{A}_0| \neq 0$$

7. Suppose that the roots of the matrix $\mathbf{A}$ are real and positive, and satisfy the relations $\lambda_1 > \lambda_2 > \ldots > \lambda_{n-1} > \lambda_n$. If the extreme roots are known approximately, show that the value of λ_1 can be improved most effectively by iteration by finding the dominant root of $\mathbf{A} - p\mathbf{I}_n$, where $p = \frac{1}{2}(\lambda_2 + \lambda_{n-1})$; likewise to improve the least root λ_n, one should take $p = \frac{1}{2}(\lambda_1 + \lambda_{n-1})$.

8. If $\mathbf{f}(\lambda)$ is the λ-matrix $\mathbf{A} - \mathbf{I}_n\lambda$, and $\mathbf{F}(\lambda)$ is its adjoint matrix (i.e. with the elements equal to the cofactors of the elements of $\mathbf{f}(\lambda)$), having the expansion

$$\mathbf{F}(\lambda) = (-1)^{n-1}(\lambda^{n-1}\mathbf{A}_0 + \lambda^{n-2}\mathbf{A}_1 + \ldots + \lambda\mathbf{A}_{n-2} + \mathbf{A}_{n-1})$$

show that the square matrices $\mathbf{A}_0, \ldots, \mathbf{A}_{n-1}$ are given by the recurrence relations

$$\mathbf{A}_0 = \mathbf{I}_n$$
$$\mathbf{A}_1 = \mathbf{A}\mathbf{A}_0 - p_1\mathbf{I}_n$$
$$\mathbf{A}_2 = \mathbf{A}\mathbf{A}_1 - p_2\mathbf{I}_n$$
$$\cdot$$
$$\mathbf{A}_k = \mathbf{A}\mathbf{A}_{k-1} - p_k\mathbf{I}_n$$

and
$$0 = \mathbf{A}\mathbf{A}_{n-1} - p_n\mathbf{I}_n$$

where the p's are the usual coefficients in the latent root function $D(\lambda)$. *Note.* Use the relation $\mathbf{f}(\lambda)\mathbf{F}(\lambda) = D(\lambda)\mathbf{I}_n$.

9. Show that $kp_k = $ trace $\mathbf{A}\mathbf{A}_{k-1}$, where $\mathbf{A}_{k-1}$ is defined in No. 8. Combine this result with No. 8 to compute both the function $D(\lambda)$ and the adjoint matrix $\mathbf{F}(\lambda)$. (Frame, 1949)

10. If $\mathbf{A}$ is a non-defective matrix having a known root λ with known column and row vectors, $\mathbf{c} = \{c_1, \ldots, c_n\}$ and $\mathbf{r} = [r_1, \ldots, r_n]$ respectively, such that $\mathbf{cr} = 1$, then the matrix

$$\mathbf{B} = \mathbf{Q}(\mathbf{A} - t\mathbf{cr})\mathbf{Q}^{-1}$$

defined by the transformation matrix $\mathbf{Q}$, has the same latent roots as $\mathbf{A}$, except that λ is replaced by $\lambda - t$ (cp. (12.33)).

If ν is another root common to $\mathbf{A}$ and $\mathbf{B}$, with respect to which $\mathbf{A}$ has vectors $\mathbf{u} = \{u_1, \ldots, u_n\}$ and $\mathbf{v} = [v_1, \ldots, v_n]$, and $\mathbf{B}$ has vectors $\mathbf{x} = \{x_1, \ldots, x_n\}$ and $\mathbf{y} = [y_1, \ldots, y_n]$, verify that $\mathbf{x} = \mathbf{Q}\mathbf{u}$ and $\mathbf{y} = \mathbf{v}\mathbf{Q}^{-1}$.

11. Show that when, in the notation of No. 10, the elements of $\mathbf{Q}$ are

$$q_{ij} = \delta_{ij}(i \neq n, \text{all } j), \quad q_{nj} = - r_j/r_n \text{ (all } j)$$

so that the reciprocal $\mathbf{Q}^{-1} = \mathbf{Q}$, then the transformed matrix

$$\mathbf{B} = \mathbf{QAQ}^{-1}$$

has elements

$$b_{ij} = a_{ij} - (r_j/r_n)a_{in} \ (i, j \neq n); \ b_{in} = - a_{in} \ (i \neq n)$$
$$b_{nj} = 0 \quad (j \neq n) \qquad \qquad ; \ b_{nn} = \lambda$$

and is effectively of order $n - 1$.

If the second root ν and its vectors $\mathbf{x}, \mathbf{y}$ are also known, show that

$$\mathbf{u} = \{x_1, \ldots, x_{n-1}, \ u_n\}$$

where

$$u_n = - \sum_{1}^{n-1} (r_i/r_n)x_i$$

and

$$\mathbf{v} = [y_1 + (r_1/r_n)v_n, \ldots, y_{n-1} + (r_{n-1}/r_n)v_n, \ v_n]$$

where

$$v_n = - \sum_{1}^{n-1} (c_i/r_n)y_i$$

Note. This is a suitable method of reduction when $\mathbf{A}$ is unsymmetrical.

(G. Blanch; see Feller and Forsythe, *Quart. Appl. Math.* (1951))

12. Let $\mathbf{A}$ be a symmetrical matrix, and $r_i = c_i$. Again using the notation of No. 10, show that when

$$q_{ij} = \delta_{ij} - \gamma c_i c_j \quad (i, j \neq n); \quad q_{in} = - c_i(i \neq n)$$
$$q_{nj} = c_j \qquad \qquad (j \neq n); \quad q_{nn} = c_n$$

where

$$\gamma = (c_n + 1)^{-1} \quad \text{and} \quad \mathbf{Q}^{-1} = \mathbf{Q}'$$

then the matrix

$$\mathbf{B} = \mathbf{Q}(\mathbf{A} - t\mathbf{cc}')\mathbf{Q}^{-1}$$

has elements

$$b_{ij} = a_{ij} - \gamma(c_i a_{nj} + c_j a_{in}) + \gamma^2 c_i c_j(a_{nn} - \lambda), \ (i, j \neq n)$$
$$b_{in} = b_{nj} = 0 \ (i, j \neq n); \quad b_{nn} = \lambda - t$$

Moreover for a second latent root

$$\mathbf{v}' = \mathbf{u} = \{x_1 + c_1 u_n, \ldots, x_{n-1} + c_{n-1} u_n, \ u_n\}$$

where

$$u_n = - \sum_{1}^{n-1} c_i x_i$$

Examine the similar transformation in which $\gamma = (c_n - 1)^{-1}$. (Change the sign of γ in q_{ij} and the sign of q_{in}.)

(Feller and Forsythe, 1951)

13. Assume that, in the notation of No. 10, $c_n = u_n = 1$. Then if $\mathbf{a}_n = [a_{n1}, a_{n2}, \ldots, a_{nn}]$, i.e. the last row of $\mathbf{A}$, and $\mathbf{B} = \mathbf{A} - \mathbf{c}\mathbf{a}_n$, show that

(a) the final row of $\mathbf{B}$ has all zero elements;

(b) $\mathbf{B}$ has the same roots as $\mathbf{A}$ except that λ is replaced by zero;

(c) the column vector $\mathbf{x}$ of $\mathbf{B}$, corresponding to the root ν, is proportional to $\mathbf{u} - \mathbf{c}$.

Hence if ν and $\mathbf{x}$ can be found (e.g. by iteration) from the matrix obtained by omitting the nth row and column of $\mathbf{B}$, show that the elements of $\mathbf{u}$ are

$$u_i = c_i + k x_i \ (i \neq n)$$

where
$$k = (\nu - \lambda)/\{\sum_1^{n-1} a_{ni} x_i\}$$

Note. This method of reduction is a suitable alternative to deflation when $\mathbf{A}$ is unsymmetrical, and can be extended to include complex roots and vectors.

14. If $\mathbf{\Lambda}$ is a diagonal matrix whose elements are the latent roots λ_j (assumed distinct and non-zero) of a symmetric matrix $\mathbf{A}$, and $\mathbf{X}$ is the matrix composed of the corresponding column vectors $\mathbf{x}_j$, show that $\mathbf{AX} = \mathbf{X\Lambda}$.

If $\mathbf{X}_0$ is an approximation to $\mathbf{X}$ such that

$$\mathbf{X}_0^{-1}\mathbf{A}\mathbf{X}_0 = \mathbf{\Lambda}_1 + \mathbf{C}$$

where $\mathbf{\Lambda}_1$ is diagonal (with elements λ_{1j}) and $\mathbf{C}$ has zero diagonal elements, show that a better approximation is given by

$$\mathbf{X}_1 = \mathbf{X}_0(\mathbf{I}_n + \mathbf{D})$$

where the elements of $\mathbf{D}$ are given in terms of those of $\mathbf{C}$ by the relations

$$d_{ij} = c_{ij}/(\lambda_{1j} - \lambda_{1i})$$

(Jahn, Collar: *Quart. J. Mech. Appl. Math.* (1948))

CHAPTER 13

INDIRECT METHODS FOR LINEAR EQUATIONS

IN a previous chapter the solution of linear simultaneous equations by direct methods was explored at some length. It is not uncommon, however, to meet sets of equations for which this kind of attack is unsuited, even pedantic, because many coefficients off the diagonal are zero or relatively small. For such equations iterative methods have been developed, on the one hand, the "classical" method of Seidel, and on the other the "relaxation" methods, developed in recent years by Southwell and others, though in origin more properly ascribed to C. F. Gauss. Indeed Gauss had a strong preference for indirect methods of solving the normal equations he met with in survey problems, partly induced perhaps by his unusual talent for mental arithmetic.* For solving differential and integral equations with suitable boundary conditions, indirect methods also have a special value.

The following account of these methods makes use of some properties of matrices introduced in the last chapter; this is not essential to the understanding of the processes involved, but it does suggest ways of accelerating the calculation in suitable cases. The problem of improving an approximation to the inverse of a matrix is also discussed.

Classical Iterative Methods

We shall describe two forms of the classical method, both straightforward in use, the second of which can be definitely ascribed to Seidel,† and perhaps the first also.

---

* One may instance the following remark from this letter to C. L. Gerling, 26 Dec., 1823, describing his method of indirect elimination (i.e. relaxation). "I recommend this method to you for imitation. You will hardly ever again eliminate directly, at least not when you have more than two unknowns. The indirect procedure can be done whilst half asleep, or while thinking about other things." (See Forsythe, *Math. Tab., Wash.,* **5** (1951), 255.)

† L. Seidel, *Abh. bayer. Akad. Wiss.,* **11** (1874), 81.

The method is often called the Gauss-Seidel method, but Gauss does not appear to have been associated with it.

Let us denote two successive approximations to the solution of equations (11.1) by

$$\mathbf{x}_k = \{x_1^{(k)}, x_2^{(k)}, \ldots, x_n^{(k)}\}$$

and
$$\mathbf{x}_{k+1} = \{x_1^{(k+1)}, x_2^{(k+1)}, \ldots, x_n^{(k+1)}\}$$

The second of these may be derived from the first by means of one or other of the following sets of iterative relations—

$$
\text{I} \quad
\left.
\begin{aligned}
a_{11}x_1^{(k+1)} + a_{12}x_2^{(k)} + a_{13}x_3^{(k)} + \ldots + a_{1n}x_n^{(k)} &= b_1 \\
a_{21}x_1^{(k)} + a_{22}x_2^{(k+1)} + a_{23}x_3^{(k)} + \ldots + a_{2n}x_n^{(k)} &= b_2 \\
\vdots \\
a_{n1}x_1^{(k)} + a_{n2}x_2^{(k)} + a_{n3}x_3^{(k)} + \ldots + a_{nn}x_n^{(k+1)} &= b_n
\end{aligned}
\right\}
\quad (13.1)
$$

$$
\text{II} \quad
\left.
\begin{aligned}
a_{11}x_1^{(k+1)} + a_{12}x_2^{(k)} + a_{13}x_3^{(k)} + \ldots + a_{1n}x_n^{(k)} &= b_1 \\
a_{21}x_1^{(k+1)} + a_{22}x_2^{(k+1)} + a_{23}x_3^{(k)} + \ldots + a_{2n}x_n^{(k)} &= b_2 \\
\vdots \\
a_{n1}x_1^{(k+1)} + a_{n2}x_2^{(k+1)} + a_{n3}x_3^{(k+1)} + \ldots + a_{nn}x_n^{(k+1)} &= b_n
\end{aligned}
\right\}
\quad (13.2)
$$

Neither procedure will necessarily give a sequence of approximations which leads to the correct solution of (11.1), although Seidel was able to prove that this must happen eventually if $\mathbf{A}$ is a symmetric matrix with all diagonal elements positive, conditions which are always satisfied by normal equations derived by the method of least squares.* These conditions, however, are often not very relevant to the practical problem of convergence, which for some sets of normal equations may be much too slow to make iteration worthwhile, whereas others, with unsymmetrical coefficients, yield to it readily enough. A more practical criterion, favourable to convergence, is that each diagonal coefficient should exceed in magnitude the sum of magnitudes of other coefficients in the same row, i.e.

$$|a_{ii}| > |a_{i1}| + \ldots + |a_{i,\,i-1}| + |a_{i,\,i+1}| + \ldots + |a_{in}|$$

This can be shown, even for unsymmetrical equations, to be sufficient for convergence, though not of course necessary.

Whether the relations (13.1) or (13.2) are used, it is an advantage

* For a recent discussion, see E. Reich, *Ann. Math. Stat.*, **20** (1949), 448. The convergence for nearly symmetric matrices has been examined by P. Stein, *Math. Tab., Wash.*, **5** (1951), 237.

to prepare the original equations by first dividing each equation by the diagonal coefficient, i.e. by forming

$$c_{ij} = a_{ij}/a_{ii}, \quad d_i = b_i/a_{ii}$$

This changes them from the form $\mathbf{Ax} = \mathbf{b}$ to $\mathbf{Cx} = \mathbf{d}$, where $\mathbf{C}$ has unit elements along the diagonal. Both methods of iteration are illustrated in the example which follows.

EXAMPLE 13.1. Solve the equations

$$
\begin{aligned}
x_1 + 0{\cdot}15x_2 + 0{\cdot}01x_3 - 0{\cdot}08x_4 - 0{\cdot}06x_5 &= 0{\cdot}57 \\
0{\cdot}17x_1 + x_2 - 0{\cdot}03x_3 + 0{\cdot}13x_4 - 0{\cdot}10x_5 &= -0{\cdot}74 \\
0{\cdot}03x_1 - 0{\cdot}08x_2 + x_3 + 0{\cdot}23x_4 - 0{\cdot}07x_5 &= 0{\cdot}54 \\
-0{\cdot}16x_1 + 0{\cdot}07x_2 + 0{\cdot}13x_3 + x_4 + 0{\cdot}09x_5 &= 0{\cdot}51 \\
0{\cdot}10x_1 - 0{\cdot}09x_2 + 0{\cdot}09x_3 - 0{\cdot}03x_4 + x_5 &= 0{\cdot}61
\end{aligned}
$$

These equations are already in the prepared form, $\mathbf{Cx} = \mathbf{d}$. We first write down the elements of $\mathbf{C}$ and $\mathbf{d}$, but omitting the diagonal elements of $\mathbf{C}$ and changing the sign of the rest. Column sums are also added. Since the non-diagonal elements are small, a good start is made by equating the unknowns to the elements of $\mathbf{d}$. This gives the row $\mathbf{x}_0$. In method I, the elements of $\mathbf{x}_1$ are given by the products of $\mathbf{x}_0$ (including the unit element added at the end) with each row of the array above. The similar product with the row of column sums provides an obvious check. Succeeding approximations are formed in the same way. In method II, the only difference is that elements in the new approximation are used to replace those in the old as soon as they become available. The check, however, cannot be applied in the same way.

$$
\mathbf{I} - \mathbf{C}
\left[
\begin{array}{rrrrr|l}
0 & -0{\cdot}15 & -0{\cdot}01 & 0{\cdot}08 & 0{\cdot}06 & \mathbf{d} \\
 & & & & & 0{\cdot}57 \\
-0{\cdot}17 & 0 & 0{\cdot}03 & -0{\cdot}13 & 0{\cdot}10 & -0{\cdot}74 \\
-0{\cdot}03 & 0{\cdot}08 & 0 & -0{\cdot}23 & 0{\cdot}07 & 0{\cdot}54 \\
0{\cdot}16 & -0{\cdot}07 & -0{\cdot}13 & 0 & -0{\cdot}09 & 0{\cdot}51 \\
-0{\cdot}10 & 0{\cdot}09 & -0{\cdot}09 & 0{\cdot}03 & 0 & 0{\cdot}61
\end{array}
\right]
$$

$$-0{\cdot}14 \quad -0{\cdot}05 \quad -0{\cdot}20 \quad -0{\cdot}25 \quad 0{\cdot}14 \quad 1{\cdot}49$$

Method I

							Sum check
$\mathbf{x}_0$	0·57	− 0·74	0·54	0·51	0·61	1	
$\mathbf{x}_1$	0·75	− 0·83	0·39	0·53	0·45	1	1·30
$\mathbf{x}_2$	0·760	− 0·880	0·361	0·597	0·441	1	1·279
$\mathbf{x}_3$	0·773	− 0·892	0·340	0·607	0·442	1	1·270
$\mathbf{x}_4$	0·7755	− 0·8959	0·3368	0·6121	0·4400	1	1·2685
$\mathbf{x}_5$	0·7764	− 0·8973	0·3351	0·6134	0·4399	1	1·2674

Method II

$\mathbf{x}_0$	0·57	− 0·74	0·54	0·51	0·61	1
$\mathbf{x}_1$	0·75	− 0·86	0·37	0·59	0·44	1
$\mathbf{x}_2$	0·769	− 0·892	0·341	0·612	0·440	1
$\mathbf{x}_3$	0·776	− 0·897	0·335	0·614	0·440	1
$\mathbf{x}_4$	0·7767	− 0·8978	0·3345	0·6140	0·4398	1
	1	− 2	0	0	− 2	
$\mathbf{x}$	0·7768	− 0·8980	0·3345	0·6140	0·4396	

It should be noted how further figures are added as the iteration proceeds. In this example, the result of four iterations by Method II is distinctly better than five iterations by Method I. It is possible to anticipate the effect of further iterations by a rough extrapolation, applying the δ^2 formula (9.29a) to each element. This gives the small corrections shown beneath $\mathbf{x}_4$, from which we may conclude that, correct to 3D,

$$x_1 = 0·777, \; x_2 = − 0·898, \; x_3 = 0·334, \; x_4 = 0·614, \; x_5 = 0·440$$

The simple extrapolation formula can be used very effectively in this type of calculation, and may reduce the number of iterations considerably. Let $\mathbf{x}_e$ denote the approximation to $\mathbf{x}$ obtained in this way; this should be substituted in the original equations, and the residual error $\mathbf{r} = \mathbf{Cx}_e − \mathbf{d}$ evaluated. If the elements of $\mathbf{r}$ are not small enough to be accepted, further iterations should be performed with the equations

$$\mathbf{Cy} = − \mathbf{r} \tag{13.3}$$

where $\mathbf{y} = \mathbf{x} − \mathbf{x}_e$, to obtain the correction to $\mathbf{x}_e$.

13.1. Interpretation and Extension Using Matrices

Although the foregoing description of the classical iterative processes may be considered adequate a further insight is obtained by expressing them in terms of matrices. This we do for each method, assuming that the equations are in the form $\mathbf{Cx} = \mathbf{d}$.

METHOD I

The iterative relations (13.1) can be written in the form

$$\mathbf{x}_{k+1} = \mathbf{d} + \mathbf{Bx}_k \tag{13.4}$$

where $\mathbf{B} = \mathbf{I} − \mathbf{C}$, and $\mathbf{I}$ is the unit matrix of order n. In Example 13.1 the solution was in fact begun by writing down the matrix $\mathbf{B}$. The solution of this difference equation can be expressed as a series

$$\mathbf{x}_k = (\mathbf{I} + \mathbf{B} + \mathbf{B}^2 + \ldots + \mathbf{B}^{k-1})\mathbf{d} + \mathbf{B}^k\mathbf{x}_0 \tag{13.5}$$

and if $\mathbf{e}_k$ represents the correction to $\mathbf{x}_k$, then

$$\mathbf{e}_r = \mathbf{x} - \mathbf{x}_k = \mathbf{x} - \mathbf{d} - \mathbf{B}\mathbf{x}_{k-1}$$
$$= \mathbf{B}(\mathbf{x} - \mathbf{x}_{k-1})$$
$$= \mathbf{B}\mathbf{e}_{k-1}$$

It follows that $\mathbf{e}_k = \mathbf{B}^k\mathbf{e}_0$, and that the sequence $\mathbf{x}_k$ will not converge to $\mathbf{x}$ unless

$$\lim_{k \to \infty} \mathbf{B}^k\mathbf{e}_0 = 0$$

This implies that all the latent roots of $\mathbf{B}$ have modulus less than unity, because if we expand $\mathbf{e}_0$ in terms of the latent column vectors of $\mathbf{B}$, say $\mathbf{u}_1 \ldots \mathbf{u}_n$, then

$$\mathbf{B}^k\mathbf{e}_0 = a_1\lambda_1{}^k\mathbf{u}_1 + a_2\lambda_2{}^k\mathbf{u}_2 + \ldots + a_n\lambda_n{}^k\mathbf{u}_n$$

and this tends to zero only if $|\lambda_i| < 0$, for all values of i. If this condition is satisfied then

$$\mathbf{x} = (\mathbf{I} + \mathbf{B} + \mathbf{B}^2 + \mathbf{B}^3 + \ldots)\mathbf{d} = \mathbf{A}^{-1}\mathbf{d}$$

where we now identify the infinite series with the expansion of

$$(\mathbf{I} - \mathbf{B})^{-1}\mathbf{d}$$

When many terms of the series are necessary, this analysis suggests several ways in which the calculation may be shortened.

1. Suppose $\mathbf{B}^2$ is evaluated; then

$$\mathbf{x}_{k+2} = (\mathbf{I} + \mathbf{B})\mathbf{d} + \mathbf{B}^2\mathbf{x}_k \tag{13.6}$$

so that alternative terms only in the sequence $\mathbf{x}_k$ need be calculated. If $\mathbf{B}^4$ is found also, then

$$\mathbf{x}_{k+4} = (\mathbf{I} + \mathbf{B}^2)(\mathbf{I} + \mathbf{B})\mathbf{d} + \mathbf{B}^4\mathbf{x}_k \tag{13.7}$$

so that every fourth term can be found.

2. In general, if $p = 2^m$, we can write

$$(\mathbf{I} + \mathbf{B} + \mathbf{B}^2 + \ldots + \mathbf{B}^{2p-1})\mathbf{d}$$
$$= (\mathbf{I} + \mathbf{B}^p) \ldots (\mathbf{I} + \mathbf{B}^4)(\mathbf{I} + \mathbf{B}^2)(\mathbf{I} + \mathbf{B})\mathbf{d}$$

Thus, given the matrices $\mathbf{B}^2$, $\mathbf{B}^4$, $\mathbf{B}^8$, etc., one need calculate only

$$\mathbf{x}_1 = (\mathbf{I} + \mathbf{B})\mathbf{d}, \ \mathbf{x}_3 = (\mathbf{I} + \mathbf{B}^2)\mathbf{x}_1, \ \mathbf{x}_7 = (\mathbf{I} + \mathbf{B}^4)\mathbf{x}_3, \ \text{etc.}$$

the term $\mathbf{B}^{2p}\mathbf{x}_0$ being omitted from (13.5). (This reduces the order of each term in the sequence roughly by one.)

In passing from (1) to (2) the iterative process has in effect been changed from one of first order to one of second order. Whether this means a saving of time depends partly on the nature of the matrix $\mathbf{B}$, partly on the number of iterations required, and partly on the number of different vectors $\mathbf{d}$ for which solutions are wanted. To form $\mathbf{x}_{2p-1}$ for a single $\mathbf{d}$ by process (2) requires that

$$n(mn + m + 1)$$

product sums of n terms each be calculated, allowing for m matrix squarings. This may be compared with $n(2p - 1)$ product sums, which is the number required to give all terms of the sequence up to $\mathbf{x}_{2p-1}$. The former may therefore be preferable if

$$2p > m(n + 1) + 2 \quad \text{or} \quad mn < 2(p - 1) - m$$

If r different $\mathbf{d}$ vectors must be considered, the inequality becomes $mn < r\{2(p - 1) - m\}$.

The following table shows conditions likely to favour the matrix-squaring process. One cannot be very precise about a point like this, because if $\mathbf{B}$ has many zero elements this acts against matrix-squaring. There are many situations, however, in which it certainly pays to calculate $\mathbf{B}^2$ and use (13.6) rather than (13.4).

	$m = 2$ $p = 4$	$m = 3$ $p = 8$	$m = 4$ $p = 16$
One $\mathbf{d}$ vector		$3n < 11$	$2n < 13$
Two $\mathbf{d}$ vectors	$n < 4$	$3n < 22$	$2n < 26$

These modifications of the classical process follow in all essentials some suggestions by Hotelling.* These dealt more directly with equations in the form $\mathbf{Ax} = \mathbf{b}$, and the suggested recurrence relation was

$$\mathbf{x}_k = h\mathbf{b} + \mathbf{B}_h \mathbf{x}_{k-1}$$

where
$$\mathbf{B}_h = \mathbf{I} - h\mathbf{A}$$

and h is a scalar constant. Again $\mathbf{e}_k = (\mathbf{B}_h)^k \mathbf{e}_0$, and the sequence therefore converges correctly if all latent roots of $\mathbf{B}_h$ have modulus less than unity, i.e. the roots of $\mathbf{A}$, if real, lie between 0 and $2/h$.

---

* H. Hotelling, *Ann. Math. Stat.*, **14** (1943), 1.

The diagonal elements of B_h, unlike those of B, are not necessarily zero. For h it is best to choose a value as large as possible consistent with satisfactory convergence.

METHOD II

Let L be a lower triangular matrix with non-zero elements on the diagonal and below the diagonal equal to those of A, and U an upper triangular matrix with non-zero elements above the diagonal only, again equal to those of A. Then

$$A = L + U$$

and the equations (13.2) take the form

$$Lx_{k+1} = b - Ux_k$$

It follows that $\qquad x_{k+1} = y + B_1 x_k \qquad\qquad$ (13.8)

where $\qquad\qquad y = L^{-1}b \quad \text{and} \quad B_1 = -L^{-1}U$

and the solution is given by

$$x_k = (I + B_1 + B_1{}^2 + \ldots + B_1{}^{k-1})y + B^k x_0 \qquad (13.9)$$

As for (13.5), convergence is certain if all the latent roots of B_1 have latent roots with modulus less than unity.

The calculation of x_k by (13.9) can be organized along the same lines as for (13.5), provided that y and B_1 are first obtained by solving the equations $Ly = b$ and $LB_1 = U$.

To those who have mastered the techniques of Chapter 11, this will present no difficulty; the first is a simple process of back-solution, and the second also can be solved without any need to tabulate L^{-1}. Example 13.2 shows the layout of the calculation. These preliminary steps take the place of the "preparation" in Method I, in which B, d are derived from A, b, and any extra labour entailed must be justified by a substantial improvement in convergence.

EXAMPLE 13.2. Solve the equations

$$\begin{bmatrix} 2 & -1 & 0 & 0 \\ -1 & 2 & -1 & 0 \\ 0 & -1 & 2 & -1 \\ 0 & 0 & -1 & 2 \end{bmatrix} \begin{bmatrix} x_1 \\ x_2 \\ x_3 \\ x_4 \end{bmatrix} = \begin{bmatrix} 1 \\ 1 \\ 1 \\ 0 \end{bmatrix}$$

It should be said at once that these equations, involving a matrix studied already in Example 12.7 are not well suited to solution by classical iteration. There is thus a good case for using any accelerating devices which matrix theory may suggest. We consider the solution both by Method I and Method II.

Method I. We first calculate $\mathbf{B}(= \mathbf{I} - \mathbf{A}/2)$, $\mathbf{B}^2$ and $\mathbf{B}^4$, and examine the sequence $\mathbf{x}_0(= \mathbf{b}/2)$, $\mathbf{x}_1$, $\mathbf{x}_3$, $\mathbf{x}_7$.

$$\mathbf{B} = \begin{bmatrix} 0 & \frac{1}{2} & 0 & 0 \\ \frac{1}{2} & 0 & \frac{1}{2} & 0 \\ 0 & \frac{1}{2} & 0 & \frac{1}{2} \\ 0 & 0 & \frac{1}{2} & 0 \end{bmatrix} \qquad \mathbf{B}^2 = \frac{1}{4}\begin{bmatrix} 1 & 0 & 1 & 0 \\ 0 & 2 & 0 & 0 \\ 1 & 0 & 2 & 0 \\ 0 & 1 & 0 & 1 \end{bmatrix}$$

$$\mathbf{B}^4 = \frac{1}{16}\begin{bmatrix} 2 & 0 & 3 & 0 \\ 0 & 5 & 0 & 3 \\ 3 & 0 & 5 & 0 \\ 0 & 3 & 0 & 2 \end{bmatrix}$$

Hence we find

$$\mathbf{x}_0 = \{0\cdot5, \quad 0\cdot5, \quad 0\cdot5, \quad 0 \quad\}$$
$$\mathbf{x}_1 = (\mathbf{I} + \mathbf{B})\mathbf{x}_0 = \{0\cdot75, \quad 1\cdot0, \quad 0\cdot75, \quad 0\cdot25 \}$$
$$\mathbf{x}_3 = (\mathbf{I} + \mathbf{B}^2)\mathbf{x}_1 = \{1\cdot125, \quad 1\cdot5625, \quad 1\cdot3125, \quad 0\cdot5625\}$$
$$\mathbf{x}_7 = (\mathbf{I} + \mathbf{B}^4)\mathbf{x}_3 = \{1\cdot5117, \quad 2\cdot1563, \quad 1\cdot9336, \quad 0\cdot9258\}$$

Convergence is obviously slow, but rather than continue the matrix squaring process (though this is not difficult), we shall derive $\mathbf{x}_9$ and $\mathbf{x}_{11}$ using (13.6), and use the δ^2-process to estimate the sequence limit for each element in turn.

Thus $\quad \mathbf{x}_9 = \mathbf{x}_1 + \mathbf{B}^2\mathbf{x}_7 = \{1\cdot6113, \ 2\cdot3096, \ 2\cdot0947, \ 1\cdot0205\}$

$\qquad \mathbf{x}_{11} = \mathbf{x}_1 + \mathbf{B}^2\mathbf{x}_9 = \{1\cdot6765, \ 2\cdot4099, \ 2\cdot2002, \ 1\cdot0825\}$

$\qquad\quad \delta^2\text{-correction} = \{0\cdot1236, \ 0\cdot1898, \ 0\cdot2002, \ 0\cdot1176\}$

Estimated limit, $\mathbf{x} = \{1\cdot8001, \ 2\cdot5997, \ 2\cdot4004, \ 1\cdot2001\}$

The δ^2-correction for the first element, using (9.29a), is

$$- (1\cdot6765 - 1\cdot6113)^2/(1\cdot6765 - 3\cdot2226 + 1\cdot5117) = 0\cdot1236$$

similarly for other elements. The exact solution

$$\mathbf{x} = \{1\cdot8, \ 2\cdot6, \ 2\cdot4, \ 1\cdot2\}$$

so the extrapolation gives results correct to 3D.

A word of warning about the use of the δ^2-correction is necessary here. A matrix symmetrical about both diagonals must have latent roots in pairs having equal magnitudes but opposite signs; for the matrix $\mathbf{B}$ in this example, the roots are $\pm 0\cdot809$, $\pm 0\cdot309$. The process then breaks down unless, as above, the sequence based on $\mathbf{B}^2$ or $\mathbf{B}^4$ is used; these matrices have double roots, but they are all positive.

Method II. The derivation of $\mathbf{B}_1$ and $\mathbf{y}$ is arranged below so that only row $\times$ row multiplications occur. By transposing all matrices, column $\times$ column products can be used if this is preferred. The elements of the transposed matrix $\mathbf{B_1}'$ are obtained one column at a time, using for the ith column the relations

$$R_i(\mathbf{L}) \times R_j(\mathbf{B_1}') = -u_{ij}$$

Check:　　　$R_i(\mathbf{L}) \times R(\mathbf{S}) = \sigma_i(i\text{th row sum of } -\mathbf{U})$

The elements of $\mathbf{y}$ are similarly given by the relations

$$R_i(\mathbf{L}) \times R(\mathbf{y}') = b_i$$

Check:　　　$R(\mathbf{s}) \times R(\mathbf{y}') = \Sigma \text{ (row sum of } \mathbf{b}')$

$$\mathbf{A} = [\mathbf{L/U}] \begin{bmatrix} l_{11} & u_{12} & u_{13} & u_{14} \\ l_{21} & l_{22} & u_{23} & u_{24} \\ l_{31} & l_{32} & l_{33} & u_{34} \\ l_{41} & l_{42} & l_{43} & l_{44} \end{bmatrix} \begin{matrix} \sigma_1 \\ \sigma_2 \\ \sigma_3 \\ 0 \end{matrix} \quad \begin{bmatrix} 2 & -1 & 0 & 0 \\ -1 & 2 & -1 & 0 \\ 0 & -1 & 2 & -1 \\ 0 & 0 & -1 & 2 \end{bmatrix} \begin{matrix} -1 \\ -1 \\ -1 \\ 0 \end{matrix}$$

$\mathbf{s}$　　$s_1 \quad s_2 \quad s_3 \quad s_4$　　　$1 \quad\quad 1 \quad\quad 1 \quad\quad 2$

$$\mathbf{B_1}' \begin{bmatrix} 0 & 0 & 0 & 0 \\ b_{12} & b_{22} & b_{32} & b_{42} \\ b_{13} & b_{23} & b_{33} & b_{43} \\ b_{14} & b_{24} & b_{34} & b_{44} \end{bmatrix} \quad \begin{bmatrix} 0 & 0 & 0 & 0 \\ \frac{1}{2} & \frac{1}{4} & \frac{1}{8} & \frac{1}{16} \\ 0 & \frac{1}{2} & \frac{1}{4} & \frac{1}{8} \\ 0 & 0 & \frac{1}{2} & \frac{1}{4} \end{bmatrix}$$

$\mathbf{S}$　　$S_1 \quad S_2 \quad S_3 \quad S_4$　　$\frac{1}{2} \quad \frac{3}{4} \quad \frac{7}{8} \quad \frac{7}{16}$

$\mathbf{b}'$　　$[b_1 \quad b_2 \quad b_3 \quad b_4]\Sigma$　　$[\ 1 \quad 1 \quad 1 \quad 0\ ]3$

$\mathbf{y}'$　　$[y_1 \quad y_2 \quad y_3 \quad y_4]$　　$[\ \frac{1}{2} \quad \frac{3}{4} \quad \frac{7}{8} \quad \frac{7}{16}]$

We proceed by forming $\mathbf{B_1}^2$, and applying (13.6) with $\mathbf{B_1}$ in place of $\mathbf{B}$ and $\mathbf{x_0} = \mathbf{y}$.

$$\mathbf{B_1}^2 = \tfrac{1}{16} \begin{bmatrix} 0 & 2 & 4 & 0 \\ 0 & 2 & 4 & 4 \\ 0 & 1 \cdot 5 & 3 & 4 \\ 0 & 0 \cdot 75 & 1 \cdot 5 & 2 \end{bmatrix}$$

$$0 \quad\quad 6 \cdot 25 \quad\quad 12 \cdot 5 \quad\quad 10$$

$$\begin{array}{rl} \mathbf{x_0} = & \{0 \cdot 50, \quad\quad 0 \cdot 75, \quad\quad 0 \cdot 875, \quad\quad 0 \cdot 4375\ \} \\ \mathbf{x_1} = (\mathbf{I} + \mathbf{B_1})\mathbf{x_0} = & \{0 \cdot 875, \quad\quad 1 \cdot 375, \quad\quad 1 \cdot 40625, \quad 0 \cdot 70312\}4 \cdot 35937 \\ \mathbf{x_3} = \mathbf{x_1} + \mathbf{B_1}^2\mathbf{x_1} = & \{1 \cdot 39844, \quad 2 \cdot 07422, \quad 1 \cdot 97461, \quad 0 \cdot 98730\}6 \cdot 43457 \\ \mathbf{x_5} = \mathbf{x_1} + \mathbf{B_1}^2\mathbf{x_3} = & \{1 \cdot 62793, \quad 2 \cdot 37467, \quad 2 \cdot 21777, \quad 1 \cdot 10889\}7 \cdot 32935 \\ \mathbf{x_7} = \mathbf{x_1} + \mathbf{B_1}^2\mathbf{x_5} = & \{1 \cdot 72629, \quad 2 \cdot 50351, \quad 2 \cdot 32194, \quad 1 \cdot 16097\}7 \cdot 71270 \\ \delta^2\text{-correction} & \{0 \cdot 07378, \quad 0 \cdot 09649, \quad 0 \cdot 07807, \quad 0 \cdot 03902\} \\ \text{Estimated limit, } \mathbf{x} = & \{1 \cdot 80007, \quad 2 \cdot 60000, \quad 2 \cdot 40001, \quad 1 \cdot 19999\} \end{array}$$

A sum check has been performed at each stage. After extrapolation, the remaining errors affect the fifth decimal, an improvement in accuracy which has been achieved by a somewhat greater effort.

The iterative formula (13.8) is the basis of a numerical procedure introduced by Morris, and extended by Frazer, Duncan and Collar (see Exercises 13, No. 2). It should also be mentioned that Lanczos has adapted his method of finding the characteristic function of a matrix to the solution of linear equations. The method cannot strictly be called an iterative one—although it is most effective when an approximate solution is available—because the solution is given explicitly in terms of a limited sequence of vectors.

13.2. Convergence and Limits of Errors

The convergence of the classical iterative processes has so far been expressed as a condition on the latent roots of the matrix $\mathbf{B}$ or $\mathbf{B}_1$. Since the evaluation of the largest latent root may involve considerable effort, a simpler criterion is very desirable, and this is partly provided by the norm of $\mathbf{B}$, a quantity usually denoted by $N(\mathbf{B})$ and defined by the equation

$$\{N(\mathbf{B})\}^2 = \Sigma b_{ij}{}^2 = \text{trace } (\mathbf{BB'}) \tag{13.10}$$

The sum includes all elements of $\mathbf{B}$, and the definition applies also to non-square matrices. It is not difficult to show that when $\mathbf{B}$ is square and has latent roots λ_i (all real), then

$$\{N(\mathbf{B})\}^2 \geqslant \Sigma \lambda_i{}^2$$

the equality sign holding when $\mathbf{B}$ is symmetric. The condition $N(\mathbf{B}) < 1$ thus ensures that for all roots, $|\lambda_i| < 1$, and hence that the iterative process converges to the desired solution. Obviously the condition on $N(\mathbf{B})$ is not necessary to convergence, but is rather favourable to it.

Norms satisfy several useful inequalities, including the following—

$$N(\mathbf{A} + \mathbf{B}) \leqslant N(\mathbf{A}) + N(\mathbf{B})$$
$$N(\mathbf{AB}) \leqslant N(\mathbf{A})N(\mathbf{B})$$

From the second, $N(\mathbf{B}^k) \leqslant \{N(\mathbf{B})\}^k$; consequently, if $N(\mathbf{B}) < 1$, $N(\mathbf{B}^k)$ tends to zero for large k, and this implies that all elements of $\mathbf{B}^k$ tend to zero.

Now Hotelling has shown that, when the condition that

$$N(\mathbf{B}) = p < 1$$

is satisfied, a limit of error can be placed on each member of the sequence defined by (13.4), if we assume for convenience that $\mathbf{x}_0 = \mathbf{d}$. We note first that

$$(\mathbf{I} - \mathbf{B})^{-1} = \mathbf{I} + \mathbf{B} + \mathbf{B}^2 + \ldots + \mathbf{B}^k + \mathbf{B}^{k+1}(\mathbf{I} - \mathbf{B})^{-1}$$

so

$$N((\mathbf{I} - \mathbf{B})^{-1}) \leqslant n^{1/2} + p + p^2 + \ldots + p^k + p^{k+1}N((\mathbf{I} - \mathbf{B})^{-1})$$

or

$$N((\mathbf{I} - \mathbf{B})^{-1}) \leqslant \frac{1}{1 - p^{k+1}}\left\{n^{1/2} - 1 + \frac{1 - p^{k+1}}{1 - p}\right\}$$

$$< n^{1/2} - 1 + \frac{1}{1 - p} \qquad (13.11)$$

But the correction

$$\mathbf{e}_k = \mathbf{x} - \mathbf{x}_k = \{(\mathbf{I} - \mathbf{B})^{-1} - (\mathbf{I} + \mathbf{B} + \mathbf{B}^2 + \ldots + \mathbf{B}^k)\}\mathbf{d}$$

$$= \mathbf{B}^{k+1}(\mathbf{I} - \mathbf{B})^{-1}\mathbf{d} \qquad (13.12)$$

so

$$N(\mathbf{e}_k) \leqslant N(\mathbf{B}^{k+1})N((\mathbf{I} - \mathbf{B})^{-1})N(\mathbf{d})$$

$$\leqslant p^{k+1}\{n^{1/2} - 1 + 1/(1 - p)\}N(\mathbf{d}) \qquad (13.13)$$

When the iterative process makes use of $\mathbf{B}^2$, so that

$$N(\mathbf{B}^2) = p_1{}^2$$

can easily be estimated, a closer limit on $N(\mathbf{e}_k)$ may be possible since $p_1 \leqslant p$. It is obviously permissible to substitute p_1 for p in (13.13), and it may sometimes happen that a limit diminishing with k is thereby obtained even when $p > 1$. (Some adjustment to $N((\mathbf{I} - \mathbf{B})^{-1})$ may be necessary.)

No element in $\mathbf{e}_k$ can exceed $N(\mathbf{e}_k)$, and if the elements are comparable in magnitude, they are likely to be of the same order as $N(\mathbf{e}_k)/n^{1/2}$. It is worth considering briefly the application of (13.13) to Example 13.1. There one finds that $p < 0.5$, $N(\mathbf{d}) < 1.4$, so that in Method I

$$N(\mathbf{e}_5) < (0.5)^6(\sqrt{5} - 1 + 2)1.4 = 0.07$$

The separate elements of $\mathbf{e}_5$ might fairly be expected not to exceed $0.07/5^{1/2}$ or 0.03. This is not very helpful, as few computers would hesitate to put much smaller limits on the errors. It should be mentioned that, from $\mathbf{B}^2$, $p_1 < 0.36$, and this would limit individual errors in $\mathbf{e}_5$ to about 0.004. Actually no error exceeds 0.001.

Little use of (13.13) can be made in Example 13.2, since $N(\mathbf{B}) > 1$. It is true that both $N(\mathbf{B}^2)$ and $N(\mathbf{B}_1{}^2)$ are less than unity, but are still too close to unity to place significant limits on the errors of later approximations. For useful results it would seem that p or p_1 should not exceed about $0 \cdot 3$, Another, perhaps more important, application of (13.11) will be made in the following section on matrix inversion.

Matrix Inversion

The inverse of a matrix, if known approximately, can often be improved conveniently by iteration. We may recall Newton's iterative formula (9.12), $x_{k+1} = x_k(2 - ax_k)$, for the reciprocal of the number a, and the fact that this gives a second-order process. The formula

$$\mathbf{C}_{k+1} = \mathbf{C}_k(2\mathbf{I} - \mathbf{A}\mathbf{C}_k) \qquad (13.14)$$

where $\mathbf{C}_k$ and $\mathbf{A}$ are square matrices of order n, will give a sequence $\mathbf{C}_k$ which tends rapidly to $\mathbf{A}^{-1}$, provided $\mathbf{C}_0$ is a sufficiently good approximation from which to start. The process is again found to be one of second order.

Let $\qquad\qquad \mathbf{D} = \mathbf{I} - \mathbf{A}\mathbf{C}_0$

Then $\qquad \mathbf{C}_0 = \mathbf{A}^{-1}(\mathbf{I} - \mathbf{D}), \quad \mathbf{C}_1 = \mathbf{A}^{-1}(\mathbf{I} - \mathbf{D}^2)$

and in general $\qquad \mathbf{C}_k = \mathbf{A}^{-1}(\mathbf{I} - \mathbf{D}^{2^k})$

as may be proved by an inductive argument. Thus $\mathbf{C}_k$ tends to $\mathbf{A}^{-1}$ if $\mathbf{D}^p$ tends to zero as p increases, i.e. if the latent roots of $\mathbf{D}$ satisfy the usual condition. In suitable cases, the properties of the norm may be used to limit the errors in the elements of $\mathbf{C}_k$. Thus

$$\mathbf{E}_k = \mathbf{A}^{-1} - \mathbf{C}_k = \mathbf{A}^{-1}\mathbf{D}^{2^k} = \mathbf{C}_0(\mathbf{I} - \mathbf{D})^{-1}\mathbf{D}^{2^k} \qquad (13.15)$$

and so, assuming $N(\mathbf{D}) = p < 1$, and using (13.11)

$$N(\mathbf{E}_k) \leqslant N(\mathbf{C}_0)\{n^{1/2} - 1 - 1/(1 - p)\}N(\mathbf{D}^{2^k}) \qquad (13.16)$$

In this expression we may use the fact that $N(\mathbf{D}^{2^k}) \leqslant p^{2^k}$, or better still, that $N(\mathbf{D}^{2^k}) \leqslant p_1^{2^k}$, where $p_1^2 = N(\mathbf{D}^2)$; or use the norm of any higher power of $\mathbf{D}$ which is available. It is quite clear, however, that the errors decrease in the way expected of a second-order process. The mean error associated with the elements of $\mathbf{E}_k$ should not exceed $N(\mathbf{E}_k)/n$.

The actual calculation may proceed as follows—

1. Given $\mathbf{C}_0$, perhaps by a direct calculation, $\mathbf{D}$ should be calculated and if necessary $\mathbf{D}^2$, to determine whether convergence is probable. Preliminary estimates of the limits of error should be made as a guide to the number of iterations required.

2. The following matrices are calculated—

$$\mathbf{C}_1 = \mathbf{C}_0 + \mathbf{C}_0\mathbf{D}$$
$$\mathbf{D}_1 = \mathbf{D}^2 \text{ (if not already done)}$$
$$\mathbf{C}_2 = \mathbf{C}_1 + \mathbf{C}_1\mathbf{D}_1$$

3. If necessary, $\mathbf{D}_2 = \mathbf{I} - \mathbf{A}\mathbf{C}_2$ (which may be checked by $\mathbf{D}_1{}^2$), $\mathbf{C}_3 = \mathbf{C}_2 + \mathbf{C}_2\mathbf{D}_2$ are calculated, and so on.

It may be observed that

$$\mathbf{C}_2 = \mathbf{C}_0(\mathbf{I} + \mathbf{D})(\mathbf{I} + \mathbf{D}^2)$$
$$\mathbf{C}_3 = \mathbf{C}_0(\mathbf{I} + \mathbf{D})(\mathbf{I} + \mathbf{D}^2)(\mathbf{I} + \mathbf{D}^4), \text{ etc.}$$

so that an interesting comparison is possible with the matrix-squaring method of solving linear equations (see Exercises 13, No. 3).

As an example of improvement of an inverse by iteration we take the matrix already considered in Example 11.7.

EXAMPLE 13.3. Find to 8D the inverse of the matrix

$$\mathbf{A} = \begin{bmatrix} 0{\cdot}855 & 0{\cdot}308 & 0{\cdot}184 & 0{\cdot}031 \\ 0{\cdot}300 & 0{\cdot}895 & 0{\cdot}218 & 0{\cdot}052 \\ 0{\cdot}104 & 0{\cdot}136 & 0{\cdot}860 & 0{\cdot}107 \\ 0{\cdot}029 & 0{\cdot}063 & 0{\cdot}122 & 0{\cdot}909 \end{bmatrix}$$

Let us take for $\mathbf{C}_0$ the inverse given in Example 11.7, but with elements curtailed to 2D. The first stage, the calculation of

$$\mathbf{D} = \mathbf{I} - \mathbf{A}\mathbf{C}_0$$

is best performed by tabulating $\mathbf{C}_0{}'$ and using row × row products. We obtain the following matrices for $\mathbf{D}$ and $\mathbf{D}^2$, the elements being exact if those of $\mathbf{A}$ and $\mathbf{C}_0$ are regarded as exact numbers. The results are checked row by row.

$$\mathbf{C}_0{}' \begin{bmatrix} 1{\cdot}34 & -0{\cdot}43 & -0{\cdot}09 & +0{\cdot}00 \\ -0{\cdot}44 & 1{\cdot}30 & -0{\cdot}15 & -0{\cdot}06 \\ -0{\cdot}18 & -0{\cdot}23 & 1{\cdot}24 & -0{\cdot}14 \\ -0{\cdot}00 & -0{\cdot}03 & -0{\cdot}13 & 1{\cdot}12 \end{bmatrix}$$

$$\begin{matrix} 0{\cdot}72 & 0{\cdot}61 & 0{\cdot}87 & 0{\cdot}92 \end{matrix}$$

$$\mathbf{D} \begin{bmatrix} 330 & 526 & 92 & -156 \\ 247 & 432 & -319 & -305 \\ -348 & 438 & -142 & -396 \\ -79 & 370 & -431 & -33 \end{bmatrix} \begin{matrix} 792 \\ 55 \\ -448 \\ -173 \end{matrix} \times 10^{-5}$$

$$\mathbf{D}_1 = \mathbf{D}^2 \begin{bmatrix} 219130 & 383388 & -83262 & -243194 \\ 323321 & 63974 & 61669 & -33903 \\ 74046 & -202548 & 19102 & -10002 \\ 217915 & -82702 & -49873 & 71239 \end{bmatrix} \begin{matrix} 276062 \\ 415061 \\ -119402 \\ 156579 \end{matrix} \times 10^{-10}$$

Rough calculations at this stage show that

$$\{N(\mathbf{C}_0)\}^2 = 6\cdot8, \quad \{N(\mathbf{D})\}^2 = 1\cdot65 \times 10^{-4}, \quad \{N(\mathbf{D}^2)\}^2 = 27\cdot7 \times 10^{-10}$$

and hence $N(\mathbf{C}_0) = 2\cdot6, \quad p = 0\cdot013, \quad p_1 = 0\cdot0072$

Accordingly, the errors in $\mathbf{C}_1$ and $\mathbf{C}_2$ may be expected to satisfy the following inequalities—

Using p, $N(\mathbf{E}_1) < 0\cdot00088$ $N(\mathbf{E}_2) < 1\cdot5 \times 10^{-6}$
Using p_1, $N(\mathbf{E}_1) < 0\cdot00027$ $N(\mathbf{E}_2) < 1\cdot4 \times 10^{-8}$

It is clear that $\mathbf{C}_2$ should provide the accuracy required. The rest of the calculation is shown below, $\mathbf{C}_1'$ and $(\mathbf{C}_1\mathbf{D}_1)'$ being derived by means of column $\times$ column products. It should be noted that the elements of $\mathbf{C}_1$ are again exact; in deriving $\mathbf{C}_1\mathbf{D}_1$, the elements of which are rounded to 8D, one may curtail the elements of $\mathbf{C}_1$, but this is not permissible when $\mathbf{C}_2$ is subsequently formed by adding $\mathbf{C}_1$ to $\mathbf{C}_1\mathbf{D}_1$.

$$\mathbf{C}_1' = \mathbf{C}_0' + (\mathbf{C}_0\mathbf{D})' \begin{bmatrix} 1\cdot3439616 & -0\cdot4273839 & -0\cdot0948800 & -0\cdot0005458 \\ -0\cdot4356408 & 1\cdot3022358 & -0\cdot1461712 & -0\cdot0567284 \\ -0\cdot1771080 & -0\cdot2340867 & 1\cdot2391952 & -0\cdot1444370 \\ -0\cdot0000356 & -0\cdot0323735 & -0\cdot1342696 & 1\cdot1203678 \end{bmatrix}$$

$$\begin{array}{cccc} 0\cdot7311772 & 0\cdot6083917 & 0\cdot8638744 & 0\cdot9186566 \end{array}$$

$$(\mathbf{C}_1\mathbf{D}_1)' \begin{bmatrix} +1405 & +3030 & -56 & +2150 \\ +5233 & -305 & -2856 & -672 \\ -1421 & +1130 & +293 & -621 \\ -3103 & +598 & +61 & +833 \end{bmatrix} \times 10^{-8}$$

$$\begin{array}{cccc} +2113 & +4454 & -2558 & +1690 \end{array}$$

The above example shows what can be done from quite a modest start, but when an inverse is required with this accuracy, it is probably most economical to obtain $\mathbf{A}^{-1}$ to 4 or 5S directly by matrix resolution as in Example 11.7, and then to refine it by iteration.

The Relaxation Method

Although the sphere of application of the classical iterative methods is not great, they have been discussed at some length— perhaps at greater length than they deserve, but the discussion may have shown once more how a simple iterative process can be advanced by an intelligent use of matrix properties. However, no iterative method must be carried to excess or the labour will surpass that of a direct solution.

In considering the method now to be described, it is instructive to bear in mind the form and limitations of the classical procedure. The relaxation method, as it is now generally called, is much more flexible, and to the computer, more interesting. When skill and experience in its use have been acquired, the convergence to the desired solution can often be made quite rapid. Although Gauss certainly used it extensively in solving simultaneous linear equations, the scope of the method has been greatly widened since about 1936 by Southwell and his colleagues,* and it is now regularly used for the solution of differential equations, both ordinary and partial, with suitable boundary conditions. This aspect will be considered in later chapters, and for the moment we are concerned with it solely as a technique for solving linear equations.

The basic principle is very simple. The set of equations (11.1) is replaced by the following—

$$\left.\begin{array}{l} a_{11}x_1 + a_{12}x_2 + \ldots + a_{1n}x_n - b_1 = r_1 \\ a_{21}x_1 + a_{22}x_2 + \ldots + a_{2n}x_n - b_2 = r_2 \\ \qquad \cdot \\ \qquad \cdot \\ \qquad \cdot \\ a_{n1}x_1 + a_{n2}x_2 + \ldots + a_{nn}x_n - b_n = r_n \end{array}\right\} \qquad (13.17)$$

where the quantities on the right are known as residuals, and are associated with a particular set of values of the x's inserted on the left. The required solution consists of that set of x's for which the residuals are zero, or at least less than some acceptably small quantity. Starting from a suitable approximate solution, with non-vanishing residuals, the process consists of a gradual reduction of these by selected changes in the x's, ordered in such a way that convergence to the wanted solution is as rapid as possible. Herein lies the first important departure from the classical method, in which the order of changes follows a definite sequence once the order of the equations has been decided upon. This rigid routine is now replaced by one largely under the control of the computer, involving no regular cycle of operations. Secondly, whereas in Seidel's method changes are made in one unknown at a time, it is practicable and often advantageous in the relaxation method to make changes simultaneously in several unknowns. However, the

---

* The account given here follows the lines of several articles by L. Fox, e.g. *Quart. J. Mech. Appl. Math.*, **1** (1948), 253.

details of this, as well as the layout of the calculations, are most easily followed in specific examples.

EXAMPLE 13.4. Find a solution of the equations

$$8x_1 - 2x_2 + 3x_3 - 55 = r_1$$
$$3x_1 + 5x_2 + x_3 - 40 = r_2$$
$$-4x_1 + 2x_2 + 9x_3 + 100 = r_3$$

for which the residuals are less than 0·005 in magnitude.

We first note the changes in the residuals produced by making unit changes in each of the variables separately. This is known as an "operations" table, and the matrix of coefficients appearing in it is the transpose of the matrix in the equations.

Δx_1	Δx_2	Δx_3	Δr_1	Δr_2	Δr_3
1			8	3	− 4
	1		− 2	5	2
		1	3	1	9

An approximate solution may be obtained by ignoring off-diagonal terms. To the nearest integer, this gives

$$x_1 = 7, \ x_2 = 8, \ x_3 = -11$$

and

$$r_1 = -48, \ r_2 = 10, \ r_3 = -11$$

The process of reducing the residuals is recorded below, each change in a variable being given separately, and on the same line, the *net* remaining residuals.

x_1	x_2	x_3	r_1	r_2	r_3	
7	8	− 11	− 48	10	− 11	
6			0	28	− **25**	
	− 5		10	3	− 35	
		4	22	7	1	
− 2			6	1	9	
		− 1	3	0	0	
11	3	− 8	3	0	− **10**	Check

At each step attention is given to reducing a dominating residual by an *integral* change in the corresponding variable. When this has proceeded as far as possible without resort to decimal changes, the net

x values are found and the residuals recalculated to ensure no slips have been made.

In this instance the check reveals that an error has occurred in the r_3 sequence (actually at the first step). No attempt to retrace steps is made, however, for the error can be retrieved in the next stage. To improve the solution it is advisable to replace the above simple operations by three others which involve more than one variable, but have the merit that their effect is concentrated on a particular residual. The "group operations" (a), (b), (c) below are suitable for this purpose, and are the only ones used in the subsequent relaxation.

	Δx_1	Δx_2	Δx_3	Δr_1	Δr_2	Δr_3
(a)	-1		3	1	0	31
(b)	1	2		4	13	0
(c)	5	-3	2	52	2	-8

	x_1	x_2	x_3	r_1	r_2	r_3
	11000	3000	-8000	$+3000$	0	-10000
(a)	-320		960	$+3320$	0	-80
(c)	-350	$+210$	-140	-320	-140	$+480$
(a)	$+15$		-45	-335	-140	$+15$
(b)	$+10$	$+20$		-295	-10	$+15$
(c)	$+30$	-18	$+12$	$+17$	$+2$	-33
(a)	-1		$+3$	$+18$	$+2$	-2
(c)	-2	$+1{\cdot}2$	$-0{\cdot}8$	$-2{\cdot}8$	$-1{\cdot}2$	$+1{\cdot}2$
	$10382{\cdot}0$	$3213{\cdot}2$	$-7210{\cdot}8$	$-2{\cdot}8$	$-1{\cdot}2$	$+1{\cdot}2$ Check

The above calcuation is expressed in units of 10^{-3}. The final residuals, which are found on checking to be correct, are within the limits specified; the corresponding solution is

$$x_1 = 10{\cdot}3820, \quad x_2 = 3{\cdot}2132, \quad x_3 = -7{\cdot}2108$$

Further relaxation would affect the fourth decimal.

EXAMPLE 13.5. Solve by relaxation the equations of Example 13.2

$$\begin{aligned} 2x_1 - x_2 &= 1 \\ -x_1 + 2x_2 - x_3 &= 1 \\ -x_2 + 2x_3 - x_4 &= 1 \\ -x_3 + 2x_4 &= 0 \end{aligned}$$

We ignore the obvious method of solving by elimination. With a symmetrical array of coefficients like this, it is easy to devise effective group-operations, and we include in the table at top of next page several more than are actually used in the relaxation which follows. The initial solution is the same as in Example 13.2 (Method I), and all numbers are given in units of 10^{-2}.

Operation	Δx_1	Δx_2	Δx_3	Δx_4	Δr_1	Δr_2	Δr_3	Δr_4
(1)	1				2	-1		
(2)		1			-1	2	-1	
(3)			1			-1	2	-1
(4)				1			-1	2
(5)	1	1	1	1	1	0	0	1
(6)		1	1		-1	1	1	-1
(7)	2	1			3	0	-1	0
(8)			1	2	0	-1	0	3
(9)	1	2			0	3	-2	0
(10)			2	1	0	-2	3	0
(11)	1	2	-2	-1	0	5	-5	0

Operation	x_1	x_2	x_3	x_4	r_1	r_2	r_3	r_4
	50	50	50	0	-50	-100	-50	-50
$75 \times$ (6)		75	75		-125	-25	25	-125
$125 \times$ (5)	125	125	125	125	0	-25	25	0
$5 \times$ (11)	5	10	-10	-5	0	0	0	0
	180	260	240	120	0	0	0	0 Check

The solution is therefore

$$\{x_1,\ x_2,\ x_3,\ x_4\} = \{1\cdot8,\ 2\cdot6,\ 2\cdot4,\ 1\cdot2\}$$

This happy result is of course rather exceptional, and compares very favourably with classical iteration, but no one with a little experience of relaxation should have much difficulty in achieving similar successes.

Now that the general procedure has been made clear by the foregoing example, some further points about the method can be stressed.

1. The most rapid convergence is not always secured by removing the largest residual remaining at a particular stage. It is more important to remove that residual which requires the largest change, or "displacement," in the variable concerned, i.e. that for which r_i/a_{ii} is largest rather than r_i.

2. It is inadvisable to choose displacements to make any residual exactly zero. Almost inevitably this residual will change again later, and the effort at precision has in fact been a waste of labour. It is much better to keep to easy operations which can often be done mentally; the calculating machine can be reserved

for checking residuals from time to time. For similar reasons the calculation need not be started with many figures, as further digits can always be added as the work proceeds, until the desired accuracy is reached.

3. Although in Examples 13.4 and 13.5 the coefficients are simple integers this will not always be so. Nevertheless there is no harm in rounding these coefficients to convenient 2- or 3-figure numbers during the process of relaxation, provided that the accurate coefficients are used later when checking residuals. There will not be exact agreement between the residuals so calculated and those obtained from the relaxation, but if the differences are significant a few more steps of relaxation will soon reduce them.

4. Although the use of group operations is one of the most effective ways of speeding the convergence there are others. Thus, if it is found that successive changes in a particular variable, say x_1, tend always to have the same sign, it may pay to "over-relax," i.e. deliberately to change the sign of r_1 with the expectation that later changes in other variables will tend to bring it nearer to zero. Or, if successive changes in x_1 have opposite signs, "under-relaxation" may be preferable, the residual r_1 being removed only partially. (A situation of this kind occurs in the first stage of Example 13.4.)

5. The occurrence of mistakes, though of course undesirable, is not serious if the residuals are regularly checked, say each time the residuals are reduced to about 1/10th of their former magnitude. The following section, however, describes a modification of the process which simplifies this checking.

13.3 Gauss' Transformation

The following device was recommended by Gauss as a substantial help in avoiding mistakes, at the cost of increasing by one the number of equations to be solved. In its simplest form the scheme introduces a set of variables

$$y_1, y_2, \cdot \cdot \cdot, y_{n+1}$$

such that

$$x_j = y_j - y_{n+1}$$

At the same time an extra equation is added which is merely minus the sum of the n equations already available. It is easily verified that the set of equations (13.17) is replaced by the following—

$$\left.\begin{array}{l} a_{11}y_1 \quad + \ldots + a_{1n}y_n + a_{1,\,n+1}y_{n+1} - b_1 = r_1 \\ \quad \cdot \\ \quad \cdot \\ \quad \cdot \\ a_{n1}y_1 \quad + \ldots + a_{nn}y_n + a_{n,\,n+1}y_{n+1} - b_n = r_n \\ a_{n+1,\,1}y_1 + \ldots + a_{n+1,\,n}y_n + a_{n+1,\,n+1}y_{n+1} \\ \qquad\qquad\qquad\qquad\qquad\qquad - b_{n+1} = r_{n+1} \end{array}\right\} \qquad (13.18)$$

where

$$a_{i,\,n+1} = -\{a_{i1} + \ldots + a_{in}\},\ i = 1, 2, \ldots, n$$
$$a_{n+1,\,j} = -\{a_{1j} + \ldots + a_{nj}\},\ j = 1, 2, \ldots, n+1$$
and $\quad b_{n+1} = -\{b_1 + \ldots + b_n\}$

The consequence of this transformation is that at every stage of the relaxation process the sum of the residuals must be zero. The current check therefore consists merely of summing residuals, and only at the end of the calculation need the final results be checked by substitution in (13.17). Although the extra equation increases the burden of relaxation, this becomes relatively smaller for larger sets of equations, and is easily offset by the convenience of the check.

Symmetric equations, it should be noted, do not lose their symmetry by this transformation. Thus the matrix occurring in Example 13.2 is replaced by—

$$\mathbf{A}_1 = \begin{bmatrix} 2 & -1 & 0 & 0 & -1 \\ -1 & 2 & -1 & 0 & 0 \\ 0 & -1 & 2 & -1 & 0 \\ 0 & 0 & -1 & 2 & -1 \\ -1 & 0 & 0 & -1 & 2 \end{bmatrix}$$

An interesting point here is that the latent roots of $\mathbf{A}_1$ include two pairs of repeated roots. The roots are in fact 0, $4 \sin^2 (2\pi/5)$ (twice), $4 \sin^2 (4\pi/5)$ (twice); those of the original matrix were

$$2\{1 \pm \cos (\pi/5)\},\ 2\{1 \pm \cos (2\pi/5)\}$$

We shall illustrate the transformation by an example taken from the letter from Gauss to Gerling, quoted earlier.

EXAMPLE 13.6. Solve approximately the equations

$$69x_1 - 50x_2 - 6x_3 - 7558 = 0$$
$$-50x_1 + 156x_2 - 78x_3 - 14604 = 0$$
$$-6x_1 - 78x_2 + 110x_3 + 22156 = 0$$

Let $\qquad x_1 = y_1 - y_4, \quad x_2 = y_2 - y_4, \quad x_3 = y_3 - y_4$

Then
$$\begin{bmatrix} 69 & -50 & -6 & -13 \\ -50 & 156 & -78 & -28 \\ -6 & -78 & 110 & -26 \\ -13 & -28 & -26 & +67 \end{bmatrix} \begin{bmatrix} y_1 \\ y_2 \\ y_3 \\ y_4 \end{bmatrix} + \begin{bmatrix} -7558 \\ -14604 \\ 22156 \\ 6 \end{bmatrix} = \begin{bmatrix} r_1 \\ r_2 \\ r_3 \\ r_4 \end{bmatrix}$$

The operations table and the relaxations (as given by Gauss) follow.

Δy_1	Δy_2	Δy_3	Δy_4	Δr_1	Δr_2	Δr_3	Δr_4
1				69	-50	-6	-13
	1			-50	156	-78	-28
		1		-6	-78	110	-26
			1	-13	-28	-26	67

y_1	y_2	y_3	y_4	r_1	r_2	r_3	r_4
0	0	0	0	-7558	-14604	$+22156$	$+6$
			-201	-6352	$+1074$	$+46$	$+5232$
$+92$				-4	-3526	-506	$+4036$
			-60	$+776$	-1846	$+1054$	$+16$
	$+112$			$+176$	$+26$	$+118$	-320
			$+5$	$+111$	-114	-12	$+15$
-2				-27	-14	0	$+41$
			-1	-14	$+14$	$+26$	-26
90	112	-201	-56				

Hence $\qquad x_1 = 146, \; x_2 = 168, \; x_3 = -145$

Note how the residuals always add up to zero.

Gauss considered that, for normal equations at least, the transformation aided the convergence of the relaxation process. This, however, is not always so: Forsythe and Motzkin,* using a generalized form of Gauss' transformation, have shown that improved convergence may be expected under certain conditions, but these are not always satisfied by the simple transformation considered here.

13.4. Limitations of the Relaxation Method

The advantage which relaxation gains over classical iterative methods by its flexibility will be sufficiently obvious from the

* G. E. Forsythe and T. S. Motzkin, *Math. Tab., Wash.*, **6** (1952), 9.

examples given. Its limitations must be understood also. First, there is no means of dealing summarily with sets of equations having the same matrix **A** but different **b** columns. Secondly, some sets of equations do not respond to the method, the convergence being far too slow to make the process practical, even though it may be certain in the long run. In this respect, relaxation is certainly not inferior to the classical method, and indeed the theoretical conditions to be satisfied by **A** are essentially the same for both.* However, there are many equations for which relaxation leads to the solution quickly whereas the classical method does not.

It is not difficult to construct sets of equations for which convergence, though guaranteed, is extremely slow, e.g. the following normal equations devised by T. S. Wilson, and satisfied if $x_1 = x_2 = x_3 = x_4 = 1$.

$$\begin{bmatrix} 5 & 7 & 6 & 5 \\ 7 & 10 & 8 & 7 \\ 6 & 8 & 10 & 9 \\ 5 & 7 & 9 & 10 \end{bmatrix} \begin{bmatrix} x_1 \\ x_2 \\ x_3 \\ x_4 \end{bmatrix} = \begin{bmatrix} 23 \\ 32 \\ 33 \\ 31 \end{bmatrix}$$

It is possible to obtain three sets of x values for which the residuals have magnitude 0.1, 0.01 and 0.001 respectively. The first set of residuals seem small, yet the x values bear no resemblance to the true solution. Even in the third row, where the residuals are less than 10^{-5} times any coefficient in the original equations, x_1 errs by more than 10 per cent. Clearly relaxation is quite impractical in such a case.

x_1	x_2	x_3	x_4	r_1	r_2	r_3	r_4
+ 14·6	− 7·2	− 2·5	+ 3·1	+ 0·1	− 0·1	− 0·1	+ 0·1
+ 2·36	+ 0·18	+ 0·65	+ 1·21	+ 0·01	− 0·01	− 0·01	+ 0·01
+ 1·136	+ 0·918	+ 0·918	+ 1·021	+ 0·001	− 0·001	− 0·001	+ 0·001

These are "ill-conditioned" equations, some of the peculiarities of which were described in § 11.14. It was there stated that ill-conditioned equations are associated with a matrix having widely distributed latent roots; in fact the ratio of the largest to the smallest latent roots has sometimes been taken as a measure of

* See G. Temple, *Proc. Roy. Soc.*, A **169** (1939), 476, for a discussion of this aspect of the relaxation method.

ill-conditioning. Knowledge of latent roots, etc., is not of course immediately available to the computer, and when it is discovered in the course of calculation that the removal of small residuals needs large changes in the unknowns, it is advisable to abandon relaxation in favour of some direct method of solution. Even this may not be free from troubles.

The above example emphasizes the difficulty of placing limits of error on a solution to simultaneous equations obtained by relaxation, a difficulty which does not arise in the same way in classical methods where the iterative cycle is equivalent to multiplication by a well-defined matrix. There are, however, many applications of the relaxation technique in which this disadvantage can be overcome, e.g. in solving differential equations, discussed in the following chapters, the accuracy of the solution can be ascertained without much trouble.

EXERCISES 13

1. Show that the iterative equation, $\mathbf{x}_{k+1} = \mathbf{d} + \mathbf{B}\mathbf{x}_k$, can also be written in the form $\mathbf{y}_{k+1} = \mathbf{T}\mathbf{y}_k$, where

$$\mathbf{y}_k = \{1, x_1^{(k)}, x_2^{(k)}, \ldots, x_n^{(k)}\}$$

and
$$\mathbf{T} = \left[\begin{array}{c|c} 1 & 0 \\ \hline \mathbf{d} & \mathbf{B} \end{array}\right]$$

a matrix with $(n + 1)$ rows and columns.

2. If $\mathbf{A} = \mathbf{V} + \mathbf{W}$, where $\mathbf{V}$ is any matrix which is easily inverted, show that the solution of $\mathbf{A}\mathbf{x} = \mathbf{b}$ is given by the sequence

$$\mathbf{x}_k = (\mathbf{I} + \mathbf{B} + \mathbf{B}^2 + \ldots + \mathbf{B}^{k-1})\mathbf{y} + \mathbf{B}^k\mathbf{x}_0$$

where $\mathbf{y} = \mathbf{V}^{-1}\mathbf{b}$ and $\mathbf{B} = -\mathbf{V}^{-1}\mathbf{W}$, provided $\mathbf{B}$ satisfies the usual conditions.

Note. (13.5) and (13.9) are special cases of this general result. Frazer, Duncan and Collar in *Elementary Matrices*, take for $\mathbf{V}$ any convenient diagonal matrix.

3. If $\mathbf{C}_0$ is an approximate inverse of the matrix $\mathbf{A}$, show how this may be used to obtain an accurate solution of the equations, $\mathbf{A}\mathbf{x} = \mathbf{b}$.

CHAPTER 14

ORDINARY DIFFERENTIAL AND FREDHOLM INTEGRAL EQUATIONS

WE shall now be concerned with the solution, mainly by indirect methods, of various problems which can be effectively expressed as a set of linear simultaneous equations. These include—

1. Ordinary differential equations, of even order, subject to two-point boundary conditions. As a special case one may include the tabulation of functions in regions where series approximations are inconvenient, but for which the second derivative is a simple analytical function.

2. Ordinary differential equations of second order, involving latent roots.

3. Similar problems for integral equations of the Fredholm type.

The differential or integral equation should preferably be linear but not necessarily homogeneous. We are therefore stepping beyond the simple procedure described in Chapter 8 for dealing with two-point conditions when the differential equation is both linear and homogeneous. Fox discusses these topics in more detail.

Two-point Boundary Conditions

Although it is the use of the relaxation method which will receive most attention in this chapter, we shall describe first a direct method of solving second-order differential equations, using matrix inversion. This is perhaps most useful in tabulating a function $G(x)$ for which series approximations are convenient for relatively small and large values of x, but inconvenient for intermediate values. If the second derivative is a known function, say $r(x)$, $G(x)$ can be regarded as the solution of the equation $G'' = r(x)$ between two points at which $G(x)$ is known from series. E.g. if $G(x) = \tan^{-1} x$, $G''(x) = -2x/(1 + x^2)^2$, the series in this example having been discussed in § 7.15.

14.1. Use of Matrix Inversion

Let us consider a set of equations of the form

$$-g_{k-1} + 2g_k - g_{k+1} + w^2 b_k = 0 \quad (k = 1, 2, \ldots, n) \quad (14.1)$$

in which g_0, g_{n+1} and the b_k are all known. These equations can be written in matrix form

$$\begin{bmatrix} 2 & -1 & 0 & & 0 \\ -1 & 2 & -1 & & 0 \\ 0 & -1 & 2 & & 0 \\ \cdot & & & & \cdot \\ \cdot & & & & \cdot \\ & & & -1 & \cdot \\ 0 & 0 & 0 & -1 & 2 \end{bmatrix} \begin{bmatrix} g_1 \\ g_2 \\ g_3 \\ \cdot \\ \cdot \\ \cdot \\ g_n \end{bmatrix} + w^2 \begin{bmatrix} b_1 \\ b_2 \\ b_3 \\ \cdot \\ \cdot \\ \cdot \\ b_n \end{bmatrix} = \begin{bmatrix} g_0 \\ 0 \\ 0 \\ \cdot \\ \cdot \\ \cdot \\ g_{n+1} \end{bmatrix}$$

or $$\mathbf{Ag} + w^2\mathbf{b} = \mathbf{g}_e \qquad (14.2)$$

The special feature of this equation is that the reciprocal matrix $\mathbf{A}^{-1}$ can be written down at once. Thus, if $n = 5$

$$\mathbf{A}^{-1} = \tfrac{1}{6} \begin{bmatrix} 5 & 4 & 3 & 2 & 1 \\ 4 & 8 & 6 & 4 & 2 \\ 3 & 6 & 9 & 6 & 3 \\ 2 & 4 & 6 & 8 & 4 \\ 1 & 2 & 3 & 4 & 5 \end{bmatrix}$$

a result which can obviously be extended to any value of n.

Hence $$\mathbf{g} = \mathbf{A}^{-1}\mathbf{g}_e - w^2\mathbf{A}^{-1}\mathbf{b} \qquad (14.3)$$

and the elements of $\mathbf{g}$ can be evaluated directly. The first term, $\mathbf{A}^{-1}\mathbf{g}_e$, is merely the result of interpolating linearly between g_0 and g_{n+1}.

The simplest application of this result is to the tabulation of $G(x)$ for $x_k = x_0 + kw$, $k = 1, 2, \ldots, n$, when $G'' = r(x)$, and $G(x_0)$, $G(x_{n+1})$ are known. By using (8.29) the differential equation can be replaced by the difference equations

$$\delta^2 G_k = w^2\{r_k + (1/12)\delta^2 r_k - (1/240)\delta^4 r_k + \ldots\}$$

or $$\delta^2\{G_k - (1/12)w^2 r_k\} = w^2\{r_k - (1/240)\delta^4 r_k + \ldots\}$$

These are equivalent to (14.1) if

$$g_k = G_k - (1/12)w^2 r_k, \quad b_k = w^2(r_k + \triangle_k)$$

and $$\triangle_k = -(1/240)\delta^4 r_k + \ldots$$

Hence by (14.3), using matrix notation again,

$$\mathbf{G} = (1/12)w^2\mathbf{r} + \mathbf{A}^{-1}\mathbf{g}_e - w^2\mathbf{A}^{-1}(\mathbf{r} + \boldsymbol{\triangle}) \qquad (14.4)$$

so that if $\mathbf{r}$ is known the elements of $\mathbf{G}$ can be tabulated directly.

EXAMPLE 14.1. Tabulate $\tan^{-1} x = \int_0^x dx/(1 + x^2)$ for $x = 0.6(0.2)1.8$ given $\tan^{-1} 0.6 = 0.540420$, $\tan^{-1} 1.8 = 1.063698$

In this example,

$$r(x) = -2x(1 + x^2)^2, \quad w = 0.2, \quad n = 5$$

Hence, if $g = G - (1/12)w^2 r$

$$g_0 = g(0.6) = 0.540420 + 0.002163 = 0.542583$$
$$g_6 = g(1.8) = 1.063698 + 0.000667 = 1.064365$$

The calculation of G_k may be summarized as follows, the differencing of r_k to obtain $\triangle_k$ being omitted. All numbers are in units of 10^{-6}.

x	0·8	1·0	1·2	1·4	1·6
$- w^2 r$	23795	20000	16125	12783	10100
$- w^2 \triangle$	5	4	2	1	0
$- w^2(r + \triangle)$	23800	20004	16127	12784	10100
g_e	542583	0	0	0	1064365
$A^{-1}g_e$	629547	716510	803474	890438	977401
$- w^2 A^{-1}(r + \triangle)$	47177	70556	73928	61175	35638
$(1/12)w^2 r$	-1983	-1667	-1344	-1065	-842
$G = \tan^{-1} x$	674741	785399	876058	951548	1012197×10^{-6}

Comparison with *Chambers* [6] shows no error greater than 1 in the 6th decimal.

In principle this method can also be applied to the equation

$$G'' + q(x)G = r(x) \tag{14.5}$$

for which

$$\delta^2 G_k = w^2\{f_k + (1/12)\delta^2 f_k - (1/240)\delta^4 f_k + \ldots\}$$

or $\delta^2 g_k = w^2\{f_k + \triangle_k\}$ (14.6)

where

$$g_k = \{1 + (1/12)w^2 q_k\}G_k - (1/12)w^2 r_k, \quad f_k = -q_k G_k + r_k$$

and $\triangle_k = -(1/240)\delta^4 f_k + \ldots$

In matrix form (14.6) is

$$Ag = g_e + w^2\{-QG + r + \triangle)$$

where Q is the diagonal matrix with diagonal elements equal to q_k. It follows that

$$g = A^{-1}g_e - w^2 A^{-1}QG + w^2 A^{-1}(r + \triangle) \tag{14.7}$$

which differs from (14.4) in that the unknown elements G_k occur on the right. The most promising line of attack would seem to be an iterative procedure in which an approximate solution $\mathbf{G}_{(0)}$ is inserted on the right, and a "better" approximation $g_{(1)}$ evaluated from the equation

$$g_{(1)} = \mathbf{A}^{-1}g_e - w^2\mathbf{A}^{-1}\{\mathbf{Q}\mathbf{G}_{(0)} - \mathbf{r}\}$$

neglecting $\triangle$. This gives $\mathbf{G}_{(1)}$ and a repetition gives $g_{(2)}$, and so on. At a suitable stage $\triangle$ can be estimated, and a correction made if necessary. Whether this is an acceptable way of dealing with two-point conditions depends very much upon the trial solution $\mathbf{G}_{(0)}$, which becomes more and more important as the exact solution departs further from the linearly interpolated function $\mathbf{A}^{-1}g_e$. Obviously more than one or two iterations would be very laborious. No numerical example of this method will be given here, but the application of relaxation methods to the same type of problem is examined in the next section.

Some other applications of matrices to the solution of differential equations are outlined in Exercises 14, Nos. 1 and 2.

14.2. Use of Relaxation

In applying the relaxation method to (14.5) we should replace (14.6) by

$$g_{k-1} - (2 - w^2q_k)g_k + g_{k+1} - w^2r_k + \triangle_k = R_k \qquad (14.8)$$

where as usual R_k is the residual at the point x_k associated with an approximate solution g_k. Some comments on this set of equations are desirable before an example of their use is given.

1. The coefficients of the g's are particularly simple, and this makes the operations table simple also (cp. Example 13.5). If $|w^2q_k| \ll 2$ it is often possible to omit this entirely when adjusting the residual R_k during relaxation, though of course it must be included when the residual is subsequently recalculated.

2. Relaxation is most successful when the coefficient of g_k exceeds 2, i.e. $q_k < 0$. This implies that the solution of the homogeneous equation, with $r(x)$ omitted, is exponential in character rather than oscillatory. The reason is that when R_k is reduced in magnitude by a change in g_k, the changes in neighbouring residuals are such that $|\Delta R_{k-1}| + |\Delta R_{k+1}| < |\Delta R_k|$. The sum of the magnitudes of all residuals is therefore reduced in steps by relaxation, and this is a guarantee of convergence to the required solution.

3. The difference term $\triangle_k$ involves the required solution. However, if w is well chosen, $\triangle_k$ is small and can be neglected in the first stage of relaxation. It can then be estimated, and its inclusion in (14.8) will only modify the residuals slightly. A little extra relaxation will again bring the residuals below the desired limit. The calculation of $\triangle_k$ also serves to show how accurately

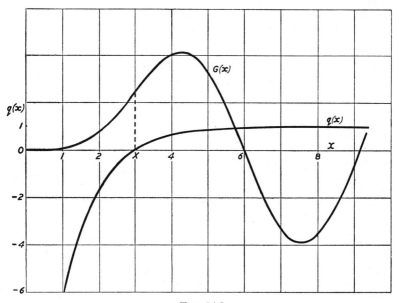

FIG. 14.1

the difference equations without $\triangle_k$ represent the differential equation.

The numerical example which follows has been chosen with the object of showing how relaxation can sometimes be combined with step-by-step integration. Fig. 14.1 illustrates the case of a homogeneous equation in which $q(x)$ changes from negative to positive values as x increases through X. The solution required is that which tends to zero for small x and behaves like $\sin(x + \delta)$ for large x. A step-by-step integration outwards from small values of x runs the risk of accumulating errors; if inward integration from X is followed, at least two integrations are required to derive the solution tending to zero, because the correct gradient at X is not known. An alternative procedure is to use relaxation in the range $(0, X)$, for which it is best suited, assuming $G(0) = 0$,

$G(X) = G_{n+1}$ (arbitrary), and then to continue the integration by steps beyond X.

EXAMPLE 14.2. Find approximately the solution of

$$G'' + (1 - 20e^{-x})G = 0$$

for which $G(0) = 0$. (Computation on p. 452.)

Here $q(x) = 1 - 20e^{-x}$, which changes sign when $x \simeq 3$. We shall use relaxation to obtain an approximate solution for $x < 4$, at intervals of 0·5. The relaxation equations (14.8) are

$$g_{k-1} - \{2 - q_k/4\}g_k + g_{k+1} - w^2 \triangle_k = R_k$$

where
$$g_k = \{1 + q_k/48\}G_k$$

$\triangle_k$ will be neglected at this stage. The initial solution is assumed to be zero up to $x = 2$, and then to increase linearly to a value of 1000 at $x = 4$.

In the first stage the residuals are reduced to about one unit by individual relaxations, and checked. All values are then increased by a factor of 10, and a similar reduction carried out, partly by group relaxations. It is an advantage to over-relax at this stage. Throughout, the value at $x = 4$ is left unchanged. Finally the values of G are derived and scaled up to give $G(4) = 10000$.

This solution is not accurate to the number of figures given. Improvement can be made by estimating $\triangle_k$ from the differences of $-q_kG_k$ and adjusting the residuals accordingly. However, if the solution is to be extended beyond $x = 4$ by a step-by-step method it may be worth deferring this correction until a few steps of forward integration have been carried out; the central differences at $x = 4$ will then be available, and the final result will be a smoother join at this point. An alternative procedure is described in § 14.4.

Another example suited to the use of relaxation is the decreasing solution of Airy's equation in the range $1 < x < 3$, for which series approximations are not convenient (see Example 8.9). This may be left as an exercise for the reader.

The equation $G'' + p(x)G' + q(x)G = r(x)$ can likewise be solved by relaxation, using the equations

$$\{1 + \tfrac{1}{2}wp_k\}G_{k-1} - (2 - w^2q_k)G_k$$
$$+ \{1 - \tfrac{1}{2}wp_k\}G_{k+1} - w^2r_k + \triangle_k = R_k \quad (14.9)$$

where

$$\triangle_k = wp_k\{-(1/6)\delta^3 + (1/30)\delta^5 + \ldots\}G_k$$
$$+ \{-(1/12)\delta^4 + (1/90)\delta^6 - \ldots\}G_k$$

The difference correction is likely to be larger than in (14.8), and therefore more difficult to apply, but the general method remains unchanged.

Values of $g_k = \{1 + (1/48)q_k\}G_k$

x	0·0	0·5	1·0	1·5	2·0	2·5	3·0	3·5	4·0
$2 - q_k/4$		4·784	3·589	2·866	2·4267	2·1604	1·9989	1·9010	
g_k	0	0	0	0	200	400	603	800	1000
		5	25	80	−11	−30		40	
			−4	−8	−6	−8	3	3	
		−1	−1	−3	−1				
g_k	0	40	200	690	1780	3620	6030	8430	10000
		3	4	−2	−6	−10	−8	−3	
					−3	−2	−3		
					−2	−3			
g_k	0	43	204	688	1769	3605	6019	8427	10000
G_k	0	57	238	751	1858	3702	6098	8468	10000

Residuals R_k

x	0·5	1·0	1·5	2·0	2·5	3·0	3·5
residual stack (top → bottom)	0 +25 +1 −3 +1 +9 +13 −1	0 +80 −10 −5 −13 −1 −2 +1 +12 +2 −1 +1 −1	+200 −29 −4 +19 −4 0 +6 −1 0 +2 +6 0 −3 +1	−85 −5 −35 +1 −7 −15 0 +3 −1 −10 +5 +5 +2 +3 0	−64 +1 −14 +3 +3 −1 −11 −17 +5 +6 +4 −1	+1 +41 +11 +3 +6 0 −3 −13 +3 −1 +1 +1	+79 +3 −3 +5 −3 0 −1
Recalculated residuals	−2	−1	+1	0	0	0	−1

14.3. Boundary Conditions Containing Derivatives

It is not essential for the use of relaxation that the boundary conditions should always specify the value of the solution at the end points. At one end, or both, the value of G', or of a combination of G and G', may be specified instead.

Let us suppose, for instance, that at x_0 G is unknown but G' has the values G'_0, and that equations (14.9) are used as a basis for relaxation. Advantage may be taken of a formula which gives G'_0 in terms of forward differences of G_{-1}, thus

$$wG'_0 = \{\Delta + (1/2)\Delta^2 - (1/6)\Delta^3 \\ - (1/12)\Delta^4 - (1/20)\Delta^5 + \ldots\}G_{-1}$$

Replacing the first four terms by tabular values this becomes

$$wG'_0 = (1/12)\{- 3G_{-1} - 10G_0 \\ + 18G_1 - G_2 - G_3\} + \triangle'_0 \quad (14.10)$$

the leading term in $\triangle'_0$ being $(- 1/20)\delta^5 G_{3/2}$. Now, when $k = 0$ in (14.9)

$$\{1 + \tfrac{1}{2}wp_0\}G_{-1} = (2 - w^2q_0)G_0 \\ - \{1 - \tfrac{1}{2}wp_0\}G_1 - w^2r_0 - \triangle_0 + R_0$$

and so we have two equations from which G_{-1} can be eliminated. The resultant equation, when allied to those for $k = 1, \ldots, n$, gives a closed set of equations for $G_0, G_1, \ldots, G_n$, and by reducing the residuals in the usual way the desired solution can be derived.

It is only a short step further to deal with a boundary condition of the form

$$G'_0 + s_0 G_0 = t_0$$

where s_0, t_0 are given. This leads in turn to the possibility of solving *first-order* differential equations by relaxation. Normally such equations would be solved by forward integration since only one end condition need be specified, but relaxation can be used if the equation is first changed to one of second order by differentiation. Thus the equation

$$G' + s(x)G = t(x) \qquad (14.11)$$

becomes $\qquad G'' + (s' - s^2)G = t' - st \qquad (14.12)$

if the term in G' is eliminated after differentiation, and this can be solved by relaxation with, for example, the conditions

$$x = x_0 \qquad G = G_0$$
$$x = x_{n+1} \qquad G'_{n+1} + s(x_{n+1})G_{n+1} = t(x_{n+1})$$

An obvious illustration is the equation

$$G' + 2xG = 1$$

which has been considered on previous occasions (Examples 7.5 and 8.1). Suppose that the solution for which $G(0) = 0$ is required in the range $0 < x < 2$. This can be obtained from the equation

$$G'' + 2(1 - 2x^2)G = -2x$$

using the conditions $x = 0$, $G = 0$; $x = 2$, $G' + 4G = 1$. By using the backward difference equivalent of (14.10), the second of these equations may be put in the form

$$(1/3)(G_{n-2} + G_{n-1}) - 7G_n + \{(16/3) + 16w + 14w^2\}G_{n+1}$$
$$- 4w(1 - w) - \triangle = 0$$

where $G_{n+1} = G(2)$, and then used as one of the relaxation equations.

14.4. Accuracy of Solutions Obtained by Relaxation

In discussing the application of relaxation to sets of simultaneous equations in general it was observed that the size of residuals is not always a reliable guide to the accuracy of the solution. Such a degree of ill-conditioning is less likely in the difference equations obtained from second-order differential equations, particularly if the solution is exponential in character, for the reasons given in § 14.2. Moreover, when a difference correction is used, this in itself gives a fair indication of the reliability of the solution, since a small $\triangle$ implies that the interval w has been suitably chosen. If the final residuals also alternate in sign, confidence is still further sustained.

When doubt still exists about the adequacy of a solution $G^{(1)}$, it may be desirable to examine the effect of reducing the interval. This usually presents little difficulty when w is halved, for then a reasonably good approximate solution is available in which missing values can be filled in by halfway interpolation. The new set of residuals is soon reduced to the same level as before. If the solution is now $G^{(2)}$, and the error of the finite difference approximation is proportional to w^2, then according to (3.41) a better result is given by

$$G = G^{(2)} + (G^{(2)} - G^{(1)})/3 \qquad (14.13)$$

In general, if the error is proportional to w^s, and the solutions available correspond to w_1 and $w_2(< w_1)$, then by (3.39) the improved solution is given by

$$G = G^{(2)} + \frac{1}{(w_1/w_2)^s - 1} (G^{(2)} - G^{(1)}) \qquad (14.14)$$

In Example 14.2, the effect of halving the interval is as follows—

x	$G^{(1)}$	$G^{(2)}$	$R^{(2)}$	G
0	0	0		0
0·25		15	0	15
0·5	57	44	− 1	43
0·75		103	0	102
1·0	238	214	0	212
1·25		409	− 1	407
1·5	751	721	1	719
1·75		1186	− 1	1184
2·0	1858	1830	− 1	1828
2·25		2665	0	2663
2·5	3702	3681	0	3680
2·75		4842	0	4841
3·0	6098	6085	− 1	6084
3·25		7323	0	7322
3·5	8468	8459	0	8458
3·75		9384	0	9384
4·0	10000	10000		10000

The formula used is such that when the difference correction $-(1/240)\delta^4 f$ is ignored the error is proportional to w^4. The final correction therefore consists of a subtraction from $G^{(2)}$ of

$$(G^{(1)} - G^{(2)})/15$$

14.5. Non-linear Equations

It must not be supposed that relaxation only works well for linear equations. Non-linearity inevitably brings in some awkwardness, but the effectiveness of the procedure need not be impaired. Fox* has quoted an interesting example which also shows how a pair of simultaneous first-order equations may be solved.

* Fox, L., *Proc. Camb. Phil. Soc.*, **45** (1948), 55.

The equations

$$dp/dx = p^2 - q^2 + A, \quad dq/dx = 2pq + B$$

in which A and B are constants, are associated with the Airy integral for a complex argument. For $x < 2$ and $x > 10$ satisfactory solutions can be obtained by series, and the problem is to fill in the range $(2,10)$ by numerical integration.

The following finite difference equations can be used for relaxation—

$$p_{-1} - 2w(p_0{}^2 + q_0{}^2) + p_1 - 2wA + 2\triangle(p_0) = R_0$$
$$q_{-1} - 4wp_0q_0 + q_1 - 2wB + 2\triangle(q_0) = S_0$$

where $$\triangle = -(1/6)\delta^3 + (1/30)\delta^5 - \ldots$$

and R_0, S_0, are two residuals associated with the values p_0, q_0. If small changes δp_0, δq_0 are made, these residuals are changed, to first order, by amounts

$$\delta R_0 = -4w(p_0\delta p_0 + q_0\delta q_0)$$
$$\delta S_0 = -4w(p_0\delta q_0 + q_0\delta p_0)$$

and hence R_0 and S_0 are reduced simultaneously if

$$\delta p_0 = \frac{p_0 R_0 + q_0 S_0}{4w(p_0{}^2 + q_0{}^2)}, \quad \delta q_0 = \frac{p_0 S_0 - q_0 R_0}{4w(p_0{}^2 + q_0{}^2)}$$

The effect on adjacent residuals is obvious. This is found to give good convergence, 4D values of p and q being obtainable with $w = 0.5$, when difference corrections are included. Since both p and q are prescribed at the two boundary points the system of equations is over-rigid, and the solution is sensitive to any incompatibility in these values.

Latent-root Problems

When the boundary conditions imposed on the solution of a differential equation can be satisfied only when a parameter in the equation has certain discrete values, we have a latent-root problem of the kind considered in Chapter 12. The equivalence becomes quite clear when the differential equation is replaced by a set of finite difference equations as in (14.6). The latent roots can then be evaluated by the methods of Chapter 12, but because of the simplicity of the matrix, which is symmetrical and only has non-zero elements near the diagonal, indirect methods can generally be used with advantage. In particular the least, i.e. most negative, latent root, and its associated function or mode, can often be found by relaxation, with the help of a well established principle due to Rayleigh. This will be described, but otherwise the problem will not be discussed in the same detail as in Chapter 12; thus it will be taken for granted that the latent roots are all distinct and well separated.

Another technique, which requires that the differential equation be first replaced by a hyperbolic partial differential equation, is described in Chapter 16.

14.6 Rayleigh's Principle

The idea here involved can be explained most simply with reference to a set of linear equations represented by

$$\mathbf{B}\mathbf{w} = \mu \mathbf{I}\mathbf{w} \tag{14.15}$$

where $\mathbf{B}$ is a symmetrical matrix. The latent roots μ_i and their vectors $\mathbf{u}_i$ then satisfy the equations

$$(\mathbf{B} - \mu_i\mathbf{I})\mathbf{u}_i = 0, \quad \mathbf{u}_i'(\mathbf{B} - \mu_i\mathbf{I}) = 0 \tag{14.16}$$

Let $\mathbf{w} = \mathbf{u}_i + \mathbf{e}_i$, where $\mathbf{e}_i$ represents a small departure from the correct vector $\mathbf{u}_i$; then the scalar equation

$$\mathbf{w}'\mathbf{B}\mathbf{w} = \bar{\mu}_i\mathbf{w}'\mathbf{I}\mathbf{w} \tag{14.17}$$

can be used to define a value $\bar{\mu}_i$ which approximates to the root μ_i. The error can be shown to be one of second order.

Thus
$$(\bar{\mu}_i - \mu_i)\mathbf{w}'\mathbf{I}\mathbf{w} = \mathbf{w}'(\mathbf{B} - \mu_i\mathbf{I})\mathbf{w}$$
$$= \mathbf{w}'(\mathbf{B} - \mu_i\mathbf{I})\mathbf{e}_i$$
$$= \mathbf{e}_i'(\mathbf{B} - \mu_i\mathbf{I})\mathbf{e}_i$$

when the two equations in (14.16) are applied in turn. This shows that the difference

$$\bar{\mu}_i - \mu_i = \mathbf{e}_i'(\mathbf{B} - \mu_i\mathbf{I})\mathbf{e}_i/\mathbf{w}'\mathbf{I}\mathbf{w}$$

is a quantity of second order in the elements of $\mathbf{e}_i$, and hence if $\mathbf{w}$ is close enough to $\mathbf{u}_i$, $\bar{\mu}_i$ is a good approximation of μ_i. Essentially the same result was used in § 12.9 in obtaining latent roots by means of scalar products. However, it can be emphasized here that the estimate of μ_i given by (14.17) is stationary with respect to small departures of $\mathbf{w}$ from $\mathbf{u}_i$. Moreover, the lowest latent root stands in a unique position, because if $\mu_1 < \mu_i$ for all $i > 1$, then always $\bar{\mu}_1 \geqslant \mu_1$, i.e. any approximation provides an upper limit to this root, equality being achieved only when $\mathbf{w}$ is identical with $\mathbf{u}_1$. This is the essence of Rayleigh's principle, and is easily proved by expanding $\mathbf{e}_1$ in terms of the vectors $\mathbf{u}_i$, when it is found that the quantity $(\mathbf{w}'\mathbf{Bw})/(\mathbf{w}'\mathbf{Iw})$ has an absolute minimum when $\mathbf{w} = \mathbf{u}_1$. These conclusions are not invalidated if the unit matrix $\mathbf{I}$ is replaced throughout by a diagonal matrix $\mathbf{Q}$ with positive elements.

The minimal property associated with μ_1 is the basis of "variational" methods of evaluating the lowest root, in which the elements of $\mathbf{w}$ are provided with suitable parameters which can then be adjusted to make $\bar{\mu}_1$ a minimum. It would be unwise to rely upon (14.17) for an estimate of a higher root unless one is certain that $\mathbf{w}$ is reasonably close to the corresponding vector, an unlikely event.* However, if μ_1 and $\mathbf{u}_1$ are known, it is possible by choosing $\mathbf{w}$ to be orthogonal to $\mathbf{u}_1$ to ensure that (14.17) gives an upper limit to μ_2 which may be improved by allowing suitable variations in $\mathbf{w}$. The process may then be extended to higher roots, or a device such as deflation may be used.

The extension to certain types of homogeneous differential equation is not difficult.† Consider an equation of the form

$$d^2G/dx^2 + q(x)G = -\mu\rho(x)G \qquad (14.18)$$

in which $q(x)$ is continuous, and $\rho(x)$ of one sign throughout the range $a \leqslant x \leqslant b$. Let G satisfy conditions at $x = a, b$, which can only be met if μ has discrete values μ_i, such that

$$\mu_1 < \mu_2 < \ldots < \mu_i < \mu_{i+1} < \ldots$$

Then if $\bar{G}^{(i)}$ is an approximation to the solution $G^{(i)}$ corresponding to μ_i, an estimate of μ_i is given by

$$\bar{\mu}_i = -\int_a^b \bar{G}^{(i)} L\bar{G}^{(i)} dx \bigg/ \int_a^b \rho\{\bar{G}^{(i)}\}^2 dx \qquad (14.19)$$

where
$$L = \frac{d^2}{dx^2} + q(x)$$

---

* However, J. B. L. Cooper, in *Quart. Appl. Math.*, **6** (1948), 179, has shown that if $\mathbf{w}$ be chosen so that $\bar{\mu}$ exceeds the largest of the diagonal elements of $\mathbf{B}$, then an iterative process such as relaxation will probably converge to the highest mode, corresponding to the greatest latent root. This fact can be used to assist the estimation of intermediate roots and vectors.

† It is described in detail, with applications to dynamical problems by G. Temple and W. G. Bickley, *Rayleigh's Principle* (Oxford 1933). A summary of the relevant theory, with possible generalizations, has also been given by K. Washizu, *Quart. Journ. Mech. Appl. Math.*, **8** (1955), 311.

If $\bar{G}^{(i)} = G^{(i)} + E^{(i)}$

$$\bar{\mu}_i - \mu_i = -\int_a^b E^{(i)} LE^{(i)} dx \Big/ \int_a^b \rho\{E^{(i)}\}^2 dx$$

Again, for the lowest root, $\bar{\mu}_1 \geqslant \mu_1$.

Rayleigh's principle is valid for the class of equations known as "self-adjoint," i.e. in which L has, for real equations of second order, the form

$$L = \frac{d}{dx}\left(p_1 \frac{d}{dx}\right) + q(x) \tag{14.20}$$

Further conditions are that p_1 and q should be continuous and differentiable functions of x in the range $a < x < b$, and $p_1 > 0$ in this range. The equation may be singular at the end points, at which the boundary conditions on G must be linear and homogeneous, e.g.

$$G(a) = c_1 G'(a), \qquad G(b) = c_2 G'(b)$$
or $\qquad G(a) = G(b), \quad p_1(a)G'(a) = p_1(b)G'(b)$

Similar conditions apply to equations of higher order. For details see Courant and Hilbert, *Methods of Mathematical Physics*, Vol. 1.

When we consider the numerical use of (14.19) the first step is to subdivide the range (a, b) suitably, e.g. by points $x_k = x_0 + kw$, where $x_0 = a$, $x_{n+1} = b$. The integrals in (14.19) can then be replaced by finite sums, involving only values of $\bar{G}$ at these tabular points, since the derivatives occurring in $L\bar{G}$ can also be replaced by their finite difference equivalents. In practice it is convenient to work directly from the difference equations which replace (14.18), and this effectively replaces the integrals by trapezoidal sums of the integrand values. The ratio of the two integrals is obtained thereby with quite sufficient accuracy. When combined with relaxation, the formula for $\bar{\mu}_1$ yields progressively better estimates of μ_1 and of the solution $G^{(1)}$.

It is worth pointing out here that, in an example such as Example 12.7, which is derived basically from a differential equation, the iterative methods described in Chapter 12 lead first of all to the larger latent roots, and the least root, there denoted by λ_4, is obtained only after a lengthy calculation. By using Rayleigh's principle, however, λ_4 and its associated vector can be derived first.

14.7. The Relaxation Procedure

To illustrate the process of finding the lowest mode of a differential equation, we consider the solution of (14.18) when $G(a)$ and

$G(b)$ have specified values G_0 and G_{n+1} respectively. The difference equations can be written as

$$G_{k-1} - (2 - w^2 q_k - v^2 \rho_k)G_k + G_{k+1} + \triangle_k = R_k \quad (14.21)$$

where

$$\triangle_k = \{-(1/12)\delta^2 + (1/90)\delta^4 - \ldots\}G_k, \quad v^2 = w^2 \mu$$

and R_k is a residual associated with the G_k's (the bar over G used in the previous section will now be omitted). Alternatively, equations similar to (14.8) and having a smaller difference correction, might be used.

Now, if G_k is a reasonable approximation to the lowest mode, an estimate of v_1^2 is given by

$$(v_1^2)_0 = -\frac{\Sigma\{G_{k-1} - (2 - w^2 q_k)G_k + G_{k+1} + \triangle_k\}G_k}{\Sigma \rho_k G_k^2} \quad (14.22)$$

In most cases this estimate will be made without including $\triangle_k$. With such a value of v_1^2 the residuals of (14.21) can be reduced by suitable changes in the G_k's; the modal solution is thereby improved and provides a better value of v_1^2; then the cycle can be repeated. At a suitable stage the residuals are modified by including $\triangle_k$, or a separate calculation with a smaller w carried out, followed by extrapolation. Both these lines of attack are illustrated in Example 14.3.

In one important respect the evaluation of latent roots by relaxation differs from the solution of a set of linear equations which are not homogeneous: the residuals in (14.21) cannot be reduced exactly to zero unless the assumed value of v^2 coincides with a latent root. The most effective course in practice is to reduce the residuals as far as possible with a particular estimate of v_1^2, but to suspend relaxation when they have roughly the same relative proportions as the values of G_k. It is then apparent from (14.21) that a small change in v_1^2 can result in an overall reduction of the residuals, and this is in fact likely to happen when v_1^2 is recalculated from the improved values of G_k.

EXAMPLE 14.3. Find to 4S the least latent root of the equation
$$G'' + \mu(1 + (2x - 1)^2)G = 0$$
when
$$G(0) = G(1) = 0$$

Here $\rho(x) = 1 + (2x - 1)^2$, which is symmetrical about $x = 1/2$. This symmetry considerably reduces the task of solution. It can be confidently assumed that the lowest mode is one without further nodes between $x = 0$ and 1. We begin with a crude solution using an interval of 0·2 in x; for this only the points $x = 0·2$, 0·4 need be considered since the solution has the same values at $x = 0·8$, 0·6. Also, since the amplitude of the mode is arbitrary, no attempt is made to alter G at $x = 0·4$, and changes at $x = 0·2$ are chosen as far as possible to leave the residuals proportional to the values of G.

The relevant difference equations are as follows—

At
$$x_1(= 0·2) \qquad - c_1 G_1 + G_2 + \triangle_1 = R_1$$
$$x_2(= 0·4) \qquad G_1 - c_2 G_2 + G_3 + \triangle_2 = R_2$$

where $\quad c_1 = 2 - 1·36 \nu_1{}^2, \quad c_2 = 2 - 1·04 \nu_1{}^2, \quad \nu_1{}^2 = 0·04 \mu$

Also $\qquad G_0 = G_5 = 0, \; G_1 = G_4, \; G_2 = G_3$

Assume $\qquad G_1 = 400, \; G_2 = 800$

Then by (14.22), ignoring $\triangle$,

$$(\nu_1{}^2)_0 = - \frac{0 \times 400 + (-400) \times 800}{1·36 \times (400)^2 + 1·04 \times (800)^2} = 0·3623$$

and accordingly $\qquad - 1·507 G_1 + \qquad G_2 = R_1$
$$G_1 - 0·623 G_2 = R_2$$

Two brief stages of relaxation are now carried out, each consisting of a single change in G_1, after which $\nu_1{}^2$, c_1 and c_2 are recalculated. This can be summarized as follows—

	G_1	G_2	$\nu_1{}^2$	c_1	c_2	R_1	R_2
	400	800	0·3623	− 1·507	− 1·623	+ 197	− 99
$\delta G_1 =$ 121						+ 15	+ 22
	521	800	0·3376	− 1·5409	− 1·6489	− 2·81	+ 1·88
$\delta G_1 = - 1·84$						+ 0·03	+ 0·04
	519·16	800	0·3375				

Note the fall in the residuals after the first recalculation of $\nu_1{}^2$. At this stage, the estimate of μ_1 is 8·437$_5$.

So far no allowance for $\triangle_k$ has been made. It is possible at this point to proceed in one of two ways—

(a) to estimate $\triangle_k$, modify the residuals accordingly, and continue the relaxation;

(b) to carry out a similar calculation, without $\triangle$, at a smaller interval, estimate $\nu_1{}^2$ again, and extrapolate to the result for a zero interval.

We show how both methods can be applied.

Continuation (a). Estimation of $\triangle_k$ with the small number of values available is rather uncertain, as the following difference table shows—

x	G	δ	δ^2	δ^3	δ^4	δ^5	δ^6	Δ
0	0		(-30)		(360)			
		519		(-208)		(-195)		
0·2	519		-238		(165)		(73)	$-13·1$
		281		-43		(-122)		
0·4	800		-281		43		(122)	$-2·2$
		0		0		0		

The bracketed values of δ^2 and δ^4 at $x = 0$ are very rough, but the choice is partly assisted by the fact that they must be consistent with the condition $G''(0) = 0$.

When $\triangle_k$ is included the residuals are much changed; the rest of the calculation can be summarized as follows—

G_1	G_2	$\triangle_1$	$\triangle_2$	$\nu_1{}^2$	R_1	R_2
519·0	800	$-13·1$	$-2·2$	0·3458	$-7·2$	$+4·7$
514·4	800	$-11·3$	$-3·8$	0·3462	$+2·1$	$-1·4$
515·8	800	$-11·9$	$-2·7$	0·3461		

The final estimate, $\nu_1{}^2 = 0·3461$, gives $\mu_1 = 8·652$.

Continuation (*b*). A similar relaxation to the original, but with $w = 0·1$, leads to the following results—

x	0·1	0·2	0·3	0·4	0·5
G	331·5	616	828	957	1000
R	0·0	$-0·1$	0·0	0·0	0·4

and $$\nu_1{}^2 = 0·01\mu_1 = 0·086367$$

It must be remembered here that when changes in G are made at $x = 0·4$ during relaxation, the effect on the residual at $x = 0·5$ must be doubled because a similar change is implicitly made at $x = 0·6$. No changes in $G(0·5)$ are made.

We now have the following estimates of μ_1, with neglect of $\triangle$—

$$w = 0·2 \quad \mu_1 \simeq 8·437$$
$$0·200$$
$$0·1 \qquad\qquad 8·637$$

The error in G is of order w^2, so the error in μ_1 is presumably of order w^4. Hence a better estimate of μ_1 according to (14.14) is obtained by adding 1/15 of the above difference, i.e. 0·013

$$\mu_1 = 8·637 + 0·013 = 8·650$$
$$\mu_1{}^{1/2} = 2·941$$

This agrees fairly well with the result in (*a*), and in this instance is probably quite as reliable because the interval of 0·2 in x is too large to enable $\triangle_k$ to be reliably estimated.

It must be observed that, although Rayleigh's formula when applied accurately to the differential equation must lead to an estimate

$\bar{\mu}_1 > \mu_1$, this is not necessarily true of the estimate obtained from difference equations which do not represent the differential equation accurately. Thus, in this example, when the difference correction $\triangle$ is ignored, the estimates of μ_1 are too small.

Relaxation is less likely to be effective in determining higher latent roots when, as usually happens, these correspond to modes having one or more intermediate nodes. As emphasized earlier, relaxation is better suited to finding solutions which are not oscillatory. When several latent roots are required it is better to adopt a quite different approach, such as that described in Chapter 16.

Fredholm Integral Equations

Although the numerical solution of integral equations is important, the subject cannot be dealt with very fully here and we shall only describe one or two methods of treating linear equations of the Fredholm type. These are usually classified into three kinds as follows, $\phi(x)$ being the unknown function.

$$\int_a^b K(x, \xi)\phi(\xi)d\xi = f(x) \tag{14.23}$$

$$\phi(x) - \mu \int_a^b K(x, \xi)\phi(\xi)d\xi = f(x) \tag{14.24}$$

$$\phi(x) - \mu \int_a^b K(x, \xi)\phi(\xi)d\xi = 0 \tag{14.25}$$

Of these (14.23) and (14.24) are inhomogeneous and are referred to as Fredholm equations of the first and second kinds respectively. The function $K(x, \xi)$ is called the kernel, and is often symmetrical in the variables x, ξ, sometimes being a function of $|x - \xi|$ only. We shall assume that $K(x, \xi)$ is a real and continuous function in the range (a, b), and likewise $f(x)$; under these conditions (14.24) can have a unique continuous solution in the same range, although there are exceptions which cannot be discussed here. Equation (14.23) may have no continuous solution unless $f(x)$ satisfies further conditions depending on the properties of $K(x, \xi)$. Equation (14.25), the homogeneous equation of the second kind, has in general non-zero solutions only if the parameter μ has certain discrete values. These are the latent roots or proper values of the equations, and there is usually an infinite number of them.

The general theory* of the continuous solutions of integral equations of the second kind is closely analogous to that for linear simultaneous equations, summarized in the introductions to Chapters 11 and 12.

When a and b are finite there is no difficulty in adjusting the scale of x and ξ to make the limits $(0, 1)$ or $(-1, 1)$. When either limit is infinite the equation is said to be singular, and the solution presents special difficulties; if $K(x, \xi)$ becomes infinite, say when $x = \xi$, we have another category of singular equations.

The importance of integral equations arises from the fact that the solution of many physical problems involving boundary conditions can be shown to satisfy such an equation. The boundary conditions are contained implicitly in the equation, and need not be stated explicitly as when a differential equation is used. It follows that many linear differential equations, with two-point conditions imposed on the solution, can be converted to Fredholm equations; in this event, the kernel $K(x, \xi)$ is closely related to the function known as the Green's function of the differential equation. It may be remarked in passing that the derivation of this Green's function† is analogous to the inversion of the matrix associated with a set of linear equations.

Of the various practical methods of solving integral equations we shall have something to say about the following—

1. Iterative methods, in which a sequence of functions is evolved which converges to the correct solution. For non-linear equations these may provide the main line of attack.

2. The conversion to a set of linear algebraic equations by substituting for the integral a finite sum involving only a discrete set of values of the integrand.

3. Methods in which the solution is fitted to a polynomial or other suitable function.

Some other methods are mentioned briefly in § 14.11.

14.8. Iterative Methods

For equations of type (14.24) it may be possible to define a sequence of functions $\phi_0(x)$, $\phi_1(x)$, . . . by the relation

$$\phi_{k+1}(x) = f(x) + \mu \int_a^b K(x, \xi)\phi_k(\xi)d\xi \qquad (14.26)$$

* It is clearly described by W V. Lovitt, *Linear Integral Equations* (1924; Dover reprint, 1950). See also F. G. Tricomi, *Integral Equations* (Interscience, 1957).
† For methods of deriving Green's functions, see Lovitt, *loc. cit.*

The choice of $\phi_0(x)$ is in principle arbitrary, but for rapid convergence it is preferably a good approximation to the desired solution. Sometimes it is convenient to assume that $\phi_0(x) = f(x)$; the process is then known as the *method of successive substitution*, and it can be shown that the sequence will converge correctly provided $|\mu| < |\mu_1|$, where μ_1 is the least latent root of the corresponding homogeneous equation (14.25).

In a few favourable cases the successive integrations may be performed analytically; more often numerical quadrature is necessary. The numerical process is apt to be tedious, since each value of x involves a separate integration and sufficient values of x must be included to make the quadrature with respect to ξ reasonably accurate. However, it may be possible, when several iterations have been performed, to anticipate the final result by applying some extrapolation technique, such as Aitken's δ^2-formula, to estimate $\phi(x)$ for each individual value of x.

The iterative procedure can be extended to find latent roots of homogeneous equations. Let us assume that $K(x, \xi)$ is symmetrical, which is sufficient to ensure that all latent roots of (14.25) are real. Then let the sequence $\phi_1, \phi_2, \ldots$ be defined by the relation

$$\phi_{k+1} = \int_a^b K(x, \xi)\phi_k(\xi)d\xi \qquad (14.27)$$

and let $$c_k = \int_a^b \phi_0\phi_k dx, \quad c_{k+1} = \int_a^b \phi_0\phi_{k+1}dx \qquad (14.28)$$

It also follows from the symmetrical property of the kernel that

$$c_k = \int_a^b \phi_j\phi_{k-j}dx \quad (j = 0, 1, \ldots, k)$$

As k increases, the ratio $\mu^{(k)} = c_k/c_{k+1}$ will in general tend to the latent root μ_1 of smallest magnitude, and ϕ_k to the corresponding modal solution $u_1(x)$ of the integral equation. The amplitude of $u_1(x)$ is of course arbitrary.

This method of determining the extreme root is essentially the same as that described on page 392 for finding the dominant latent root of a matrix $\mathbf{A}$. The repeated integration of ϕ_0 with $K(x, \xi)$ is equivalent to repeated multiplication of an arbitrary vector by the matrix $\mathbf{A}$, and the constants c_k correspond exactly to the scalar products defined in (12.17). The equivalence becomes clearer still when the integral in (14.27) is replaced by a finite sum as in the following section. There is a slight change in notation in that μ replaces $1/\lambda$, and the limit of the sequence $\mu^{(k)}$ is therefore the least in magnitude of the latent roots of (14.25).

As for matrices, it is possible to envisage a generalization of this iterative procedure to include further roots, multiple roots, complex roots (arising from unsymmetrical kernels) and so on, but it would be unprofitable to follow such a course here. It should also be mentioned that the Lanczos technique can in principle be extended to include integral equations.

A brief reference must now be made to the possible use of iteration in solving non-linear integral equations. For instance the equation

$$\phi(x) = \int_0^1 \frac{\{\phi(\xi)\}^2}{1 + x + \xi} \, d\xi \qquad (14.29)$$

may be solved by means of a sequence defined by

$$\phi_{k+1}(x) = \int_0^1 \frac{\{\phi_k(\xi)\}^2}{1 + x + \xi} \, d\xi, \quad \phi_0 = \text{constant}$$

However, it is essential to the success of this operation that $\phi_0{}^2$ should be left unspecified, so that the sequence actually derived is

$$\phi_1/\phi_0{}^2, \ \phi_2/\phi_0{}^4, \ \phi_3/\phi_0{}^8, \ \cdots$$

By taking ratios of successive terms in this sequence it is soon found that the correct value of $\phi_0{}^2$ is about 3·54. Collatz* has given other examples of non-linear equations.

14.9. Use of Finite Sums

The device of replacing the integral by a sum, using a convenient quadrature formula, is an obvious one, and for non-singular equations of type (14.24) or (14.25) it is usually quite effective. For equations of the first kind, (14.23), it is often unsatisfactory because the set of linear equations which result are very ill-conditioned.

Let us consider equations of the second kind, first dividing the range of integration into n equal intervals so that

$$x_j = x_0 + jw, \quad x_0 = a, \quad x_n = b$$

---

* L. Collatz, *N.T.D.E.* This book discusses integral equations more fully than has been possible here.

Then (14.24) is replaced by a set of algebraic equations

$$\phi_j - w\{t_0 K_{j0}\phi_0 + t_1 K_{j1}\phi_1 + \ldots + t_n K_{jn}\phi_n + \triangle_j\} = f_j$$
$$(j = 0, 1, \ldots, n) \quad (14.30$$

where $\qquad \phi_j = \phi(x_j),\ f_j = f(x_j),\ K_{jk} = K(x_j,\ \xi_k)$

the t's are weighting factors associated with the quadrature formula, and $\triangle_j$ is a correction term for higher differences ignored by this formula.

Two decisions have to be made, first the interval w must be chosen and this determines the number of equations, and secondly the quadrature formula. Clearly, if w is small enough for the differences of the integrand to decrease rapidly, the quadrature formula can be a simple one, but the number of equations may be large. The final choice must be a compromise, related to the accuracy required of the solution.

The linear equations may be solved either by a direct method, or by indirect methods such as iteration or relaxation. It often happens that the kernel $K(x, \xi)$ favours an indirect method, and then there is much to be said for a simple quadrature formula such as the trapezoidal rule or Simpson's rule, a correction for higher differences of the integrand being introduced later, as in other applications of relaxation. One reason for this is that it is not usually known in advance what order of differences may contribute significantly to the integral for a given choice of w, and it is obviously an advantage to be able to make adjustments at a later stage. Alternatively, the $\triangle$ terms in (14.30) may be entirely ignored, and a second calculation made with a smaller value of w, with a view to extrapolating the solution later to zero w.

Further details of the procedure are shown in the following numerical examples, the second of which is a latent-root problem.

EXAMPLE 14.4. Solve the equation

$$\phi(x) + \int_{-1}^{1} K(x,\ \xi)\phi(\xi)d\xi = 1$$

where $\qquad \begin{aligned} K(x,\ \xi) &= 1 - (x - \xi)^2,\ |x - \xi| \leqslant 1 \\ &= 0 \qquad\qquad\quad ,\ |x - \xi| \geqslant 1 \end{aligned}$

Because $K(-x,\ -\xi) = K(x,\ \xi)$ the solution of this equation has the property that $\phi(-x) = \phi(x)$, and this simplifies the computation.

We propose to do calculations at intervals of 0·5 and 0·25 in x, and the relevant values of $K(x, \xi)$, are given in the following table—

$$16K(x, \xi)$$

$\xi - 1$	$-\frac{3}{4}$	$-\frac{1}{2}$	$-\frac{1}{4}$	0	$\frac{1}{4}$	$\frac{1}{2}$	$\frac{3}{4}$	1
x								
0	0	7	12	15	16	15	12	7	0
$\frac{1}{4}$	0	0	7	12	15	16	15	12	7
$\frac{1}{2}$	0	0	0	7	12	15	16	15	12
$\frac{3}{4}$	0	0	0	0	7	12	15	16	15
1	0	0	0	0	0	7	12	15	16

We use the notation $\phi_k = \phi(k/4)$.

$w = 1/2$. Let the trapezoidal rule be used to approximate to the integrals, e.g. for $x = 1/2$, using the fact that $\phi_{-k} = \phi_k$,

$$\int_{-1}^{1} K(\tfrac{1}{2}, \xi)\phi(\xi)d\xi = \tfrac{1}{2}[(12\phi_0 + 16\phi_2 + 6\phi_4)/16 + \triangle_2]$$

The integral equation, multiplied by 16 for convenience, is replaced by the three equations—

$$24\phi_0 + 12\phi_2 \qquad\quad = 16(1 - \triangle_0/2)$$
$$6\phi_0 + 24\phi_2 + \ 3\phi_4 = 16(1 - \triangle_2/2)$$
$$6\phi_2 + 20\phi_4 = 16(1 - \triangle_4/2)$$

Ignoring the $\triangle$'s, the solution

$$(\phi_0, \phi_2, \phi_4) = (86/201, 96/201, 132/201) = (0{\cdot}428, 0{\cdot}478, 0{\cdot}657)$$

$w = 1/4$. There are now 5 linear equations. Using the trapezoidal rule again, and introducing a factor 128, these may be written in matrix form

$$\begin{bmatrix} 160 & 60 & 46 & 28 & 0 \\ 30 & 184 & 44 & 24 & 7 \\ 24 & 44 & 160 & 30 & 12 \\ 14 & 24 & 30 & 160 & 15 \\ 0 & 14 & 24 & 30 & 144 \end{bmatrix} \begin{bmatrix} \phi_0 \\ \phi_1 \\ \phi_2 \\ \phi_3 \\ \phi_4 \end{bmatrix} = 128 \begin{bmatrix} 1 - \triangle_0/4 \\ 1 - \triangle_1/4 \\ 1 - \triangle_2/4 \\ 1 - \triangle_3/4 \\ 1 - \triangle_4/4 \end{bmatrix}$$

The solution is easily derived by iteration; the result, when the difference corrections are ignored, is given in the second row of the following table, the first row containing the previous estimates for comparison.

	ϕ_0	ϕ_1	ϕ_2	ϕ_3	ϕ_4
$w = 1/2$	0·428		0·478		0·657
	− 23		− 7		− 2
$w = 1/4$	0·405	0·420	0·471	0·552	0·655
	− 8	− 4	− 2	− 1	− 1
$w = 0$	0·397	0·416	0·469	0·551	0·654

The final row is obtained by assuming that errors using the trapezoidal rule are proportional to w^2. Extrapolation to $w = 0$ is then achieved by corrections equal to one-third of the differences between the estimates for $w = 1/2$ and $1/4$.

Alternatively, the approximate solution for $w = 1/4$ can be used to give estimates of $\triangle_j$ corresponding to a more accurate quadrature formula, e.g. Gregory's. It should be remarked that Simpson's rule cannot be satisfactorily applied here when $x = 1/4$, $3/4$, because the integrand has a discontinuous derivative at the point $\xi = x$, which occurs in the middle of a range to which Simpson's rule would be applied. Neglect of this fact introduces serious errors. However, using Gregory's formula we find

$$32(\triangle_0, \triangle_{21}, \triangle_{32}, \triangle_{43}, \triangle_{54}) = (1\cdot8, 1\cdot3, 0\cdot19, 0\cdot5, 0\cdot3)$$
$$(\phi_0, \phi_1, \phi_2, \phi_3, \phi_4) = (0\cdot396, 0\cdot415, 0\cdot468_5, 0\cdot551, 0\cdot654)$$

It appears therefore that the above extrapolation procedure does not involve errors exceeding $0\cdot001$.

EXAMPLE 14.5. Find the smallest latent root and mode of the equation

$$\phi(x) = \mu \int_0^1 K(x, \xi)\phi(\xi)d\xi$$

where
$$\begin{aligned} K(x, \xi) &= (x^2/6)(3\xi - x)\rho(\xi), & x \leqslant \xi \\ &= (\xi^2/6)(3x - \xi)\rho(\xi), & x \geqslant \xi \end{aligned}$$

and
$$\rho(\xi) = 1 + (2\xi - 1)^2$$

It is obvious here from the definition of $K(x, \xi)$ that $\phi(0) = 0$, but $\phi(1) \neq 0$. We assume $w = 1/4$, and obtain the following table for $1536K(x_j, \xi_k)$.

$$1536K_{jk}$$

j \ k	1	2	3	4
1	10	20	40	88
2	25	64	140	320
3	40	112	270	648
4	55	160	405	1024 Note $K_{jk} \neq K_{kj}$

Again the first stage is best carried out using the trapezoidal rule. Since $\phi_0 = 0$, four linear equations replace the integral equation as follows—

$$\begin{bmatrix} X_1 \\ X_2 \\ X_3 \\ X_4 \end{bmatrix} = \begin{bmatrix} 10 & 20 & 40 & 44 \\ 25 & 64 & 140 & 160 \\ 40 & 112 & 270 & 324 \\ 55 & 160 & 405 & 512 \end{bmatrix} \begin{bmatrix} \phi_1 \\ \phi_2 \\ \phi_3 \\ \phi_4 \end{bmatrix} + 1536 \begin{bmatrix} \triangle_1 \\ \triangle_2 \\ \triangle_3 \\ \triangle_4 \end{bmatrix} = \kappa \begin{bmatrix} \phi_1 \\ \phi_2 \\ \phi_3 \\ \phi_4 \end{bmatrix}$$

where $\kappa = 6144/\mu$. Our first estimate of κ, neglecting $\triangle_j$, is given by

$$(\kappa)_0 = (X_1\phi_1 + X_2\phi_2 + X_3\phi_3 + X_4\phi_4)/(\phi_1{}^2 + \phi_2{}^2 + \phi_3{}^2 + \phi_4{}^2)$$

in accordance with Rayleigh's principle.

Assuming $(\phi_1, \phi_2, \phi_3, \phi_4) = (1, 2, 3, 4)$

then $(X_1, X_2, X_3, X_4) = (346, 1213, 2370, 3638)$

and $(\kappa)_0 = 24434/30 \simeq 814$

With this estimate of κ the solution can be improved by relaxation, using residuals defined by the equations (still neglecting $\triangle$)

$$-804\phi_1 + 20\phi_2 + 40\phi_3 + 44\phi_4 = R_1$$
$$25\phi_1 - 750\phi_2 + 140\phi_3 + 160\phi_4 = R_2$$
$$40\phi_1 + 112\phi_2 - 544\phi_3 + 324\phi_4 = R_3$$
$$55\phi_1 + 160\phi_2 + 405\phi_3 - 302\phi_4 = R_4$$

The first few steps appear as follows, all values being multiplied by 100—

ϕ_1	ϕ_2	ϕ_3	ϕ_4	R_1	R_2	R_3	R_4
100	200	300	400	-46800	-41500	-7200	$+38200$
		-50		-48800	-48500	$+20000$	$+17950$
	-70			-50200	$+4000$	$+12160$	$+6750$
-70				$+6080$	$+2250$	$+9360$	$+2900$
		$+10$		$+6480$	$+3650$	$+3920$	$+6950$
$+5$				$+2460$	$+3775$	$+4120$	$+7225$
35	130	260	400				

Note that ϕ_4 is deliberately left unchanged.

For the next estimate of κ, it is important to include a contribution from $\triangle$, as this is relatively large. Using Simpson's rule, the correction to each integral has the form

$$\triangle = -(1/6)\{\delta^2(K\phi)_1 + \delta^2(K\phi)_3\}$$

and the values obtained are as follows—

$$1536(\triangle_1, \triangle_2, \triangle_3, \triangle_4) = (-3150, -11680, -24190, -39460)$$

When these are included with the improved value of ϕ

$$(X_1, X_2, X_3, X_4) = (27800, 99580, 191570, 293365)$$

and $(\kappa)_1 \simeq 737$

The residuals are now recalculated, including the $\triangle$'s, and the next stage of relaxation can be summarized as follows—

ϕ_1	ϕ_2	ϕ_3	ϕ_4	R_1	R_2	R_3	R_4
35	130	260	400	$+2005$	$+2105$	-50	-1435
3	8	1					
38	138	261	400	$+24$	$+266$	$+499$	$+415$

Slight modifications in the $\triangle$'s now follow, and the next estimate of κ is

$$(\kappa)_2 = 736 \cdot 1$$

whence $$\mu = 8 \cdot 34_7$$

The δ^4 terms in $\triangle$ are not negligible, and no further improvement can be made without making some allowance for them.

The solution of the integral equation just derived also represents the lowest mode of the differential equation

$$d^4\phi/dx^4 + \mu\rho(x)\phi = 0$$

subject to the conditions

$$\phi(0) = \phi^{(1)}(0) = \phi^{(2)}(1) = \phi^{(3)}(1) = 0$$

The Green's function $G(x, \xi)$ for the solution of this equation provides the link between the two formulations of the same problem, since

$$K(x, \xi) = G(x, \xi)\rho(\xi)$$

It may be worth mentioning that if a quadrature formula requires central differences depending on values of $K\phi$ outside the range of the integral in the equation, e.g. the Gauss-Encke formula (5.38), it may be feasible to obtain such values with sufficient accuracy by using the integral equation itself.

14.10. Approximation by Polynomials

A rather different approach to the solution of integral equations has been followed by Crout.* The general idea is that the solution is represented approximately by a linear sum of suitable functions, e.g.

$$\phi_m(x) = a_0 v_0(x) + a_1 v_1(x) + \ldots + a_m v_m(x) \qquad (14.31)$$

The integral equation is used to give enough linear equations to determine the coefficients a_j. More particularly, Crout has developed the use of polynomials for this purpose. Thus suppose the range (a, b) is divided into m equal intervals as usual, and that $\bar{\phi}_k$ is a good approximation to ϕ_k or $\phi(x_k)$. Then if $x = x_0 + rw$, $x_0 = a$, $x_m = b$,

$$\bar{\phi}(x) = L_0(r)\bar{\phi}_0 + L_1(r)\bar{\phi}_1 + \ldots + L_m(r)\bar{\phi}_m \qquad (14.32)$$

where $L_k(r)$ is defined by (3.6), is a polynomial of degree m which is likely to represent $\phi(x)$ fairly closely throughout (a, b). $\bar{\phi}(x)$ has the form of the Lagrange interpolation polynomial, although in

---

* P. D. Crout, *J. Math. Phys.*, **19** (1940), 34. Somewhat similar methods have also been developed by A. Young, *Proc. Roy. Soc. A*, **224** (1954), 552 and 561.

this instance it does not pass through any specified points of $\phi(x)$. However, assume now that $\bar{\phi}(x)$ satisfies the integral equation (14.24) at each of the points $x_0, x_1, \ldots, x_m$. For a typical point x_j this would give an equation

$$\bar{\phi}_j - \mu \sum_{k=0}^{m} \bar{\phi}_k J_{jk} = f_j \qquad (14.33)$$

where $\qquad J_{jk} = \int_a^b K(x_j, \xi) L_k(\rho) d\xi, \quad \xi = x_0 + \rho w$

The number of such equations is just sufficient to determine the coefficients $\bar{\phi}_j$ in (14.32).

The integrals J_{jk} may have to be evaluated numerically although in favourable cases the integrals

$$I_s = \int_a^b K(x, \xi) \xi^s d\xi$$

may be amenable to analytical treatment, and then J_{jk} can be derived analytically. This possibility allows some equations with singular kernels to be handled by this method, whereas solution by the method of § 14.9 would be out of the question. Another advantage of Crout's method is that equations of type (14.23) can often be solved satisfactorily. The prevailing disadvantage is that the degree of the polynomial used for fitting $\phi(x)$ must be decided at the start, and the adequacy of the result cannot readily be checked without a separate and perhaps longer calculation using a polynomial of higher degree.

When numerical quadrature is used to evaluate J_{jk} it is not necessary to use the same subdivision of the range (a, b) if a finer one is desirable. Thus if $\xi_i = a + iw'$, $\xi_n = b$, then

$$J_{jk} = \int_a^b K(x_j, \xi) L_k(\rho) d\xi \simeq w' \sum_{i=0}^{n} K_{ji} t_i L_{ik} \qquad (14.34)$$

where $\qquad K_{ji} = K(x_j, \xi_i), \quad L_{ik} = L_k(\xi_i)$

and t_i is a weighting factor associated with the quadrature formula. If written in matrix form, (14.34) becomes

$$\mathbf{J} = w'\mathbf{K(TL)} \qquad (14.35)$$

where $\mathbf{T}$ is a diagonal matrix with elements t_i; $\mathbf{K}$ and $\mathbf{TL}$ are $(m + 1, n + 1)$ and $(n + 1, m + 1)$ matrices respectively.

It is an important point that whereas $\mathbf{K}$ depends on the kernel of the particular equation, $(\mathbf{TL})$ depends only on the procedure adopted for solution, and its elements can be tabulated and used for a variety of problems. The elements of **L** have of course been extensively tabulated (see § 3.4). It may be most convenient to use tables of Lagrange polynomials of the central type

$$\bar{\phi}(x) = L_{-p}(r)\bar{\phi}_{-p} + \ldots + L_0(r)\bar{\phi}_0 + \ldots + L_p(r)\bar{\phi}_p \quad (14.36)$$

where
$$r = \{x - \tfrac{1}{2}(b - a)\}/w$$

In this case, it is necessary to modify (14.33) by extending the sum over k from $-p$ to p and in (14.34) the sum over i from $-s$ to s, where s may differ from p. (14.36) represents a polynomial of degree $2p$, and it must be remembered that for quadrature, a polynomial of even degree is preferable to one of odd degree.

For a homogeneous integral equation, (14.33) is replaced by

$$(1/\mu)\bar{\phi}_j - \sum_k J_{jk}\bar{\phi}_k = 0 \quad (14.37)$$

the latent roots and vectors of which should, at least for the lowest mode, approach those of the integral equation. The first illustration is of this kind.

EXAMPLE 14.6. Find the lowest root of the equation

$$\phi(x) - \mu \int_0^1 K(x,\, \xi)\phi(\xi)d\xi = 0$$

where $K(x,\, \xi) = G(x,\, \xi)\rho(\xi)$ $G(x,\, \xi) = \xi(1 - x),\ x \leqslant \xi$
$\rho(\xi) = 1 + (2\xi - 1)^2$ $= x(1 - \xi),\ x \geqslant \xi$

This problem is identical with Example 14.3, as it is easily shown by two differentiations that

$$\phi''(x) + \mu\rho(x)\phi(x) = 0$$

and from the definition of $G(x,\, \xi)$ it is obvious that $\phi(0) = \phi(1) = 0$.

Let $x = (2 + r)/4$, and ϕ be replaced by the central quartic polynomial

$$\bar{\phi}(x) = L_{-1}(r)\bar{\phi}_{-1} + L_0(r)\bar{\phi}_0 + L_1(r)\bar{\phi}_1$$

where
$\bar{\phi}_{-1} = \bar{\phi}(1/4)$ $L_{-1} = -r(r - 1)(r^2 - 4)/6$
$\bar{\phi}_0 = \bar{\phi}(1/2)$ $L_0 = (r^2 - 1)(r^2 - 4)/4$
$\bar{\phi}_1 = \bar{\phi}(3/4)$ $L_1 = -r(r + 1)(r^2 - 4)/6$

Since $\bar{\phi}_{-2} = \bar{\phi}_2 = 0$, the polynomials L_{-2}, L_2 can be ignored, and equations (14.37) are only three in number.

Though it is not essential, we evaluate the integrals J_{jk} numerically, assuming $w' = 1/8$; K_{ji} and L_{ik} have then to be tabulated for

$$j,\ k = -1,\ 0,\ 1 \quad \text{and} \quad i = 2r = \pm 3,\ \pm 2,\ \pm 1,\ 0$$

Let Simpson's rule be used for integration, so that the weighting factors are

$$t_{-3} = t_{-1} = t_1 = t_3 = 1/6, \quad t_{-2} = t_0 = t_2 = 1/12$$

We obtain tables as follows, introducing suitable factors to avoid decimals—

i		-3	-2	-1	0	1	2	3
	$j = -1$	3	6	5	4	3	2	1
$32G_{ji}$	0	2	4	6	8	6	4	2
	1	1	2	3	4	5	6	3
$16\rho_i$		25	20	17	16	17	20	25
	$k = -1$	70	64	30	0	-10	0	14
$64L_{ik}$	0	-35	0	45	64	45	0	-35
	1	14	0	-10	0	30	64	70
$6t_i$		1	$\frac{1}{2}$	1	$\frac{1}{2}$	1	$\frac{1}{2}$	1

$$512\mathbf{K} = \begin{bmatrix} 75 & 120 & 85 & 64 & 51 & 40 & 25 \\ 50 & 80 & 102 & 128 & 102 & 80 & 50 \\ 25 & 40 & 51 & 64 & 85 & 120 & 75 \end{bmatrix}$$

$$384(\mathbf{TL})' = \begin{bmatrix} 70 & 32 & 30 & 0 & -10 & 0 & 14 \\ -35 & 0 & 45 & 32 & 45 & 0 & -35 \\ 14 & 0 & -10 & 0 & 30 & 32 & 70 \end{bmatrix}$$

Only the relevant parts of the matrices $\mathbf{K}$ and $(\mathbf{TL})'$ are given, the rows and columns corresponding to $x, \xi = 0$ and 1 being omitted. The elements of $\mathbf{J}$ are now obtained by row $\times$ row multiplication.

$$49152\mathbf{J} = \begin{bmatrix} 2870 & 1167 & 1190 \\ 2200 & 2444 & 2200 \\ 1190 & 1167 & 2870 \end{bmatrix}$$

The linear equations are therefore

$$(2870 - \kappa)\bar{\phi}_{-1} + 1167\bar{\phi}_0 + 1190\bar{\phi}_1 = 0$$
$$2200\bar{\phi}_{-1} + (2240 - \kappa)\bar{\phi}_0 + 2200\bar{\phi}_1 = 0$$
$$1190\bar{\phi}_{-1} + 1167\bar{\phi}_0 + (2870 - \kappa)\bar{\phi}_1 = 0$$

where $\kappa = 49152/\mu$. For modes of even symmetry it can be further assumed that $\bar{\phi}_{-1} = \bar{\phi}_1$; for the odd mode that $\bar{\phi}_{-1} = -\bar{\phi}_1$. The roots of the determinantal equation are thus easily separated and found to be

$$\kappa_1 = 5657 \cdot 8, \quad \kappa_2 = 1680, \quad \kappa_3 = 846 \cdot 2$$

The smallest latent root is therefore approximately

$$\mu_1 = 49152/5657 \cdot 8 = 8 \cdot 687$$

This is within $\frac{1}{2}$ per cent of the final value 8·650 in Example 14.3; it is better than the value obtained there with $w = 0 \cdot 2$, but less accurate than that obtained with $w = 0 \cdot 1$. The estimates of higher roots obtained from κ_2 and κ_3 cannot be expected to be very reliable.

For the lowest mode we now obtain $\bar{\phi}_{-1} = \bar{\phi}_1 = 0 \cdot 7305$. Computation using the Lagrange polynomial gives the following values for comparison with those in Example 14.3.

x	0·1	0·12	0·25	0·3	0·4	0·5
$\bar{\phi}(x)$	336	616	730	826	956	1000
From Example 14.3	332	616	(732)	828	957	1000

The agreement is reasonably good, and the labour not excessive. It is unfortunate that there is no easy check on the accuracy of $\bar{\phi}(x)$ or μ_1.

The next example is one discussed by Crout and involves an equation of the first kind, with a singular kernel.

EXAMPLE 14.7. Solve the equation

$$\int_0^1 K(x, \xi)\phi(\xi)d\xi = a - bx^2$$

where $K(x, \xi) = - \log (\xi^2 - x^2), \quad x < \xi$
$$= - \log (x^2 - \xi^2), \quad x > \xi$$

and the value of a is such that $\phi(1) = 0$.

Let ϕ be replaced by a quartic polynomial as before, but of the form

$$\bar{\phi}(\xi) = L_0(\rho)\bar{\phi}_0 + L_1(\rho)\bar{\phi}_1 + L_2(\rho)\bar{\phi}_2 + L_3(\rho)\bar{\phi}_3 + L_4(\rho)\bar{\phi}_4$$

where $\rho = 4\xi, \quad \bar{\phi}_k = \phi(k/4)$

and $L_0(\rho) = (\rho - 1)(\rho - 2)(\rho - 3)(\rho - 4)/24$
$$L_1(\rho) = - \rho(\rho - 2)(\rho - 3(\rho - 4)/6$$
$$L_2(\rho) = \rho(\rho - 1)(\rho - 3)(\rho - 4)/4$$
$$L_3(\rho) = - \rho(\rho - 1)(\rho - 2)(\rho - 4)/6$$

Since $\bar{\phi}_4 = 0$, the last term can be omitted.

In this instance it is possible (and necessary) to evaluate the integrals J_{jk} mainly by analytical methods.

Thus let $I_s(x) = \int_0^1 \xi^s K(x, \xi)d\xi, \quad I_s(x_j) = I_{js}$

and $L_k(\rho) = \sum_{s=0}^{4} c_{sk}\xi^s$

Then $J_{jk} = \int_0^1 K(x_j, \xi)L_k(\rho)d\xi = \sum_{s=0}^{4} I_{js}c_{sk}$

so that it is necessary to evaluate the elements of two matrices $\mathbf{I}$ and $\mathbf{C}$ such that $\mathbf{J} = \mathbf{IC}$.

Details of the analysis need not be given here. One obtains the following analytical expressions for $I_s(x)$—

$$I_0 = \{2 - (1 - x) \log (1 - x) - (1 + x) \log (1 + x)\}$$
$$2I_1 = \{1 - 2x^2 \log x - (1 - x^2) \log (1 - x^2)\}$$
$$3I_2 = \{2/3 + 2x^2 - (1 - x^3) \log (1 - x) - (1 + x^3) \log (1 + x)\}$$
$$4I_3 = \{1/2 + x^2 - 2x^4 \log x - (1 - x^4) \log (1 - x^2)\}$$
$$5I_4 = \{2/5 + (2/3)x^2 - (1 - x^5) \log (1 - x) - (1 + x^5) \log (1 + x)\}$$

from which

$$\mathbf{I} = [I_{js}] = \begin{bmatrix} 2\cdot00000 & 0\cdot50000 & 0\cdot22222 & 0\cdot12500 & 0\cdot08000 \\ 1\cdot93683 & 0\cdot61690 & 0\cdot28274 & 0\cdot15940 & 0\cdot10270 \\ 1\cdot73838 & 0\cdot78117 & 0\cdot43901 & 0\cdot27659 & 0\cdot18900 \\ 1\cdot36725 & 0\cdot84266 & 0\cdot59914 & 0\cdot45242 & 0\cdot35454 \\ 0\cdot61371 & 0\cdot50000 & 0\cdot42679 & 0\cdot37500 & 0\cdot33607 \end{bmatrix}$$

From the expansions of the polynomials $L_k(\rho)$ one also obtains

$$3\mathbf{C}' = 3[c_{sk}]' = \begin{bmatrix} 3 & -25 & 70 & -80 & 32 \\ 0 & 48 & -208 & 288 & -128 \\ 0 & -36 & 228 & -384 & 192 \\ 0 & 16 & -112 & 224 & -128 \end{bmatrix}$$

Here the fifth row, which would correspond to L_4, has been omitted. The elements of $\mathbf{J}$ are then derived by row $\times$ row multiplication of $\mathbf{I}$ and $\mathbf{C}'$.

In the linear equations which result it is necessary to treat a as the fifth unknown in place of ϕ_4.

$$\begin{bmatrix} 0\cdot53852 & 1\cdot17926 & 0\cdot00889 & 0\cdot29037 & -1 \\ 0\cdot23806 & 1\cdot18772 & 0\cdot25488 & 0\cdot25459 & -1 \\ 0\cdot11255 & 0\cdot54898 & 0\cdot68372 & 0\cdot36425 & -1 \\ 0\cdot04238 & 0\cdot24695 & 0\cdot20424 & 0\cdot77950 & -1 \\ -0\cdot00972 & 0\cdot07000 & -0\cdot05514 & 0\cdot39397 & -1 \end{bmatrix} \begin{bmatrix} \bar{\phi}_0 \\ \bar{\phi}_1 \\ \bar{\phi}_2 \\ \bar{\phi}_3 \\ a \end{bmatrix} = \begin{bmatrix} 0 \\ -0\cdot0625 \\ -0\cdot2500 \\ -0\cdot5625 \\ -1\cdot0 \end{bmatrix} b$$

The solution of these equations is

$$\{\bar{\phi}_0, \bar{\phi}_1, \bar{\phi}_2, \bar{\phi}_3, \bar{\phi}_4\} = \{0\cdot616, 0\cdot604, 0\cdot538, 0\cdot412, 0\}b$$

and
$$a = 1\cdot169b$$

14.11. Other Methods

There are several other methods of solving integral equations which usually involve fitting the solution by a convenient analytical function. Some of these will be described here very briefly; for further details reference can be made to Collatz, *N.T.D.E.*

1. METHOD OF LEAST SQUARE ERROR

Suppose the solution of (14.24) is represented, as suggested in (14.31), by a function

$$\bar{\phi}(x) = a_0 v_0(x) + a_1 v_1(x) + \ldots + a_m v_m(x)$$

We can associate with $\bar{\phi}$ an error function $\varepsilon(x)$ defined by

$$\varepsilon(x) = \bar{\phi}(x) - \mu \int_a^b K(x, \xi)\bar{\phi}(\xi)d\xi - f(x) \qquad (14.38)$$

$$= \sum_{j=0}^m a_j(v_j - J_j(x)) - f(x) \qquad (14.39)$$

where
$$J_j(x) = \mu \int_a^b K(x, \xi) v_j(\xi) d\xi$$

The condition $\quad \int_a^b \varepsilon^2(x) dx = \text{minimum}$ \hfill (14.40)

may be used to determine the coefficients a_j; thus by equating to zero the derivative of this integral with respect to a_j, one obtains the equation

$$\sum_{k=0}^m a_k \int_a^b (v_j - J_j)(v_k - J_k) dx = \int_a^b f(x)(v_j - J_j) dx \qquad (14.41)$$

If $j = 0, 1, \ldots, m$, there are sufficient equations to determine all the coefficients. The condition (14.40) is rather special in that the whole range of x is uniformly weighted.

Alternatively, a number of values in the range (a, b), say $x_0, x_1, \ldots, x_n$, may be picked out, and the sum $\sum_i \varepsilon_i^2$, where $\varepsilon_i = \varepsilon(x_i)$, minimized instead of the integral. The integrals in (14.41) are then also replaced by sums.

2. Collocation

Another method, sometimes called "collocation," uses $(m + 1)$ points in the range (a, b), and the conditions

$$\varepsilon_j = 0 \quad (j = 0, 1, \ldots, m) \qquad (14.42)$$

to determine a_j. It is clear that Crout's method is a special form of collocation. It should be mentioned that both this and the method of least square error are applicable also to differential equations; in fact collocation was introduced in this connexion.* Collocation may sometimes be used to solve non-linear integral equations.

3. Variational Method of Ritz

A general variational principle, applicable to a wide variety of differential and integral equations, was formulated by Ritz. In the form in which it applies to the integral equation (14.24), with a symmetrical kernel, the principle states that the integral (Collatz, *N.T.D.E.* p. 425)

$$I = \tfrac{1}{2}\mu \int_a^b \int_a^b K(x, \xi) \bar\phi(x) \bar\phi(\xi) dx d\xi + \int_a^b [f(x)\bar\phi(x) - \tfrac{1}{2}\{\bar\phi(x)\}^2] dx$$

has an extreme value, normally a minimum, when $\bar\phi$ coincides with the exact solution ϕ of (14.24), and is otherwise stationary for small departures from ϕ.

* See Frazer, Duncan and Collar, *Elementary Matrices*, p. 224.

The obvious application of this result is to take for $\bar{\phi}$ a suitable function containing parameters which can be adjusted to give I a minimum value. When the variation or trial function has the linear form (14.31), the condition that $\partial I/\partial a_j = 0$ leads to the equation

$$\mu \sum_k a_k \int_a^b v_j(v_k - J_k)dx = \int_a^b f(x)v_j dx$$

or

$$\int_a^b \varepsilon(x)v_j(x)dx = 0 \qquad (14.43)$$

The $(m + 1)$ equations of this kind determine the parameters a_j, and ensure that certain averages of the error function, depending on the functions v_j, all vanish.

It is an instructive exercise to compare the results of applying (14.40), (14.42) and (14.43) to an equation such as that in Example 14.4, with trial functions of the form $a_0 + a_2 x^2$ and $a_0 + a_2 x^2 + a_4 x^4$.

For the homogeneous equation (14.25), the extreme value of I is necessarily zero; the variation principle then reduces to that of Rayleigh discussed earlier. In particular the inequality

$$\int_a^b \bar{\phi}^2 dx \Big/ \int_a^b \int_a^b K(x, \xi)\bar{\phi}(x)\bar{\phi}(\xi)dxd\xi \geqslant \mu_1 \qquad (14.44)$$

sets an upper limit to the least latent root μ_1. This result was used in Example 14.5 with sums in place of integrals. Comparison with (14.17) and (14.19) brings out again the analogy between the kernel and the inverse of a matrix or differential operator.

EXERCISES 14

1. Show how a solution of the equation $G'' + q(x)G = r(x)$, satisfying two-point boundary conditions, may be obtained by means of the matrix resolution described in Exercises 11, No. 2. For this purpose express the difference equations in the form

$$g_{k-1} - (2 - w^2 q_k)g_k + g_{k+1} = w^2(r_k + \triangle_k)$$

as in (14.6).

Repeat by this method the problem which was solved by relaxation in Example 14.2.

2. Show that the same type of problem may be solved using the matrix resolution introduced in Exercises 11, No. 3, in conjunction with difference equations of the form (8.8). Extend this procedure, with any necessary modifications, to equations of the form

$$G'' + p(x)G' + q(x)G = r(x)$$

using difference equations as in (14.9).

CHAPTER 15

FUNCTIONS OF TWO VARIABLES

PROCESSES of interpolation, integration and differentiation for tabular functions of two real variables x and y, though naturally more laborious than for functions of one variable, involve little change in principle when the polynomial approximation is satisfactory. Indeed this is true for many functions of more than two variables, although the chance of meeting functions which are not well represented by polynomials over a reasonable range of the variables is much greater. In the following treatment we shall write

$$f_{jk} = f(x_j, y_k)$$

where x_j, y_k are values for which the function $f(x, y)$ is tabulated, and usually assume that the tabular intervals are constant, i.e.

$$(x_j, y_k) = (x_0 + jw_1, y_0 + kw_2)$$

where j, k are integers. Sometimes it is convenient to use, instead of (x, y), continuous variables (r, s) such that

$$(x, y) = (x_0 + rw_1, y_0 + sw_2)$$

and then $f(x, y)$ may be denoted by f_{rs}. This function is therefore tabulated at unit intervals in r and s.

In deriving formulas for interpolation, etc., it is most expeditious to use the symbolic methods introduced in Chapter 6. We therefore make use of the following symbols, which are partial operators in the sense that they affect only one or other of the variables concerned.

Displacement operators
$$E_x, E_y$$

Difference operators
$$\delta_x, \delta_y \text{ (central)}; \quad \Delta_x, \Delta_y \text{ (forward)}$$

Averaging operators
$$\mu_x, \mu_y \text{ (in association with } \delta_x, \delta_y)$$

Differential operators
$$D_x, D_y(= \partial/\partial x, \partial/\partial y) \quad \text{or} \quad D_r, D_s(= \partial/\partial r, \partial/\partial s)$$

The essential relations between these operators are the following—

$$E_x = 1 + \Delta_x = e^{D_r}, \quad \Delta_x = E_x^{1/2}\delta_x$$
$$\delta_x = E_x^{1/2} - E_x^{-1/2} = 2\sinh(D_r/2), \quad (\mu\delta)_x = (E_x - E_x^{-1})/2$$

and similar relations in which y, s replace x, r.

There is another field, rather different in character, in which calculations involving two variables may arise; that is the use of functions of a complex variable, e.g. $f(z)$, where $z = x + iy$. This is touched on briefly at the end of the chapter.

Interpolation

Several methods of applying polynomials to the problem of interpolating in a double-entry table suggest themselves.

1. The Lagrange polynomial may be generalized for two variables. Thus if $f(x, y)$ is given at an irregular set of $(N + 1)$ points (x_s, y_s) where $s = 0, 1, \ldots, N$, then by an obvious extension of (3.2) and (3.3)

$$f(x, y) = \sum_s \frac{\phi_N(x)\psi_N(y)}{(x - x_s)\phi_N'(x_s)(y - y_s)\psi_N'(y_s)} f_{s,\,s} + R \quad (15.1)$$

where
$$\phi_N(x) = (x - x_0)(x - x_1) \ldots (x - x_N)$$
$$\psi_N(y) = (y - y_0)(y - y_1) \ldots (y - y_N)$$

If the points are $(m + 1)(n + 1)$ in number, and form a rectangular array (x_j, y_k) where

$$j = 0, 1, \ldots, m \quad \text{and} \quad k = 0, 1, \ldots, n$$

the polynomial takes the form

$$f(x, y) = \sum_{j=0}^m \sum_{k=0}^n \frac{\phi_m(x)}{(x - x_j)\phi_m'(x_j)} \cdot \frac{\psi_n(y)}{(y - y_k)\psi_n'(y_k)} f_{jk} + R \quad (15.2)$$

In (15.1) the polynomial is of degree N in x and y; in (15.2) it is of degree $m + n$. For practical purposes the degree of the polynomial may be unduly high, but these expressions also suffer from the serious disadvantage that all points are given equal prominence, no distinction being made between points close to the region of interpolation and those far distant. Their use should therefore be avoided if possible, unless the irregular placing of the points at which $f(x, y)$ is known makes it necessary (see (15.47)).

2. When $f(x, y)$ is tabulated at points involving constant intervals in both x and y it might seem feasible to develop interpolation formulas by fitting a polynomial of suitable degree at a

chosen pattern of points near the region of interpolation. Several cases of common occurrence are shown in Fig. 15.1 (p. 487). To take this pattern as example, a polynomial might be fitted at the 5 central points marked o, for interpolation within the shaded area. By adding further rings of points, fitting may take place at 9, 13, 21 . . . points. One difficulty of this procedure, which has been fully discussed by K. Pearson,* is that the number of points in a symmetrical pattern rarely coincides with the number of independent coefficients in a general polynomial of given degree (6, 10, 15, 21 . . . coefficients in general quadratic, cubic, quartic, quintic, etc.). Some terms have therefore to be excluded, and there is no obvious rule for choosing these. The method is finally ruled out by the fact that, if a polynomial symmetrical in x and y can be picked out with the desired number of coefficients, its form is likely to imply certain unacceptable relations between the values of $f(x, y)$ at some of the tabular points, e.g. the 9-term cubic polynomial

$$f(x, y) = a_0 + a_1 x + a_2 y + a_3 x^2 + a_5 y^2$$
$$+ a_6 x^3 + a_7 x^2 y + a_8 x y^2 + a_9 y^3$$

implies that $\quad f_{1, 1} - f_{-1, 1} = f_{1, -1} - f_{-1, -1}$

3. A third method, which is in fact the easiest to pursue when the tabular points are uniformly spaced, uses an extension of the method of differences to two variables. This has the prime advantage that the interpolation formula is a series of terms involving ascending powers of the variables, and differences of the function of increasing order, which can be terminated at fairly obvious points. Moreover, the nature of the error introduced by truncating the series is seen fairly easily.

Various types of interpolation formula can be derived, according to the way in which the available data are distributed round the region of interpolation. For one variable it was found that the Stirling and Bessel formulas, containing central differences symmetrical about $r = 0$, $r = 1/2$ respectively, are the most useful, although at the ends of a table the Newton formulas containing forward or backward differences must be used. With two variables, combinations of central and forward (or backward) differences are possible and sometimes necessary. Of the many combinations possible we shall consider the following in detail.

* Karl Pearson, "On the construction of tables and on interpolation," Part II (*Tracts for Computers*, No. 3, Cambridge Univ. Press, 1920).

(a) The midpoint formula, using central differences symmetrical about the point $(r, s) = (0, 0)$ (see Fig. 15.1). This corresponds to the use of a Stirling formula for both variables.

(b) The mid-panel formula, based on four central points (Fig. 15.2) and symmetrical about the point $(r, s) = \frac{1}{2}, \frac{1}{2}$. This corresponds to the use of Everett's formula for both variables.

(c) The corner-panel formula, using forward (or backward) differences for both variables (Fig. 15.3).

(d) An edge-panel formula, combining central differences (as in Everett's formula) for one variable with forward differences for the other (Fig. 15.4).

In all cases the basic interpolation formula is

$$f_{rs} = E_x{}^r E_y{}^s f_{00} \tag{15.3}$$

in which $E_x{}^r$, $E_y{}^s$ must be replaced by the appropriate difference operators.

15.1. Midpoint Formula

From the relations, $E_x = \mu_x + \delta_x/2$ and $E_y = \mu_y + \delta_y/2$, and the expansion (6.11), it follows that

$$f_{rs} = \{1 + r(\mu\delta)_x + r_{[2]}\delta_x{}^2 + r_{\{3\}}(\mu\delta^3)_x + r_{[4]}\delta_x{}^4 + \ldots\}$$
$$\times \{1 + s(\mu\delta)_y + s_{[2]}\delta_y{}^2 + s_{\{3\}}(\mu\delta^3)_y + s_{[4]}\delta_y{}^4 + \ldots\} f_{00}$$

Direct multiplication of these series would give f_{rs} in terms of bivariate central differences of f_{00}. A more practical form, however, is obtained if all odd order differences and most cross-differences are eliminated by using relations of the type—

$$(\mu\delta)_x f_{00} = \tfrac{1}{2}(E_x - E_x{}^{-1})f_{00} = \tfrac{1}{2}(f_{1,\,0} - f_{-1,\,0})$$
$$(\mu\delta^3)_x f_{00} = \tfrac{1}{2}\delta_x{}^2(f_{1,\,0} - f_{-1,\,0})$$
$$(\mu\delta)_x(\mu\delta)_y f_{00} = \tfrac{1}{4}(E_x - E_x{}^{-1})(E_y - E_y{}^{-1})f_{00}$$
$$= \tfrac{1}{4}(f_{1,\,1} - f_{1,\,-1} - f_{-1,\,1} + f_{-1,\,-1})$$

The resulting formula, retaining all terms up to fourth degree in r and s, may be written as follows—

$$\begin{aligned}
f_{rs} = f_{00} \\
&+ \tfrac{1}{2}r(f_{1,\,0} - f_{-1,\,0}) + \tfrac{1}{2}s(f_{0,\,1} - f_{0,\,-1}) + (r_{[2]}\delta_x{}^2 + s_{[2]}\delta_y{}^2)f_{00} \\
&+ \tfrac{1}{4}rs(f_{1,\,1} - f_{1,\,-1} - f_{-1,\,1} + f_{-1,\,-1}) + r_{[2]}s_{[2]}\delta_x{}^2\delta_y{}^2 f_{00} \\
&+ \tfrac{1}{2}(r_{\{3\}}\delta_x{}^2 + rs_{[2]}\delta_y{}^2)(f_{1,\,0} - f_{-1,\,0}) \\
&+ \tfrac{1}{2}(r_{[2]}s\delta_x{}^2 + s_{\{3\}}\delta_y{}^2)(f_{0,\,1} - f_{0,\,-1}) + (r_{[4]}\delta_x{}^4 + s_{[4]}\delta_y{}^4)f_{00} \\
&+ \tfrac{1}{4}(r_{\{3\}}s\delta_x{}^2 + rs_{\{3\}}\delta_y{}^2)(f_{1,\,1} - f_{1,\,-1} - f_{-1,\,1} + f_{-1,\,-1}) \tag{15.4}
\end{aligned}$$

in which
$$r_{[2]} = r^2/2$$
$$r_{\{3\}} = r(r^2 - 1)/6$$
$$r_{[4]} = r^2(r^2 - 1)/24$$
$$r_{\{5\}} = r(r^2 - 1)(r^2 - 4)/120, \text{ etc.}$$

The terms have been grouped so that the first row involves only the points marked o in Fig. 15.1, the second row brings in the × points, the 3rd and 4th rows the + points, and the final row involves the · points. If this last row be omitted we have a quartic which coincides with $f(x, y)$ at the midpoint and 12 neighbouring points; the r^3s and rs^3 terms are omitted from the general quartic which contains 15 terms. Inclusion of the last row of (15.4) does not of course give a quartic which in general passes through the · points; only a sextic polynomial can do this, and one must add the following terms—

$$(r_{[4]}s\delta_x{}^4 + r_{[2]}s_{\{3\}}\delta_x{}^2\delta_y{}^2)(f_{0,\,1} - f_{0,\,-1})$$
$$+ (rs_{[4]}\delta_y{}^4 + r_{\{3\}}s_{[2]}\delta_x{}^2\delta_y{}^2)(f_{1,\,0} - f_{-1,\,0})$$
$$+ (r_{[4]}s_{[2]}\delta_x{}^4\delta_y{}^2 + r_{[2]}s_{[4]}\delta_x{}^2\delta_y{}^4)f_{00} \qquad (15.5)$$

These may be comparable in size with the last row of (15.4), which is therefore best omitted unless these other terms are also included. Still further terms are given by Pearson.

The midpoint formula is best used for $|r|$, $|s| < 1/2$. It is important to notice the requirements which (15.4) makes of a double-entry table; in addition to the function value at each point, one needs five associated differences, $\delta_x{}^2$, $\delta_y{}^2$, $\delta_x{}^4$, $\delta_y{}^4$ and $\delta_x{}^2\delta_y{}^2$. Incidentally, the last of these provides a valuable check on the calculation of the second-order differences, if it is verified that

$$\delta_x{}^2\delta_y{}^2f_{00} = \delta_x{}^2(f_{0,\,1} - 2f_{00} + f_{0,\,-1})$$
$$= \delta_y{}^2(f_{1,\,0} - 2f_{00} + f_{-1,\,0}) = \delta_y{}^2\delta_x{}^2f_{00}$$

In printed tables, by an extension of Comrie's throwback device, it is possible to have a pair of modified second differences only and yet retain nearly the full accuracy of 4th degree interpolation.

Before we present further formulas and detailed numerical examples of their use, some general cautionary remarks about interpolation in a double-entry table are necessary. First, it is important to be sure that interpolation to 4th order differences, say, gives the desired accuracy, particularly as functions of two variables are often tabulated at rather wide intervals. Differences of odd order sometimes give larger contributions than those of even order, so that terms of 5th order differences should certainly be examined; or, if even differences predominate, terms in 6th order differences may be more important than those in 5th order. Hence ideally, terms of two orders beyond those actually retained should be examined in cases of doubt. Another point is that although the tabulation with respect to one of the variables may be satisfactory, differences associated with changes in the other variable may be relatively large and correspondingly more differences should be included.

Finally, if the function becomes very large or has a singularity at some point, it is advisable if possible to "subtract" this singularity before interpolating in its neighbourhood, e.g. to subtract terms of the form r^{-n}, $\log r$, etc., where r is the distance from the singularity, when these are known to be present.

The examples given on the following pages to illustrate the use of (15.4), (15.6), (15.8) and (15.9) are founded on Table 15.1, containing values of the elliptic integral $E(\theta, \phi)$ at 15° intervals. At this rather wide spacing, interpolation using 4th differences is satisfactory in the upper half of the table, but becomes increasingly inaccurate as the point $E(90°, 90°)$ is approached. In this corner the differences are distressingly large, and interpolation to 5D requires either that more differences be included, or, preferably, that a smaller interval of tabulation be used. The points considered in Examples 15.3 and 15.4 have been specially chosen to emphasize this. It should be noticed, however, that although these examples are primarily intended to show the use of edge-panel and corner-panel formulas, more accurate results could be obtained by using the periodic properties of $E(\theta, \phi)$ to provide the extra central differences for midpanel interpolation.

CONSTANTS USED IN EXAMPLES 15.1, 15.2 AND 15.4—

r	0·2	0·4	0·6	0·8	
$r_{[2]}$	0·02	0·08	0·18	0·32	
$r_{\{3\}}$	$-0·032$	$-0·056$	$-0·064$	$-0·048$	
$r_{[4]}$	$-0·0016$	$-0·0056$	$-0·0096$	$-0·0096$	
$r_{\{5\}}$	0·0063	0·0108	0·0116	0·0081	(to 4D)

TABLE 15.1

$$E(\theta, \phi) = \int_0^\phi (1 - \sin^2\theta \sin^2\phi)^{1/2} d\phi$$

ϕ		θ						
		0°	15°	30°	45°	60°	75°	90°
0°		0	0	0	0	0	0	0
15°		26180	26160	26106	26032	25957	25902	25882
	δ_θ^2		− 34	− 20	− 1	+ 20	+ 35	
	δ_ϕ^2	0	− 112	− 424	− 859	− 1305	− 1639	− 1764
	δ_θ^4			+ 5	+ 2	− 6		
	$\delta_\theta^2\delta_\phi^2$		− 200	− 123	− 11	+ 112	+ 209	
30°		52360	52208	51788	51205	50609	50165	50000
	δ_θ^2		− 268	− 163	− 13	+ 152	+ 279	
	δ_ϕ^2	0	− 197	− 750	− 1559	− 2439	− 3139	− 3407
	δ_θ^4			+ 45	+ 15	− 38		
	δ_ϕ^4	0	+ 55	+ 180	+ 321	+ 377	+ 306	+ 231
	$\delta_\theta^2\delta_\phi^2$		− 356	− 256	− 71	+ 180	+ 432	
45°		78540	78059	76720	74819	72822	71289	70711
	δ_θ^2		− 858	− 562	− 96	+ 464	+ 955	
	δ_ϕ^2	0	− 227	− 896	− 1938	− 3196	− 4333	− 4819
	δ_θ^4			+ 170	+ 94	− 69		
	δ_ϕ^4	0	+ 57	+ 239	+ 492	+ 683	+ 572	+ 329
	$\delta_\theta^2\delta_\phi^2$		− 442	− 373	− 216	+ 121	+ 651	
60°		104720	103683	100756	96495	91839	88080	86603
	δ_θ^2		− 1890	− 1334	− 395	+ 897	+ 2282	
	δ_ϕ^2	0	− 200	− 803	− 1825	− 3270	− 4955	− 5902
	δ_θ^4			+ 383	+ 353	+ 93		
	δ_ϕ^4	0	+ 57	+ 234	+ 579	+ 1117	+ 1466	+ 402
	$\delta_\theta^2\delta_\phi^2$		− 403	− 419	− 423	− 240	+ 738	
75°		130900	129107	123989	116346	107586	99916	96593
	δ_θ^2		− 3325	− 2525	− 1117	+ 1090	+ 4347	
	δ_ϕ^2	0	− 116	− 476	− 1133	− 2227	− 4111	− 6583
	δ_θ^4			+ 608	+ 799	+ 1050		
	$\delta_\theta^2\delta_\phi^2$		− 244	− 297	− 437	− 790	− 588	
90°		157080	154415	146746	135064	121106	107641	100000
	δ_θ^2		− 5004	− 4013	− 2276	+ 493	+ 5824	
	δ_θ^4			+ 746	+ 1032	+ 2562		

All values in units of 10^{-5}

MIDPOINT FORMULA

	$(-1, -1)$	$(0, -1)$	$(1, -1)$
f	51788	51205	50609
δ_x^2		$-\ 13$	
δ_y^2		$-\ 1559$	

	$(-1, 0)$	$(0, 0)$	$(1, 0)$
f	76720	74819	72822
δ_x^2	$-\ 562$	$-\ 96$	$+\ 464$
δ_y^2	$-\ 896$	$-\ 1938$	$-\ 3196$
δ_x^4		$+\ 94$	
δ_y^4		$+\ 492$	
$\delta_x^2\delta_y^2$		$-\ 216$	

	$(-1, 1)$	$(0, 1)$	$(1, 1)$
f	100756	96495	91839
δ_x^2		$-\ 395$	
δ_y^2		$-\ 1825$	

FIG. 15.1

$$f_{rs} = f_{00}$$
$$+ \tfrac{1}{2}r(f_{1,0} - f_{-1,0}) + \tfrac{1}{2}s(f_{0,1} - f_{0,-1}) + (r_{[2]}\delta_x^2 + s_{[2]}\delta_y^2)f_{0,0}$$
$$+ \tfrac{1}{4}rs(f_{1,1} - f_{1,-1} - f_{-1,1} + f_{-1,-1}) + r_{[2]}s_{[2]}\delta_x^2\delta_y^2 f_{0,0}$$
$$+ \tfrac{1}{2}(r_{\{3\}}\delta_x^2 + rs_{[2]}\delta_y^2)(f_{1,0} - f_{-1,0}) + \tfrac{1}{2}(r_{[2]}s\delta_x^2 + s_{\{3\}}\delta_y^2)(f_{0,1} - f_{0,-1})$$
$$+ (r_{[4]}\delta_x^4 + s_{[4]}\delta_y^4)f_{0,0}$$

First row, o points. Second and third rows, × points. Fourth row, + points. For terms involving · points, see § 15.1.

EXAMPLE 15.1. Estimate the value of E (48°, 51°).

Use data from Table 15.1, with $f_{0,0} = E(45°, 45°)$, $x = \theta$, $y = \phi$. For the required value $r = 0.2$, $s = 0.4$, $\sigma = 0.6$, $\rho = 0.8$. Then

$$f_{rs} = E(48°, 51°)$$
$$= 74819$$

$$+ 0.1(-3898) + 0.2(45290) + 0.02(-96) + 0.08(-1938)$$
$$+ 0.02(91839 - 50609 - 100756 + 51788) + 0.0016(-216)$$
$$+ 0.008(-3196 + 896) + 0.004(-395 + 13)$$
$$- 0.016(464 + 562) - 0.028(-1825 + 1559)$$
$$- 0.0016(94) - 0.0056(492)$$

$$= 74819 - 389.8 + 9058.0 - 1.9 - 155.0 = 83330.3 = 83143.3$$
$$ - 154.8 - 0.3 \qquad\qquad - 155.1$$
$$ - 18.4 - 1.5 \qquad\qquad - 19.9$$
$$ - 16.4 + 7.4 - 0.2 - 2.8 \qquad - 12.0$$

The correct value to 6D (Legendre-Pearson tables) is 0.831396. There is thus a residual error of about 4 units in the fifth decimal. In fact the next group of terms involving · points contributes -5.1×10^{-5},

15.2. Mid-panel Formula

It would be possible to extend the Bessel type of formula to two variables by using the expansion (6.12) for $E_x{}^{r-1/2}$ and $E_y{}^{s-1/2}$. However, since we wish to avoid odd order differences, the Everett formula is a more suitable starting point, and leads to the following direct derivation. Let s for the moment be considered constant; then interpolation for r using (5.14) gives

$$f_{rs} = \{\rho + \rho_{\{3\}}\delta_x{}^2 + {}_{\{\rho 5\}}\delta_x{}^4 + \ldots\}f_{0,\,s}$$
$$+ \{r + r_{\{3\}}\delta_x{}^2 + r_{\{5\}}\delta_x{}^4 + \ldots\}f_{1,\,s}$$

where $\rho = 1 - r$.

Likewise, if $\sigma = 1 - s$, and s varies,

$$f_{0s} = \{\sigma + \sigma_{\{3\}}\delta_y{}^2 + \sigma_{\{5\}}\delta_y{}^4 + \ldots\}f_{00}$$
$$+ \{s + s_{\{3\}}\delta_y{}^2 + s_{\{5\}}\delta_y{}^4 + \ldots\}f_{0,\,1}$$

$$f_{1s} = \{\sigma + \sigma_{\{3\}}\delta_y{}^2 + \sigma_{\{5\}}\delta_y{}^4 + \ldots\}f_{1,\,0}$$
$$+ \{s + s_{\{3\}}\delta_y{}^2 + s_{\{5\}}\delta_y{}^4 + \ldots\}f_{1,\,1}$$

After substitution, and grouping the terms suitably, one obtains the mid-panel formula (15.6) on page 489, which would normally* be used for $0 < r < 1$, $0 < s < 1$. On comparison with Fig. 15.2 it is clear that the terms in the first column involve the o points, the quartic terms in the second and third columns involve the × points, the sextic terms in the next three columns involve the + points, and so on. Thus the quartic approximation is a polynomial giving coincidence with $f(x, y)$ at 12 points, the terms in r^4, r^2s^2, s^4 being omitted from the general quartic; the sextic approximation coincides at 24 points, compared with the 28 possible to the most general sextic.

It is worth noting the numerical checks which can be made using the sums of the coefficients in each column, thus

$$\rho\sigma + \rho s + r\sigma + rs = 1, \quad \rho_{\{3\}}(\sigma + s) + r_{\{3\}}(\sigma + s) = \rho_{\{3\}} + r_{\{3\}}, \text{ etc.}$$

Comparison with the midpoint formula shows that with the same 5 associated differences available at each point, a higher level of accuracy is generally obtainable with (15.6). Again, modified second differences might simplify the tabulation considerably without much loss of accuracy.

---

* However, Pearson points out that when $|r|$ and $|s| < 1/4$ it is slightly more satisfactory to use the midpoint formula.

MID-PANEL FORMULA

	$(0, 0)$	$(1, 0)$
f	74819	72822
δ_x^2	$-\ 96$	$+\ 464$
δ_y^2	$-\ 1938$	$-\ 3196$
δ_x^4	$+\ 94$	$-\ 69$
δ_y^4	$+\ 492$	$+\ 683$
$\delta_x^2\delta_y^2$	$-\ 216$	$+\ 121$

	$(0, 1)$	$(1, 1)$
f	96495	91839
δ_x^2	$-\ 395$	$+\ 897$
δ_y^2	$-\ 1825$	$-\ 3270$
δ_x^4	$+\ 353$	$+\ 93$
δ_y^4	$+\ 579$	$+\ 1117$
$\delta_x^2\delta_y^2$	$-\ 423$	$-\ 240$

FIG. 15.2

Values of $E(\theta, \phi)$ etc.

$$
\begin{aligned}
f_{rs} = &\ (\rho\sigma + \rho_{\{3\}}\sigma\delta_x^2 + \rho\sigma_{\{3\}}\delta_y^2 + \rho_{\{5\}}\sigma\delta_x^4 \\
&\quad + \rho_{\{3\}}\sigma_{\{3\}}\delta_x^2\delta_y^2 + \rho\sigma_{\{5\}}\delta_y^4 + \ldots)f_{0,\,0} \\
&+ (\rho s + \rho_{\{3\}}s\delta_x^2 + \rho s_{\{3\}}\delta_y^2 + \rho_{\{5\}}s\delta_x^4 \\
&\quad + \rho_{\{3\}}s_{\{3\}}\delta_x^2\delta_y^2 + \rho s_{\{5\}}\delta_y^4 + \ldots)f_{0,\,1} \\
&+ (r\sigma + r_{\{3\}}\sigma\delta_x^2 + r\sigma_{\{3\}}\delta_y^2 + r_{\{5\}}\sigma\delta_x^4 \\
&\quad + r_{\{3\}}\sigma_{\{3\}}\delta_x^2\delta_y^2 + r\sigma_{\{5\}}\delta_y^4 + \ldots)f_{1,\,0} \\
&+ (rs + r_{\{3\}}s\delta_x^2 + rs_{\{3\}}\delta_y^2 + r_{\{5\}}s\delta_x^4 \\
&\quad + r_{\{3\}}s_{\{3\}}\delta_x^2\delta_y^2 + rs_{\{5\}}\delta_y^4 + \ldots)f_{1,\,1} \quad (15.6)
\end{aligned}
$$

EXAMPLE 15.2. Estimate the value of $E\,(48°, 51°)$.

The essential data from Table 15.1 are given above with
$$f_{0,\,0} = E(45°, 45°),\ x = \theta,\ y = \phi$$

As in Example 15.1
$$r = 0\!\cdot\!2,\ s = 0\!\cdot\!4,\ \sigma = 0\!\cdot\!6,\ \rho = 0\!\cdot\!8$$

With terms arranged as in (15.6)

$$
\begin{aligned}
f_{rs} = &\ 0\!\cdot\!48\,(74819) - 0\!\cdot\!0288\,(-96)\quad - 0\!\cdot\!0512\,(-1938) \\
&\ 0\!\cdot\!32\,(96495) - 0\!\cdot\!0192\,(-395)\quad - 0\!\cdot\!0448\,(-1825) \\
&\ 0\!\cdot\!12\,(72822) - 0\!\cdot\!0192\,(464)\qquad - 0\!\cdot\!0128\,(-3196) \\
&\ 0\!\cdot\!08\,(91839) - 0\!\cdot\!0128\,(897)\qquad - 0\!\cdot\!0112\,(-3270) \\
&\qquad + 0\!\cdot\!0049\,(94)\qquad + 0\!\cdot\!0031\,(-216) + 0\!\cdot\!0093\,(492) \\
&\qquad + 0\!\cdot\!0032\,(353)\qquad + 0\!\cdot\!0027\,(-423) + 0\!\cdot\!0086\,(579) \\
&\qquad + 0\!\cdot\!0038\,(-69)\qquad + 0\!\cdot\!0020\,(+121) + 0\!\cdot\!0023\,(683) \\
&\qquad + 0\!\cdot\!0025\,(93)\qquad + 0\!\cdot\!0018\,(-240) + 0\!\cdot\!0022\,(1117)
\end{aligned}
$$

$$
\begin{aligned}
&= 35913{\cdot}1 + \quad 2{\cdot}8 + 99{\cdot}2 + 0{\cdot}5 - 0{\cdot}7 + 4{\cdot}6 \\
&+ 30878{\cdot}4 + \quad 7{\cdot}6 + 81{\cdot}8 + 1{\cdot}1 - 1{\cdot}1 + 5{\cdot}0 \\
&+ \;\; 8738{\cdot}6 - \quad 8{\cdot}9 + 40{\cdot}9 - 0{\cdot}3 + 0{\cdot}2 + 1{\cdot}6 \\
&+ \;\; 7347{\cdot}1 - \;\; 11{\cdot}5 + 36{\cdot}6 + 0{\cdot}2 - 0{\cdot}4 + 2{\cdot}5 \\
&= 82877{\cdot}2 + 248{\cdot}5 + 13{\cdot}2 = 83138{\cdot}9
\end{aligned}
$$

In this approximation the error does not exceed 1 unit in the 5th place.

15.3. Corner-panel Formula

When the requisite central differences are not available, as in the corner of a table, a procedure similar to the use of forward differences with one variable must be followed. We can, as in Newton's formula (5.1), use the expansion

$$
E_x{}^r = (1 + \Delta_x)^r = (1 + r\Delta_x + r_{(2)}\Delta_x{}^2 + r_{(3)}\Delta_x{}^3 + \ldots)
$$

with a similar expansion for $E_y{}^s$. However, in order to retain the advantage of a uniform notation, it is preferable to translate this into central difference notation, and at the same time remove odd order differences, by using the relations

$$
\Delta_x = E_x - 1, \quad \Delta_x{}^2 = E_x \delta_x{}^2
$$

The above expansion then becomes

$$
E_x{}^r = \rho + E_x + (r_{(2)} - r_{(3)})(E\delta^2)_x + r_{(3)}(E^2\delta^2)_x \\
\qquad\qquad + (r_{(4)} - r_{(5)})(E^2\delta^4)_x + \ldots \quad (15.7)
$$

When this is multiplied by the similar expansion for $E_y{}^s$, and all displacement operators removed, formula (15.8) is obtained. Referring to Fig. 15.3, it will be seen that the first row involves the o points only, the 2nd row brings in × points, the 3rd and 4th bring in + points, and the 5th and 6th · points. At this stage we have a sextic which coincides with $f(x, y)$ at 19 points. Further terms are easily derived.

The above formula can be adapted for use in any of the other three corners of a table by suitably adjusting the signs of r and s; since only even differences appear their signs will be unaffected.

CORNER-PANEL FORMULA

	(0, 0)	(1, 0)	(2, 0)
f	100000	107641	121106
$\delta_x{}^2$		+ 5824	+ 493
$\delta_x{}^4$			+ 2562

	(0, 1)	(1, 1)	(2, 1)
f	96593	99916	107586
$\delta_x{}^2$		+ 4347	+ 1091
$\delta_y{}^2$	− 6583	− 4111	
$\delta_x{}^4$			+ 1050
$\delta_x{}^2\delta_y{}^2$		− 588	− 790

	(0, 2)	(1, 2)
f	86603	88080
$\delta_y{}^2$	− 5902	− 4955
$\delta_y{}^4$	+ 402	+ 1466
$\delta_x{}^2\delta_y{}^2$		+ 738

Fig. 15.3

DATA FROM TABLE 15.1

$$f_{rs} = \rho\sigma f_{0,\,0} + \rho s f_{0,\,1} + r\sigma f_{1,\,0} + r s f_{1,\,1}$$
$$+ (r_{(2)} - r_{(3)})(\sigma\delta_x{}^2 f_{1,\,0} + s\delta_x{}^2 f_{1,\,1}) + (s_{(2)} - s_{(3)})(\rho\delta_y{}^2 f_{0,\,1} + r\delta_y{}^2 f_{1,\,1})$$
$$+ r_{(3)}(\sigma\delta_x{}^2 f_{2,\,0} + s\delta_x{}^2 f_{2,\,1}) + s_{(3)}(\rho\delta_y{}^2 f_{0,\,2} + r\delta_y{}^2 f_{1,\,2})$$
$$+ (r_{(2)} - r_{(3)})(s_{(2)} - s_{(3)})\delta_x{}^2\delta_y{}^2 f_{1,\,1}$$
$$+ (r_{(4)} - r_{(5)})(\sigma\delta_x{}^4 f_{2,\,0} + s\delta_x{}^4 f_{2,\,1}) + (s_{(4)} - s_{(5)})(\rho\delta_y{}^4 f_{0,\,2} + r\delta_y{}^4 f_{1,\,2})$$
$$+ r_{(3)}(s_{(2)} - s_{(3)})\delta_x{}^2\delta_y{}^2 f_{2,\,1} + (r_{(2)} - r_{(3)})s_{(3)}\delta_x{}^2\delta_y{}^2 f_{1,\,2}$$
$$+ \text{6th and higher order terms} \qquad\qquad (15.8)$$

EXAMPLE 15.3. Estimate the value of E (87°, 87°).

The necessary data from Table 15.1 are given above, with
$$f_{0,\,0} = E(90°,\,90°), \quad x = -\,\theta, \quad y = -\,\phi$$
For the required value, $r = s = 0\!\cdot\!2$, $\sigma = \rho = 0\!\cdot\!8$.
In view of the large 4th differences, an interpolation accurate to 5 figures is not to be expected. We find, using (15.8), f_{rs}

$$= 0\!\cdot\!64\,(100000) + 0\!\cdot\!16\,(107641) + 0\!\cdot\!16\,(96593) + 0\!\cdot\!04\,(99916)$$
$$- 0\!\cdot\!128\,\{0\!\cdot\!8\,(5824) + 0\!\cdot\!2\,(4347)\} - 0\!\cdot\!128\,\{0\!\cdot\!8\,(-6583) + 0\!\cdot\!2\,(-4111)\}$$
$$+ 0\!\cdot\!048\,\{0\!\cdot\!8\,(493) + 0\!\cdot\!2\,(1091)\} + 0\!\cdot\!048\,\{0\!\cdot\!8\,(-5902) + 0\!\cdot\!2\,(-4955)\}$$
$$+ (0\!\cdot\!128)^2\,(-588)$$
$$- 0\!\cdot\!0591\,\{0\!\cdot\!8\,(2562) + 0\!\cdot\!2\,(1050)\} - 0\!\cdot\!0591\,\{0\!\cdot\!8\,(402) + 0\!\cdot\!2\,(1466)\}$$
$$- 0\!\cdot\!0061\,(-790) \qquad\qquad - 0\!\cdot\!0061\,(+738)$$
$$= 100674\!\cdot\!1 - 707\!\cdot\!7 + 29\!\cdot\!4 - 133\!\cdot\!5$$
$$+ 779\!\cdot\!3 - 274\!\cdot\!2 - 36\!\cdot\!3$$
$$- 9\!\cdot\!6 + 4\!\cdot\!8$$
$$- 4\!\cdot\!5$$
$$= 100674\!\cdot\!1 + 71\!\cdot\!6 - 254\!\cdot\!4 - 169\!\cdot\!5 = 100322$$

The correct value is 1·00211, and an error of the order of 0·001 is in keeping with the size of the contributions from 4th differences.

15.4. Mixed Difference Formulas

It is obviously possible, by combining say a Stirling expansion for $E_x{}^r$ with an Everett expansion for $E_y{}^{s-1/2}$, to obtain a formula intermediate to the midpoint and mid-panel formulas. Likewise forward or backward differences in one direction can be combined with central differences in the other. The most useful formula of this kind is certainly a Newton-Everett combination which can be used near the edge of a table, and is conveniently termed an *edge-panel formula*. The reader should have no difficulty in verifying formula (15.9) using an Everett formula for $f_{r,\,s}$ in terms of $f_{0,\,s}$ and $f_{1,\,s}$ as in §15.2, and expanding $f_{0,\,s} = E_y{}^s f_{0,\,0}$, $f_{1,\,s} = E_y{}^s f_{1,\,0}$ in the manner of § 15.3. In this arrangement, the first row, the second and third rows, the fourth and fifth rows, introduce the o, ×, + points respectively (Fig. 15.4). This is by no means a hard and fast grouping of terms, as the best arrangement in any particular application depends on how the differences fall off in both the x and y directions.

Formula (15.9) is of course but one example of many intermediate cases, most of which need separate investigation. An extensive study of them has been made by K. Pearson.

EDGE-PANEL FORMULA

	(0, 0)	(1, 0)
f	70711	86603
$\delta_x{}^2$	− 4819	− 5902
$\delta_x{}^4$	+ 329	+ 402
	(0, 1)	(1, 1)
f	71289	88080
$\delta_x{}^2$	− 4333	− 4955
$\delta_y{}^2$	+ 955	+ 2282
$\delta_x{}^4$	+ 572	+ 1466
$\delta_x{}^2\delta_y{}^2$	+ 651	+ 738
	(0, 2)	(1, 2)
f	72822	91839
$\delta_y{}^2$	+ 464	+ 897
$\delta_y{}^4$	− 69	+ 93
$\delta_x{}^2\delta_y{}^2$	+ 121	− 240

FIG. 15.4

$$f_{rs} = (\rho\sigma f_{0,\,0} + \rho s f_{0,\,1} + r\sigma f_{1,\,0} + rs f_{1,\,1})$$
$$+ (s_{(2)} - s_{(3)})(\rho\delta_y{}^2 f_{0,\,1} + r\delta_y{}^2 f_{1,\,1})$$
$$+ \rho_{\{3\}}(\sigma\delta_x{}^2 f_{0,\,0} + s\delta_x{}^2 f_{0,\,1}) + r_{\{3\}}(\sigma\delta_x{}^2 f_{1,\,0} + s\delta_x{}^2 f_{1,\,1})$$
$$+ s_{(3)}(\rho\delta_y{}^2 f_{0,\,2} + r\delta_y{}^2 f_{1,\,2})$$
$$+ (s_{(2)} - s_{(3)})(\rho_{\{3\}}\delta_x{}^2\delta_y{}^2 f_{0,\,1} + r_{\{3\}}\delta_x{}^2\delta_y{}^2 f_{1,\,1})$$
$$+ \rho_{\{5\}}(\sigma\delta_x{}^4 f_{0,\,0} + s\delta_x{}^4 f_{0,\,1}) + r_{\{5\}}(\sigma\delta_x{}^4 f_{1,\,0} + s\delta_x{}^4 f_{1,\,1})$$
$$+ s_{(3)}(\rho_{\{3\}}\delta_x{}^2\delta_y{}^2 f_{0,\,2} + r_{\{3\}}\delta_x{}^2\delta_y{}^2 f_{1,\,2})$$
$$+ (s_{(4)} - s_{(5)})(\rho\delta_y{}^4 f_{0,\,2} + r\delta_y{}^4 f_{1,\,2}) + \text{etc.} \qquad (15.9)$$

EXAMPLE 15.4. Estimate the value of $E\,(87°, 51°)$.

The necessary data from Table 15.1 are given on page 492, with
$$f_{0,\,0} = E(90°, 45°), \quad x = \phi, \quad y = \theta$$
For the required value, $r = 0·4$, $s = 0·2$, $\sigma = 0·8$, $\rho = 0·6$.

Also
$$s_{(2)} - s_{(3)} = -0·128, \quad s_{(3)} = 0·048, \quad s_{(4)} - s_{(5)} = -0·0591$$

Hence, from (15.9), $E(87°, 51°)$
$$= 0·48\,(70711) + 0·12\,(71289) + 0·32\,(86603) + 0·08\,(88080)$$
$$- 0·128\,\{0·6\,(955) + 0·4\,(2282)\}$$
$$- 0·064\,\{0·8\,(-4819) + 0·2\,(-4333)\}$$
$$- 0·056\,\{0·8\,(-5902) + 0·2\,(-4955)\}$$
$$+ 0·048\,\{0·6\,(464) + 0·4\,(897)\} - 0·128\,\{-0·064\,(651) - 0·056\,(738)\}$$
$$+ 0·0116\,\{0·8\,(329) + 0·2\,(572)\} + 0·0108\,\{0·8\,(402) + 0·2\,(1466)\}$$
$$+ 0·048\,\{-0·064\,(121) - 0·056\,(-240)\}$$
$$- 0·0591\,\{0·6\,(-69) + 0·4\,(93)\}$$
$$= 77255·3 - 190·2$$
$$+ 302·2 + 319·9$$
$$+ 30·6 + 10·6$$
$$+ 4·4 + 6·6$$
$$+ 0·3 + 0·2$$
$$= 77065·1 + 663·3 + 11·5 = 77740\ (\times 10^{-5})$$

The correct value to 5D is $0·77750$. The deficiency is largely made up by contributions from the points $(0, 4)$, $(1, 4)$.

In concluding these numerical examples, we would refer the reader once again to the general remarks about double-entry interpolation on pages 484 and 485.

Cubature

When suitable interpolation formulas have been derived, the problem of cubature, i.e. integration of $f(x, y)$ over a rectangular area in the (x, y) plane, is relatively simple. There is, however, an enormous variety of possible formulas to meet slightly different circumstances, and only a few of these which have fairly wide applicability will be considered here.

15.5. Integration Over a Single Panel

From the mid-panel formula (15.6) it follows at once by integrating over the central panel that

$$\int_{x_0}^{x_0+w_1} dx \int_{y_0}^{y_0+w_2} dy\, f(x,\, y) = w_1 w_2 \int_0^1 \int_0^1 f_{rs} drds$$

$$= (w_1 w_2/4)\{1 - (\delta_x^2 + \delta_y^2)/12$$

$$+ (11\delta_x^4 + 5\delta_x^2\delta_y^2 + 11\delta_y^4)/720$$

$$- (191\delta_x^6 + 77\delta_x^4\delta_y^2 + 77\delta_x^2\delta_y^4 + 191\delta_y^6)/60480$$

$$+ \ \cdot \ \cdot \ \cdot\}(f_{0,\,0} + f_{0,\,1} + f_{1,\,0} + f_{1,\,1}) \quad (15.10)$$

Although this result is obtained most easily when the interpolation formula is given in terms of differences, its practical value is increased when it is expressed in Lagrangian form involving values of f_{jk} only. The results of doing this when second, fourth and sixth differences are neglected are shown in (15.11), (15.12) and (15.13) (Fig. 15.5). In each case the truncation error can be expressed in terms of derivatives of the integrand, e.g. for (15.12)

$$R = w_1 w_2\{11w_1^4(\partial^4 f/\partial x^4) + 5w_1^2 w_2^2(\partial^4 f/\partial x^2 \partial y^2)$$

$$+ 11w_2^4(\partial^4 f/\partial y^4)\}/2880$$

where the partial derivatives are evaluated at some points within the range of the data. Such a form may have little practical value, however.

When the midpoint formula (15.4) is integrated over the panel, $|r| \leqslant 1/2$, $|s| \leqslant 1/2$, one finds that

$$\int_{x_0-w_1/2}^{x_0+w_1/2} dx \int_{y_0-w_2/2}^{y_0+w_2/2} dy\, f(x,\, y) = w_1 w_2 \int_{-1/2}^{1/2} \int_{-1/2}^{1/2} f_{rs} drds$$

$$= w_1 w_2\{1 + (\delta_x^2 + \delta_y^2)/24$$

$$- (17\delta_x^4 - 10\delta_x^2\delta_y^2 + 17\delta_y^4)/5760$$

$$+ (367\delta_x^6 - 119\delta_x^4\delta_y^2 - 119\delta_x^2\delta_y^4$$

$$+ 367\delta_y^6)/967680 - \ \cdot \ \cdot \ \cdot\}f_{0,\,0} \quad (15.18)$$

Some conversions to Lagrangian form, including second and fourth differences and using quartic and sextic polynomials

MID-PANEL FORMULAS

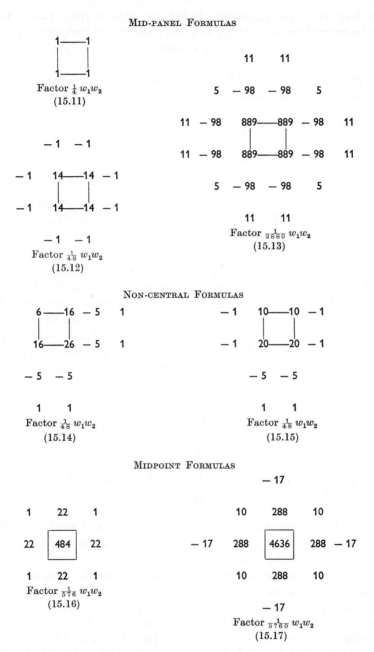

Factor $\frac{1}{4} w_1 w_2$
(15.11)

Factor $\frac{1}{48} w_1 w_2$
(15.12)

Factor $\frac{1}{2880} w_1 w_2$
(15.13)

NON-CENTRAL FORMULAS

Factor $\frac{1}{48} w_1 w_2$
(15.14)

Factor $\frac{1}{48} w_1 w_2$
(15.15)

MIDPOINT FORMULAS

Factor $\frac{1}{576} w_1 w_2$
(15.16)

Factor $\frac{1}{5760} w_1 w_2$
(15.17)

FIG. 15.5. INTEGRATION OVER SINGLE PANEL (SHOWN BY FULL LINES)

respectively, are shown in (15.16) and (15.17) (Fig. 15.5). The non-central formulas (15.8) and (15.9) can be similarly integrated; some results based on quartic polynomials for corner and edge panels are shown in (15.14) and (15.15).

One other formula of interest is obtained by integrating (15.14) over four panels. This gives

$$\int_{x_0-w_1}^{x_0+w_1} dx \int_{y_0-w_2}^{y_0+w_2} dy\, f(x, y)$$
$$= w_1 w_2 \{4 + (5/9)(\delta_x{}^2 + \delta_y{}^2) - (\delta_x{}^4 + \delta_y{}^4)/45$$
$$+ (5\delta_x{}^6 + 7\delta_x{}^4\delta_y{}^2 + 7\delta_x{}^2\delta_y{}^4 + 5\delta_y{}^6)/1890 + \ldots\} f_{0,0} \quad (15.19)$$

When fourth and higher differences are ignored, we obtain the bivariate form of Simpson's rule, shown in (15.20) (Fig. 15.6).

15.6. Closed Cubature Formulas

When the integral over a rectangular region is required, there are two simple ways in which a suitable formula may be obtained.

(a) An appropriate Lagrangian formula for integration with one variable may be "squared." Formula (15.20) can be regarded as an example of this kind, as the coefficients in the square array are also given by the outer product of a column and a row matrix, each containing the coefficients in Simpson's rule for one variable; thus if

$$L = (1/3)[1,\ 4,\ 1]$$

then
$$L'L = (1/9)\begin{bmatrix}1\\4\\1\end{bmatrix}[1,\ 4,\ 1] = (1/9)\begin{bmatrix}1 & 4 & 1\\4 & 16 & 4\\1 & 4 & 1\end{bmatrix}$$

A similar process with the three-eighths rule, with

$$L = (3/8)[1,\ 3,\ 3,\ 1]$$

leads to formula (15.22) for cubature over a 3×3 rectangle. The same formulas can of course be derived by integrating Lagrange polynomials of the type shown in (15.2).

(b) One can combine suitable formulas giving the integrals over the separate panels forming the rectangle. Thus by combining (15.12), (15.14) and (15.15), one obtains both (15.21) for a 2×2 rectangle and (15.23) for a 3×3 rectangle. (15.21) is an interesting variant of (15.20), and (15.23) of (15.22), differing only in the form of the neglected remainder (see Exercises 15, No. 2).

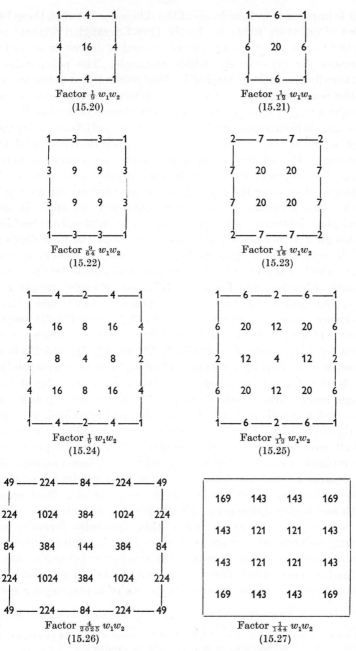

Fig. 15.6. Closed Cubature Formulas

504 NUMERICAL METHODS

It is important to bear in mind the difference between these two types of cubature formula. In the true Lagrangian formula (a), applied to a $n \times n$ rectangle, a polynomial of degree $2n$ is used to represent $f(x, y)$ over the whole rectangle. The polynomial is not usually the most general of its kind, some terms being absent. In the composite type of formula, a different polynomial is used to represent $f(x, y)$ over each panel, the degree being usually less than $2n$. Whether one or other type is more satisfactory depends very much on the behaviour of the higher derivatives of the integrand. It may happen that the composite formula is better when the integrand varies much more rapidly over part of the rectangle than over the rest. There is an obvious advantage in having two formulas of comparable accuracy, to apply in any particular instance, for the results are mutually checking. Although it is not always permissible to treat the final digits in which both answers agree as being accurate, it is evident that digits which disagree are not significant and should be discarded.

Some other formulas for use with larger rectangles are given in Figs. 15.6 and 15.7. For 4×4 rectangles, (15.24) and (15.25) obviously involve a repeated use of (15.20) and (15.21) respectively; (15.26) is based on Boole's rule and the coefficients are given by $L'L$, where $L = (2/45)[7, 32, 12, 32, 7]$. (15.27) is an example of a midpoint formula, and arises from the corresponding quadrature formula in which $L = (1/12)[13, 11, 11, 13]$; it is of course less accurate than (15.26), as it uses far fewer points, but on occasion (15.27) and (15.24) can be happily combined, as shown in Example 15.5. For 5×5 and 6×6 rectangles, (15.28) and (15.29) can be used; only the essential coefficients are given, and the remainder can be filled in by symmetry. These two formulas are composite, and are derived by combining results for separate panels given by Irwin,* using sextic polynomials; they ignore sixth and higher differences. Finally for $n \times m$ rectangles, where m, $n \geqslant 8$, (15.30) can be used; this composite formula uses quartic polynomials for each panel and retains third differences only. One corner only is shown, the symmetry being obvious.

Another type of cubature formula may be briefly mentioned, in which function values at selected points of a rectangular mesh

---

* J. O. Irwin, *Tracts for Computers, X; On Quadrature and Cubature* (Cambridge, 1923). This contains many more results than have been quoted here.

A more recent survey is that of J. C. P. Miller, *Math. Comp.*, **14** (1960), pp. 13, 130, and 240. A bibliography on approximate integration has been prepared by A. H. Stroud, *Math. Comp.*, **15** (1960), 52.

are used, the values at other points being omitted. It is reasonable
to suppose that an n-point formula which selects n points from a
regular mesh covering the area, instead of using *all* points of a

62	249	164	.	.	.
.	973	653	.	.	.
.	.	433	.	.	.
.	.	.	.	.	.
.	.	.	.	.	.
.	.	.	.	.	.

Factor $\frac{1}{576}\, w_1 w_2$
(15.28)

278	1336	395	1490	.	.	.
.	5357	2650	5290	.	.	.
.	.	548	2858	.	.	.
.	.	.	5348	.	.	.
.	.	.	.	.	.	.
.	.	.	.	.	.	.

Factor $\frac{1}{2880}\, w_1 w_2$
(15.29)

4	23	12	17	16	16	.
23	76	54	64	62	62	.
12	54	32	42	40	40	.
17	64	42	52	50	50	.
16	62	40	50	48	48	.
16	62	40	50	48	48	
.	.	.	.	.	.	.

Factor $\frac{1}{48}\, w_1 w_2$
(15.30)

Fig. 15.7. Closed Cubature Formulas

similar but coarser mesh, might in fact give better results for the
same labour. Such formulas have been devised by Tyler,* not
only for integrating functions of two variables, but also functions
of three variables over regions with rectangular boundaries, when
a judicious choice of points is even more important.

* G. W. Tyler, *Canad. J. Math.*, **5** (1953), 393. Other work on the evaluation of
multiple integrals is that of P. C. Hammer and associates; see A. H. Stroud, *Math.
Comp.*, **15** (1960), 143 for references.

We now give a numerical example of cubature over a 4×4 rectangle.

EXAMPLE 15.5. Estimate by cubature the value of the integral

$$I = \frac{1}{2\pi} \cdot \frac{1}{(1-r^2)^{1/2}} \int_0^{0.8} \int_0^{0.8} \exp\{-(x^2 - 2rxy + y^2)/2(1-r^2)\}dx\,dy$$

where $r = 0.2$.

1. We use intervals of 0.2 in both x and y. The following values of the Gaussian function

$$g(x, y) = (2\pi)^{-1/2} \exp\{-(x^2 - 0.4xy + y^2)/1.92\}$$

have been given by Irwin (*loc. cit.*)

y	x				
	0	0·2	0·4	0·6	0·8
0	39894	39071	36704	33073	28585
0·2	39071	38586	36552	33211	28945
0·4	36704	36552	34914	31989	28113
0·6	33073	33211	31989	29554	26191
0·8	28585	28945	28113	26191	23404

Units of 10^{-5}

The first step is to add together those values which are to be multiplied by the same numerical coefficient in the cubature formula, of which (15.24) is typical. This leads in an obvious way to the symmetrized values

$$
\begin{array}{ccc}
120468 & 254560 & 129634 \\
 & 134562 & 137082 \\
 & & 34914
\end{array}
$$

The results of applying the cubature formulas (15.24), (15.25) and (15.26) are given below. The integral I_1 obtained from the above values of $g(x, y)$ is multiplied by $(1.92\pi)^{-1/2}$ ($= 0.4071689$) to give I.

Formula	I_1	I
(15.24)	0.212768_0	0.086632_5
(15.25)	0.212765_9	0.086631_7
(15.26)	0.212758_3	0.086628_6
Analytical		0.086629_6

The integral can be evaluated analytically by expanding as a power series in r, the coefficients involving tetrachoric functions (for details see Irwin). This leads to the analytical value quoted above. In this example (15.25) is slightly more accurate than (15.24), though the best result is given by (15.26) in which the error term involves 6th order derivatives of $f(x, y)$ as compared with 4th order derivatives for the other two.

2. An alternative procedure uses the midpoint formula (15.27), for which we may take the following values—

y	x			
	0·1	0·3	0·5	0·7
0·1	39563	38107	35207	31199
0·3	38107	37011	34481	30812
0·5	35207	34481	32391	29187
0·7	31199	30812	29187	26520

These provide symmetrized values

$$128481 \qquad 266626$$
$$138364$$

Thence by (15.27)

$$I_1 = 0.212730_1, \; I = 0.086617_1$$

This is a much poorer result than given by any of the panel formulas tried above. However, it can be shown that the errors associated with (15.24) and (15.27) are similar in form, being as follows—

(15.24) $\qquad R = - (32/360)w_1w_2(w_1{}^4D_x{}^4 + w_2{}^4D_y{}^4)f(\xi, \eta)$

(15.27) $\qquad R = + (103/360)w_1w_2(w_1{}^4D_x{}^4 + w_2{}^4D_y{}^4)f(\xi', \eta')$

where the derivatives are all evaluated at certain points within the rectangle. If the fourth derivatives are not varying rapidly and do not change sign within the rectangle it might be expected that a better result would be obtained by combining (15.24) and (15.27) in the ratio 103 : 32. In fact

$$(103 \times 0.086632_5 + 32 \times 0.086617_1)/135 = 0.086628_9$$

which is a much improved estimate of the integral.

15.7. Integration with a Curved Boundary

When the integral is required over an area in the (x, y) plane with a curved boundary, the foregoing method is not applicable. Usually each case must be treated on its merits. If the integrand is an analytical function it may be that a simple transformation will convert the boundary to a rectangular one; thus if the area is a sector of a circle, a change to polar coordinates is indicated.

Otherwise, resort to a separate integration over the x and y variables may be necessary. For example, the area may be subdivided into strips of equal width parallel to the y axis, and quadrature performed along each strip assuming x constant and the interval adjusted to the length of the strip. The integral is finally obtained by a further quadrature with respect to x as variable. For an example of this kind the tract by Irwin may be consulted.

Differentiation

The evaluation of partial derivatives from a table of the function at regular intervals presents no particular difficulties and needs no detailed comment. From the interpolation formulas expressions can be derived for derivatives at tabular points, at halfway or other intermediate points, in terms of differences. The expressions for "straight" derivatives ($\partial f/\partial x$, $\partial^2 f/\partial x^2$, etc.) at tabular points will be found to reduce to those obtained in Chapter 5 for functions of one variable. Symbolic methods can be used to derive them, if expansions for D_r, D_s in terms of difference operators are applied.

We shall be mainly concerned here to obtain suitable operators for such important combinations of derivatives as occur in the Laplacian, etc., to be used later in the solution of partial differential equations.

15.8. The Laplacian Operator

We shall assume here that $w_1 = w_2 = w$ and use the symbols ∇^2 and Q^4 to denote the following operators—

$$\nabla^2 = \partial^2/\partial x^2 + \partial^2/\partial y^2 = (1/w^2)(D_r^2 + D_s^2)$$
$$Q^4 = \partial^4/(\partial x^2 \partial y^2) = (1/w^4)D_r^2 D_s^2$$

If we apply the expansions of D_r^2, D_s^2 in terms of δ_x^2, δ_y^2 respectively, as given in (5.31), then

$$w^2 \nabla^2 f_{0,\,0} = \{\delta_x^2 + \delta_y^2 - (\delta_x^4 + \delta_y^4)/12$$
$$+ (\delta_x^6 + \delta_y^6)/90 - (\delta_x^8 + \delta_y^8)/315 + \ldots\} f_{0,\,0} \quad (15.31)$$

In Lagrangian form the first and second approximations to $\nabla^2 f_{00}$ are shown in (15.32) and (15.33). The "box" notation, suggested by Hartree, is self-explanatory; the coefficient attached to f_{00} is shown in heavy type, and the surrounding coefficients are those which multiply adjacent f values.

Another simple approximation to $\nabla^2 f_{00}$ is given by $X f_{00}$, where X is the operator shown in (15.34). This is obvious if we consider

$$
Hf_{00} = \begin{array}{|ccc|}
 & 1 & \\
1 & -4 & 1 \\
 & 1 &
\end{array} f_{00}
$$

$$= w^2 \nabla^2 f_{00} + 0(w^4)$$

(15.32)

$$
\begin{array}{|ccccc|}
 & & -1 & & \\
 & & 16 & & \\
-1 & 16 & -60 & 16 & -1 \\
 & & 16 & & \\
 & & -1 & &
\end{array} f_{00} = 12w^2 \nabla^2 f_{00} \\ + 0(w^6)
$$

(15.33)

$$
2Xf_{00} = \begin{array}{|ccc|}
1 & & 1 \\
 & -4 & \\
1 & & 1
\end{array} f_{00}
$$

$$= 2w^2 \nabla^2 f_{00} + 0(w^4)$$

(15.34)

$$
N^2 f_{00} = \begin{array}{|ccc|}
1 & -2 & 1 \\
-2 & 4 & -2 \\
1 & -2 & 1
\end{array} f_{00}
$$

(15.35)

the x and y axes rotated through $45°$, and the tabular intervals increased by a factor $\sqrt{2}$; if the rotation is carried out analytically one finds that

$$\partial^2/\partial x^2 + \partial^2/\partial y^2 = \partial^2/\partial x_1^2 + \partial^2/\partial y_1^2$$

where $\quad x_1 = (x+y)/\sqrt{2},\ y_1 = (x-y)/\sqrt{2}$

X is also a simple combination of the operators

$$H = \delta_x^2 + \delta_y^2 \quad \text{and} \quad N^2 = \delta_x^2 \delta_y^2$$

(the latter is shown in (15.35)), as it can be seen by inspection that

$$2X = 2H + N^2 \qquad (15.36)$$

Now a combination of H and X can be found which is generally a better approximation to ∇^2 than either H or X separately, and commonly very much better. To see this we first examine the inverse expansions of H and X in terms of ∇^2 and Q^4. By direct expansion of δ_x and δ_y in powers of D_r and D_s it follows that

$$H = w^2 \nabla^2 + \frac{w^4}{2 \cdot 3!}(\nabla^4 - 2Q^4) + \frac{w^6}{3 \cdot 5!}(\nabla^6 - 3Q^4 \nabla^2)$$

$$+ \frac{w^8}{4 \cdot 7!}(\nabla^8 - 4Q^4 \nabla^4 + 2Q^8) + \cdots \qquad (15.37)$$

$$X = w^2\nabla^2 + \frac{w^4}{2 \cdot 3!}(\nabla^4 + 4Q^4) + \frac{w^6}{3 \cdot 5!}(\nabla^6 + 12Q^4\nabla^2)$$

$$+ \frac{w^8}{4 \cdot 7!}(\nabla^8 + 24Q^4\nabla^4 + 16Q^8) + \ldots \quad (15.38)$$

Now if $K = 4H + 2X$ so that*

$$Kf_{00} = \begin{vmatrix} 1 & 4 & 1 \\ 4 & -20 & 4 \\ 1 & 4 & 1 \end{vmatrix} f_{00} \quad (15.39)$$

then the expansion of $K/6$ has $w^2\nabla^2$ as the leading term but no term in w^4Q^4; thus

$$\frac{1}{6}K = w^2\nabla^2 + \frac{w^4}{2 \cdot 3!}\nabla^4 + \frac{w^6}{3 \cdot 5!}(\nabla^6 + 2Q^4\nabla^2)$$

$$+ \frac{w^8}{4 \cdot 7!}\left(\nabla^8 + \frac{16}{3}Q^4\nabla^4 + \frac{20}{3}Q^8\right) + \ldots \quad (15.40)$$

This is particularly valuable when $\nabla^2 f$ is a specified function as in Poisson's equation, $\nabla^2 f = g(x, y)$. Then

$$\frac{1}{6}Kf_{00} = w^2\left\{1 + \frac{w^2}{2 \cdot 3!}\nabla^2 + \frac{w^4}{3 \cdot 5!}(\nabla^4 + 2Q^4)\right\}g_{00} + 0(w^8) \quad (15.41)$$

and this difference equation in two variables, with the terms up to w^6 included on the right, is a very good approximation to Poisson's equation. It is especially simple for Laplace's equation, in which $g(x, y) = 0$.

Reverting to (15.31) for a moment, we can express this expansion for ∇^2 in a form given by Milne, by noting that

$$\delta_x^2 + \delta_y^2 = K_1 - N_1^2, \quad \delta_x^4 + \delta_y^4 = (K_1 - N_1^2)^2 - 12N_1^2$$

where K_1, N_1^2 have been written for $K/6$, $N^2/6$. Thus

$$w^2\nabla^2 = K_1\{1 - (1/12)K_1 + (1/90)(K_1^2 - 3N_1^2)\}$$

$$+ \text{4th order terms} \quad (15.42)$$

---

* For uniformity the symbols H, X, N^2, K used by Milne, *N.S.D.E.*, have also been adopted here.

This provides a difference correction to K_1 when this is used as an approximation to ∇^2.

15.9. The Operators Q^2 and Q^4

To obtain a difference approximation to the operator

$$Q^2(= \partial^2/\partial x \partial y)$$

applicable at a tabular point, it is necessary to use the expansions

$$D_r = (\mu\delta)_x\{1 - (1/6)\delta_x^2 + (1/30)\delta_x^4 - \ldots\}$$
$$D_s = (\mu\delta)_y\{1 - (1/6)\delta_y^2 + (1/30)\delta_y^4 - \ldots\}$$

The first approximation is clearly

$$w^2 Q^2 f_{00} = (\mu\delta)_x(\mu\delta)_y f_{00} + 0(w^4) = Y f_{00} + 0(w^4) \quad (15.43)$$

where

$$4 Y f_{00} = \begin{bmatrix} 1 & & -1 \\ & 0 & \\ -1 & & 1 \end{bmatrix} f_{00} \quad (15.44)$$

Y is an operator prominent in the midpoint formula (15.4). Higher approximations can obviously be derived, and expressed in terms of K and N^2 if desired.

It is obvious that

$$w^4 Q^4 = \delta_x^2 \delta_y^2 \{1 - (1/12)(\delta_x^2 + \delta_y^2)$$
$$+ (1/90)(\delta_x^4 + \delta_y^4) + (1/144)\delta_x^2\delta_y^2 - \ldots\}$$
$$= N^2\{1 - K/72 + K^2/540 - N^2/120 - \ldots\} \quad (15.45)$$

The inverse expansion for N^2 is

$$N^2 = w^4 Q^4 + \frac{w^6}{2 \cdot 3!} Q^4 \nabla^2 + \frac{w^8}{3 \cdot 5!} Q^4 \left(\nabla^4 + \frac{1}{2}Q^4\right) + \ldots \quad (15.46)$$

All results obtained so far have been based essentially on the midpoint formula (15.4). The mid-panel formula also has its uses, providing, for example, values of the Laplacian and other derivatives at halfway points (see Exercises 15, No. 5).

15.10. Irregular Intervals

We conclude by deriving an approximate formula which enables an estimate of $\nabla^2 f_{00}$ to be made when f is known only at points irregularly spaced along two perpendicular lines through O, as indicated in Fig. 15.8.

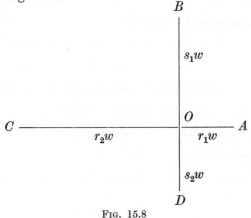

Fig. 15.8

If $O = (x_0, y_0)$ and COA the direction of the x-axis, we can represent $f(x, y_0)$ by a parabola fitted at C, O and A; thus

$$f(x, y_0) = \frac{r(r - r_1)}{r_2(r_1 + r_2)} f_C - \frac{(r + r_2)(r - r_1)}{r_1 r_2} f_O + \frac{r(r + r_2)}{r_1(r_1 + r_2)} f_A$$

whence
$$\left(\frac{\partial^2 f}{\partial x^2}\right)_0 \simeq \frac{2}{w^2} \left\{ \frac{1}{r_1 + r_2} \left(\frac{f_C}{r_2} + \frac{f_A}{r_1} \right) - \frac{f_O}{r_1 r_2} \right\}$$

Similarly
$$\left(\frac{\partial^2 f}{\partial y^2}\right)_0 \simeq \frac{2}{w^2} \left\{ \frac{1}{s_1 + s_2} \left(\frac{f_B}{s_1} + \frac{f_D}{s_2} \right) - \frac{f_O}{s_1 s_2} \right\}$$

Hence, in the usual notation

$$w^2 \nabla^2 f_{0,\,0} \simeq 2 \left\{ \frac{1}{r_1 + r_2} \left(\frac{f_{r_1,\,0}}{r_1} + \frac{f_{-r_2,\,0}}{r_2} \right) + \frac{1}{s_1 + s_2} \left(\frac{f_{0,\,s_1}}{s_1} + \frac{f_{0,\,-s_2}}{s_2} \right) \right.$$
$$\left. - \left(\frac{1}{r_1 r_2} + \frac{1}{s_1 s_2} \right) f_{0,\,0} \right\} \quad (15.47)$$

This reduces to $Hf_{0,\,0}$ when all the spacings are equal to w. Another form, which may be easier for computation, and which has an obvious geometrical interpretation, is the following—

$$w^2 \nabla^2 f_{0,\,0} \simeq \frac{2}{r_1 + r_2} \left\{ \frac{f_{r_1,\,0} - f_{0,\,0}}{r_1} + \frac{f_{-r_2,\,0} - f_{0,\,0}}{r_2} \right\}$$
$$+ \frac{2}{s_1 + s_2} \left\{ \frac{f_{0,\,s_1} - f_{0,\,0}}{s_1} + \frac{f_{0,\,-s_2} - f_{0,\,0}}{s_2} \right\} \quad (15.48)$$

This result will be found useful in Chapter 16.

Functions of a Complex Variable

Computation with complex numbers does not in itself involve unusual difficulties, and we need not do more than make the obvious comment that addition and subtraction are most easily carried out when numbers are expressed in Cartesian form, $z = x + iy$, and multiplication and division when in polar form, $z = re^{i\theta}$. Tables for converting one form into the other are particularly useful, e.g. those by E. H. Neville (*Royal Society Math. Tables*, Vol. 2).

However, direct numerical calculations with functions of a complex variable, e.g. $f(z) = g(x, y) + ih(x, y)$, do present a special problem in that the real functions g and h normally satisfy Laplace's equation in two variables, and formulas for interpolation, integration, etc., should take account of this fact. Perhaps too little attention has so far been given to the development of suitable methods, though the work of H. E. Salzer has done much to remedy this. The following references to original papers may be helpful.

Interpolation—

(a) Cartesian. Lowan and Salzer, *Journ. Math. Phys.*, **23** (1944), 151; Salzer, ibid., **27** (1948), 136 and **28** (1949), 200. See also Salzer, ibid., **26** (1947), 294.

(b) Polar. Salzer, ibid., **24** (1945), 141; **26** (1946), 56 and **29** (1950), 96.

Differentiation—

Salzer, ibid., **31** (1952), 155.

Integration—

G. Birkhoff and D. Young, *ibid.*, **29** (1950), 217 and D. Young, ibid., **31** (1951), 42.

Differential equations (first and second order)—

Salzer, ibid., **29** (1950), 207.

EXERCISES 15

1. Derive the formula

$$f_{0, 0} = \tfrac{1}{2}(f_{1, 0} + f_{-1, 0} + f_{0, 1} + f_{0, -1})$$
$$- \tfrac{1}{4}(f_{1, 1} + f_{1, -1} + f_{-1, 1} + f_{-1, -1})$$

which gives $f_{0, 0}$ in terms of the values on the right.

Compare the error of this bivariate formula with those of the formulas

$$f_{0,\,0} = (-f_{0,\,-2} + 4f_{0,\,-1} + 4f_{0,\,1} - f_{0,\,2})/6$$
$$f_{0,\,0} = (-f_{-2,\,0} + 4f_{-1,\,0} + 4f_{1,\,0} - f_{2,\,0})/6$$

which involve interpolation in one variable only.

2. Verify the formula for "halfway interpolation,"

$$f_{1/2,\,1/2} = (1/4)\{1 - (\delta_x^2 + \delta_y^2)/8$$
$$+ (3\delta_x^4 + 2\delta_x^2\delta_y^2 + 3\delta_y^4)/128 - \cdots\}(f_{0,\,0} + f_{0,\,1} + f_{1,\,0} + f_{1,\,1})$$

and derive the Lagrangian form for the second approximation. Show that it agrees with Bessel's formula when f is independent of y.

3. Verify the following expressions for the remainder terms in cubature formulas given in the text.

(15.20) $R = - (1/45)w_1w_2(D_r^4 + D_s^4)f$

(15.21) $R = w_1w_2\{- (1/45)(D_r^4 + D_s^4) + (1/36)D_r^2D_s^2\}f$

(15.22) $R = - (9/80)w_1w_2(D_r^4 + D_s^4)f$

(15.23) $R = w_1w_2\{- (9/80)(D_r^4 + D_s^4) + (1/16)D_r^2D_s^2\}f$

(15.27) $R = (103/360)w_1w_2(D_r^4 + D_s^4)f$

(15.26) $R = - (32/945)w_1w_2(D_r^6 + D_s^6)f$

Note that $D_r^4 = w_1^4 D_x^4$, $D_s^4 = w_2^4 D_y^4$, etc., and that each derivative is evaluated at some point (not always the same point) within the rectangle of integration.

4. Show that

$$w^2 \int_{-m}^{m} dr \int_{-n}^{n} ds\, f_{r,\,s} = 4w^2 \frac{\sinh mD_r \sinh nD_s}{D_r D_s} f_{0,\,0}$$

and express this result as a series in powers of ∇^2 and Q^4. By comparison with the expansion of

$$w^2\{4 + B(H - X) + (2/3)X\}f_{0,\,0}$$

where B has a suitable value, show that, when $\nabla^2 f_{0,\,0} = 0$,

$$w^2 \int_{-1}^{1} dr \int_{-1}^{1} ds\, f_{r,\,s} = (1/45)w^2 \begin{array}{|ccc|} 7 & 16 & 7 \\ 16 & \mathbf{88} & 16 \\ 7 & 16 & 7 \end{array} f_{0,\,0} + 0(w^{10})$$

(Bickley, 1948)

Note. For harmonic functions this result is definitely superior to (15.20) and (15.21), but it is not so in general.

5. Use the mid-panel formula (15.6) to derive the following expressions for the Laplacian at halfway points—

$$w^2 \nabla^2 f_{1/2,\,0}$$
$$= \tfrac{1}{2}\{(\delta_x{}^2 + \delta_y{}^2) - (\delta_x{}^4 + \delta_y{}^4)/12 - (1/8)\delta_x{}^2\delta_y{}^2 + \ldots\}$$
$$(f_{0,\,0} + f_{1,\,0})$$

$$w^2 \nabla^2 f_{1/2,\,1/2}$$
$$= \tfrac{1}{4}\{(\delta_x{}^2 + \delta_y{}^2) - (\delta_x{}^4 + \delta_y{}^4)/12 - (1/4)\delta_x{}^2\delta_y{}^2 + \ldots\}$$
$$(f_{0,\,0} + f_{0,\,1} + f_{1,\,0} + f_{1,\,1})$$

Derive Lagrangian forms for the first approximations.

6. If Y is the operator defined in (15.44), show that Y^2 is equivalent to $N^2/16$, when N^2 is applied at twice the normal interval.

7. If $\nabla^2 f = 0$, show that

(a) $\qquad\qquad Hf = (a_1 w^4 + a_2 w^8 + a_3 w^{12} + \ldots)$

(b) $\qquad\qquad Xf = -2(a_1 w^4 - 4a_2 w^8 + 16a_3 w^{12} - \ldots)$

(c) $\qquad\qquad Kf = 20(a_2 w^8 - 3a_3 w^{12} + \ldots)$

where a_1, a_2, etc., depend only on x, y. Examine the possibility of deriving a finite difference approximation to Laplace's equation with an error depending on w^{12}.

Note. Assume that f is the real part of a function $F(z)$, where

$$z = x + iy \quad \text{and} \quad F(z) = \sum_s b_s(z - z_0)^s$$

Write $\qquad\qquad z - z_0 = re^{i\theta}, \ b_s = c_s e^{i\alpha_s}$

8. If $\nabla^4 f = 0$, show from (15.37), (15.38) and (15.40) that

(a) $\qquad\qquad H^2 f = b_1 w^6 + b_2 w^8 + b_3 w^{10} + \ldots$

(b) $\qquad\qquad X^2 f = -2(b_1 w^6 - 2b_2 w^8 + 4b_3 w^{10} - \ldots)$

(c) $\qquad\qquad K^2 f = 8b_3 w^{10} + O(w^{14})$

Verify the following Lagrangian forms of the operators H^2 and K^2, and examine that for $8H^2 + 4X^2$.

$$H^2 f_{00} = \begin{bmatrix} & & 1 & & \\ & 2 & -8 & 2 & \\ 1 & -8 & +20 & -8 & 1 \\ & 2 & -8 & 2 & \\ & & 1 & & \end{bmatrix} f_{00}
\qquad
K^2 f_{00} = \begin{bmatrix} 1 & 8 & 18 & 8 & 1 \\ 8 & -8 & -144 & -8 & 8 \\ 18 & -144 & 468 & -144 & 18 \\ 8 & -8 & -144 & -8 & 8 \\ 1 & 8 & 18 & 8 & 1 \end{bmatrix} f_{00}$$

CHAPTER 16

PARTIAL DIFFERENTIAL EQUATIONS

THE numerical solution of partial differential equations is now such a wide subject that the present chapter must be regarded merely as an introduction to it. For this reason only the simplest linear equations of the second order involving two variables will be considered although some of the methods described are easily extended to some equations in three variables. We begin by recounting briefly the types of equation which occur most often, and the nature of the boundary conditions necessary to determine a particular solution.

Classification of Second-order Equations

It is customary to classify linear second-order equations of the form

$$\left\{A \frac{\partial^2}{\partial x^2} + 2B \frac{\partial^2}{\partial x \partial y} + C \frac{\partial^2}{\partial y^2}\right\} f(x, y) = g\left(x, y, f, \frac{\partial f}{\partial x}, \frac{\partial f}{\partial y}\right) \quad (16.1)$$

as elliptic if $\qquad AC - B^2 > 0$

as hyperbolic if $\qquad AC - B^2 < 0$

as parabolic if $\qquad AC - B^2 = 0$

If A, B, and C are functions of x, y the character of the equation can of course vary from one part of the (x, y) plane to another; however, these quantities are often constant and then the elliptic or other property is preserved throughout. Simple examples of each type are as follows—

Elliptic

$$(\partial^2/\partial x^2 + \partial^2/\partial y^2)f = g(x, y) \text{ (Poisson's equation)} \quad (16.2)$$

Hyperbolic

$$\{\partial^2/\partial x^2 - (1/c^2)\partial^2/\partial t^2\}f = 0 \text{ (wave equation)} \quad (16.3)$$

Parabolic

$$\{\partial^2/\partial x^2 - (1/\kappa)\partial/\partial t\}f = 0 \text{ (heat conduction equation)} \quad (16.4)$$

In the latter two, the variable t is used to represent time, and replaces y.

16.1. Characteristics

It is generally possible* to derive a unique solution of (16.1) at all points near a curve Γ in the (x, y) plane when both f and the derivative $\partial f/\partial n$ along the normal are specified at all points of Γ. There are, however, important exceptions to this general rule associated with certain sets of curves in the (x, y) plane, known as characteristics of the equation. These are defined by the differential relation

$$\Delta = A\,dy^2 - 2B\,dx\,dy + C\,dx^2 = 0 \qquad (16.5)$$

which in general determines two directions through each point (x, y) and hence two families of intersecting curves. However, it is obvious from the definition above that for elliptic equations the roots of (16.5) are complex and there are no real characteristics; also for parabolic equations the two families degenerate into one. Only in regions where the equation is hyperbolic do two real sets of characteristics exist, and, provided A, B, C depend only on x, y, these curves are uniquely determined and remain the same for all solutions of the equation.

One way in which characteristics can be used is in deriving a "normal form" for each type of equation. Thus, if the characteristics are represented by the equations $\phi(x, y) = \text{constant}$, $\psi(x, y) = \text{constant}$, and the variables transformed as indicated below, simpler equations are obtained. The process is analogous to transforming a conic to its principal axes.

Elliptic $\xi + i\eta = \phi,\ \xi - i\eta = \psi$

$$(\partial^2/\partial\xi^2 + \partial^2/\partial\eta^2)f = G(\xi, \eta, f, \partial f/\partial\xi, \partial f/\partial\eta) \qquad (16.6)$$

Hyperbolic $\xi = \phi,\ \eta = \psi$

$$\partial^2 f/\partial\xi\partial\eta = G(\xi, \eta, f, \partial f/\partial\xi, \partial f/\partial\eta) \qquad (16.7)$$

Parabolic $\xi = \phi = \psi,\ \eta = x$

$$\partial^2 f/\partial\eta^2 = G(\xi, \eta, f, \partial f/\partial\xi, \partial f/\partial\eta) \qquad (16.8)$$

We see that (16.2) and (16.4) are already in normal form; (16.3) can be made so by the transformation

$$\xi = x + ct,\ \eta = x - ct$$

In regions where an equation is hyperbolic, the characteristics have a special importance, because the solution is uniquely

---

* For a simple justification of this and subsequent statements in this section see Sommerfeld, *Partial Differential Equations* (Academic Press, 1949).

determined throughout such a region if it is specified at all points along two intersecting characteristics, i.e. one condition at each point is adequate instead of two, as in the case of a general curve Γ. This can be seen most easily for the simple equation

$$(\partial^2 f / \partial \xi \partial \eta) = 0$$

which has a general solution of the form

$$f = f_1(\xi) + f_2(\eta)$$

The variation of f along one characteristic, $\eta = \text{constant}$, determines the function $f_1(\xi)$; and that along one characteristic, $\xi = \text{constant}$, determines $f_2(\eta)$, and hence the solution at all other points.

In physical problems leading to hyperbolic equations it is not usual for the natural boundaries to be characteristics, and so the conditions to be specified at the boundaries are not affected.* In problems of heat conduction and similar diffusion processes, however, typified by equation (16.4), the lines $t = \text{constant}$ are characteristics. It is well known from experience that, provided suitable end conditions (at $x = 0$, l, say) are specified for all $t > 0$, the subsequent behaviour of the system is determined if f only is given at $t = 0$ over the range $0 \leqslant x \leqslant l$. This is because the initial boundary is a characteristic; if the equation were hyperbolic it would be necessary to specify $\partial f / \partial t$ also at $t = 0$.

16.2. Boundary Conditions

We now summarize the facts most relevant to the numerical solution of (16.2), (16.3) and (16.4) and similar equations, showing in particular the boundary conditions likely to be met. Three cases of common occurrence are illustrated in Fig. 16.1. The general behaviour of the characteristics is indicated by dotted lines. The boundary conditions in (a) and (b), in which we interpret t and x as time and space variables respectively, consist of "initial conditions," referring to $t = 0$, and "end conditions," referring to $x = 0$ and l. It is envisaged that the end conditions have the form

$$af + b\partial f / \partial x = c$$

in which a, b and c may be functions of t. Although it is usual for one condition to be applied at each end as shown, it can also

---

* However, the properties of the characteristics can sometimes be used to assist the process of numerical solution (see Hartree, *N.A.*, p. 257).

happen that two conditions are applied at one end, effectively determining both f and $\partial f/\partial x$ there.

It will be noticed that in (a) and (b) the regions of integration are open in the sense that boundary conditions are applied only on three sides of the rectangle. Such problems are amenable to step-by-step methods of numerical solution, analogous to those used in solving ordinary differential equations with one-point boundary conditions. These are described in § 16.4–§ 16.7. The

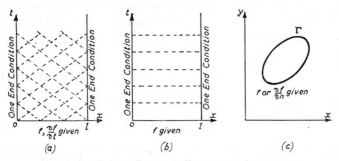

FIG. 16.1. THREE CASES OF BOUNDARY CONDITIONS

(a) Hyperbolic equations, usually associated with oscillatory systems. Two initial conditions, two end conditions required. Discontinuities, etc., in f and its first derivatives on the boundaries normally persist throughout the solution.

(b) Parabolic equations, associated with diffusion or equalization processes (e.g. conduction of heat or electric charge, mass diffusion), and having non-oscillatory solutions unless these are "forced" by the boundary conditions (Schrodinger's wave equation, although parabolic, is an exception, as the constant k is imaginary). One initial condition, two end conditions required. Abrupt changes in f on the boundaries do not persist through the region of integration.

(c) Elliptic equations, associated with equilibrium states, and particularly potential problems. The boundary conditions usually refer to a closed curve, and the solution *within* the curve is uniquely determined if $af + b\partial f/\partial n$ is specified at all points of the boundary; this solution is finite and continuous (analytic) even if discontinuities occur on the boundary.

elliptic problem has a closed boundary, however, and appropriate methods of solution are necessary; of these, relaxation will be found to be one of the most valuable. Parabolic equations can also be associated with a closed boundary, e.g. when the usual initial condition is replaced by one requiring the solution to be periodic in time. Sections 16.8–16.13 are devoted to closed boundary problems.

16.3. Other Linear Equations

Although the discussion so far has referred only to equations with two independent variables, many of the ideas can be extended to equations with three or more variables. Thus the solutions of

$$(\partial^2/\partial x^2 + \partial^2/\partial y^2 + \partial^2/\partial z^2)f = g(x, y, z) \qquad (16.9)$$

$$\{\partial^2/\partial x^2 + \partial^2/\partial y^2 - (1/c^2)\partial^2/\partial t^2\}f = 0 \qquad (16.10)$$

$$\{\partial^2/\partial x^2 + \partial^2/\partial y^2 - (1/\kappa)\partial/\partial t\}f = 0 \qquad (16.11)$$

retain many of the features of elliptic, hyperbolic and parabolic equations respectively, and require similar boundary conditions. This is true also of some equations of higher order, the best known being those which arise in the theory of elastic bodies, e.g. the biharmonic equation

$$\nabla^4 f = \{\partial^4/\partial x^4 + 2\,\partial^4/(\partial x^2\partial y^2) + \partial^4/\partial y^4\}f = 0 \qquad (16.12)$$

and the corresponding vibrational equation

$$\{\nabla^4 - (1/c^2)\partial^2/\partial t^2\}f = 0 \qquad (16.13)$$

Being of fourth order, the number of boundary conditions required is effectively twice as many as for second-order equations.

Parabolic Equations

This section is concerned with the development of step-by-step methods for solving partial differential equations, particularly the simple parabolic equation (16.4) for which the boundary conditions are most often of the open kind. Most attention will be given to methods using finite differences for both variables as these are best suited to hand computation. There is little difficulty in extending these methods to equations in which the right side is replaced by a function of f, even when this is not linear. Other lines of attack are described briefly in § 16.6.

The use of a difference equation is attended by two important requirements concerning convergence.

1. The solution of the difference equations, which refers to a mesh of points at regular intervals, must tend to the required solution of the differential equation as the finite intervals tend suitably to zero. This is the fundamental problem of convergence which cannot be properly discussed here.*

---

* Useful discussions of convergence, and the stability of particular difference formulas, have been given by H. Lewy (see footnote on p. 525), by G. G. O'Brien, M. A. Hyman and S. A. Kaplan, *J. Math. Phys.*, **29** (1951), 223, by E. C. du Fort and S. P. Frankel, *Math. Tab. Wash.*, **7** (1953), 135 and by S. H. Crandall, *Quart. Appl. Math.*, **13** (1955), 318. See also end of chapter.

2. The difference equations must not possess undesirable solutions which, if introduced through rounding errors, grow to large proportions and swamp the solution which is sought. This is the problem of "stability," of great practical importance, which arose earlier in a simple form in connexion with ordinary differential equations (Chapter 8, pages 233–235). The difficulty of unstable solutions can usually be avoided either by relating the intervals in the two variables suitably, or by a good choice of difference equation.

16.4. Finite Difference Methods

Let us first replace the variables x, y (or t) by r, s where

$$x = x_0 + rw, \quad y = y_0 + s(\alpha w^2/\kappa)$$

α being a constant which relates the standard intervals in x and y. The differential equation then becomes

$$(D_s - \alpha D_r{}^2)f = 0 \tag{16.14}$$

where D_s, D_r have the usual meaning. The aim is then to tabulate the solution f_{jk}, where j, k are integral values of r and s. Most finite difference methods make use of recurrence relations between f values at a simple pattern of points such as those shown below; from a knowledge of the solution for k, $k - 1$, etc., that for $k + 1$ is derived, and so on.

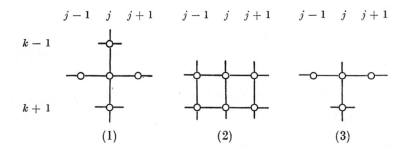

The first of these patterns can be dealt with very briefly. By using the obvious approximations

$$D_s \simeq \tfrac{1}{2}(E_y - E_y{}^{-1}), \quad D_r{}^2 \simeq \delta_x{}^2 = E_x{}^{-1} - 2 + E_x$$

one obtains at once a finite difference approximation to (16.14) which, in the box notation of § 15.8–§ 15.10, appears as

$$\boxed{\begin{array}{ccc} & -1 & \\ -2\alpha & 4\alpha & -2\alpha \\ & 1 & \end{array}}\, f_{jk} = 0(w^4) \qquad (16.15)$$

Although this gives $f_{j,\ k+1}$ in a very simple way, it was shown by Crank and Nicolson* that the formula is unstable in the sense described above for all values of α, and it should not therefore be used. By omitting the centre point of pattern (1), however, it is possible to devise a formula which is stable for all values of α and therefore most useful. This will be presented shortly, but we shall first construct a fairly general formula for pattern (2), treating pattern (3) as a special case.

The Lagrange polynomial coinciding with f at the six points of pattern (2) can be written in the form

$$p(r, s) = \{(1 - s) + sE_y\}\{\tfrac{1}{2}r(r - 1)E_x + 1 - r^2 + \tfrac{1}{2}r(r + 1)E_x\}f_{00}$$

For convenience (j, k) is replaced temporarily by $(0, 0)$. The procedure now is to satisfy the differential equation as nearly as possible at two symmetrical points $(\pm r_0, s_0)$. The derivatives at these two points of the polynomial are easily evaluated, and then by taking the mean

$$\tfrac{1}{2}\{(D_s - \alpha D_r{}^2)p(r_0, s_0) + (D_s - \alpha D_r{}^2)p(- r_0, s_0)\}$$

we obtain the following finite difference approximation to (16.14)

$$\boxed{\begin{array}{ccc} -(\alpha + \gamma/2) & \underline{-(1 - 2\alpha) + \gamma} & -(\alpha + \gamma/2) \\ \gamma/2 & 1 - \gamma & \gamma/2 \end{array}}\, f_{00} \simeq 0 \qquad (16.16)$$

where $\gamma = r_0{}^2 - 2\alpha s_0$. The coefficient attached to f_{00} is here underlined.

The first point to make about (16.16) is that it does not lead to instability provided $\alpha + \gamma \leqslant 1/2$, negative values of γ being

* J. Crank and P. Nicolson, *Proc. Camb. Phil. Soc.*, **43** (1947), 50.

permitted. One method of demonstrating this is suggested in Exercises 16, No. 1. We can also examine the truncation error of (16.16) before imposing any further restriction on α or γ. Thus in symbolic form the left side is

$$\{(E_y - 1)(1 + \tfrac{1}{2}\gamma\delta_x{}^2) - \alpha\delta_x{}^2\}f_{00}$$

and when difference operators are replaced by differential this becomes

$$\{(e^{D_s} - 1)(1 + \gamma(\cosh D_r - 1)) - 2\alpha(\cosh D_r - 1)\}f_{00}$$

$$= \left[\frac{1}{2!}\,\alpha\left(\alpha + \gamma - \frac{1}{6}\right)D_r{}^4\right.$$

$$\left. + \frac{1}{3!}\,\alpha\left(\alpha^2 - \frac{1}{60} + \frac{3}{2}\gamma\left(\alpha + \frac{1}{6}\right)\right)D_r{}^6 + \ldots\right]f_{00}$$

This last expression, in which use has been made of the equalities $D_s = \alpha D_r{}^2$, $D_s{}^2 = \alpha^2 D_r{}^4$, etc., represents the truncation error of (16.16). There seems to be an obvious merit in choosing α and γ so that the term in $D_r{}^4$ disappears, and we therefore pick out the following special cases for further examination.

1. Let $\gamma = 0$. Then replacing $(0, 0)$ by (j, k), (16.16) becomes

$$\boxed{\begin{array}{ccc} -\alpha & -(1-2\alpha) & -\alpha \\ & \underline{} & \\ & 1 & \end{array}}\,f_{jk} = \tfrac{1}{2}\alpha\{(\alpha - \tfrac{1}{6})D_r{}^4 + \tfrac{1}{3}(\alpha^2 - \tfrac{1}{60})D_r{}^6 + \ldots\}f_{jk}$$

$$(16.17)$$

From the general result quoted above it follows that this formula is stable provided $\alpha \leqslant 1/2$. However, if the higher derivatives of f are well-behaved, the best value of α, in the sense that the solution of the difference equation approaches most closely that of the differential equation, is clearly $1/6$, and we obtain the very simple result

$$\boxed{\begin{array}{ccc} -1 & -4 & -1 \\ & \underline{} & \\ & 6 & \end{array}}\,(f_{jk}/6) = \{(1/3240)D_r{}^6 + \ldots\}f_{jk} = O(w^6)$$

$$(16.18)$$

It will be seen that (16.17) involves only the four points of pattern (3), and like (16.15) it provides $f_{j,\,k+1}$ at once in terms of prior values.

It must be said at once that the small value of α can be a serious limitation. Thus suppose that the value of f for $x = 0$ is specified, and that a substantial change in $f(x, y)$ due to this value on another line at $x = 4$ is sought. This may well require the solution to be pursued as far as $y = 16$. Suppose also that the range of x is divided into 40 intervals of length $0 \cdot 1$. If $\alpha = 1/6$ each interval in y must then be $1/600$; consequently about 10,000 values of y, and 400,000 values of f, would be involved, a task which might tax even a fast electronic computor!

For this reason a modification of (16.17) due to du Fort and Frankel which imposes no such restriction on α, has real advantages. By using a very simple polynomial which fits f at the four outer points of pattern (1) (see Exercises 16, No. 2), the differential equation at the centre point can be expressed in the form

$$
\begin{array}{ccc}
 & -(1-2\alpha') & \\
-\alpha' & 0 & -\alpha' \\
 & \underline{} & \\
 & 1 &
\end{array}
\quad
f_{jk} = \tfrac{1}{2}\alpha'\{2(\alpha^2 - \tfrac{1}{12})D_r{}^4 + \tfrac{1}{3}(\alpha^2 - \tfrac{1}{60})D_r{}^6 + \ldots\}f_{jk} \quad (16.17a)
$$

where $\alpha' = 2\alpha/(1 + 2\alpha)$. Now this formula is identical with (16.17) when $\alpha = 1/2$, but unlike (16.17) it can be shown that omission of the right side does not lead to instability for larger values of α. The authors also show by means of simple examples that a fairly good representation of the solution of the differential equation is possible throughout when $\alpha = 1/2$; for larger α it is still possible but such use may be better deferred to a later stage in the calculation defined crudely by the condition, $k \gg 4\alpha$. A good compromise may be to start the solution with a value of $1/2$ or less for α, and then after a sufficient number of cycles to increase α, preferably by an odd integral factor such as 5.

It should be noticed that the difference relation in (16.17a) is such that solution values are obtained over a diamond-shaped mesh, and these can be built up either along lines of constant k, or along diagonal lines corresponding to constant (even) values of $j + k$.

We now return to the consideration of (16.16).

2. Let $\alpha + \gamma = 1/6$. This condition is consistent with stability and gives

$$\frac{1}{12}\begin{vmatrix} -(1+6\alpha) & \underline{-10+12\alpha} & -(1+6\alpha) \\ \\ 1-6\alpha & 10+12\alpha & 1-6\alpha \end{vmatrix} f_{jk} = \{(\alpha/12)(-\alpha^2 + \tfrac{1}{20})D_r^6 + \ldots\}f_{jk} \quad (16.19)$$

The chief demerit of this more general formula is that, unless $\alpha = 1/6$ (when it reverts to (16.18)), the values of $f_{j,\,k+1}$ for different j are not given separately, but only by a set of coupled relations involving all values of j. Each row of the solution must then be derived by a more elaborate calculation, using relaxation or some iterative process to solve the simultaneous equations. There may be good reason for following this line if the intervals in y corresponding to $\alpha = 1/6$ are much too brief to be practicable. To this extent (16.19) is a possible alternative to (16.17a), with the advantage that the leading error term is that in D_r^6.

It has also been suggested by Milne that (16.19) may be used as a check on results obtained by (16.18). Thus if $\alpha = 1/3$, we have

$$\frac{1}{12}\begin{vmatrix} -3 & -6 & -3 \\ \cdot & \cdot & \cdot \\ -1 & 14 & -1 \end{vmatrix} f_{j,\,k} = \{-(11/6480)D_r^6 + \ldots\}f_{j,\,k} \quad (16.20)$$

linking the values in alternate rows obtained by (16.18). It should be observed that the check is purely numerical, and not corrective, as the truncation errors of (16.18) and (16.20) are comparable.

We conclude this discussion of difference formulas with a brief reference to other types of linear parabolic equation, e.g. the equation

$$\{(1/\kappa)D_y - D_x^2\}f = af \quad (16.21)$$

or the inhomogeneous equation

$$\{(1/\kappa)D_y - D_x^2\}f = g(x, y) \quad (16.22)$$

For each of these equations it is possible to obtain finite difference formulas in which the truncation error varies as w^6 rather than w^4, by following an argument similar to that by which (16.19) was derived. The principal change is that, whereas for the homogeneous equation (16.14) the values of r_0 and s_0 were irrelevant, it is now necessary to assume that $r_0{}^2 = 1/6$ and $s_0 = 1/2$, these values being consistent with the condition, $\alpha + \gamma = 1/6$. For (16.22) the formula again involves only four points as in (16.18) if $\alpha = 1/6$; for (16.21) this is true only if α is given a value which depends on the constant a, and if w is not too large (see Exercises 16, Nos. 3 and 4). Alternatively, formulas similar to (16.17a) can be developed.

Equations with variable coefficients multiplying the derivatives, or with a non-linear function of f on the right side, may sometimes yield to difference methods of the kind described here. One must usually accept a formula with a truncation error of $0(w^4)$, e.g. Crank and Nicolson (*loc. cit.*) solved a non-linear equation using (16.16) with $\alpha + \gamma = 0$, although this involved all six points of pattern (2).

16.5. Numerical Procedure

There is a classical type of heat conduction problem based on equation (16.4), in which the initial temperature distribution $f(x, 0)$ is given, and the ends of the system are subsequently kept at a constant temperature which may be taken as zero. If the solution in such a case should be required in detail it can always be obtained from Fourier's analytical solution which takes the form

$$f(x, t) = \sum_{n=1}^{\infty} \exp\left(-\kappa(n\pi/l)^2 t\right) a_n \sin\left(n\pi x/l\right) \qquad (16.23)$$

where
$$a_n = (2/l) \int_0^l f(x, 0) \sin\left(n\pi x/l\right) dx$$

The coefficients a_n are of course the Fourier coefficients in the expansion of $f(x, 0)$ as a sine series. However, the solution in such a case can also be tabulated by a finite difference method, and, provided $f(x, 0)$ is not a discontinuous function, the process is simple and free from difficulty. It is in fact far quicker in general to tabulate a row of f_{jk} values by means of (16.18) than to calculate the same values from (16.23). This is equally true of many problems of greater difficulty, for which an analytical solution may be available but is often extremely cumbersome.

It is hardly necessary to give a numerical example of the elementary "equalization" problem, as the method of using (16.18) is obvious and extremely simple. The example given below brings in two difficulties: (1) the derivative $\partial f/\partial t$ becomes infinite at the point $(0, 0)$, since $f \propto \sqrt{t}$ when $x = 0$; (This type of infinity is rather frequent in heat conduction problems, and makes it necessary to develop a series solution in the immediate vicinity; in addition the use of a small mesh of points in this region will reduce the risk of errors due to taking finite differences infecting the solution further away. Of course, if an analytical solution is available this may be used as far away as is convenient); (2) the condition at $x = 0$ is such that a special formula must be developed for this boundary.

EXAMPLE 16.1. Tabulate the solution of $(D_t - D_x^2)f = 0$ which satisfies the conditions

(i) $\qquad\qquad f = 0 \quad$ when $\quad t = 0,\ x \geqslant 0$

(ii) $\qquad\qquad \partial f/\partial x = -A + Bf \quad$ when $\quad x = 0$
(iii) $\qquad\qquad \partial f/\partial x \to 0 \quad$ as $\quad x \to \infty$
$\left.\vphantom{\begin{array}{c}a\\b\end{array}}\right\}t > 0$

assuming the values $A = 30000$, $B = 3$.

This describes the temperature variation in a long bar, initially at zero temperature, into which heat flows at one end at a constant rate (given by A), but is also lost at a rate proportional to the excess temperature. The analytical solution is

$$f = (A/B)\{1 - \operatorname{erf} q - e^{p^2 - q^2}(1 - \operatorname{erf} p)\}$$

where $\qquad\qquad q = \tfrac{1}{2}x/\sqrt{t}, \quad p = q + B\sqrt{t}$

The steady state corresponds to a uniform temperature A/B along the bar. It is found that

$$\partial f/\partial t = Ae^{-q^2}\{1/(2\sqrt{t}) - Be^{p^2}(1 - \operatorname{erf} p)\}$$
$$\sim \tfrac{1}{2}A/\sqrt{t}$$

when $x = 0$ and t is small.

We assume the interval in x, $w = 1/10$; the interval in t, with $\alpha = 1/6$, is then $w^2/6$ or $1/600$.

Then if $x = jw$, $t = (1/6)kw^2$ it follows that

$$q = j\sqrt{(3/2k)}, \quad p = q + \sqrt{(0{\cdot}015k)}, \quad p^2 - q^2 = 0{\cdot}3j + 0{\cdot}015k$$

Because of the infinite derivative at the point $(0, 0)$ the analytical solution is continued until $k = 5$, and it is checked that the values for $k = 5$ can be obtained with sufficient accuracy by applying (16.18) to the values for $k = 4$. Errors at this stage do not exceed one unit. Thereafter all values in row $k + 1$ are obtained from row k by using (16.18), except the value $f_{0,\ k+1}$ which is obtained by the following device incorporating condition (ii).

Let a fictitious value $f_{-1,\ k}$ be assumed, and the derivative $\partial f/\partial x$

at $x = 0$ be expressed in terms of $f_{-1, k}, f_{0, k}$, etc., by some formula like the following—

$$w(\partial f/\partial x)_{0, k} = \{-6f_{-1, k} - 20f_{0, k} + 36f_{1, k} - 12f_{2, k} + 2f_{3, k}\}/4\,!$$
$$= w(-A + Bf_{0, k})$$
$$= -3000 + 0{\cdot}3f_{0, k}$$

Now eliminate $f_{-1, k}$ by using the relation given by the differential equation—

$$f_{0, k+1} = \{f_{-1, k} + 4f_{0, k} + f_{1, k}\}/6$$

with the result that

$$f_{0, k+1} = 2000 + (-3{\cdot}2f_{0, k} + 42f_{1, k} - 12f_{2, k} + f_{3, k})/36 \quad (A)$$

A similar formula not involving $f_{3, k}$ is

$$f_{0, k+1} = 1500 + (3{\cdot}2f_{0, k} + 8f_{1, k} - f_{2, k})/12 \quad (B)$$

This method is much more satisfactory than any attempts to extrapolate $f_{0, k+1}$ from the values in the same row, as this introduces an error which subsequently builds up. It is advisable to use both (A) and (B), although (A) should be more accurate, both as a numerical check and to make sure that the values of $f_{0, k+1}$ are not too disparate.

The calculation to $k = 12$ appears as follows—

k		0	1	2	3	4	5	6	7	8	
1		1246	56	0							
2		1693	236	11	0						
3		2006	439	46	1	0		Analytical			
4		2257	635	105	9	0					
5		2470	817	176	23	2	0				
											Check s
6	2676	(2655)	986	257	45	5	0				− 3
7	2828	(2814)	1146	343	74	11	1	0			+ 2
8	2973	(2962)	1292	432	108	20	3	0			− 2
9	3102	(3095)	1429	521	147	32	5	1	0		− 1
10	3222	(3216)	1556	610	190	47	9	2	0		+ 1
11	3331	(3328)	1676	698	236	64	14	3	0		− 4
12	3433		1789	784	284	84	20	4	1	0	− 5
(Anal.	3433		1786	783	284	84	20	4	1	0)	

It will be seen that the value of $f_{0, 6}$ given by (A) is appreciably in error, but this error is steadily reduced in subsequent values and beyond $k = 12$ does not exceed one or two units (values from the analytical solution are shown in brackets). A sum check has been applied to each row, using the obvious fact that

$$s = 6(f_{1, k+1} + f_{2, k+1} + \ldots - f_{1, k} - f_{2, k} - \ldots)$$
$$+ f_{1, k} - f_{0, k} \simeq 0$$

Values of s up to 6 are satisfactory, but it is preferable that these should alternate in sign. The check can be modified to include one on $f_{0, k+1}$ if desired. Another procedure would be to apply (16.20) at each point.

A check on the adequacy of the integration formula can be obtained by examining values of $(1/15)\delta_t{}^3 f_{jk}$, which should represent very nearly the truncation error of (16.18), i.e. $D_r{}^6 f/3240$ or $D_s{}^3 f/15$. In this example the formula appears to be quite accurate enough.

Later in the calculation it would be possible to increase the interval in x. It is very simple to double w, but it must be remembered that the interval in t is then increased fourfold. Conversely, if a smaller interval had been assumed initially it would have been possible to restrict the use of the analytical solution to a shorter range of t.

We shall not consider here the solution of equations in three variables, such as (16.11), although this is not difficult so long as the boundary in the (x, y) plane is rectilinear. A finite difference approximation to ∇^2 is necessary, and for this the operator H, or preferably K (see (15.39)), can be used. Numerical examples have been given by Milne (*N.S.D.E.*, sec. 63).

16.6. Other Methods of Integration

We shall mention briefly some alternatives to the finite difference method just described, applicable to an equation such as (16.21), but with $G(x, t, f)$ on the right, when the boundary conditions are open.*

1. Simultaneous Equations in the t Variable

If finite differences are used to replace the continuous x variable, so that for example $\partial^2 f/\partial x^2$ is replaced by

$$\{f_{j+1}(t) - 2f_j(t) + f_{j-1}(t)\}/w^2$$

where
$$f_j(t) = f(x_j, t)$$

then the partial differential equation is replaced by a set of simultaneous ordinary differential equations of the form

$$\frac{1}{\kappa} \frac{df_j}{dt} + \frac{2}{w^2} f_j = G(x_j, f_j, t) + \frac{1}{w^2} (f_{j+1} + f_{j-1}) + 0(w^2)$$

The solution of these simultaneous equations, together with one or two special equations representing the boundary conditions which may have a different form, presents no difficulty in principle but may offer a major problem in hand computation. For this reason it should preferably not be attempted without special equipment, e.g. differential analyser; even so the solution of more than six coupled equations is likely to be beyond the capacity of most machines. The method has a wide field of application, however, and can be extended to equations with two space variables, e.g. (16.11).

2. Ordinary Differential Equations in the x Variable

An alternative method is to use finite differences in place of the t variable so reducing the problem to that of solving an ordinary differential equation with x as variable, for each of a discrete sequence of t values. The solution of the kth equation is used in the solution of the $(k+1)$th and so on. Each equation is of course likely to be subject to two-point boundary conditions, with all the numerical difficulties this entails.

This approach is clearly similar to that in § 16.4; indeed, except when a continuous analogue machine such as a differential analyser is used, it often reduces to using (16.16) in a disguised form. Although a variety of finite difference methods of solving the equation may be available, including relaxation, each needs to be carefully examined to ensure that rounding errors do not accumulate seriously. For hand computing it seems preferable to use finite differences directly for both variables, as in § 16.4, when this can be done, though a possible exception occurs when restrictions on the solution are applied at one boundary only.

3. Use Of Relaxation

Relaxation is not well suited to solving an ordinary differential equation when boundary conditions refer to one point only; so for a partial equation it is not generally suitable when the boundary conditions are of the open kind. However, Allen and Severn have suggested that relaxation methods might often be applied in the solution of heat conduction and similar problems if the second order equation is replaced by one of fourth order

e.g. $\dfrac{\partial f}{\partial t} = \kappa \dfrac{\partial^2 f}{\partial x^2}$ replaced by $\dfrac{\partial^2 g}{\partial t^2} = \kappa^2 \dfrac{\partial^4 g}{\partial x^4}$

where $\dfrac{\partial g}{\partial t} + \kappa \dfrac{\partial^2 g}{\partial x^2} = f$

Suitable conditions can then be applied on all four boundaries and the solution by relaxation should in principle proceed smoothly. However, since the equation is one of fourth order, the process is not simple, and one would not resort to it unless there were special difficulties which make the course worthwhile.

Hyperbolic Equations

The direct numerical solution of hyperbolic equations has so far been developed less fully than that of other types, perhaps because the solutions of greatest interest are often periodic; a linear hyperbolic equation can then be reduced to an ordinary differential equation or an elliptic partial equation and solved by appropriate methods.

For a simple equation such as (16.3) it is obvious that a possible finite difference equivalent has the form

$$(\delta_t^2 - \beta^2\delta_x^2)f \simeq 0$$

or
$$\begin{array}{|ccc|}\hline & 1 & \\ -\beta^2 & -2(1-\beta^2) & -\beta^2 \\ & 1 & \\ \hline \end{array} f_{jk} = 0(w_1^4) \qquad (16.24)$$

where $\beta = aw_2/w_1$, w_1 and w being the intervals in x and t respectively. It can be shown* that the use of this approximation is not subject to instability arising from rounding errors provided $\beta \leqslant 1$. The simplest formula for $f_{j,\,k+1}$ in terms of prior values clearly arises when $\beta = 1$, and this choice has the peculiar advantage that the truncation error of (16.24) is seemingly eliminated whatever the value of w_1. Thus from the assumption that $\delta_t^2 f = \delta_x^2 f$, it follows that $\delta_t^{2p}f = \delta_x^{2p}f$, and hence that a higher difference approximation to the differential equation, such as

$$\{\delta_t^2 - (1/12)\delta_t^4 + (1/90)\delta_t^6\}f_{jk}$$
$$= \{\delta_x^2 - (1/12)\delta_x^4 + (1/90)\delta_x^6\}f_{jk}$$

is automatically satisfied.

---

* The point is discussed by H. Lewy, *Studies and Essays presented to R. Courant* (Interscience Pub., 1948). The abrupt change which occurs when w_1/w_2 falls below the velocity a arises from the fact that the solution at points on the two characteristics through a point (j, k) cannot be influenced by any change in f_{jk}, when (16.24) is used. This is in marked contrast to the differential equation which represents the propagation of influences along the characteristics.

It is of course essential that this expansion in terms of differences should converge well. Otherwise the condition $\beta = 1$ is not such a severe restriction on the interval in the t variable as that in (16.17) for parabolic equations. In practice, however, both w_1 and w_2 must be adjusted so that the detailed variation of the solution at interior points, which is similar to the prescribed variation on the boundaries, is not obscured by having too coarse a mesh of points.

We shall not pursue here in detail the application of (16.24), or its obvious extension to equations of the form (16.10).* Instead a subsidiary use of the formula will be described; this is in the estimation of latent roots for certain ordinary differential equations of second order, when the solutions are subject to two-point boundary conditions, following a method devised by Milne.†

16.7. Latent Roots of Ordinary Differential Equations

We consider the linear hyperbolic equation of the form

$$\partial^2 f/\partial t^2 = \{\partial^2/\partial x^2 + p(x)\partial/\partial x + q(x)\}f \qquad (16.25)$$

where $p(x)$, $q(x)$ are continuous functions of x in the range $a \leqslant x \leqslant b$, and investigate the solution of such an equation which satisfies initial conditions of the form

$$f(x, 0) = F(x), \quad (\partial f/\partial t)_{t=0} = 0 \qquad (16.26)$$

and end conditions of the form

$$f + A\partial f/\partial x = 0, \ x = a; \quad f + B\partial f/\partial x = 0, \ x = b \qquad (16.27)$$

It is always possible to find harmonic solutions of (16.25) of the form $u(x) \cos \mu t$, provided

$$\{d^2/dx^2 + p(x)d/dx + q(x) + \mu^2\}u(x) = 0 \qquad (16.28)$$

However, when end conditions such as (16.27) are imposed, they will be satisfied only when μ is one of the latent roots μ_m associated with these conditions. The general solution of (16.25) is in fact a linear combination

$$f(x, t) = \sum_m c_m u_m(x) \cos \mu_m t \qquad (16.29)$$

---

* A more detailed study of hyperbolic equations has been made by R. Courant, E. Isaacson and M. Rees, *Comm. Pure Appl. Math.*, **5** (1952), 243. The use of characteristics in solving the more complicated types of equation has also been described by Hartree, *N.A.* p. 237.

† W. E. Milne, *J. Res. Nat. Bur. Stand.*, **45** (1950), 245; see also Milne, *N.S.D.E.*, Ch. 11.

where $u_m(x)$ is the solution of (16.28) corresponding to μ_m, and subject to the conditions

$$u + Adu/dx = 0, \; x = a; \quad u + Bdu/dx = 0, \; x = b$$

The solution of (16.25) is thus reduced to the problem of finding latent roots and functions of (16.28) corresponding to the conditions at a and b. Conversely, if a solution of (16.25) can be found by a convenient numerical technique, using a suitable initial function $F(x)$, it may be possible to analyse this solution to obtain estimates of μ_m and $u_m(x)$. It is this aspect of the problem which will be pursued here. The latent roots of (16.28) are of course likely to be infinite in number, and as the first step is to replace the differential equation by a matrix of finite order n, the procedure will only lead to estimates of the first n latent roots.

We first write $x_j = x_0 + jw$, where $x_0 = a$, $x_{n+1} = b$, and $t_k = kw$, and use the approximation

$$w(\partial f/\partial x)_{j, \, k} = \tfrac{1}{2}(f_{j+1, \, k} - f_{j-1, \, k}) + 0(w^2)$$

With the condition $\beta = 1$ thus satisfied, the difference approximation to (16.25), corresponding to (16.24), is given by

$$\left|\begin{array}{ccc} & 1 & \\ -(1 - \tfrac{1}{2}wp_j) & -w^2q_j & -(1 + \tfrac{1}{2}wp_j) \\ & 1 & \end{array}\right| f_{jk} = 0(w^4) \qquad (16.30)$$

where $p_j = p(x_j)$, $q_j = q(x_j)$. This relation defines $f_{j, \, k+1}$ in terms of f_{jk} and other prior values, and can be used to build up a table of f_{jk} from any initial values f_{j0}, assuming only that $f_{j, \, 1} = f_{j, \, -1}$ (consistent with the initial condition $\partial f/\partial t = 0$) and certain end conditions relating to f_{j0} and $f_{j, \, n+1}$. In effect (16.29) has now been replaced by the expansion of n terms

$$f_{jk} = \sum_{m=1}^{n} \bar{c}_m \bar{u}_{jm} \cos k\bar{\nu}_m \qquad (16.31)$$

where $\bar{\nu}_m = w\bar{\mu}_m$, $\bar{u}_{jm} = \bar{u}_m(x_j)$; $\bar{\mu}_m$ and $\bar{u}_m(x)$ are approximations to μ_m and $u_m(x)$ for $m \leqslant n$.

Let this be done for an initial function such that $f_{j0} = 0$ when

$j > 1$ (only $f_{1,\,0}$ being finite), and simple end conditions of the form

$$f(a, t) = f_{0k} = 0, \quad f(b, t) = f_{n+1,\,k} = 0$$

The application of (16.30) as far as $k = n - 1$ leads to the following triangular array—

$\mathbf{b}_0$	f_{10}	0	0	$\ldots 0$
$\mathbf{b}_1$	f_{11}	f_{21}	0	$\ldots 0$
$\mathbf{b}_2$	f_{12}	f_{22}	f_{32}	$\ldots 0$
.				
.				
.				
$\mathbf{b}_{n-1}$	$f_{1,\,n-1}$	$f_{2,\,n-1}$	$f_{3,\,n-1} \cdots f_{n,\,n-1}$	

The elements in these n rows can be regarded as composing a set of "vectors," $\mathbf{b}_0, \mathbf{b}_1 \ldots, \mathbf{b}_{n-1}$, the elements of $\mathbf{b}_k$ being generated from those of $\mathbf{b}_{k-1}$ and preceding vectors by means of (16.30). It should be noticed that

$$f_{21} = \tfrac{1}{2}\{1 - \tfrac{1}{2}wp_2\}f_{10}, \quad f_{32} = \{1 - \tfrac{1}{2}wp_3\}f_{21},$$
$$f_{43} = \{1 - \tfrac{1}{2}wp_4\}f_{32}, \text{ etc.}$$

so that none of the diagonal elements are zero, provided only that $\tfrac{1}{2}|wp_j| < 1$ for all $j \leqslant n$. This implies that all the above vectors are linearly independent, since each vector contains one more non-zero element than the preceding vector. Now the finite difference matrix which has replaced the differential equation (16.28) can have no more than n independent vectors associated with it; hence if (16.30) is applied again to give the elements of one more vector

$$\mathbf{b}_n \qquad f_{1n} \qquad f_{2n} \qquad f_{3n} \cdots f_{nn}$$

then it is clear that $\mathbf{b}_n$ must be a linear combination of $\mathbf{b}_0, \ldots, \mathbf{b}_{n-1}$, i.e.

$$a_0\mathbf{b}_0 + a_1\mathbf{b}_1 + \ldots + a_{n-1}\mathbf{b}_{n-1} + \mathbf{b}_n = 0$$

or $\qquad\qquad \displaystyle\sum_{k=0}^{n-1} a_k f_{jk} + f_{jn} = 0 \quad (j = 1, \ldots, n) \qquad\qquad$ (16.32)

This is a set of triangular equations from which

$$a_{n-1}, a_{n-2}, \ldots, a_0$$

(in that order) can be found in the usual way. The basic similarity in principle of this method to that of Lanczos (§ 12.15) for finding the latent roots of a matrix is now apparent. In Milne's application of the principle the hyperbolic equation is used as a device for generating the set of independent vectors, without attempting to make these orthogonal.

The equation which in this case actually provides the latent roots is easily derived as follows. By substituting for f_{jk} in (16.32) from (16.31), we have

$$\sum_{m=1}^{n} \bar{c}_m \bar{u}_{jm} \sum_{k=0}^{n} a_k \cos k\bar{\nu}_m = 0$$

in which $a_n = 1$; and since the values of $\bar{c}_m$ are essentially arbitrary it follows that

$$\sum_{k=0}^{n} a_k \cos k\bar{\nu}_m = 0 \quad (m = 1, \ldots, n) \tag{16.33}$$

This is the equation from which the roots $\bar{\nu}_m$, and hence $\bar{\mu}_m$, can be calculated. Milne has given a simple procedure for deriving the elements $\bar{u}_{jm}$ of the corresponding latent vectors (see Exercises 16, No. 9). The derivation and solution of (16.33) is illustrated in the following example.

EXAMPLE 16.2. Estimate the first few latent roots of the equation
$$d^2u/dx^2 + \mu^2(1 + (2x - 1)^2)u = 0$$
when $u(0) = u(1) = 0$.

This is the equation that was considered in Example 14.3. In order to apply Milne's method it is first necessary to bring the equation to the form of (16.28) by changing the independent variable to y, where
$$dy/dx = A(1 + (2x - 1)^2)^{1/2}$$
or $y = y_0 + \frac{1}{4}A\{(2x - 1)(1 + (2x - 1)^2)^{1/2} + \sinh^{-1}(2x - 1)\}$

If we assume that y ranges from -1 to $+1$ when x ranges from 0 to 1 it follows that
$$d^2u/dy^2 + p(y)du/dy + (\mu^2/A^2)u = 0$$
where $p(y) = (2/A)(2x - 1)\{1 + (2x - 1)\}^{-3/2}$
and $1/A = \frac{1}{4}(2^{1/2} + \sinh^{-1} 1) = 0.57390$

Details of the tabulation of $p(y)$ need not be given here, and we only quote the following results—

y	0	0·1	0·2	0·3	0·4	0·5
$p(y)$	0	0·12893	0·24220	0·32985	0·38945	0·42412
y		0·6	0·7	0·8	0·9	1·0
$p(y)$		0·43945	0·44115	0·43396	0·42137	0·40581

When y is negative the values are similar but opposite in sign.

One consequence of the antisymmetry of $p(y)$ about $y = 0$ is that successive modal solutions of the equation are alternately symmetrical and antisymmetrical about this point. We can use this fact to reduce the calculation appreciably, by considering only positive values of y, and deriving even and odd latent roots separately. We consider first those roots for which $u = 0$ when $y = 0$.

1. ROOTS WITH ANTISYMMETRICAL SOLUTIONS

We choose an interval of $0 \cdot 2$ in y, giving $n = 4$. The table of f_{jk} values, constructed by applying (16.30), appears as follows. The constant multipliers, $1 \pm wp_j/2$, are shifted laterally so that they appear vertically above the elements they multiply; in this example $q_j = 0$.

j	0	1	2	3	4	5		
$1 - wp_{j+1}/2$		0·96106	0·95606	0·95660				
$1 + wp_{j-1}/2$			1·02422	1·03894	1·04394			
s_j		0·96106	1·98028	1·99554	1·04394			
			Values of f_{jk}				σ_k	a_k
$k = 0$	0	100000	0	0	0	0	100000	0·51523
1	0	0	48053	0	0	0	48053	0
2	0	− 50783	0	45942	0	0	− 4841	1·02373
3	0	0	− 49128	0	43948	0	− 5180	0
4	0	465	0	− 47032	0	0	− 46567	1

A few comments on this table are necessary. First, the row containing s_j (merely the sum of the two previous rows), and the column of row sums σ_k, are included for checking purposes. It is an obvious corollary of (16.30) that

$$\text{row } \mathbf{s} \times \text{row } \mathbf{b}_k - \sigma_{k-1} = \sigma_{k+1}$$

This should be used to check the row $\mathbf{b}_{k+1}$ as soon as it is completed. Also, at the completion of the back-substitution process giving the column of a_k values, the check

$$\text{column } \boldsymbol{\sigma} \times \text{column } \mathbf{a} = 0$$

should be applied.

From the above table the equation giving the latent roots is

$$D(\nu) = \cos 4\nu + 1 \cdot 02373 \cos 2\nu + 0 \cdot 51523 = 0$$

where $\nu = 0 \cdot 2\mu/A$. It is found without much difficulty that the first three roots of this equation are such that

$$\bar{\mu}_2/A = 3 \cdot 1680 = \pi + 0 \cdot 0264$$
$$\bar{\mu}_4/A = 6 \cdot 2908 = 2\pi + 0 \cdot 0076$$
$$\bar{\mu}_6/A = 9 \cdot 4172 = 3\pi - 0 \cdot 0076$$

If roots to 4 or 5D are sufficient, the NBS tables of sines and cosines for radian arguments up to 25 are here most valuable; $D(\nu)$ is tabulated in the neighbourhood of the root, which is then found by a linear inverse interpolation. Thus for the first of the above roots—

$5\nu(=\mu/A)$	$\cos 4\nu$	$1{\cdot}02373\cos 2\nu$	$D(\nu)$	
3·150	− 0·81295	+ 0·31308	+ 0·01536	
				− 853
3·160	− 0·81758	+ 0·30918	+ 0·00683	
				− 849
3·170	− 0·82216	+ 0·30527	− 0·00166	

2. ROOTS WITH SYMMETRICAL SOLUTIONS

The results of a similar calculation for the even latent roots are given below. These differ from the odd roots in that the corresponding solutions are finite when $x = 1/2$, i.e. $y = 0$; hence we assume a finite value for f_{00} instead of f_{10}, and also that $f_{-1,\,k} = f_{1,\,k}$. Since the first column now contains non-zero elements it is necessary to derive one additional row before proceeding to derive a_k. In connexion with the calculation of these elements in the first column it should be noticed that the multiplier $(1 - wp_0/2)$ (in brackets) is doubled. As before, $w = 0{\cdot}2$.

	0	1	2	3	4	5
$1 - wp_{j+1}/2$	0·97578	0·96106	0·95606	0·95660		
$1 - wp_{j-1}/2$		(2·0)	1·02422	1·03894	1·04394	
s_j	0·97578	2·96106	1·98028	1·99554	1·04394	

	Values of f_{jk}						σ_k	a_k
$k = 0$	100000	0	0	0	0		100000	0
1	0	48789	0	0	0	0	48789	0·08692
2	− 2422	0	46889	0	0	0	44467	0
3	0	− 3128	0	44829	0	0	41701	0·07221
4	− 3834	0	− 3321	0	42883	0	35728	0
5	0	− 4015	0	− 3237	0	0	− 7252	1

From the final column the equation for the latent roots is

$$\cos 5\nu + 0{\cdot}07221\cos 3\nu + 0{\cdot}08692\cos \nu = 0$$

The first three roots are found to give

$$\bar{\mu}_1/A = 1{\cdot}6912 = \pi/2 + 0{\cdot}1204$$
$$\bar{\mu}_3/A = 4{\cdot}7305 = 3\pi/2 + 0{\cdot}0181$$
$$\bar{\mu}_5/A = 7{\cdot}8540 = 5\pi/2 \text{ exactly}$$

A similar calculation using a smaller interval, $w = 0.1$, leads to the estimates 1.6930, 4.7370 and 7.8673 respectively for these roots. It is interesting that the estimates obtained from the difference equations are smaller than the correct values for the differential equation, as in Example 14.3. For the first root a comparison can be made with the result obtained in Example 14.3; the final value there obtained for μ_1 was 2.941, from which $\mu_1/A \simeq 1.688$. Admittedly a high precision was not sought in that calculation, and the result is now seen to be rather too low.

The improvement of the alternate roots in (1) by a similar calculation with $w = 0.1$ is a suitable exercise for the reader.

As a further illustration of the kind of accuracy attainable by this method, we give below the first seven latent roots of the equation

$$d^2u/dx^2 + 2du/dx + \mu^2 u = 0$$

for which $u(0) = u(1) = 0$, as given by Milne (loc. cit.). These were calculated (a) with an interval $w = 1/8$, (b) with an interval, $w = 1/16$, and are compared with exact analytical results.

m	$w = 1/8$ $\mu_m^{(1)}$	$w = 1/16$ $\mu_m^{(2)}$	Exact μ_m	$\mu_m - \mu_m^{(2)}$	$(\mu_m^{(2)} - \mu_m^{(1)})/3$
1	3·2898	3·2952	3·2969	0·0017	0·0018
2	6·3457	6·3583	6·3623	0·0040	0·0042
3	9·4507	9·4715	9·4777	0·0062	0·0069
4	12·5664	12·5976	12·6061	0·0085	0·0104
5	15·6820	15·7289	15·7398	0·0109	0·0156
6	18·7870	18·8625	18·8761	0·0136	0·0252
7	21·8430	21·9974	22·0139	0·0165	0·0515

It will be seen that the relative error of the values $\mu_m^{(1)}$ increases from -0.00215 to -0.00776, whereas that of $\mu_m^{(2)}$ increases from -0.00052 only to -0.00072 for these roots. It is instructive to see how far the estimates given by $\mu_m^{(2)}$ can be improved by assuming that the error due to the finite difference approximation is proportional to w^2. The last column shows the correction which would be made to $\mu_m^{(2)}$ on this basis; when compared with the previous column, it is seen that a substantial betterment would result for the first 2 or 3 roots, but the "correction" is increasingly unsatisfactory for the later roots.

Milne has also given examples of the use of the method when the differential equation has a singularity at one of the end boundary points, and has also shown how it can be extended, though with some difficulty, to find the latent roots of simple elliptic equations with two independent variables. Although it is usually most convenient to derive latent roots with the help of a hyperbolic partial equation, as has been done here, this is not an essential feature of the method. A parabolic equation might also be used, with a suitable expansion in place of (16.29).

Elliptic Equations

At the present time the numerical solution of elliptic partial differential equations by difference methods has been more highly developed than that of parabolic and hyperbolic equations, and generally speaking, rather more certainty is attached to the results obtained. This is mainly because it is easier to assess the errors associated with the solution of a problem in which conditions are specified over a closed boundary than when the boundary is open, as usually happens with parabolic and hyperbolic equations. For elliptic equations, questions of stability and convergence are much less acute; nevertheless it is still important to examine carefully the precision of any solution based on a finite difference approximation.

It is not proposed to consider in detail here any equation more complicated than Poisson's equation in the Cartesian form (16.2). Finite difference approximations to this equation have already been discussed in § 15.8–§ 15.10; assuming now a rectangular mesh of points in the (x, y) plane, such that

$$x_i = x_0 + iw, \quad y_j = y_0 + jw$$

it is obvious that we might use one or more of the following approximations—

$$Hf_{ij} = w^2 g_{ij} + \triangle_1 \qquad (16.34)$$

$$2Xf_{ij} = 2w^2 g_{ij} + \triangle_2 \qquad (16.35)$$

$$Kf_{ij} = 6w^2 g_{ij} + \triangle_3 \qquad (16.36)$$

where H, X and K are defined in (15.32), (15.34) and (15.39), and $g_{ij} = g(x_i, y_j)$. The error terms $\triangle_1$, $\triangle_2$ and $\triangle_3$ are normally proportional to w^4; however, for Laplace's equation, $\triangle_3$ is proportional to w^8, and as was seen in (15.41), a slight modification to (16.36) will give a similar accuracy of approximation to Poisson's equation. It is sometimes valuable to express $\triangle$ in terms of differences of the solution; in particular, for (16.34)

$$\triangle_1 = \{(1/12)(\delta_x{}^4 + \delta_y{}^4) - (1/90)(\delta_x{}^6 + \delta_y{}^6) + \ldots\}f_{ij}$$

This may be verified by reference to (15.31). Most difference methods of solving (16.2) are based on the approximation (16.34). This provides a set of linear equations relating the approximation solution values at the mesh points, and when combined with the relations which arise at the boundary points, these equations have a well defined solution. It is usually convenient to find this solution by some kind of iterative procedure, which will be applicable even when the boundary is not rectilinear. However, it is worth emphasizing that for regions which are rectangular or have certain other simple shapes, an analytical solution of the difference equations can be found which may yield numerical results without too long a computation. We shall in the following sections derive such a solution for the particular case of a rectangular boundary, and somewhat special boundary conditions. An example is given in which the exact solution of the difference equations is compared with that of the differential equation which they represent. Various iterative procedures, including relaxation, are described in § 16.9, § 16.10, § 16.11 and § 16.12.

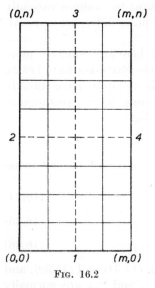

FIG. 16.2

16.8. Analytical Solution of Difference Equations for a Rectangular Boundary

We first consider the solution of the difference equations

$$Hf_{ij} = 0 \qquad (16.37)$$

representing Laplace's equation, over the rectangular mesh shown in Fig. 16.2. It will be sufficient for the present purpose to consider a simplified set of boundary values, in which $f_{i,\,0}$ and $f_{i,\,n}$ are specified for $i = 1, 2, \ldots, m - 1$, and all values on boundaries 2 and 4 are zero. A solution f^A satisfying these conditions can be combined by addition with another, f^B, having zero values on boundaries 1 and 3 and non-zero values on 2 and 4. If it is further desired that f should have non-zero values at the corner points, it will be necessary to include also a trivial solution of the form

$$f^C = a + bi + cj + dij$$

in which a, b, c, d are chosen to give the required corner values; and to adjust the boundary conditions on f^A and f^B accordingly.

It is now easily shown, either by direct substitution or by assuming a solution of the form $f_{ij} = \phi_i \psi_j$ in which the variables are separated, that

$$\sin{(si\pi/m)}(P\lambda_s^{\ j} + Q\lambda_s^{-j})$$

is a solution of (16.37) which vanishes on boundaries 2 and 4, provided s is an integer and

$$\lambda_s = \mu_s + \sqrt{(\mu_s^2 + 1)}$$

where $$\mu_s = 1 - \cos{(s\pi/m)} \geqslant 1$$

The general solution of this kind then takes the form

$$f_{ij} = \sum_{s=1}^{N} \sin{(si\pi/m)}\{P_s\lambda_s^{\ j} + Q_s\lambda_s^{-j}\} \qquad (16.38)$$

where P_s, Q_s must be consistent with the prescribed values, $2(m-1)$ in number, on boundaries 1 and 3. To determine these constants uniquely we must take $N = m - 1$.

Equation (16.37) can be conveniently written in terms of matrices. Thus if $c_{is} = \sin{(si\pi/m)}$ and $t_{sj} = P_s\lambda_s^{\ j} + Q_s\lambda_s^{-j}$, and f_{ij}, c_{is}, t_{sj} are regarded as elements of matrices $\mathbf{F}$, $\mathbf{C}$, $\mathbf{T}$ respectively, then

$$\mathbf{F} = \mathbf{CT} \quad \text{and} \quad \mathbf{T} = \mathbf{C}^{-1}\mathbf{F}$$

It is a very fortunate consequence of the properties of trigonometrical functions that the inverse matrix

$$\mathbf{C}^{-1} = (2/m)\mathbf{C}$$

and hence $$\mathbf{T} = (2/m)\mathbf{CF}$$

or $$t_{sj} = (2/m)\sum_{i=1}^{m-1} f_{ij}\sin{(si\pi/m)} \qquad (16.39)$$

In particular, on the boundaries 1 and 3

$$t_{s0} = P_s + Q_s \qquad = (2/m)\sum_{i=1}^{m-1} f_{i0}\sin{(si\pi/m)} = A_s, \text{ say}$$

$$t_{sn} = P_s\lambda_s^{\ n} + Q_s\lambda_s^{-n} = (2/m)\sum_{i=1}^{m-1} f_{in}\sin{(si\pi/m)} = B_s, \text{ say} \qquad (16.40)$$

Since A_s and B_s can be calculated from the given boundary values for each value of s, P_s and Q_s are determined by this pair of linear equations, from which

$$P_s\lambda_s{}^n = B_s + (B_s\lambda_s{}^{-n} - A_s)/(\lambda_s{}^n - \lambda_s{}^{-n})$$
$$Q_s = A_s + (A_s\lambda_s{}^{-n} - B_s)/(\lambda_s{}^n - \lambda_s{}^{-n}) \qquad (16.41)$$

The solution values can now be tabulated directly from (16.38). When n is large, clearly $P_s\lambda_s{}^n \simeq B_s$ and $Q_s \simeq A_s$, since $\lambda_s > 1$. It is worth remarking that the elements of $\mathbf{C}$ depend only on the method of subdividing the rectangle, and may be used repeatedly for different sets of boundary values.

It should be observed that, as a consequence of the simple relation between $\mathbf{C}$ and $\mathbf{C}^{-1}$, the $2(m - 1)$ constants P_s and Q_s are obtained by inverting $(m - 1)$ matrices of order 2, whereas the direct solution of the equations for the boundary values given by (16.38) would require the inversion of one matrix of order $2(m - 1)$. The analytical procedure followed here in solving the difference equations is basically the same as the method of solving Laplace's equation with the help of Fourier series expansions to represent the solution on boundaries 1 and 3.

EXAMPLE 16.3. Tabulate an approximate solution of Laplace's equation over a rectangle with corners at the points $(0, 0)$, $(1, 0)$, $(0, 2)$ and $(1, 2)$ in the (x, y) plane, satisfying the conditions

$$f = 0 \quad \text{when} \quad x = 0 \quad \text{and} \quad 1$$
$$f = 64x(1 - x) \quad \text{when} \quad y = 0 \quad \text{and} \quad 2$$

We assume a common interval in x and y of size $1/8$, so that $m = 8$, $n = 16$. At the mesh points on both boundaries 1 and 3 (Fig. 16.2), the solution values are given by

$$\mathbf{f_0} = \{0,\ 7,\ 12,\ 15,\ 16,\ 15,\ 12,\ 7,\ 0\}$$

One consequence of the symmetry about $y = 1$ is that $A_s = B_s$ and

$$P_s\lambda_s{}^{16} = Q_s = A_s/(1 + \lambda_s{}^{-16})$$

Referring to (16.4) it is seen that the quantities A_s are the elements of a single-column matrix $\mathbf{A} = (1/4)\mathbf{Cf_0}$. Written in full this equation appears as follows—

$$\frac{1}{4}
\begin{bmatrix}
0\cdot383 & 0\cdot707 & 0\cdot924 & 1\cdot0 & 0\cdot924 & 0\cdot707 & 0\cdot383 \\
0\cdot707 & 1\cdot0 & 0\cdot707 & 0 & -0\cdot707 & -1\cdot0 & -0\cdot707 \\
0\cdot924 & 0\cdot707 & -0\cdot383 & -1\cdot0 & -0\cdot383 & 0\cdot707 & 0\cdot924 \\
1\cdot0 & 0 & -1\cdot0 & 0 & 1\cdot0 & 0 & -1\cdot0 \\
0\cdot924 & -0\cdot707 & -0\cdot383 & 1\cdot0 & -0\cdot383 & -0\cdot707 & 0\cdot924 \\
0\cdot707 & -1\cdot0 & 0\cdot707 & 0 & -0\cdot707 & 1\cdot0 & -0\cdot707 \\
0\cdot383 & -0\cdot707 & 0\cdot924 & -1\cdot0 & 0\cdot924 & -0\cdot707 & 0\cdot383
\end{bmatrix}
\begin{bmatrix} 7 \\ 12 \\ 15 \\ 16 \\ 15 \\ 12 \\ 7 \end{bmatrix}
=
\begin{bmatrix} 16\cdot5111 \\ 0 \\ 0\cdot6061 \\ 0 \\ 0\cdot1208 \\ 0 \\ 0\cdot0258 \end{bmatrix}$$

with $\mathbf{C}$, $\mathbf{f_0}$, and $\mathbf{A}$ labelling the three matrices respectively.

The elements of **C** have been abbreviated to save space; to 6D, the relevant values are 0·382683, 0·707107 and 0·923880.

Since $A_s = 0$ when s is even, the corresponding values of Q_s also vanish, and it is unnecessary to evaluate λ_s except for odd values of s. With $\mu_s = 1 - \cos (s\pi/8)$, we find that

$$\lambda_1^{-1} = 0·67858, \quad \lambda_3^{-1} = 0·34621, \quad \lambda_5^{-1} = 0·22000, \quad \lambda_7^{-1} = 0·17632$$

$$Q_1 = 16·4778, \quad Q_3 = 0·6061, \quad Q_5 = 0·1208, \quad Q_7 = 0·0258$$

The values of f_{ij} are then derived from (16.38) in the simpler form

$$f_{ij} = \sum_{s=1}^{7} \sin (si\pi/8) . Q_s(\lambda_s^{-16+j} + \lambda_s^{-j}) \qquad (H)$$

It is particularly interesting to compare the values obtained from this formula, representing the exact solution of the difference equations, with those from the exact solution of the differential equation. The latter can be found without difficulty for the boundary conditions considered here and is

$$f(x, y) = \sum_{s=1}^{\infty} \sin s\pi x \ \{\bar{P}_s e^{s\pi y} + \bar{Q}_s e^{-s\pi y}\} \qquad (E)$$

where $\qquad \bar{P}_s e^{2s\pi} = \bar{Q}_s = 512/\{(s\pi)^3(1 + e^{-2s\pi})\}$, s odd

$$= 0 \qquad , s \text{ even}$$

Comparative values of f_{ij} are shown in the following table—

i	j								
	0	1	2	3	4	5	6	7	8
1 (E)	7000	4468	2958	1997	1373	971	723	588	545
(H)		4518	3004	2036	1406	999	747	611	567
2 (E)	12000	8020	5401	3671	2531	1792	1335	1086	1007
(H)		8068	5463	3733	2588	1842	1380	1128	1048
3 (E)	15000	10248	6982	4773	3300	2339	1743	1419	1316
(H)		10290	7048	4845	3370	2403	1801	1473	1369
4 (E)	16000	11002	7527	5157	3569	2531	1886	1536	1424
(H)		11043	7592	5231	3642	2599	1949	1594	1481

The discrepancies, which reach 4 per cent near the centre of the rectangle, are an indication of the truncation errors to be expected in similar cases. Methods of improving the finite difference solution will be considered later.

The foregoing analysis, which is in the form given by Hyman,* can be modified to give solutions of the difference equations over

* M. A. Hyman, *Appl. Sci. Res.*, **2** (1952), 325.

other regions with simple boundaries, circular, annular, ellipsoidal, etc., provided suitable coordinates are chosen to define the mesh-points. It can also be extended to include Poisson's equation (16.2), if we can tabulate a particular solution of this equation, say f^D, which is zero at all boundary points. When f^D is added to the solution of Laplace's equation, $f^A + f^B + f^C$, having the required boundary values, the problem is completed.

The nature of the particular solution of Poisson's equation can be shown by considering once again the rectangular boundary. For this we first expand $g_{ij}(= g(x_i, y_j))$ as a double Fourier series of the form

$$g_{ij} = \sum_{s=1}^{m-1} \sum_{t=1}^{n-1} q_{st} c_{is} d_{tj} \tag{16.42}$$

where $c_{is} = \sin{(is\pi/m)}$ as before, $d_{tj} = \sin{(tj\pi/n)}$, and q_{st} is a numerical coefficient. In matrix form, (16.42) becomes

$$\mathbf{G} = \mathbf{CQD}$$

and it is then obvious that the elements q_{st} can be derived from the known values g_{ij} at all interior mesh-points by means of the equation

$$\mathbf{Q} = \mathbf{C^{-1}GD^{-1}} = (4/mn)\mathbf{CGD} \tag{16.43}$$

Assuming now a similar expansion for the solution f^D, such that

$$f_{ij} = \sum_s \sum_t p_{st} c_{is} d_{tj} \quad (\text{or } \mathbf{F} = \mathbf{CPD}) \tag{16.44}$$

it is easily verified by direct substitution in the difference equations (16.34), neglecting $\triangle_1$, that

$$p_{st} = -\tfrac{1}{4}w^2 \frac{q_{st}}{\sin^2{(\pi s/2m)} + \sin^2{(\pi t/2n)}}$$

Although straightforward, the tabulation of f_{ij} is lengthy, and we shall not give a numerical illustration. However, it should be noted that if $g(x, y) = $ constant, the tabulation depends on the two parameters m and n, and once carried out is available for all kinds of boundary conditions.

16.9. Iterative Methods of Solution

To appreciate the significance of the iterative methods most commonly used to solve difference equations such as (16.34), it is instructive to examine first the diffusion equation

$$(\partial^2/\partial x^2 + \partial^2/\partial y^2)f(x, y, t) - g(x, y) = \partial f/\partial t \tag{16.45}$$

We shall assume the same mesh in the (x, y) plane as hitherto, and also a regular sequence of t values, $t_k = k\alpha w^2$, where k is integral and α is the same parameter as in (16.14). The corresponding solution values will be denoted by $f_{ij}^{(k)}$. By an obvious extension of (16.17) it is possible to replace (16.45) by an approximate set of difference equations relating the solution at the point (x_i, y_j) and time t_{k+1} to solution values at time t_k; thus, corresponding to (16.17)

$$f_{ij}^{(k+1)} = f_{ij}^{(k)} + \alpha H f_{ij}^{(k)} - \alpha w^2 g_{ij} \qquad (16.46)$$

Such equations provide an obvious iterative scheme for deriving the solution of (16.34), which is now seen to correspond to the ultimate steady-state solution of a simple diffusion equation. In the process it may be possible to take advantage of techniques already developed for parabolic equations. Several methods of applying (16.46) will now be discussed.

1. THE LIEBMANN AND RICHARDSON METHODS*

It was emphasized earlier with reference to (16.17) that for a stable solution it is essential that α should be less than $1/2$, and preferably much smaller. It is very convenient here to assume that $\alpha = 1/4$, for (16.46) then takes on a simple numerical form

$$f_{ij}^{(k+1)} = 1/4 \begin{array}{|ccc|} \hline & 1 & \\ 1 & 0 & 1 \\ & 1 & \\ \hline \end{array} f_{ij}^{(k)} - (w^2/4) g_{ij} \qquad (16.47)$$

This relation is the basis of what is generally called the Liebmann iterative process for solving (16.34). A suitable set of starting values $f_{ij}^{(0)}$ is chosen, perhaps partly by guesswork with whatever help can be obtained from the boundary values, and the iterative relations (16.47) applied until the solution values are constant to the precision required.

The more general formula (16.46) is ascribed to Richardson, and can be used similarly. There is now no reason to prefer the value of $1/6$ for α, as in (16.18), because we are not seeking an accurate solution of the diffusion equation throughout, but only the

---

* H. Liebmann, *Sitz. Bayer Akad. München* (1918), 385. L. F. Richardson, *Phil. Trans. Roy. Soc.*, A **210** (1910), 307.

limiting solution. The best choice of α is a matter which depends largely on the particular boundary conditions, and if any general rule can be given it is that α should be chosen as large as possible consistently with the iteration remaining reasonably stable.

In discussing later the application of relaxation methods to this problem, much importance will be attached to the residuals associated with the solution values at any stage. It will clarify the relation between relaxation and routine iterative methods, and perhaps throw some light on the choice of α, to introduce the residuals at this point. They are defined as

$$R_{ij}^{(k)} = Hf_{ij}^{(k)} - w^2 g_{ij} \qquad (16.48)$$

so that (16.46) can be written in the form

$$f_{ij}^{(k+1)} - f_{ij}^{(k)} = \alpha R_{ij}^{(k)} \qquad (16.49)$$

It should also be noticed that the residuals at successive stages of iteration satisfy the relation

$$R_{ij}^{(k+1)} - R_{ij}^{(k)} = \alpha H R_{ij}^{(k)} \qquad (16.50)$$

When $\alpha = 1/4$, the change made in each f_{ij} would be just sufficient to cancel the residual R_{ij} were no change made at adjacent points. However, when all the changes are superimposed there is no net change in the sum total of residuals over those points which are more than one interval distant from the boundary, merely because the elements of H add up to zero. Any change in ΣR for the whole region can arise only through changes at points adjacent to the boundary, by which residuals are pushed out to the boundary, as it were, and "sunk." However, we must note a second effect of applying (16.49), which is that residuals are more evenly spread over the region, and if they are not all of one sign this may lead to a significant reduction in $\Sigma |R|$, if not of ΣR. It must be remembered here that if the iteration is to succeed both $\Sigma |R|$ and ΣR must tend to zero. Indeed, if positive and negative residuals are more or less balanced, the spreading effect is likely to be more important than the sinking of residuals at the boundary, and may control the convergence to the desired solution, at least in the initial stages.

The opposite extreme occurs when residuals are predominantly of one sign, and the reduction of ΣR and $\Sigma |R|$ must then proceed hand-in-hand by sinking residuals at the boundary. The rate at which this occurs is generally increased by increasing α, as may be verified by summing (16.49) over the whole mesh, and it is quite safe to do this provided the iteration shows evidence of being stable,* i.e. the solution values vary monotonically. However, if successive values of f_{ij} oscillate strongly, and $\Sigma|R|$ shows signs of increasing instead of decreasing, this is clear evidence of instability in the iteration, and it is wiser to decrease α below the normal value of $1/4$. It should be observed that if $\alpha > 1/4$, the change in f_{ij} alone is sufficient to reverse the sign of the residual R_{ij}. This corresponds in the relaxation method to "over-relaxation"; likewise if $\alpha < 1/4$ we have under-relaxation.

2. Milne's Extension of the Liebmann-Richardson Method

Milne† has suggested that (16.49) be replaced by

$$f_{ij}^{(k+1)} - f_{ij}^{(k)} = \beta L R_{ij}^{(k)} \tag{16.51}$$

where L is a suitable differencing operator, and β a parameter playing the same rule as α. At the same time (16.50) is replaced by

$$R_{ij}^{(k+1)} - R_{ij}^{(k)} = \beta H L R_{ij}^{(k)} \tag{16.52}$$

The operator L can be chosen to distribute the residual R_{ij} more widely than is done by the operator H alone; thus one such operator proposed by Milne is

$$L = 1/16 \begin{vmatrix} 1 & 2 & 1 \\ 2 & 6 & 2 \\ 1 & 2 & 1 \end{vmatrix} \text{ for which } HL = 1/16 \begin{vmatrix} & 1 & 2 & 1 & \\ 1 & 0 & 0 & 0 & 1 \\ 2 & 0 & -16 & 0 & 2 \\ 1 & 0 & 0 & 0 & 1 \\ & 1 & 2 & 1 & \end{vmatrix}$$

The effect is thus to spread each residual over 12 points at a distance of about 2 intervals, instead of over the 4 nearest points. At the same time the sinking of residuals at the boundary is enhanced because all points at a distance of two intervals from the

---

* Considerable attention has been given to methods of using over-relaxation to the best advantage. See for instance B. A. Carré, *Computer J.*, **4** (1961), 73.
† See Milne, *N.S.D.E.* § 86.

boundary now contribute to this effect. On both counts (16.51) may be expected to be a more effective iterative formula than (16.49). This gain is obtained, however, at the cost of using a 12- or 13-point formula to improve the f values, instead of a 4- or 5-point formula. The process may be interpreted in terms of a diffusion equation, though this will naturally be more complicated than (16.45).

The choice of β is governed by similar considerations to those discussed above. The value $\beta = 1$ corresponds to $\alpha = 1/4$, since the change in f_{ij} alone is then just sufficient to cancel R_{ij}; iteration with $\beta > 1$ or $\beta < 1$ corresponds to over- and under-relaxation respectively.

3. The Method of Shortley and Weller

The following practical procedure developed by Shortley and Weller* was originally based on the Liebmann formula (16.47), but many of the ideas embodied in the method can be applied equally to (16.49) or (16.51). We shall describe it in terms of (16.49), leaving α unspecified.

The important modifications of the iterative routine are—

(a) The changes made to solution values during a particular iteration are not entirely independent. Thus the mesh-points are traversed in a certain order, and whenever improved solution values are available they are inserted in the iterative formula in the course of completing the round. The principle is precisely similar to that of the second iterative method of solving linear equations described in § 13.1 and § 13.2, where it was found that the rate of convergence was slightly greater than in the first.

(b) When the first iteration has been completed, subsequent iterations are carried out on the difference function $\delta = f^{(1)} - f^{(0)}$, which is zero at all boundary points. This has the further advantage that calculations are made with smaller numbers than would otherwise be the case, and as will be shown in a moment, extrapolation towards the correct solution is made much easier.

The first of these modifications introduces an element of flexibility, because the route through the mesh-points is at the discretion of the computer. It will often be found that the process converges more rapidly along certain routes than along others. A typical

---

* G. Shortley and R. Weller, *J. Appl. Phys.*, **9** (1938), 334; Shortley, Weller and Fried, *J. Appl. Phys.*, **11** (1940) 283; Shortley, Weller, Darby and Gamble, *J. Appl. Phys.*, **18** (1947) 116.

route is shown in Fig. 16.3 (Example 16.4). In the first iteration the routine is to replace value $f_{ij}{}^{(0)}$ in turn by

$$\alpha \text{ (sum of values at 4 nearest points)} + (1 - 4\alpha)f_{ij}{}^{(0)} - \alpha w^2 g_{ij}$$

and in forming the sum to use such improved values as are available.

If this procedure were repeated using solution values we should obtain a sequence of solutions $f^{(1)}, f^{(2)}, f^{(3)}, \ldots$ Let the exact solution values of the difference equations be denoted by $\bar{f}_{ij}$, and the error of the kth iterate by $e_{ij}{}^{(k)}$, so that

$$f_{ij}{}^{(k)} = \bar{f}_{ij} + e_{ij}{}^{(k)}$$

Then $\qquad H'e_{ij}{}^{(k)} = H'f_{ij}{}^{(k)} - H'\bar{f}_{ij} = H'f_{ij}{}^{(k)} - w^2 g_{ij}$

where H' is used instead of H to indicate the modification made in (a) above. Since

$$f_{ij}{}^{(k+1)} - f_{ij}{}^{(k)} = e_{ij}{}^{(k+1)} - e_{ij}{}^{(k)}$$

it follows from (16.49) that

$$e_{ij}{}^{(k+1)} = (1 + \alpha H')e_{ij}{}^{(k)} \qquad (16.53)$$

It should be noted that g_{ij} has vanished from this iterative relation. The boundary values of $e_{ij}{}^{(k)}$ are of course zero.

From this point the argument is most easily presented in terms of matrices. Let $\mathbf{e}^{(k)}$ be a single-column matrix with N elements, equal in number to the interior points of the mesh and listed in the order in which they are traversed in iteration, the element corresponding to (i, j) having the value $e_{ij}{}^{(k)}$. Matrices $\mathbf{f}^{(k)}, \bar{\mathbf{f}}$ can be defined similarly. Now (16.53) can be written in the form

$$\mathbf{e}^{(k+1)} = \mathbf{T}\mathbf{e}^{(k)} \qquad (16.54)$$

where $\mathbf{T}$ is a square matrix of order N, the elements of which are independent of any boundary values and can readily be found for any particular route. The details of $\mathbf{T}$, however, are of no concern at the moment.

Now let $\boldsymbol{\delta}^{(1)}$ be the difference matrix

$$\boldsymbol{\delta}^{(1)} = \mathbf{f}^{(1)} - \mathbf{f}^{(0)} = \mathbf{e}^{(1)} - \mathbf{e}^{(0)}$$

and suppose a sequence $\boldsymbol{\delta}^{(1)}, \boldsymbol{\delta}^{(2)}, \ldots$ be formed such that

$$\boldsymbol{\delta}^{(k+1)} = \mathbf{T}\boldsymbol{\delta}^{(k)} \qquad (16.55)$$

again assuming zero boundary values throughout.

Then
$$\delta^{(1)} = (\mathbf{T} - \mathbf{I})\mathbf{e}^{(0)}$$
$$\delta^{(2)} = (\mathbf{T}^2 - \mathbf{T})\mathbf{e}^{(0)}$$
.
.
.
$$\delta^{(p)} = (\mathbf{T}^p - \mathbf{T}^{p-1})\mathbf{e}^{(0)}$$

so that
$$\sum_{k=1}^{p} \delta^{(k)} = (\mathbf{T}^p - \mathbf{I})\mathbf{e}^{(0)}$$

Now if the sequence $\mathbf{f}^{(k)}$ converges to $\bar{\mathbf{f}}$, $\mathbf{T}^p\mathbf{e}^{(0)}$ tends to zero for large p; consequently

$$\sum_1^{\infty} \delta^{(k)} = -\mathbf{e}^{(0)} \quad \text{and} \quad \bar{\mathbf{f}} = \mathbf{f}^{(0)} + \sum_1^{\infty} \delta^{(k)} \qquad (16.56)$$

To determine $\bar{\mathbf{f}}$, therefore, it is only necessary to estimate the sum of the infinite series formed from $\delta^{(k)}$. Usually after a few terms have been obtained by iteration it is found that the elements of $\delta^{(k)}$ are mainly of one sign, and the elements of $\delta^{(k+1)}$, $\delta^{(k+2)}$, . . . are roughly λ, λ^2, . . . times those of $\delta^{(k)}$. The sum of the infinite series can then be estimated on the assumption that it is geometric, i.e.

$$\bar{\mathbf{f}} \simeq \mathbf{f}^{(0)} + \sum_{k=1}^{p} \delta^{(k)} + \delta^{(p)}\lambda/(1 - \lambda) \qquad (16.57)$$

This equation is to be interpreted as applying to each element $\bar{f}_{ij}$.

An extrapolation of this kind should be followed up by treating the solution obtained as a new $\mathbf{f}^{(0)}$, evaluating $\mathbf{f}^{(1)}$ and repeating the iterative process with $\mathbf{f}^{(1)} - \mathbf{f}^{(0)}$, until the required precision is attained.

The behaviour of the series (16.56) can be understood through an argument similar to that in § 13.1. Assuming that the matrix $\mathbf{T}$ has real and distinct latent roots λ_i, with latent column matrices $\mathbf{u}_i$ satisfying the equation $\mathbf{T}\mathbf{u}_i = \lambda_i\mathbf{u}_i$, then any matrix such as $\delta^{(1)}$ can be expanded in the form

$$\delta^{(1)} = a_1\mathbf{u}_1 + a_2\mathbf{u}_2 + \ldots + a_N\mathbf{u}_N$$

and
$$\delta^{(k+1)} = \mathbf{T}^k\delta^{(1)} = a_1\lambda_1^k\mathbf{u}_1 + a_2\lambda_2^k\mathbf{u}_2 + \ldots + a_N\lambda_N^k\mathbf{u}_N$$

If there is a numerically largest root, say λ_1, then when k is large

$$\delta^{(k+1)}/\delta^{(k)} \simeq \lambda_1$$

provided
$$|\lambda_1| < 1$$

The condition for the convergence of the iteration is the familiar one that all latent roots of **T** are numerically less than unity.

Now if $\alpha = 1/4$ and H is not replaced by H', it can be shown that **T** is a symmetric matrix whose latent roots do satisfy the above condition (for proof, see Shortley and Weller, *loc. cit.*). It also happens (see Milne, *N.S.D.E.*, sec. 85) that positive and negative roots occur in pairs, so that λ_1 and $-\lambda_1$ are both roots. This would lead to a situation such as that in Example 9.16, in which $\delta^{(k+2)}/\delta^{(k)}$ and $\delta^{(k+1)}/\delta^{(k-1)}$ form separate sequences for large k. However, when **T** is formed from H', the symmetric property is lost and the largest root is almost certainly a distinct root. It is then also more difficult to prove that convergence occurs in general, although the departure from symmetry seems unlikely to be so serious as to destroy this result. It may also be expected to hold so long as $\alpha < 1/2$.

We conclude this section by an application of Shortley and Weller's method to the problem of Example 16.3.

EXAMPLE 16.4. Derive a solution of the difference equations in Example 16.3 by iteration.

We shall derive solutions of the difference equations, first when the mesh-points are at intervals of $1/4$ in x and y, and secondly for intervals of $1/8$ as in Example 16.3. This will enable the error arising from the use of finite difference approximations to be estimated subsequently.

Calculation at Intervals of $1/4$. It is sufficient to consider only the eight points shown in Fig. 16.3 (*a*), since the solution at other points within the rectangle is given by symmetry. The iteration is performed along the path shown, starting at the point (4, 8) and ending at (2, 8), and assuming that $\alpha = 1/4$. A typical calculation is shown in Fig. 16.4. The initial solution $f^{(0)}$ is quite crude, and is iterated once to give the values $f^{(1)}$ shown in brackets. Thereafter the difference function is iterated until, after 5 iterations, all values are declining, and the sums of the elements of $\delta^{(4)}$ and $\delta^{(5)}$ are 36·6 and 25·2 respectively. This suggests that $\lambda \simeq 25·2/36·6 = 0·69$ and $\lambda/(1-\lambda) \simeq 2·3$. The "tail" values are estimated accordingly, and the resulting values of f are shown on the left of the vertical lines. A direct iteration with these values shows only one change of one unit in the final digit.

Calculation at Intervals of $1/8$. Starting values over the finer mesh are first obtained. At points for which both coordinates are odd, e.g. (1, 1), (1, 3), etc., the mean of 4 values on diagonal lines can be used; for those which remain values are then available at the 4 nearest points. The initial values shown in Fig. 16.5 are derived in this way. The first stage of iteration is set out as in Fig. 16.4, the path being that shown in Fig. 16.3 (*b*), beginning at the point (4, 1). With the value of $1/4$ for α, the iteration is very stable and converges slowly. The contributions to $\delta^{(5)}$, $\delta^{(6)}$ and $\delta^{(7)}$ shown in the figure total 226, 199 and 176 respectively, giving a geometric ratio of 0·88. Extrapolation is performed at this stage, the tail values being assumed to be $7\delta^{(7)}$. Comparison with the exact solution of the difference equations for this mesh in Example 16.3 shows that the remaining errors are greatest round the central point (4, 8), the largest errors being 55 and the error total over the quarter rectangle about 550.

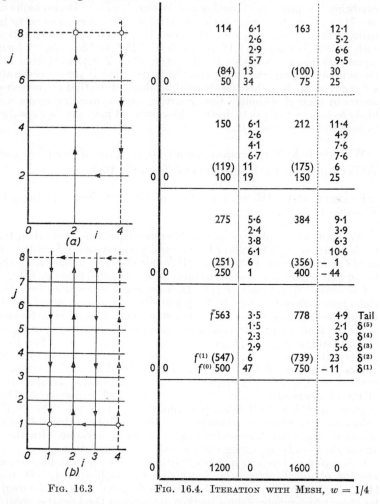

FIG. 16.3

FIG. 16.4. ITERATION WITH MESH, $w = 1/4$

The next stage of iteration is not shown, but is of length comparable with that in Fig. 16.5. Provided a guarding figure is used throughout, the solution values attained differ at most by one unit from those given in Example 16.3. A summary of results is given in a later section (§ 16.12).

One or two comments can be made on this computation. First the path through the mesh has been carefully chosen to *end* at the point

	578	− 21	1073	− 35	1412	− 42	1533	− 42	
		− 3		− 5		− 6		− 6	
		− 3		− 5		− 6		− 6	
		− 3		− 5		− 6		− 6	
		− 3		− 4		− 6		− 6	
		− 2		− 4		− 5		− 5	
	(614)	− 1	(1135)	− 4	(1487)	− 4	(1611)	− 7	
0 0	615	− 1	1140	− 5	1492	− 5	1630	− 19	
	621	− 21	1154	− 35	1518	− 42	1649	− 42	
		− 3		− 5		− 6		− 6	
		− 3		− 5		− 6		− 6	
		− 3		− 5		− 6		− 6	
		− 3		− 5		− 6		− 7	
						− 6		− 8	
	(660)	− 3	(1219)	− 5	(1596)	6	(1730)	− 8	
0 0	660	0	1224	− 5	1598	− 2	1736	− 6	
	757	− 21	1407	− 35	1839	− 49	1989	− 56	
		− 3		− 5		− 7		− 8	
		− 3		− 6		− 8		− 8	
		− 4		− 6		− 8		− 8	
		− 4		− 6		− 8		− 9	
		− 4		− 7		− 8		− 9	
	(800)	− 4	(1480)	− 8	(1936)	− 9	(2094)	− 7	
0 0	805	− 5	1500	− 20	1942	− 6	2120	− 26	
	1009	− 21	1860	− 42	2431	− 56	2622	− 70	
		− 3		− 6		− 8		− 10	
		− 3		− 7		− 10		− 10	
		− 4		− 8		− 11		− 12	
		− 5		− 9		− 12		− 12	
		− 6		− 10		− 12		− 11	
	(1058)	− 7	(1954)	− 12	(2549)	− 10	(2758)	− 11	
0 0	1062	− 4	1966	− 12	2552	− 3	2766	− 8	
	1412	− 21	2603	− 42	3382	− 63	3658	− 70	
		− 3		− 6		− 9		− 10	
		− 4		− 7		− 10		− 12	
		− 4		− 8		− 13		− 14	
		− 4		− 10		− 15		− 16	
		− 8		− 12		− 16		− 16	
	(1464)	− 8	(2704)	− 16	(3526)	− 18	(3807)	− 11	
0 0	1477	− 13	2750	− 46	3536	− 10	3840	− 33	
	2038	− 21	3737	− 42	4844	− 63	5234	− 70	
		− 3		− 6		− 9		− 10	
		− 3		− 7		− 10		− 12	
		− 4		− 8		− 12		− 15	
		− 3		− 9		− 16		− 19	
		0		− 14		− 22		− 17	
	(2086)	− 14	(3846)	− 23	(4994)	− 18	(5392)	− 15	
0 0	2095	− 9	3869	− 23	5000	− 6	5405	− 13	
	3007	− 14	5470	− 28	7054	− 42	7590	− 56	
		− 2		− 4		− 6		− 8	
		− 2		− 5		− 8		− 10	
		− 3		− 6		− 9		− 12	
		− 3		− 7		− 11		− 15	
		0		− 6		− 18		− 21	
	(3009)	+ 22	(5544)	− 18	(7176)	− 30	(7726)	− 14	
0 0	3033	− 24	5630	− 86	7190	− 14	7780	− 54	
	4520	− 7	8073	− 14	10292	− 21	$\tilde{f}$ 11043	− 28	Tail
		− 1		− 2		− 3		− 4	$\delta^{(7)}$
		− 1		− 3		− 4		− 6	$\delta^{(6)}$
		− 2		− 3		− 5		− 7	$\delta^{(5)}$
		− 1		− 3		− 6		− 8	$\delta^{(4)}$
		− 1		− 4		− 6		− 10	$\delta^{(3)}$
	(4526)	7	(8097)	+ 5	(10349)	− 12	$f^{(1)}$ (11121)	− 15	$\delta^{(2)}$
0 0	4408	118	8098	1	10352	− 3	$f^{(0)}$ 11121	0	$\delta^{(1)}$
	7000	0	12000	0	15000	0	16000	0	

FIG. 16.5. ITERATION WITH MESH, $w = 1/8$

(1, 1). This is because the solution in this region is varying rapidly, and the iteration there tends to be rather unstable. Evidence of this is given by the large positive change at (1, 1) and the slight oscillations at neighbouring points. Had the iteration been started in this corner, a large number of positive changes would have resulted, so delaying the convergence.

Secondly, the stability of the iteration over most of the region suggests that an increase in α would improve the convergence. A particularly simple formula is obtained if $\alpha = 1/3$; with this value, a computation like that in Fig. 16.5 leaves smaller residual errors at the corresponding stage. Thus after 8 iterations followed by extrapolation, the largest error is found to be 40 (near the point (3, 4)) and the sum of errors is about 350, compared with 55 and 550 when $\alpha = 1/4$. The improved convergence is also shown by the fact that $\lambda \simeq 0.82$. However, if α is increased to $1/2$ the iteration soon becomes unstable.

16.10. Improvement of Convergence

Although the method illustrated in the last section already offers opportunities for improving the rate of convergence, by comparison with a simple Liebmann process, Shortley and Weller emphasize that a more substantial improvement may result by using another device. This requires that the mesh-points be grouped together as far as possible in square blocks of say 4 or 9 points, and that the values over each block be improved as a whole before proceeding to the next block. The method of doing this will be made clear by quoting the iterative formulas for 4- and 9-point blocks.

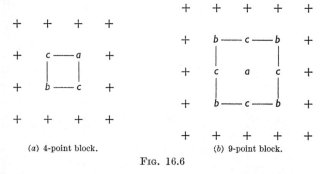

(a) 4-point block.   (b) 9-point block.

Fig. 16.6

Nine-point Blocks. We consider these first as the treatment is more symmetrical. Referring to Fig. 16.6 (b), the centre value at a is first improved by using the difference operators L and LH already defined in § 16.9, the formula for Poisson's equation being

$$f_a^{(1)} = (1 + LH)f_a^{(0)} - w^2 Lg_a \qquad (16.58)$$

This does not involve any $f^{(0)}$ values at points within the block, but does involve values of g at all nine points. The four values at the points marked b are improved next, in each case using the improved value at a and the values at three other points diagonally placed and exterior to the block. A typical formula can be written

$$f_b^{(1)} = \{1 + \tfrac{1}{4}X'\}f_b^{(0)} - \tfrac{1}{2}w^2g_b \qquad (16.59)$$

where X' takes the place of X to show that the improved value at a is being used. Finally the usual Liebmann formula supplies the values at the points c, with the help of the improved b values; thus

$$f_c^{(1)} = \{1 + \tfrac{1}{4}H'\}f_c^{(0)} - \tfrac{1}{4}w^2g_c \qquad (16.60)$$

It will be observed that the improved values within the block are all expressed in terms of values at 16 points external to the block.

Four-point Blocks. Here there is an arbitrary choice to be made of the first value to be improved. Suppose this is the point a in Fig. 16.6 (a), and that the values at b and the two points c are derived subsequently. The formulas are

$$f_a^{(1)} = (1 + L_1H)f_a^{(0)} - w^2L_1g_2 \qquad (16.61)$$

where
$$L_1 = 1/24 \begin{bmatrix} 2 & 7 \\ 1 & 2 \end{bmatrix} \quad 1 + L_1H = 1/24 \begin{bmatrix} 0 & 2 & 7 & 0 \\ 2 & 0 & \underline{0} & 7 \\ 1 & 0 & 0 & 2 \\ 0 & 1 & 2 & 0 \end{bmatrix}$$

and the elements underlined refer to point a.

$$f_b^{(1)} = \{1 + \tfrac{1}{4}X'\}f_b^{(0)} - \tfrac{1}{2}w^2g_b \qquad (16.62)$$

$$f_c^{(1)} = \{1 + \tfrac{1}{4}H'\}f_c^{(0)} - \tfrac{1}{4}w^2g_c \qquad (16.63)$$

The use of these formulas, for 9- or 4-point blocks, can be embodied in the general procedure described in § 16.9, i.e. after the first iteration, the difference function can be introduced and further iterations carried out upon this, assuming all boundary values to be zero. The iterative formulas for $\delta^{(k)}$ are exactly as above, except that all terms involving g are omitted.

By examining the matrix $\mathbf{T}$ associated with iteration over blocks of points, and in particular the largest latent root of this matrix, Shortley and Weller conclude that convergence should be more rapid with the use of 4- or 9-point blocks than by a simple iteration from point to point. From a consideration of square regions with many interior points it appears that iteration with 4-point blocks should proceed twice as rapidly, and with 9-point blocks $3\frac{1}{2}$ times as rapidly. Larger blocks might be taken, with further reduction in the number of iterations required, but the formulas become more varied and cumbersome; Shortley and Weller conclude that the 9-point block is the most convenient.

A word of warning is, however, necessary. It is obvious that the difference equations which are solved when, for instance, (16.58), (16.59) and (16.60) are used, are not the same as when (16.47) is used throughout. The exact solution of the difference equations which is approached by the iterative process may in fact be significantly different. Thus in Example 16.4, if a 9-point block with corners at (1, 1), (1, 3), (3, 1) and (3, 3) were used, the final value at the point (1, 1) would differ from that actually derived in the second digit. This is because the 9-point scheme would derive the value at (1, 1) using the operator $1 + X/4$, and the result is quite different from that using $1 + H/4$. In this region the solution values are sensitive to the size of the mesh, and for accurate results, i.e. accurate in relation to the differential equation, a smaller mesh is desirable. The example emphasizes that if blocks of points are used, it is advisable, when a stable solution has been achieved, to follow up with a simple iteration using (16.47). This will show up any inconsistencies and indicate where it is most necessary to reduce the mesh size. It may not of course be necessary or desirable to reduce the mesh over the whole region, and Shortley and Weller have given formulas for use at points on or near a boundary between regions in which the mesh is different.

16.11. Use of Relaxation

It will have been evident from preceding sections that the difference equations which replace Laplace's or Poisson's equation are admirably suited to solution by relaxation. Thus when the residuals are defined by (16.48) a positive increase of 1 unit in the value at any mesh point reduces the residual at this point by 4 units and increases those at four neighbouring points by 1 unit. This is shown schematically in Fig. 16.7 (*a*). In solving difference equations in one variable it was found that the process could often be hastened by using group relaxations; so here, it is convenient to make simultaneous changes along a line of points, or over a rectangular block of points, as shown in Fig. 16.7 (*b*) and (*c*)

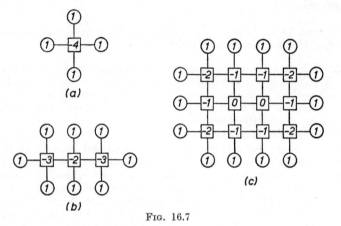

(a)

(b)

(c)

Fɪɢ. 16.7

respectively. In each case a unit positive change is made at all points represented by a square, and the numbers within the squares and circles show the resulting changes in the residuals. Relaxation over a rectangular block is often most valuable when the residuals are mainly of one sign; if a suitable block relaxation is then applied over the whole region the algebraic sum of the residuals can be reduced nearly to zero through the effect described earlier as "sinking residuals at the boundary." Those residuals which remain, being a balanced set of positive and negative values, are more easily reduced by the "spreading effect" of relaxations made at interior points.

It is the ability to combine group and single point relaxations which constitutes the main strength of this method in comparison with more routine iterative processes. The other devices of the method which were described in Chapter 13 can also be used in the present context, in particular those of over- or under-relaxation. The Gauss transformation, however, is no longer a practical proposition. At the same time it must be remembered that relaxation is essentially a procedure for hand computing; its very flexibility makes it unsuitable for translation to automatic machines, on which routine methods can be much better controlled.

Of the two numerical illustrations which follow the first is yet another treatment of the problem initiated in Example 16.3. The second introduces a simple form of Poisson's equation, and shows how some of the difficulties arising from a curved boundary can be treated.

EXAMPLE 16.5. Improve by relaxation the starting values used in Example 16.3 for the mesh of interval 0·1.

Fig. 16.8 shows how the first stage of relaxation might be carried out. No doubt better combinations of relaxations could be found, but those chosen are at least reasonable and would probably suggest themselves to anyone not having a great deal of experience of the method. The layout is slightly different to that in Fig. 16.5, as the starting values of the solution, and subsequent *changes* made in them, all appear on the left of the vertical lines, and the initial and subsequent values of the residuals appear on the right. The residual R_{ij} is given by Hf_{ij}. As an aid to following the steps of the process, whenever a change is made in the solution at any point the amount of this is placed level with the value of the residual at the point *after* the change. The order in which the changes have been made is indicated by the numbers in brackets; the sequence is also given below, with a few explanatory notes. One general remark is that in this problem it is profitable to over-relax, as was discovered in Example 16.4, and in making point changes this principle has been applied to the extent of changing a residual $- R$ into $+ R/2$, approximately. It is also assumed that any change within the quarter-rectangle shown is accompanied by similar changes at symmetrical points in the other three-quarters.

1. Change of $+ 125$ at $(1, 1)$. This removes the dominant positive residual.

2. Block change of $- 100$ over the rectangle with corners at $(2, 2)$, $(6, 2)$, $(6, 14)$ and $(2, 14)$. This change is intended to leave comparable positive and negative residuals along the edges of this rectangle. The amount is a matter of judgment.

3, 4. Block changes of $- 60$ along lines joining $(1, 3)$ to $(1, 13)$ and $(3, 1)$ to $(5, 1)$. These changes follow naturally on (2).

5 to 8. Point changes of $- 60$ at $(4, 2)$, $- 50$ at $(2, 2)$, $- 40$ at $(2, 4)$, $- 30$ at $(2, 1)$ and $(1, 2)$, to reduce some of the dominant residuals.

9. Block change of $- 50$ along the line joining $(4, 3)$ to $(4, 15)$.

10. Block change of $- 40$ along the line joining $(3, 2)$ to $(3, 16)$. Note that the effect on the residuals on the axis of symmetry is doubled by reason of a similar change in the adjacent quarter rectangle.

11, 12. Changes of $- 30$ at $(4, 4)$, $- 25$ at $(4, 6)$ and $- 15$ at $(4,8)$, followed by $- 20$ at $(4, 1)$ and $(4, 2)$.

	Column 1 (→ 7000)	Column 2 (→ 12000)	Column 3 (→ 15000)	Column 4 (→ 16000)	Residuals
0	(3) − 60; + 20; − 100; **615**; 0	(2) − 100; **1140**	− 5; + 35; + 95; − 5; (10) − 40; (2) − 100; **1492**	+ 13; + 28; − 52; − 2; (11) − 15; (9) − 50; (2) − 100; **1630**	+ 16; − 44; + 36; − 64
0	(3) − 60; + 24; − 96; + 4; **660**	(2) − 100; **1224**	− 18; + 2; + 42; + 102; + 2; (10) − 40; (2) − 100; **1598**	+ 32; − 48; + 2; (9) − 50; (2) − 100; **1736**	− 18; + 22; + 102; + 2
0	(3) − 60; + 2; + 22; − 98; + 2; **805**	(13) − 20; (2) − 100; **1500**	− 3; − 63; + 37; − 63; (10) − 40; (2) − 100; **1942**	− 13; + 7; + 32; − 48; + 2; (11) − 25; (9) − 50; (2) − 100; **2120**	+ 26; − 74; + 6; − 94
0	(3) − 60; − 15; 0; + 20; − 100; **1062**	(13) − 20; (2) − 100; **1966**	0; − 40; + 40; + 100; 0; (10) − 40; (2) − 100; **2552**	− 8; + 12; + 32; − 48; + 2; (9) − 50; (2) − 100; **2766**	− 35; + 20; + 100; 0
0	(16) − 15; (3) − 60; + 19; − 41; − 21; + 19; − 101; − 1; **1477**	(13) − 20; (7) − 40; (2) − 100; **2750**	− 2; + 18; + 33; + 48; + 8; + 48; − 112; − 52; − 152; (17) − 20; (10) − 40; (2) − 100; **3536**	+ 18; − 62; − 42; − 12; − 92; − 42; − 2; (11) − 30; (9) − 50; (2) − 100; **3840**	− 17; + 23; − 97; − 17; − 117
0	(3) − 60; − 1; + 14; + 29; + 49; + 79; − 101; − 1; **2095**	(14) − 15; (13) − 20; (2) − 100; **3869**	+ 9; − 51; − 91; − 51; − 11; + 39; + 99; − 1; (10) − 40; (2) − 100; **5000**	− 25; − 5; + 10; + 30; − 50; (9) − 50; (2) − 100; 0; **5405**	− 40; − 20; + 10; + 90; − 60; 0
0	(8) − 30; + 1; + 16; + 36; − 84; − 34; + 26; + 126; + 1; **3033**	(13) − 20; (6) − 50; (2) − 100; **5630**	+ 15; + 30; − 30; + 10; + 70; − 130; − 330; (10) − 40; (2) − 100; **7190**	+ 12; + 32; + 52; − 68; − 18; + 42; + 102; + 2; (12) − 20; (5) − 60; (2) − 100; **7780**	− 4; − 64; + 16; + 65; − 174; − 114; − 214
0	(15) − 15; (1) 125; − 1; − 61; − 1; + 499; **4408**	(8) − 30; **8098**	− 2; + 13; + 33; − 87; − 37; + 23; + 123; − 2; (4) − 60; **10352**	− 9; + 11; + 51; + 81; − 99; + 1; (12) − 20; (4) − 60; **11121**	+ 20; − 40; + 20; − 100; 0
	7000	**12000**	**15000**	**16000**	

Fig. 16.8. REDUCTION OF RESIDUALS BY RELAXATION

13, 14. Block change of -20 along line joining $(2, 2)$ to $(2, 6)$, followed by point change of -15 at $(2, 3)$.

15 to 17. Changes of -15 at $(1, 1)$ and $(1, 4)$, and -20 at $(3, 4)$.

At this stage the largest remaining residual is -40 at $(4, 3)$. Further changes of -15 at $(4, 3)$, $(4, 4)$ and $(4, 5)$, and -10 at $(4, 7)$ and $(3, 3)$ would bring all residuals below 25 in magnitude. Comparison with the exact solution of the difference equations given in Example 16.3 then shows that most of the errors which remain are less than 10 units, although the largest is -17.

It is now very desirable to recalculate all residuals from the revised solution values to ensure that no mistakes have been made, before embarking on a further series of relaxations. It is fairly easy to reproduce the correct solution with errors of one or two units only in the 4th significant figure, though to do this satisfactorily it is advisable to introduce an extra figure into the residuals.

EXAMPLE 16.6. Derive the solution of Poisson's equation

$$\nabla^2 f + 6400 = 0$$

inside the same rectangle as in Example 16.3, subject to the conditions that $f = 0$ at all points of the rectangle boundary and on the perimeter of a centrally placed circle of radius 3/16 (Fig. 16.9).

The first step in the solution of this problem is to find starting values over a mesh of 1/4 interval, in preparation for solving difference equations of the form (16.34). This can be done by making use of the approximate formula (15.47) for $\nabla^2 f$, which is suitable when the four neighbouring points are not equidistant. The iterative formula (16.48) then becomes

$$f^{(k+1)} = (1 + \alpha'H')f^{(k)} - \alpha'w^2g \qquad (16.64)$$

or

$$f^{(k+1)} = f^{(k)} + \alpha'R^{(k)}$$

where

$$R^{(k)} = H'f^{(k)} - w^2g \qquad (16.65)$$

and

$$H' = \begin{array}{|ccc|} \hline & t_3 & \\ t_2 & -t_0 & t_1 \\ & t_4 & \\ \hline \end{array}$$

$$t_0 = 2(1/r_1r_2 + 1/s_1s_2)$$
$$t_1 = 2/\{r_1(r_1 + r_2)\}$$
$$t_2 = 2/\{r_2(r_1 + r_2)\}$$
$$t_3 = 2/\{s_1(s_1 + s_2)\}$$
$$t_4 = 2/\{s_2(s_1 + s_2)\}$$

H' reduces to H when $r_1 = r_2 = s_1 = s_2 = 1$.

(16.64) can be made to provide starting values $f^{(0)}$ if the points defined by r_1, r_2, s_1 and s_2 are all chosen to lie on the boundary, and also $\alpha' = 1/t_0$.

It is now clear that one can start at the point $(4, 4)$, as shown in Fig. 16.9, and proceed in turn to $(2, 6)$, $(2, 2)$, $(2, 8)$, etc., using each

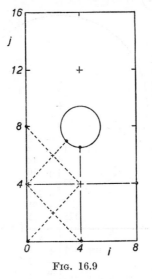

FIG. 16.9

result wherever possible to find others. The relevant data for the problem in hand are summarized in the following table—

(i, j)	r_1	r_2	s_1	s_2	t_0	t_1	t_2	t_3	t_4	$f_{ij}^{(0)}$
$(4, 4)$	2	2	$5/4$	2	$1\cdot30$					307
$(2, 6)$	$\sqrt{2} - 3/4$	$\sqrt{2}$	$\sqrt{2}$	$\sqrt{2}$	$3\cdot13$				$0\cdot5$	177
$(2, 8)$	$1/4$	1	1	1	10	$6\cdot4$	$1\cdot6$	1	1	66
$(4, 6)$	1	1	$1/4$	1	10	1	1	$6\cdot4$	$1\cdot6$	114
$(2, 2)$	$\sqrt{2}$	$\sqrt{2}$	$\sqrt{2}$	$\sqrt{2}$	2	$0\cdot5$	$0\cdot5$	$0\cdot5$	$0\cdot5$	275

$$(w^2 g = 400)$$

The values at the points $(2, 4)$ and $(4, 2)$ are obtained by the standard formula, and are 290 and 314 respectively.

The calculation of residuals is now straightforward. It is necessary to use (16.65) at two points only, viz. $(2, 8)$ and $(4, 6)$, at which

$$R_{2,8}^{(0)} = f_{2,6}^{(0)} + f_{2,10}^{(0)} - 10f_{2,8}^{(0)} + 400$$
$$R_{4,6}^{(0)} = f_{6,6}^{(0)} + f_{2,6}^{(0)} + 1\cdot6f_{4,4}^{(0)} - 10f_{4,6}^{(0)} + 400$$

The relaxation patterns corresponding to point changes in solution values are quite normal except at the points $(2, 8)$, $(4, 6)$ and $(4, 4)$.

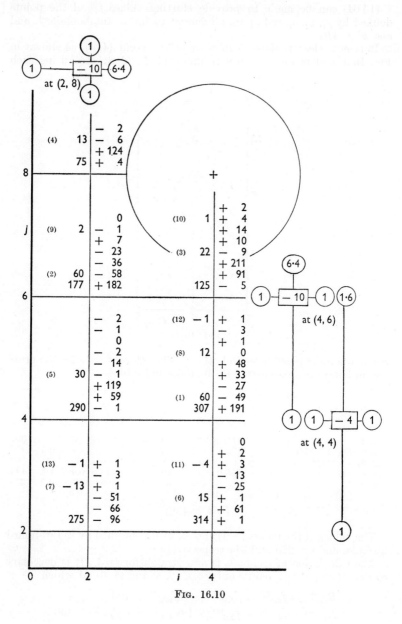

FIG. 16.10

For these anomalous points the complete patterns are shown in Fig. 16.10, although the only significant effects (all boundary values being zero) are (a) that a unit increase in $f_{2,8}$ lowers the residual at this point by 10, (b) a similar effect at (4, 6), and (c) that a unit increase in $f_{4,4}$ increases $R_{4,6}$ by 1·6. At other points the usual pattern (Fig. 16.5 (a)) applies, although the demands made by symmetry in this particular problem must be carefully remembered, e.g. the residual changes produced by a unit change in $f_{2,6}$ must be doubled at both (2, 8) and (4, 6).

The first stage of relaxation following this scheme is outlined in Fig. 16.10. All the changes are point relaxations, and, as these are numbered in the same way as in the previous problem, the various steps may be followed on the figure without much difficulty. It is instructive, however, to do the relaxation independently when it will be found that initially it is very profitable to over-relax to some extent at (4, 4) and (2, 6), but all later changes should be chosen to bring the corresponding residuals close to zero.

The results of a further stage of relaxation following interpolation to an interval of 1/8 are shown in the table below, and compared with those at 1/4. Some of the changes are considerable and indicate that the results are still some way from the correct solution of Poisson's equation. However, the estimation of truncation errors due to using finite differences is discussed in the following section.

VALUES OF f_{ij} (and R_{ij})

j	i			
	1	2	3	4
8	1052 (− 1)	**880** 805 (+ 2)		
7	1201 (0)	1216 (− 1)		
6	1536 (− 1, − 53)	**2390** 2107 (+ 1)	1862 (+ 1)	**1480** 1493 (− 2)
5	1835 (0, − 11)	2816 (0, − 20)	3148 (− 1)	3172 (0)
4	1989 (0, − 1)	**3200** 3170 (+ 2, + 2)	3742 (− 1, + 31)	**3780** 3898 (+ 1, 0)
3	1951 (− 1, + 6)	3136 (+ 1, + 10)	3751 (+ 2, + 16)	3937 (+ 1, + 20)
2	1678 (0, + 17)	**2610** 2673 (+ 2, + 17)	3191 (0, + 13)	**3250** 3350 (0, + 13)
1	1092 (− 1, + 50)	1689 (− 1, + 18)	1990 (+ 2, + 12)	2082 (+ 1, + 9)

Note. Values of f_{ij} in bold type refer to the larger interval. Residuals are given in brackets, those in light type being given by $Hf_{ij} + 1000$

or $H'f_{ij} + 1000$. The significance of residuals in bold type is discussed in the next section (§ 16.12).

In the relaxation at the finer interval it is necessary to introduce special relaxation patterns at the points (1, 8), (2, 8), (1, 7), (2, 7), (3, 6), (4, 6), (3, 5) and (3, 6). The details of these are easily worked out from (16.64) and (16.65).

Before closing this introduction to the relaxation method of solving elliptic equations it should be said that the above treatment of a curved boundary is not the only one which may be practicable. It is often feasible to introduce further points on the standard square mesh lying close to the curved boundary but outside the region of integration, e.g. inside the circle in Example 16.6. "Fictitious" solution values are then introduced at these points and so adjusted that the boundary values, at points where the boundary cuts the mesh-lines, are correctly reproduced by polynomials which fit the solution values at the mesh-points. These boundary conditions introduce sufficient extra relations for the "fictitious" values to be eliminated, and the ultimate effect is to modify the relaxation patterns at internal points in much the same way as the method followed in Example 16.6. For details of the alternative approach the writings of Southwell, Fox and others may be consulted.

16.12. Improving the Solution

In the discussion of iterative and relaxation methods so far given the important question of the accuracy of the results as a solution of the differential equation has been largely ignored. Halving the interval in a finite difference approximation does of course indicate how many digits in the results are reliable in this sense, and the process of reducing the interval could be carried to the stage at which a sufficient number of digits are unlikely to be affected by any further reduction. This would be laborious and fortunately there are other expedients by which the finite difference solution can be brought nearer to the correct differential solution.

We shall discuss some of these briefly.

1. *Extrapolation to Zero Interval*. The approximation to ∇^2 by the difference operator H/w^2 involves a truncation error proportional to w^2. It is therefore reasonable to assume that the solution values contain a similar error, and to apply the type of correction which by this time has become quite familiar. Thus, when two

solutions have been obtained corresponding to intervals of $2w$ and w, a correction equal to one-third of the difference is applied at each point common to the two meshes, as in (14.13). If the correction varies smoothly it can be extended by interpolation to points not belonging to the coarser mesh.

2. *Use of K Operator Instead of H*. It has been seen that for many equations the use of $K/6w^2$ for ∇^2 involves a truncation error with a leading term proportional to w^6. A much better result is therefore to be expected from the use of this operator, both in routine iteration and in relaxation, and the only disadvantage is that each application involves twice as many points as the simpler operator H. However, even if H is used in the earlier stages of solution, a final stage using K to refine the solution may be very profitable. In computing with an automatic machine it may be preferable to use K throughout.

The introduction of K into the iterative method leaves equation (16.49) formally unchanged, but now

$$R_{ij}^{(k)} = (K/6)f_{ij}^{(k)} - w^2 g_{ij} \qquad (16.66)$$

and in (16.50), H is also replaced by $K/6$. Alternatively, all residuals may be multiplied by 6. The value of α in (16.49) can be adjusted in the same way and for the same reasons as before, but a value which is often convenient is $3/10$, since the formula for $f_{ij}^{(k+1)}$ is then independent of $f_{ij}^{(k)}$. The use of the difference function $f^{(1)} - f^{(0)}$, and the Shortley-Weller method of estimating the series limit, can be carried over unchanged.

3. *Use of a Difference Correction*. Although relaxation can be applied directly to solve equations of the form $Kf_{ij} = 6w^2 g_{ij}$, with residuals defined by (16.66), the relaxation pattern is rather complicated and also leads to difficulties when there are curved boundaries. It is usually quite satisfactory to modify the residuals by a difference correction, as was done in the solution of ordinary differential equations. In the case of (16.34), a convenient expression for the difference correction has already been given, and when $g = $ constant or $\nabla^2 g = 0$, this reduces to the very simple form

$$\triangle_1 = -(1/6)\delta_x^2\delta_y^2 f_{ij} + 0(w^8) \qquad (16.67)$$

Hence, if $\bar{f}_{ij}$ denotes the solution of the difference equations, $Hf_{ij} = w^2 g_{ij}$, the modified residuals are given by

$$R_{ij} = Hf_{ij} - w^2 g_{ij} + (1/6)\delta_x^2\delta_y^2 \bar{f}_{ij} \qquad (16.68)$$

and values of f_{ij} are found, either by relaxation or iteration, which reduce these residuals near to zero. If these differ markedly from $\bar{f}_{ij}$, the difference correction must be revised and the residuals reduced again.

The above form of the difference correction, using the mixed difference $\delta_x{}^2\delta_y{}^2$, seems more satisfactory than the alternative which is sometimes used

$$\triangle_1 = \{(1/12)(\delta_x{}^4 + \delta_y{}^4) - (1/90)(\delta_x{}^6 + \delta_y{}^6) + \ldots\}f_{ij}$$

This is less easy to calculate and gives rise to more difficulty near boundaries. The simpler form does involve a restriction on the behaviour of g, but even when g does not satisfy Laplace's equation the extra terms in $\triangle_1$ are easily calculated, either analytically or in terms of differences.

Examples 16.4 and 16.6 can be reconsidered in the light of the above suggestions. The results obtained for the rectangular problem of Example 16.4 are summarized in the table on page 561. There it will be seen that the result of introducing K into the difference equations, either directly or through a difference correction, is to give solution values very close to the analytical values (E) for the differential equation calculated in Example 16.3. Of the discrepancies which remain, the negative errors in the bottom left corner are genuine and due to the approximation; the small positive errors in the centre of rectangle could probably be reduced still further by another iteration with one more guarding figure.

The results of using H with intervals of $1/4$ and $1/8$ have been included in the table. From the differences given, it can be deduced that the crude extrapolation to zero interval described in (1) above would leave errors of 10 units or less in the extrapolated values. The extrapolation could be extended fairly easily to all values over the finer mesh as the errors vary regularly and all have the same sign.

In Example 16.6, the interval of $1/8$ is still too large for the extrapolation method to be applied successfully, mainly because the changes which take place in reducing the interval from $1/4$ to $1/8$ vary rapidly and change sign. The effect on the residuals of including a difference correction of the form (16.67) is shown in the final table accompanying Example 16.6. The residuals shown there in heavy type contain this difference correction: the corrections have not been made for points near the circular hole because in this region they vary rapidly and are probably not reliable. If the solution to this problem were to be improved it would seem desirable that the interval should first be reduced to $1/16$ near the hole (it is probably unnecessary to do this over the whole region), and when good solution values at the new mesh-points have been derived, all residuals should be modified by including a difference correction and reduced by standard methods.

		i			
		1	2	3	4
8	$H\ (w = 1/4)$		1140		1630
				− 92		− 149
	$H\ (w = 1/8)$	567	1048	1368	1481
				− 40		− 56
	$K\ (w = 1/8)$	545·4	1007·9	1316·6	1425·0
	E	545·2	1007·4	1316·0	1424·4
7	$H\ (1/8)$	610	1127	1474	1594
	K	588·0	1086·5	1419·3	1536·1
	E	587·9	1086·1	1418·8	1535·6
6	$H\ (1/4)$		1500		2120
				− 121		− 171
	$H\ (1/8)$	747	1379	1801	1949
				− 44		− 62
	K	722·8	1335·0	1743·5	1886·8
	E	722·6	1334·6	1743·1	1886·3
5	$H\ (1/8)$	999	1842	2403	2600
	K	971·0	1792·5	2339·7	2531·5
	E	970·8	1792·2	2339·4	2531·1
4	$H\ (1/4)$		2750		3840
				− 162		− 197
	$H\ (1/8)$	1406	2588	3370	3643
				− 57		− 74
	K	1373·0	2531·4	3300·2	3569·2
	E	1373·0	2531·3	3300·1	3568·9
3	$H\ (1/8)$	2036	3734	4846	5232
	K	1996·8	3671·0	4773·4	5156·8
	E	1996·9	3671·1	4773·4	5156·7
2	$H\ (1/4)$		5630		7780
				− 166		− 187
	$H\ (1/8)$	3005	5464	7048	7593
				− 64		− 66
	K	2956·9	5400·0	6981·9	7526·6
	E	2957·6	5400·5	6982·1	7526·7
1	$H\ (1/8)$	4518	8068	10290	11043
	K	4465·2	8019·3	10247·0	11002·4
	E	4468·2	8020·1	10248·4	11002·5
0		7000	12000	15000	16000

16.13. Further Developments

An attempt has been made in this chapter to explain the basic principles of methods which can be used to solve elliptic equations numerically. To do more than this would require a much longer discussion, and we shall conclude with a very brief outline of some fairly obvious extensions of the methods which have received considerable applications. Further references are given at the end of the section. The following developments have arisen mainly in the use of the relaxation method, but of course if suitable difference equations can be set up, a routine iterative procedure may also solve them effectively.

1. LATENT ROOTS

If a problem, such as the free vibration of a membrane, requires the solution of the equation

$$\nabla^2 f + \lambda f = 0$$

and the determination of latent roots λ_i consistent with the conditions at the boundary, this may be done numerically by the methods already described, with the aid of Rayleigh's principle to provide approximate values of the latent root. For the above equation, Rayleigh's principle gives

$$\lambda = - \iint f \nabla^2 f \, dx dy / \iint f^2 dx dy$$

although, when a square difference mesh is used, it is generally satisfactory to replace the integrals by finite sums over the interior mesh-points; thus

$$\lambda \simeq - \Sigma f_{ij} H f_{ij} / \Sigma f_{ij}^2$$

with a difference correction to the operator H if necessary. The procedure is essentially the same as that described in Chapter 14 in connexion with ordinary differential equations, and is most satisfactory for the lowest mode of vibration, for which Rayleigh's quotient tends to an absolute minimum. Higher modes can sometimes be dealt with by this method, though it may be advisable to use approximate solutions which are orthogonal to those for lower modes.

Milne's method of obtaining several latent roots simultaneously has already been mentioned in § 16.7. Reference (4) below is also of interest.

2. OTHER TYPES OF MESH

In all illustrations of difference equations in two dimensions given here, a rectangular mesh has been used. This is most natural if the boundaries are mainly rectangular. It is not essential, however, and Southwell for instance introduced triangular and hexagonal meshes when these were suited to the form of the boundaries. The appropriate difference equations are easily derived (see reference (1)).

Another point may be mentioned here. In the examples given, reduction of the mesh has been carried out by halving the interval. This is usually convenient, but a less drastic step, when an approximate solution over a mesh of interval $2w$ has been obtained, is to introduce only those points at the centre of each square. This rotates the mesh-lines through $45°$, and gives an interval of $\sqrt{2}w$. Iteration or relaxation is applied to this mesh using the operator X instead of H; then the further points required to give a mesh of interval w can be introduced if necessary.

3. Other Types of Boundary Condition

With rectangular boundaries there is usually no difficulty in dealing with boundary points at which the normal derivative $\partial f/\partial n$ or the combination $f + A\partial f/\partial n$ is specified instead of f. The procedure is similar to that followed in Example 16.1, where a fictitious solution value at a point outside the boundary was introduced and used in a difference formula for the normal derivative. The fictitious value is eliminated by means of the difference equation satisfied by the solution at the boundary point. For each boundary point so treated one more equation is added to the set to be solved by iteration or relaxation.

At points on curved boundaries normal derivatives present a serious difficulty, because the direction of the normal is rarely parallel to the mesh-lines. Possible methods are described in references (1) and (3) below.

There are some problems in which the form of the boundary, or part of it, is not known in advance. An example of this occurs when fluid seeps through a porous wall. The pressure in the steady state satisfies Laplace's equation at all points, but the free boundary inside the wall on which the pressure vanishes is not initially known. There is, however, a second condition to be satisfied on such a boundary, and this enables its shape to be discovered by a trial and error process using relaxation.

4. Problems with Axial Symmetry

The solution of elliptic equations in three variables, when the solution is the same in all planes through an axis of symmetry, is only slightly more difficult than similar two-dimensional problems. Thus, in cylindrical coordinates (ρ, z, ϕ) Laplace's equation becomes

$$\partial^2 f / \partial \rho^2 + (1/\rho)\partial f / \partial \rho + \partial^2 f / \partial z^2 = 0$$

when f is independent of ϕ. The finite difference equation, corresponding to (16.37), is

$$\left. \begin{array}{ccc} & 1 & \\ 1 - \tfrac{1}{2}w/\rho_i & -4 & 1 + \tfrac{1}{2}w/\rho_i \\ & 1 & \end{array} \right| f_{ij} + \triangle = 0$$

where the leading term in the difference correction $\triangle$ may be of the form $-(w/6\rho_i)\mu\delta_\rho{}^3 f_{ij}$. This is applied in the usual way. Problems involving latent roots can also be solved.

It may be that the axis $\rho = 0$ is a boundary of the region of integration; if so, it is necessary that $\partial f / \partial \rho$ should vanish on this boundary, otherwise the solution would be singular there and could not be derived numerically.

5. CONFORMAL TRANSFORMATIONS

If $w = F(z)$ is a regular function of the complex variable, $z = x + iy$, and $F(z) = \phi(x, y) + i\psi(x, y)$, it is well known that ϕ and ψ must satisfy Laplace's equation in two dimensions. There is also a simple correspondence between points in the z and w planes which is such that corresponding small elements of area have the same essential shape although they may differ in size and orientation. It is possible by such a correspondence to transform an area in the z plane having curved or otherwise complicated boundaries into an area with a simple boundary, e.g. the interior of a circle, or an infinite rectangular strip, in the w plane. The details of the transformation can be worked out numerically without specific knowledge of the function F, and, since this requires only the solution of Laplace's equation for ϕ (or ψ) with quite simple boundary conditions, it obviously falls within the scope of the relaxation method. The results may have direct physical significance, e.g. in many electrostatic problems, or may be valuable as a first step in solving a potential problem having a difficult boundary which can with advantage be transformed to a simpler shape (see reference (1)).

6. Equations of Higher Order

Elliptic equations of fourth order arise frequently in the bending, torsion and vibration of flat elastic plates, and in viscous flow, the most familiar being the biharmonic equation (16.12). In some cases the problem can be reduced to the solution of two simultaneous second-order equations. Some finite difference representations of ∇^4 have been given in Exercises 15, No. 7, but the detailed treatment of such problems is beyond the scope of this chapter. A good discussion of them has been given by Fox (reference (3)).

7. Equations in Three Independent Variables

In general the numerical solution of Laplace's or Poisson's equation in three dimensions by a finite difference method involves a major computation. We need only mention here that many such problems can be made tractable by means of a Fourier or Laplace transform which effectively yields a limited set of two-dimensional equations. These can be solved by relaxation or other suitable method. The procedure has been described by Tranter (reference (5) below).

Finally, although it has been assumed throughout that the partial differential equation and its associated boundary conditions are linear, and the solution free from singularities, the methods which have been described may occasionally be adapted to solve problems in which either the differential equation or the boundary condition is non-linear. It should also be remembered that if the solution has singularities of a type which can be recognized, it may be possible to remove these analytically, leaving a problem without singularities to be solved numerically.

References for Elliptic Equations

1. R. V. Southwell, *Relaxation Methods in Theoretical Physics* (Oxford, Vol. 1, 1946; Vol. 2, 1956).
2. L. Fox, "Some improvements in the use of relaxation methods for the solution of ordinary and partial differential equations," *Proc. Roy. Soc.*, A **190** (1947), 31, and "A short account of relaxation methods," *Quart. J. Mech. Appl. Math.*, **1** (1948), 253.
3. L. Fox, "The numerical solution of elliptic differential equations when the boundary conditions involve a derivative," *Phil. Trans. Roy. Soc.*, **242** (1950), 345.
4. D. A. Flanders and G. Shortley, "The numerical determination of fundamental modes," *J. Appl. Phys.*, **21** (1950), 1326.

5. C. J. Tranter, "The combined use of relaxation methods and Fourier transforms in the solution of some three-dimensional boundary value problems," *Quart. J. Mech. Appl. Math.*, **1** (1948), 281.

6. F. S. Shaw, *Introduction to Relaxation Methods* (Dover, 1953).

7. D. N. de G. Allen, *Relaxation Methods* (McGraw-Hill, 1954).

8. M. Engeli, Th. Ginsburg, H. Rutishauser and E. Stiefel, *Refined Iterative Methods for Computation of the Solution and the Eigenvalues of Self-adjoint Boundary-value Problems* (Birkhäuser, 1959).

9. G. E. Forsythe and W. R. Wasow, *Finite Difference Methods for Partial Differential Equations* (Wiley, 1960).

FURTHER REFERENCES FOR PARABOLIC AND HYPERBOLIC EQUATIONS

1. J. Crank, *The Mathematics of Diffusion* (Oxford, 1956).

2. D. W. Peachman and H. H. Rachford, "The numerical solution of parabolic and elliptic differential equations," *J. Soc. Indust. Appl. Math.*, **3** (1955), 28.

3. R. D. Richtmyer, *Difference Methods for Initial-value Problems* (Interscience, 1957).

4. J. Douglas, "On the relation between stability and convergence in the numerical solution of linear parabolic and hyperbolic differential equations," *J. Soc. Indust. Appl. Math.*, **4** (1956), 20.

5. A. N. Lowan, "The operator approach to problems of stability and convergence of solutions of difference equations and the convergence of various iteration procedures, *Scripta Mathematica* (New York, 1957). Includes elliptic equations.

Additional references will be found in *Modern Computing Methods*.

EXERCISES 16

1. Show that any solution of the difference equation

$$\{(E_y - 1)(1 + \tfrac{1}{2}\gamma\delta_x^2) - \alpha\delta_x^2\}f_{j,\,k} = 0$$

satisfying the conditions $f_{-p,\,k} = f_{p,\,k} = 0$ for all $k > 0$, tends to zero as k becomes large, provided $\alpha > 0$ and $\alpha + \gamma < 1/2$.

Note. Assume that

$$f_{j,\,k} = \sum_{l=1}^{p} g_l(k) \cos j\beta \quad \text{where} \quad \beta = (2l - 1)\pi/2p$$

and show that

$$\left| \frac{g_l(k + 1)}{g_l(k)} \right| = \left| 1 - \frac{2\alpha(1 - \cos\beta)}{1 + \gamma(1 - \cos\beta)} \right| < 1$$

2. Derive formula (16.17a) for the solution of

$$\{(1/\kappa)D_y - D_x^2\}f = 0$$

using the polynomial

$$[\tfrac{1}{2}(1 - r^2)\{(1 - s)E_y^{-1} + (1 + s)E_y\}$$
$$+ \tfrac{1}{2}(1 - s^2)\{r(r - 1)E_x^{-1} + r(r + 1)E_x\}]f_{j,\,k}$$

3. If $\{(1/\kappa)D_y - D_x^2\}f = g(x, y)$, show that

$$\begin{array}{|ccc|}
\hline
-(\alpha + \gamma/2) & -(1 - 2\alpha) + \gamma & -(\alpha + \gamma/2) \\
\gamma/2 & 1 - \gamma & \gamma/2 \\
\hline
\end{array} f_{00}$$

$$- \tfrac{1}{2}\alpha w^2(g_{r_0, s_0} + g_{-r_0, s_0})$$

$$= \tfrac{1}{2}\alpha(\alpha + \gamma - 1/6)D_r^4 f_{00} + \alpha w^2(\tfrac{1}{2} - s_0)(D_s + \alpha D_r^2)g_{00} + 0(w^6)$$

where w, α and γ have the usual meaning.

4. If $\{(1/\kappa)D_y - D_x^2\}f = af$, show that

$$\begin{array}{|ccc|}
\hline
-\alpha(1 + aw^2/2) & -1 + 2\alpha(1 + aw^2/2) & -\alpha(1 + aw^2/2) \\
0 & 1 - a\alpha w^2 & 0 \\
\hline
\end{array} f_{j, k}$$

$$= 0(w^6)$$

provided $\alpha = 1/(6 + \tfrac{1}{2}aw^2)$.

5. Examine the formula

$$\begin{array}{|ccc|}
\hline
0 & -1 + \alpha & -\alpha \\
-\alpha & 1 + \alpha & 0 \\
\hline
\end{array} f_{j, k} = 0$$

for the solution of the equation $\{(1/\kappa)D_y - D_x^2\}f = 0$, and show that the leading term in the truncation error is $\alpha^2 w^3 D_x^3 f$.

6. Examine the use of difference methods for the solution of the equation $(D_y - p(x)D_x^2)f = 0$, where $p(x)$ is finite and a slowly varying function of x.

7. Examine difference methods of solving the radial diffusion equation
$$\partial^2 f/\partial r^2 + (1/r)\partial f/\partial r = \partial f/\partial t$$

Show in particular that the transformation $r = e^x$ leads to an equation of the form considered in No. 6.

8. Derive the approximate difference equation

$$\begin{array}{|ccc|}
\hline
\beta^2 a & -(1 + 2\beta^2 a) & \beta^2 a \\
\beta^2(1 - 2a) & 2 - 2\beta^2(1 - 2a) & \beta^2(1 - 2a) \\
\beta^2 a & -(1 + 2\beta^2 a) & \beta^2 a \\
\hline
\end{array} f_{j, k} = 0$$

for the hyperbolic equation $\partial^2 f/\partial x^2 = \partial^2 f/\partial t^2$, a being an arbitrary parameter, and β the ratio of the intervals, $\Delta t/\Delta x$.

Show that for stability β is unrestricted if $a > 1/4$, but if $a \leqslant 1/4$, then $\beta \leqslant 1/\sqrt{(1 - 4a)}$.

9. In Milne's method for the evaluation of latent roots, show by substituting $f_{j, k} = \bar{u}_{j, m} \cos k\bar{\nu}_m$ in (16.30) that the elements $\bar{u}_{j, m}$ of the latent vector corresponding to $\bar{\nu}_m$ satisfy the equation

$$\{1 + \tfrac{1}{2}wp_j\}\bar{u}_{j+1, m} = (2 \cos \bar{\nu}_m - w^2 q_j)\bar{u}_{j, m} - \{1 - \tfrac{1}{2}wp_j\}\bar{u}_{j-1, m}$$

Apply this recurrence relation to find the elements of the vector corresponding to $\bar{\mu}_1$ in Example 16.2, assuming $\bar{u}_{01} = 0$, $\bar{u}_{11} = 1$. Verify that $\bar{u}_{n+1, 1} = 0$ within the accuracy of the calculation.

RELATIONS BETWEEN POWERS AND FACTORIALS

Many occasions arise when it is advantageous to expand powers in terms of factorials, or vice versa, and it is therefore useful to have tables of the coefficients occurring in these expansions.

For convenience the definitions of factorials given in Chapter 2 are repeated here—

Descending factorial $\quad r^{(m)} = r(r-1)\ldots(r-m+1)$

Ascending factorial $\quad {}^{(m)}r = r(r+1)\ldots(r+m-1)$

Inverse factorial $\quad r^{(-m)} = 1/\{(r+1)(r+2)\ldots(r+m)\}$

Central factorials $\quad r^{\{2p\}} = (r^2 - 1/4)(r^2 - 9/4)\ldots$
$$(r^2 - (p - 1/2)^2)$$
$$r^{\{2p+1\}} = r(r^2 - 1)(r^2 - 4)\ldots(r^2 - p^2)$$

Mean central factorials $r^{[2p]} = r \cdot r^{\{2p-1\}}, \quad r^{[2p+1]} = r \cdot r^{\{2p\}}$

Reduced factorials $\quad r_{(m)} = r^{(m)}/m!$, etc.

Expansion of Factorials in Terms of Powers

1. Descending Factorials

Let $\qquad\qquad r^{(m)} = \sum_{j=1}^{m} S_m{}^j r^j$

The numbers $S_m{}^j$, often called Stirling numbers of the first kind, satisfy the recurrence relation

$$S_{m+1}{}^j = S_m{}^{j-1} - m S_m{}^j$$

and $\qquad S_m{}^m = 1, \quad S_m{}^j = 0$ if $j = 0$ or $j > m$

2. Ascending Factorials

Since ${}^{(m)}r = (-1)^m (-r)^{(m)}$, the expansion of the ascending factorial is

$${}^{(m)}r = \sum_{j=1}^{m} (-1)^{j+m} S_m{}^j r^j = \sum_{j=1}^{m} |S_m{}^j| r^j$$

3. Central Factorials

Let $\qquad\qquad r^{[m]} = \sum_{j=1}^{m} T_m{}^j r^j$

The numbers $T_m{}^j$ satisfy the recurrence relation

$$T_{m+2}{}^j = T_m{}^{j-2} - (m/2)^2 T_m{}^j$$

and $T_m{}^m = 1$, $T_m{}^j = 0$ if $j = 0, j > m$ or $j + m$ is odd.

The expansion of $r^{[2p+1]}$ contains only odd, and that of $r^{[2p]}$ only even powers of r.

Expansion of Powers in Terms of Factorials

1. DESCENDING FACTORIALS

Let $r^m = \sum\limits_{j=1}^{m} s_m{}^j r^{(j)}$

The numbers $s_m{}^j$, Stirling numbers of the second kind, satisfy the recurrence relation

$$s_{m+1}{}^j = s_m{}^{j-1} + j s_m{}^j$$

and $s_m{}^m = 1$, $s_m{}^j = 0$ if $j = 0$ or $j > m$

2. ASCENDING FACTORIALS

It follows that $r^m = \sum\limits_{j=1}^{m} (-1)^{j+m} s_m{}^j \cdot {}^{(j)}r$

3. CENTRAL FACTORIALS

Let $r^m = \sum\limits_{j=1}^{m} t_m{}^j r^{[j]}$

The numbers $t_m{}^j$ satisfy the recurrence relation

$$t_{m+2}{}^j = t_m{}^{j-2} + (j/2)^2 t_m{}^j$$

and $t_m{}^m = 1$, $t_m{}^j = 0$ if $j = 0, j > m$ or $j + m$ is odd.

For m up to 12, values of $S_m{}^j$, $T_m{}^j$, $s_m{}^j$, $t_m{}^j$ are given in Tables 1, 2, 3, 4, respectively.

Derivatives and Differences of Zero

$S_m{}^j$, $T_m{}^j$ are related to the derivatives of zero; thus

$$S_m{}^j = D^j 0^{(m)}/j!, \quad T_m{}^j = D^j 0^{[m]}/j!$$

where $D^j 0^{(m)}$, $D^j 0^{[m]}$ are the jth derivatives of $r^{(m)}$, $r^{[m]}$ respectively when $r = 0$.

Likewise $s_m{}^j$, $t_m{}^j$ are related to the differences of zero, $\triangle^j 0^m$, $\delta^j 0^m$, defined as the forward and central differences of r^m respectively when $r = 0$. We have

$$s_m{}^j = \triangle^j 0^m/j!, \quad t_m{}^j = \delta^j 0^m/j!$$

TABLE 1
VALUES OF S_m^j

j	m							
	1	2	3	4	5	6	7	8
1	1	− 1	2	− 6	24	− 120	720	− 5040
2		1	− 3	11	− 50	274	− 1764	13068
3			1	− 6	35	− 225	1624	− 13132
4				1	− 10	85	− 735	6769
5					1	− 15	175	− 1960
6						1	− 21	322
7							1	− 28
8								1
9								
10								
11								
12								

j	m			
	9	10	11	12
1	40320	− 362880	3628800	− 39916800
2	− 109584	1026576	− 10628640	120543840
3	118124	− 1172700	12753576	− 150917976
4	− 67284	723680	− 8409500	105258076
5	22449	− 269325	3416930	− 45995730
6	− 4536	63273	− 902055	13339535
7	546	− 9450	157773	− 2637558
8	− 36	870	− 18150	357423
9	1	− 45	1320	− 32670
10		1	− 55	1925
11			1	− 66
12				1

TABLE 2

VALUES OF $T_m{}^j$

j	m					
	1	3	5	7	9	11
1	1	$-1/4$	$9/16$	$-225/64$	$11025/256$	$-893025/1024$
3		1	$-5/2$	$259/16$	$-3229/16$	$1057221/256$
5			1	$-35/4$	$987/8$	$-86405/32$
7				1	-21	$4389/8$
9					1	$-165/4$
11						1

j	m					
	2	4	6	8	10	12
2	1	-1	4	-36	576	-14400
4		1	-5	49	-820	21076
6			1	-14	273	-7645
8				1	-30	1023
10					1	-55
12						1

TABLE 3

VALUES OF $s_m{}^j$

j	m											
	1	2	3	4	5	6	7	8	9	10	11	12
1	1	1	1	1	1	1	1	1	1	1	1	1
2		1	3	7	15	31	63	127	255	511	1023	2047
3			1	6	25	90	301	966	3025	9330	28501	86526
4				1	10	65	350	1701	7770	34105	145750	611501
5					1	15	140	1050	6951	42525	246730	1379400
6						1	21	266	2646	22827	179487	1323652
7							1	28	462	5880	63987	627396
8								1	36	750	11880	159027
9									1	45	1155	22275
10										1	55	1705
11											1	66
12												1

TABLE 4

VALUES OF $t_m{}^j$

j	m					
	1	3	5	7	9	11
1	1	1/4	1/16	1/64	1/256	1/1024
3		1	5/2	91/16	205/16	7381/256
5			1	35/4	483/8	12485/32
7				1	21	2541/8
9					1	165/4
11						1

j	m					
	2	4	6	8	10	12
2	1	1	1	1	1	1
4		1	5	21	85	341
6			1	14	147	1408
8				1	30	627
10					1	55
12						1

Applications

In addition to their immediate use in the expansions of powers and factorials, the numbers $S_m{}^j$, etc., have many applications, which are described in detail by Jordan (*Calculus of Finite Differences*, Ch. IV). We quote the following—

1. RELATIONS BETWEEN DIFFERENCES AND DERIVATIVES

Derivatives, as shown in Chapter 5, are expressible in terms of ordinary differences, with coefficients depending on $S_m{}^j$, $T_m{}^j$. These formulas are summarized in Appendix 2, but for completeness we give here the infinite series representing differences in terms of derivatives.

If $u(r)$ is tabulated for integral values of r

$$\Delta^j{}_0 = \sum_{k=j}^{\infty} \frac{j!}{k!} s_k{}^j u^{(k)}(0) \qquad\qquad \nabla^j{}_0 = \sum_{k=j}^{\infty} (-1)^{j+k} \frac{j!}{k!} s_k{}^j u^{(k)}(0)$$

$$\delta^{2p}{}_0 = \sum_{s=p}^{\infty} \frac{(2p)!}{(2s)!} t_{2s}{}^{2p} u^{(2s)}(0) \qquad\qquad \delta^{2p-1}{}_0 = \sum_{s=p}^{\infty} \frac{(2p-1)!}{(2s-1)!} t_{2s}{}^{2p} u^{(2s-1)}(0)$$

At midpoints—

$$\delta^{2p}_{1/2} = \sum_{s=p}^{\infty} \frac{(2p)!}{(2s)!} \, t_{2s+1}{}^{2p+1} u^{(2s)}(\tfrac{1}{2})$$

$$\delta^{2p+1}_{1/2} = \sum_{s=p}^{\infty} \frac{(2p+1)!}{(2s+1)!} \, t_{2s+1}{}^{2p+1} u^{(2s+1)}(\tfrac{1}{2})$$

2. RELATIONS BETWEEN POWER MOMENTS AND FACTORIAL MOMENTS

The mth power moment about $r = 0$ of $u_0, u_1, \ldots, u_n$, is

$$M_m(0) = \sum_{k=0}^{n} k^m u_k$$

The kth factorial moment is likewise

$$M^{(m)} = \sum_{k=0}^{n} k^{(m)} u_k$$

Then $\qquad M_m = \sum_{j=1}^{m} s_m{}^j M^{(j)}, \quad M^{(m)} = \sum_{j=1}^{m} S_m{}^j M_j$

3. EXPANSIONS OF RECIPROCAL POWERS AND FACTORIALS

$$r^{-j} = \sum_{k=j}^{\infty} |S_k{}^j| / (r+k)^{(k)} = \sum_{k=j}^{\infty} |S_k{}^j| r^{(-k)}$$

$$r^{(-j)} = 1/(r+j)^{(j)} = \sum_{k=j}^{\infty} (-1)^{j+k} s_k{}^j \, r^{-k}$$

Also $\qquad 1/r^{(j+1)} = \sum_{k=j}^{\infty} s_k{}^j r^{-(k+1)}$ $\quad$ (convergent if $r > j$)

4. RELATIONS BETWEEN LOGARITHMIC AND ORDINARY DERIVATIVES

Let $\qquad\qquad \Theta = r(d/dr) = rD$

Then symbolically

$$\Theta^m = \sum_{j=1}^{m} s_m{}^j r^j D^j, \quad r^m D^m = \sum_{j=1}^{m} S_m{}^j \, \Theta^j$$

Similarly, if $\qquad\qquad \Psi = r\Delta$

$$\Psi^m = \sum_{j=1}^{m} s_m{}^j \cdot {}^{(j)}r \cdot \Delta^j, \quad {}^{(m)}r \cdot \Delta^m = \sum_{j=1}^{m} S_m{}^j \, \Psi^j$$

Definitions of $S_m{}^j$, $T_m{}^j$, $s_m{}^j$, $t_m{}^j$ in terms of Bernoulli polynomials will be found in the *Index*, Section 4.

SUMMARY OF DIFFERENCE FORMULAS, WITH REMAINDERS

Interpolation

Unequal Intervals

Newtons's d.d. formula:

$$f(x) = p_n(x) + R_{n+1}$$

where $p_n(x)$ is given by (3.1).

$$R_{n+1} = \phi(x)[x, 0, 1, 2, \ldots n] \quad \text{or} \quad \frac{\phi(x)}{(n+1)!} f^{(n+1)}(\xi)$$

$$\phi(x) = (x - x_0)(x - x_1) \ldots (x - x_n)$$

Equal Intervals

$$x = x_0 + rw, \quad f(x) = u(r); \quad x_k = x_0 + kw, \quad f(x_k) = u_k$$

Newton F (5.1)

$$u(r) = u_0 + \sum_1^n r_{(k)} \Delta^k{}_0 + r_{(n+1)} u^{(n+1)}(\rho)$$

Newton B (5.5)

$$u(r) = u_0 + \sum_1^n (-1)^k s_{(k)} \nabla^k{}_0 + (-1)^{n+1} s_{(n+1)} u^{(n+1)}(\rho)$$

$$\text{where } s = -r$$

Stirling (5.9)

$$u(r) = u_0 + \sum_1^q \{r_{\{2s-1\}} \delta^{2s-1}{}_0 + r_{[2s]} \delta^{2s}{}_0\} + r_{\{2q+1\}} u^{(2q+1)}(\rho)$$

Bessel (5.13)

$$u(r) = u_0 + \tfrac{1}{2} r \delta^1{}_{1/2} + \sum_1^{q-1} \{(r - \tfrac{1}{2})_{\{2s\}} \delta^{2s}{}_{1/2} + (r - \tfrac{1}{2})_{[2s+1]} \delta^{2s+1}{}_{1/2}\}$$
$$+ (r - \tfrac{1}{2})_{\{2q\}} u^{(2q)}(\rho)$$

Everett (5.14)

$$u(r) = \sum_0^{q-1} \{t_{\{2s+1\}} \delta^{2s+1}{}_0 + r_{\{2s+1\}} \delta^{2s+1}{}_1\} + (r - \tfrac{1}{2})_{\{2q\}} u^{(2q)}(\rho)$$

$$\text{where } t = 1 - r$$

Definitions of factorials are given in Appendix 1, and references to tables of interpolation coefficients will be found on p. 115.

Note that $u^{(m)}(\rho) = (d^m u/dr^m)_\rho = w^m(d^m f/dx^m)_\xi$

where $\xi = x_0 + \rho w$.

Also ρ is some value of r in the range covered by 0 to n, and including the interpolated value r.

Differentiation

UNEQUAL INTERVALS

$$f^{(m)}(x) = D^m p_n(x) + R_{n+1}$$

where $R_{n+1} = \{D^m \phi(x)/(n+1)!\}f^{(n+1)}(\xi)$ if x is not interior to

$$x_0, x_1, \ldots, x_n.$$

$$= \sum_{j=0}^{m} \{(m!/j!)D^j\phi(x)\}f^{(m+n-j+1)}(\xi_j)/(m+n-j+1)!$$

for general x.

For proof, see Steffensen, § 69.

EQUAL INTERVALS

Newton F $u^{(j)}(0) = \sum_{k=j}^{n} \frac{j!}{k!} S_k{}^j \nabla^k{}_0 + \frac{j!}{(n+1)!} S_{n+1}{}^j u^{(n+1)}(\rho)$

Newton B $u^{(j)}(0) = \sum_{k=j}^{n} \frac{j!}{k!} |S_k{}^j| \nabla^k{}_0 + \frac{j!}{(n+1)!} |S_{n+1}{}^j| u^{(n+1)}(\rho)$

Stirling $\begin{cases} u^{(2p-1)}(0) = \sum_{s=p}^{q-1} \frac{(2p-1)!}{(2s-1)!} T_{2s}{}^{2p}\delta^{2s-1}{}_0 + R_{2q-1} \\[2ex] u^{(2p)}(0) = \sum_{s=p}^{q-1} \frac{(2p)!}{(2s)!} T_{2s}{}^{2p}\delta^{2s}{}_0 + R_{2q} \end{cases}$

Bessel $\begin{cases} u^{(2p)}(\frac{1}{2}) = \sum_{s=p}^{q-1} \frac{(2p)!}{(2s)!} T_{2s+1}{}^{2p+1}\delta^{2s}{}_{1/2} + R_{2q} \\[2ex] u^{(2p+1)}(\frac{1}{2}) = \sum_{s=p}^{q-1} \frac{(2p+1)!}{(2s+1)!} T_{2s+1}{}^{2p+1}\delta^{2s+1}{}_{1/2} + R_{2q+1} \end{cases}$

Coefficients of differences in Stirling and Bessel type formulas are given in *I.A.T.* (pp. 61 and 65) and *Chambers* [6] (Table XIVA). General expressions for R_{2q}, etc., are given by Steffensen

(§§ 70–73): these are complicated, however, and have little practical value.

Single Integration and Summation

Note that
$$\int_{x_0}^{x_n} f(x)dx = w \int_0^n u(r)dr$$

Trapezoidal sum
$$T_n = \tfrac{1}{2}u_0 + u_1 + \ldots + u_{n-1} + \tfrac{1}{2}u_n$$

LAPLACE FORMULAS

Gregory:
$$\int_0^n u(r)dr = T_n - \sum_{k=1}^{m-1} L_{k+1}(\Delta^k{}_0 + (-1)^k \nabla^k{}_n) + nL_{m+1}u^{(m+1)}(\rho)$$
where
$$k!L_k = \int_0^1 r^{(k)}dr = \sum_{j=1}^k S_k{}^j/(j+1)$$

Gauss I:
$$\int_{-1/2}^{n+1/2} u(r)dr = \sum_0^n u_k + \sum_{s=1}^{p-1} K_{2s}(\delta^{2s-1}{}_{n+1/2} - \delta^{2s-1}{}_{-1/2})$$
$$+ (n+1)K_{2p}u^{(2p)}(\rho)$$
where
$$(2s)!K_{2s} = \int_{-1/2}^{1/2} r^{[2s]}dr = \sum_{p=1}^s T_{2s}{}^{2p}/\{2^{2p}(2p+1)\}$$

Gauss-Encke (or Gauss II):
$$\int_0^n u(r)dr = T_n + \sum_{s=1}^{p-1} M_{2s}(\delta^{2s-1}{}_n - \delta^{2s-1}{}_0) + nM_{2p}u^{(2p)}(\rho)$$
where
$$(2s)!M_{2s} = \int_{-1/2}^{1/2} r^{\{2s\}}dr = \sum_{p=0}^s T_{2s+1}{}^{2p+1}/\{2^{2p}(2p+1)\}$$

Stirling:
$$\int_0^{2n} u(r)dr = 2\sum_{k=1}^n u_{2k-1} + \sum_{s=1}^{p-1} N_{2s}\left(\sum_{k=1}^n \delta^{2s}{}_{2k-1}\right) + nN_{2p}u^{(2p)}(\rho)$$
where
$$(2s)!N_{2s} = \int_{-1}^1 r^{[2s]}dr = 2\sum_{p=1}^s T_{2s}{}^{2p}/(2p+1)$$

EULER FORMULAS

Euler-Maclaurin I:
$$T_n = \int_0^n u(r)dr + \sum_{s=1}^{p-1} \frac{B_{2s}}{(2s)!}\left[u^{(2s-1)}(r)\right]_0^n + \frac{nB_{2p}}{(2p)!}u^{(2p)}(\rho)$$

Euler-Maclaurin II:

$$\sum_{0}^{n-1} u(k + \tfrac{1}{2}) = \int_0^n u(r)dr + \sum_{s=1}^{p-1} \frac{B_{2s}(\tfrac{1}{2})}{(2s)!}\left[u^{(2s-1)}(r)\right]_0^n$$
$$+ \frac{nB_{2p}(\tfrac{1}{2})}{(2p)!}u^{(2p)}(\rho)$$

where $B_{2s} = \sum_{j=1}^{2s}\frac{j!}{j+1}(-1)^j s_{2s}{}^j, \quad B_{2s}(\tfrac{1}{2}) = -\left(1 - \frac{1}{2^{2s-1}}\right)B_{2s}$

Numerical Coefficients in Integration Formulas

GREGORY

k	$k!\,L_k$	L_k	$k!$
2	$-1/6$	$-0\cdot08333\ 33$	2
3	$1/4$	$0\cdot04166\ 67$	6
4	$-19/30$	$-0\cdot02638\ 89$	24
5	$9/4$	$0\cdot01875\ 00$	120
6	$-10\ (23/84)$	$-0\cdot01426\ 92$	720
7	$57\ (7/24)$	$0\cdot01136\ 74$	5040
8	$-377\ (23/90)$	$-0\cdot00935\ 65$	40320
9	$2864\ (1/20)$	$0\cdot00789\ 26$	362880
10	$-24624\ (65/132)$	$-0\cdot00678\ 58$	3628800
11	$236469\ (3/8)$	$0\cdot00592\ 41$	39916800
12	$-2508385\ (3007/5460)$	$-0\cdot00523\ 67$	479001600

For coefficients up to $k = 20$, Lowan and Salzer, *J. Math. Phys.*, 22 (1943), 49.

GAUSS I

k	$k!\,K_k$	K_k
2	$1/12$	$0\cdot04166\ 67$
4	$-17/240$	$-0\cdot00295\ 14$
6	$367/1344$	$0\cdot00037\ 93$
8	$-27859/11520$	$-0\cdot00006\ 00$
10	$38\ (11707/33792)$	$0\cdot00001\ 06$
12	$-953\ (981707/5591040)$	$-0\cdot00000\ 20$

GAUSS-ENCKE

k	$k!M_k$	M_k
2	$-1/6$	$-0.08333\ 33$
4	$11/30$	$0.01527\ 78$
6	$-191/84$	$-0.00315\ 81$
8	$27\ (47/90)$	$0.00068\ 81$
10	$-560\ (65/132)$	$-0.00015\ 45$
12	$16928\ (229/4620)$	$0.00003\ 53$

STIRLING

k	$k!N_k$	N_k
2	$2/3$	$0.33333\ 33$
4	$-4/15$	$-0.01111\ 11$
6	$20/21$	$0.00132\ 28$
8	$-8\ (8/45)$	$-0.00020\ 28$
10	$127\ (17/33)$	$0.00003\ 51$
12	$-3135\ (1363/1365)$	$-0.00000\ 65$

EULER-MACLAURIN I　　　　　EULER-MACLAURIN II

k	B_k	$B_k/k!$	$B_k(1/2)$	$B_k(1/2)/k!$
2	$1/6$	$0.08333\ 33333$	$-1/12$	$-0.04166\ 66667$
4	$-1/30$	$-0.00138\ 88889$	$7/240$	$0.00121\ 52778$
6	$1/42$	$0.00003\ 30688$	$-31/1344$	$-0.00003\ 20354$
8	$-1/30$	$-0.00000\ 08267$	$127/3640$	$0.00000\ 08203$
10	$5/66$	$0.00000\ 00209$	$-2555/33792$	$-0.00000\ 00208$
12	$-691/2730$	$-0.00000\ 00005$	$\dfrac{1414477}{2^{12}.1365}$	$0.00000\ 00005$

LAGRANGIAN FORMULAS FOR DIFFERENTIATION AND INTEGRATION

Differentiation

General formula (using a polynomial of degree n)

$$(w^m/m!)(d^m f/dx^m)_j = (1/n!) \sum_{k=0}^{n} A_k f_k + R$$

where $f_k = f(x_0 + kw)$ and derivative is evaluated at $x_0 + jw$.

Note that

$$(-1)^m (w^m/m!)(d^m f/dx^m)_{n-j} = (1/n!) \sum_{k=0}^{n} A_{n-k} f_k + (-1)^{n-1} R$$

First Derivatives ($m = 1$)

j	n	A_0	A_1	A_2	A_3	A_4	A_5	A_6	R
0	2	-3	4	-1					$(1/3)w^3 f^{(3)}$
	3	-11	18	-9	2				$-(1/4)w^4 f^{(4)}$
	4	-50	96	-72	32	-6			$(1/5)w^5 f^{(5)}$
	5	-274	600	-600	400	-150	24		$-(1/6)w^6 f^{(6)}$
	6	-1764	4320	-5400	4800	-2700	864	-120	$(1/7)w^7 f^{(7)}$
1	2	-1	0	1					$-(1/6)w^3 f^{(3)}$
	3	-2	-3	6	-1				$(1/12)w^4 f^{(4)}$
	4	-6	-20	36	-12	2			$-(1/20)w^5 f^{(5)}$
	5	-24	-130	240	-120	40	-6		$(1/30)w^6 f^{(6)}$
	6	-120	-924	1800	-1200	600	-180	24	$-(1/42)w^7 f^{(7)}$
2	4	2	-16	0	16	-2			$(1/30)w^5 f^{(5)}$
	5	6	-60	-40	120	-30	4		$-(1/60)w^6 f^{(6)}$
	6	24	-288	-420	960	-360	96	-12	$(1/105)w^7 f^{(7)}$
3	6	-12	108	-540	0	540	-108	12	$-(1/140)w^7 f^{(7)}$

Second Derivatives ($m = 2$)

j	n	A_0	A_1	A_2	A_3	A_4	A_5	A_6	R
0	2	1	-2	1					$-(1/2)w^3 f^{(3)}$
	3	6	-15	12	-3				$(11/24)w^4 f^{(4)}$
	4	35	-104	114	-56	11			$-(5/12)w^5 f^{(5)}$
	5	225	-770	1070	-780	305	-50		$(137/360)w^6 f^{(6)}$
	6	1624	-6264	10530	-10160	5940	-1944	274	$-(7/20)w^7 f^{(7)}$
1	2	1	-2	1					$-(1/24)w^4 f^{(4)}$
	3	3	-6	3	0				$-(1/24)w^4 f^{(4)}$
	4	11	-20	6	4	-1			$(1/24)w^4 f^{(4)}$
	5	50	-75	-20	70	-30	5		$-(13/360)w^6 f^{(6)}$
	6	274	-294	-510	940	-570	186	-26	$(11/360)w^7 f^{(7)}$
2	4	-1	16	-30	16	-1			$(1/180)w^6 f^{(6)}$
	5	-5	80	-150	80	-5	0		$(1/180)w^6 f^{(6)}$
	6	-26	456	-840	400	30	-24	4	$-(1/180)w^7 f^{(7)}$
3	6	4	-54	540	-980	540	-54	4	$-(1/1120)w^8 f^{(8)}$

Further coefficients for $m = 3$, 4 and $n = 8$, 10 are given by W. G. Bickley, *Math. Gaz.*, **25** (1941), 19.

Integration

General formula

$$F_m - F_0 = \int_{x_0}^{x_0 + mw} f(x)dx = wC \sum_{k=0}^{n} B_k f_k + R$$

n	m	C	B_0	B_1	B_2	B_3	B_4	B_5	B_6	R	Type
1	1	1/2	1	1	Trapezoidal					$-(1/12)w^3 f^{(2)}$	a
	2	2	0	1	Modified Euler Mid-ordinate					$+(1/2)$ —	b
2	1	1/12	5	8	−1					$+(1/24)w^4 f^{(3)}$	c
	2	1/3	1	4	1	Simpson				$-(1/90)w^5 f^{(4)}$	a
	3	3/4	1	0	3	Heun				$+(3/8)w^4 f^{(3)}$	b
	4	4/3	2	−4	5					$+(8/3)$ —	b
3	1	1/24	9	19	−5	1				$-(19/720)w^5 f^{(4)}$	c
	2	1/3	1	4	1	0				$-(1/90)$ —	c
	3	3/8	1	3	3	1	Three-eighths			$-(3/80)$ —	a
	4	4/3	0	2	−1	2	Milne			$+(14/45)$ —	b
4	1	1/720	251	646	−264	106	−19			$+(3/160)w^6 f^{(5)}$	c
	2	1/90	29	124	24	4	−1			$+(1/90)$ —	c
	3	3/80	9	34	24	14	−1			$+(3/160)$ —	c
	4	2/45	7	32	12	32	7	Boole		$-(8/945)w^7 f^{(6)}$	b
	5	5/144	19	−10	120	−70	85			$+(95/288)w^6 f^{(5)}$	b
	5	5/24	0	11	1	1	11			$+(25/36)\ w^5 f^{(4)}$	b
5	1	1/1440	475	1427	−798	482	−173	27		$-(863/60480)w^7 f^{(6)}$	c
	2	1/90	28	129	14	14	−6	1		$-(37/3780)$ —	c
	3	3/160	17	73	38	38	−7	1		$-(29/2240)$ —	c
	4	2/45	7	32	12	32	7	0		$-(8/945)$ —	c
	5	5/288	19	75	50	50	75	19		$-(275/12096)$ —	a
	6	3/10	0	11	−14	26	−14	11		$+(41/140)$ —	b
6	1	1/60480	19087	65112	−46461	37504	−20211	6312	−863	$+(275/24192)w^8 f^{(7)}$	c
	2	1/3780	1139	5640	33	1328	−807	264	−37	$+(8/945)$ —	c
	3	1/2240	685	3240	1161	2176	−729	216	−29	$+(9/896)$ —	c
	4	2/945	143	696	192	752	87	24	−4	$+(8/945)$ —	c
	5	5/12096	743	3480	1275	3200	2325	1128	−55	$+(275/24192)$ —	c
	6	1/140	41	216	27	272	27	216	41	$-(9/1400)w^9 f^{(8)}$	a
	7	7/1440	0	611	−453	562	562	−453	611	$w^7 f^{(6)}$	b
6	6	3/10	1	5	1	6	1	5	1	$-(1/140)w^7 f^{(6)}$	a
							Weddle				
	6	1/100	28	162	0	22	0	162	28	$+(9/700)$ —	b
							Hardy				

Type *a*. Closed formulas (Newton-Cotes), convenient for quadrature. Formulas with n even are to be preferred.

Type *b*. Open formulas (Steffensen), applicable to step-by-step integration of first-order differential equations.

Type *c*. Partial-range formulas.

OTHER QUADRATURE FORMULAS

	$m = n = 8$		$m = n = 10$	
	Newton-Cotes		Newton-Cotes	Shovelton
B_0 B_8	989	B_0 B_{10}	16067	8
B_1 B_7	5888	B_1 B_9	106300	35
B_2 B_6	− 928	B_2 B_8	− 48525	15
B_3 B_5	10496	B_3 B_7	272400	35
B_4	− 4540	B_4 B_6	− 260550	15
		B_5	427368	36
C	4/14175	C	5/299376	5/126
R	$-\dfrac{2368}{467775}\, w^{11} f^{(10)}$	R	$-\dfrac{134635}{326918592}\, w^{13} f^{(12)}$	$-(25/756) w^7 f^{(6)}$

Gauss I formula (see Appendix 2):

$$F(n + \tfrac{1}{2}) - F(-\tfrac{1}{2}) = (w/D)\Sigma B_k f_k + R$$

		δ^3 neglected $n \geqslant 1$	δ^5 neglected $n = 2 \; n > 2$		δ^7 neglected		
				$n = 2$	3	4	> 4
B_{-3}	B_{n+3}			367	367	367	367
B_{-2}	B_{n+2}		− 17 − 17	− 4691	− 4691	− 4691	− 4691
B_{-1}	B_{n+1}	1	291 291	52558	52558	52558	52558
B_0	B_n	23	5469 5469	914755	915122	915122	915122
B_1	B_{n-1}	D	5794 5777	977062	972004	972371	972371
B_2	B_{n-2}	D	D			966946	967313
B_3	B_{n-3}	D	D				D
D		24	5760		967680		

Intermediate values of B_k, when they occur, are all equal to D.

Stirling quadrature formula (Appendix 2):

$$F(n) - F(0) = (w/D)\Sigma B_k f_k + R \quad (n \text{ even})$$

		δ^4 neglected $n = 4 \;\; \geqslant 8$	δ^6 neglected $n = 4$ 6 $\geqslant 8$			δ^8 neglected $n = 4$ 6 $\geqslant 8$		
B_{-2}	B_{n+2}					5	5	5
B_{-1}	B_{n+1}		− 1	− 1	− 1	− 72	− 72	− 72
B_0	B_n	1 1	34	34	34	1508	1508	1508
B_1	B_{n-1}	4 4	113	113	113	4616	4616	4616
B_2	B_{n-2}	2 2	68	68	68	3006	3011	3011
B_3	B_{n-3}	**4**			112	**112**		4544	**4544**
B_4	B_{n-4}	**2**				**68**			**3016**
D		3	90			3780		

Intermediate values of B_k, when they occur, have the alternating values shown in heavy type.

For remainder terms, see Appendix 2. Similar coefficients for Gregory and Gauss-Encke formulas are given in *Chambers* [6] p. 549.

CHECK FORMULAS

The following formulas, some of which have great accuracy, may be used to check the results of step-by-step integrations. They are not suitable for performing such integration because of the relatively small coefficient of F_n.

$n = 3$

$$11F_3 + 27F_2 - 27F_1 - 11F_0$$
$$= 3w(f_3 + 9f_2 + 9f_1 + f_0) - (3/140)w^7 f^{(6)}$$

$$3(F_3 - F_2 - F_1 + F_0)$$
$$= w(f_3 + 3f_2 - 3f_1 - f_0) - (1/30)w^6 f^{(5)}$$

$$F_3 + 9F_2 - 9F_1 - F_0$$
$$= 6w(f_2 + f_1) \qquad\qquad + (1/10)w^5 f^{(4)}$$

$n = 4$

$$25F_4 + 160(F_3 - F_1) - 25F_0$$
$$= 6w(f_4 + 16f_3 + 36f_2 + 16f_1 + f_0) - (1/105)w^9 f^{(8)}$$

$$11F_4 + 16F_3 - 54F_2 + 16F_2 + 11F_0$$
$$= 3w(f_4 + 8f_3 - 8f_1 - f_0) - (3/140)w^8 f^{(7)}$$

$n = 6$

$$49F_6 + 924F_5 + 2625(F_4 - F_2) - 924F_1 - 49F_0$$
$$= 10w(f_6 + 36f_5 + 225f_4 + 400f_3 + 225f_2 + 36f_1 + f_0)$$
$$- (5/6006)w^{13} f^{(12)}$$

$$137F_6 + 1488F_5 + 375F_4 - 4000F_3 + 375F_2 + 1488F_1 + 137F_0$$
$$= 30w(f_6 + 24f_5 + 75f_4 - 75f_2 - 24f_1 - f_0)$$
$$- (5/462)w^{12} f^{(11)}$$

These formulas, and most of the preceding integration formulas, are taken from the paper by W. G. Bickley, *Math. Gaz.*, **23** (1939), 352.

APPENDIX 4

GAUSSIAN QUADRATURE

LET
$$\int_a^b f(x)dx = \sum_{j=1}^n D_j f(x_j) + R$$

When $f(x)$ is approximated by a polynomial with an arbitrary choice of the x_j the quadrature error will normally depend on the nth or $(n+1)$th derivative of $f(x)$. However, it was shown by Gauss that with suitable choice of x_j the error depends on the $(2n)$th derivative and the formula is then accurate for polynomials of degree up to $(2n-1)$. By comparison with formulas based on ordinates at equal intervals in x the number of points required for a given precision is roughly halved.

Writing $\quad x_0 = \tfrac{1}{2}(b+a), \quad d = \tfrac{1}{2}(b-a), \quad x = x_0 + yd$

the best choice of the n values of x is given by the zeros y_k of the Legendre polynomial $P_n(y)$ in the range $(-1, 1)$. The integral now becomes

$$\int_{x_0-d}^{x_0+d} f(x)dx = d\left[C_0 f(x_0) + \sum_{k=1}^\alpha C_k\{f(x_0 + y_k d) + f(x_0 - y_k d)\} \right] + R$$

where $C_0 = 0$, $\alpha = \tfrac{1}{2}n$ when n is even; $\alpha = \tfrac{1}{2}(n-1)$ when n is odd.

Also
$$C_k = \frac{2(1 - y^2_k)}{(n+1)^2[P_{n+1}(y_k)]^2}$$

and
$$R = \frac{(n!)^4(2d)^{2n+1} f^{(2n)}(\xi)}{[(2n)!]^3(2n+1)}$$

where ξ lies in (a, b)

For proof of these results see Hildebrand, *Introduction to Numerical Analysis* (McGraw-Hill, 1956), p. 319 *et seq.*

For integrals of the form $\int_a^b w(x)f(x)dx$, where $w(x)$ is a simple weight function, similar formulas may be available using the zeros of other appropriate types of polynomial, e.g. Laguerre, Hermite, Chebyshev (see Chapter 10).

589

TABLE 1

ZEROS OF $P_n(y)$ AND VALUES OF C_k

n	k	Y_k	C_k
2	1	0·57735 02691 90	1·00000 00000 00
3	0	0·00000 00000 00	0·88888 88888 89
	1	0·77459 66692 41	0·55555 55555 56
4	1	0·33998 10435 85	0·65214 51548 63
	2	0·86113 63115 94	0·34785 48451 37
5	0	0·00000 00000 00	0·56888 88888 89
	1	0·53846 93101 06	0·47862 86704 99
	2	0·90617 98459 39	0·23692 68850 56
6	1	0·23861 91860 83	0·46791 39245 73
	2	0·66120 93864 66	0·36076 15730 48
		0·93246 95142 03	0·17132 44923 79
8	1	0·18343 46424 96	0·36268 37833 78
	2	0·52553 24099 16	0·31370 66458 78
	3	0·79666 64774 14	0·22238 10344 53
	4	0·96028 98564 98	0·10122 85362 90
10	1	0·14887 43389 82	0·29552 42247 15
	2	0·43339 53941 29	0·26945 67193 10
	3	0·67940 95682 99	0·21967 63625 16
	4	0·86506 33666 89	0·14926 13491 51
	5	0·97390 65285 17	0·06608 13443 09

A longer table providing 15 D values for all n up to 16 is given by A. N. Lowan, N. Davids and A. Levenson, *Bul. Amer. Math. Soc.*, **48** (1942), 739. See also "Tables of functions and zeros of functions" (Ed. A. N. Lowan), *Nat. Bur. Stand. Appl. Math. Series*, **37** (1954), and P. Davis and P. Rabinowitz, *J. Res. Nat. Bur. Stand.*, **56** (1956), 35 and **60** (1958), 613.

APPENDIX 5

ORTHOGONAL POLYNOMIALS FOR CURVE-FITTING

THE following tables are for use with the methods described in § 10.6 (Tables 1, 2) and § 10.8 (Table 3).

TABLE 1
VALUES OF V_{rj} AND N_j

n	r	V_1	V_2	V_3	V_4	V_5	n	r	V_1	V_2	V_3	V_4	V_5
3	1	$+1$	$+1$				4	3/2	$+3$	$+1$	$+1$		
	0	0	-2					1/2	$+1$	-1	-3		
	N_j	2	6					N_j	20	4	20		
5	2	$+2$	$+2$	$+1$	$+1$		6	5/2	$+5$	$+5$	$+5$	$+1$	$+1$
	1	$+1$	-1	-2	-4			3/2	$+3$	-1	-7	-3	-5
	0	0	-2	0	$+6$			1/2	$+1$	-4	-4	$+2$	$+10$
	N_j	10	14	10	70			N_j	70	84	180	28	252
7	3	$+3$	$+5$	$+1$	$+3$	$+1$	8	7/2	$+7$	$+7$	$+7$	$+7$	$+7$
	2	$+2$	0	-1	-7	-4		5/2	$+5$	$+1$	-5	-13	-23
	1	$+1$	-3	-1	$+1$	$+5$		3/2	$+3$	-3	-7	-3	$+17$
	0	0	-4	0	$+6$	0		1/2	$+1$	-5	-3	$+9$	$+15$
	N_j	28	84	6	154	84		N_j	168	168	264	616	2184
9	4	$+4$	$+28$	$+14$	$+14$	$+4$	10	9/2	$+9$	$+6$	$+42$	$+18$	$+6$
	3	$+3$	$+7$	-7	-21	-11		7/2	$+7$	$+2$	-14	-22	-14
	2	$+2$	-8	-13	-11	$+4$		5/2	$+5$	-1	-35	-17	$+1$
	1	$+1$	-17	-9	$+9$	$+9$		3/2	$+3$	-3	-31	$+3$	$+11$
	0	0	-20	0	$+18$	0		1/2	$+1$	-4	-12	$+18$	$+6$
	N_j	60	2772	990	2002	468		N_j	330	132	8580	2860	780
11	5	$+5$	$+15$	$+30$	$+6$	$+3$	12	11/2	$+11$	$+55$	$+33$	$+33$	$+33$
	4	$+4$	$+6$	-6	-6	-6		9/2	$+9$	$+25$	-3	-27	-57
	3	$+3$	-1	-22	-6	-1		7/2	$+7$	$+1$	-21	-33	-21
	2	$+2$	-6	-23	-1	$+4$		5/2	$+5$	-17	-25	-13	$+29$
	1	$+1$	-9	-14	$+4$	$+4$		3/2	$+3$	-29	-19	$+12$	$+44$
	0	0	-10	0	$+6$	0		1/2	$+1$	-35	-7	$+28$	$+20$
	N_j	110	858	4290	286	156		N_j	572	12012	5148	8008	15912

Extended tables, all for $j \leqslant 5$, may be found as follows—

Max. n

30   Birge: *Rev. Mod. Phys.*, **19** (1947), 341.

75   Fisher and Yates: *Statistical Tables* (5th edition, 1957).

104   Anderson and Houseman: *Research Bull.*, **297**: Agric. Expt. Station, Iowa State College (1942).

TABLE 2

VALUES OF S_{ij} AND f_j

$$V_j(r) = T_j(r)/f_j = \sum_i S_{ij} r^i$$

Note that recurring decimals are replaced by fractional equivalents.

n		V_1	V_3	V_5		V_2	V_4
3	r	1	—	—	$1/r^2$	-2	—
	r^3	—	—	—		3	—
	f	2	—	—		1	—
4	r	2	$-6{\cdot}8(1/3)$	—	$1/r^2$	$-1{\cdot}25$	—
	r^3	—	$3(1/3)$	—		1	—
	f_j	1	1	—		3	—
5	r	1	$-2{\cdot}8(1/3)$	—	$1/r^2$	-2	6
	r^3	—	$5/6$	—	$1/r^4$	1	$-12{\cdot}9(1/6)$
		—		—		—	$2{\cdot}9(1/6)$
	f_j	2	4	—		3	1
6	r	2	$-8{\cdot}4(1/6)$	$24{\cdot}0979(1/6)$	$1/r^2$	$-4{\cdot}375$	$2{\cdot}953(1/8)$
	r^3	—	$1(2/3)$	$-16{\cdot}9(1/6)$	$1/r^4$	$1{\cdot}5$	$-3{\cdot}95(5/6)$
	r^5	—	—	$2{\cdot}1$		—	$0{\cdot}58(1/3)$
	f_j	1	2	1		2	5
7	r	1	$-1{\cdot}1(2/3)$	$8{\cdot}7(1/3)$	$1/r^2$	-4	6
	r^3	—	$1/6$	$-4{\cdot}08(1/3)$	$1/r^4$	1	$-5{\cdot}58(1/3)$
	r^5	—	—	$0{\cdot}35$		—	$0{\cdot}58(1/3)$
	f_j	2	20	6		3	5
8	r	2	$-6{\cdot}1(2/3)$	$16{\cdot}36354(1/6)$	$1/r^2$	$-5{\cdot}25$	$10{\cdot}828(1/8)$
	r^3	—	$2/3$	$-11{\cdot}08(1/3)$	$1/r^4$	1	$-7{\cdot}45(5/6)$
	r^5	—	—	$0{\cdot}7$		—	$0{\cdot}58(1/3)$
	f_j	1	5	3		3	5
9	r	1	$-9{\cdot}8(1/3)$	$11{\cdot}9(1/3)$	$1/r^2$	-20	18
	r^3	—	$5/6$	$-3{\cdot}08(1/3)$	$1/r^4$	3	$-9{\cdot}58(1/3)$
	r^5	—	—	$0{\cdot}15$		—	$0{\cdot}58(1/3)$
	f_j	2	4	14		1	5
10	r	2	$-24{\cdot}4(1/6)$	$12{\cdot}6395(5/6)$	$1/r^2$	$-4{\cdot}125$	$20{\cdot}109(3/8)$
	r^3	—	$1(2/3)$	$-2{\cdot}58(1/3)$	$1/r^4$	$0{\cdot}5$	$-8{\cdot}54(1/6)$
	r^5	—	—	$0{\cdot}1$		—	$0{\cdot}4(1/6)$
	f_j	1	2	21		6	7
11	r	1	$-14{\cdot}8(1/3)$	$4{\cdot}76(2/3)$	$1/r^2$	-10	6
	r^3	—	$5/6$	$-0{\cdot}79(1/6)$	$1/r^4$	1	$-2{\cdot}08(1/3)$
	r^5	—	—	$0{\cdot}025$		—	$0{\cdot}08(1/3)$
	f_j	2	4	84		3	35
12	r	2	$-14{\cdot}1(2/3)$	$41{\cdot}4177(1/12)$	$1/r^2$	$-35{\cdot}75$	$30{\cdot}164(1/16)$
	r^3	—	$2/3$	$-5{\cdot}708(1/3)$	$1/r^4$	3	$-8{\cdot}729(1/6)$
	r^5	—	—	$0{\cdot}15$		—	$0{\cdot}29(1/6)$
	f_j	1	5	14		1	10

Birge's table extends to $n = 30$.

TABLE 3
VALUES OF g_{ij}, h_{ij} AND M_j

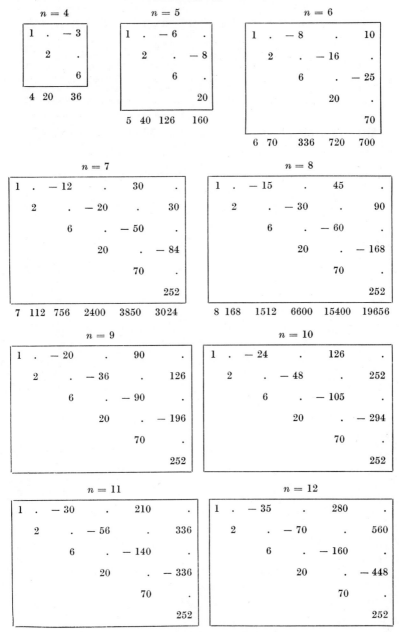

n = 4

```
1  .  − 3
   2  .
         6
4  20  36
```

n = 5

```
1  .  − 6   .
   2  .  − 8
      6  .
             20
5  40  126  160
```

n = 6

```
1  .  − 8    .    10
   2  .  − 16   .
      6   .   − 25
          20    .
                   70
6  70  336  720  700
```

n = 7

```
1  .  − 12   .    30    .
   2   .  − 20   .    30
       6   .  − 50   .
           20    .  − 84
                70    .
                       252
7  112  756  2400  3850  3024
```

n = 8

```
1  .  − 15   .    45    .
   2   .  − 30   .    90
       6   .  − 60   .
           20    .  − 168
                70    .
                       252
8  168  1512  6600  15400  19656
```

n = 9

```
1  .  − 20   .    90    .
   2   .  − 36   .   126
       6   .  − 90   .
           20    .  − 196
                70    .
                       252
```

n = 10

```
1  .  − 24   .   126    .
   2   .  − 48   .   252
       6   .  − 105   .
           20    .  − 294
                70    .
                       252
```

n = 11

```
1  .  − 30   .   210    .
   2   .  − 56   .   336
       6   .  − 140   .
           20    .  − 336
                70    .
                       252
```

n = 12

```
1  .  − 35   .   280    .
   2   .  − 70   .   560
       6   .  − 160   .
           20    .  − 448
                70    .
                       252
```

n	Values of M_j					
	$j = 0$	1	2	3	4	5
4–8	Shown below rectangles					
9	9	240	2772	15840	50050	91728
10	10	330	4752	34320	140140	343980
11	11	440	7722	68640	350350	1100736
12	12	572	12012	128700	800800	3118752

Aitken's table (*Proc. Roy. Soc. Edin.*, **53** (1932) 54), extends to $n = 25$.

INDEX OF
USEFUL FORMULAS IN TEXT

INDEX

ADJOINT matrix, 358, 373, 420
Airy's equation, 183, 215, 236
Aitken, A. C., 93, 102, 262, 272, 277, 286, 304, 312, 319, 389, 401, 586
Aitken's δ^2 process, 260, 283, 393, 430
Algebraic equations, linear, 336
  conditions for solution, 336
  elimination without division, 356
  escalator method, 357
  Gauss-Doolittle method, 339, 343
  ill-conditioned equations, 362, 444
  improvement of solution, 359
  matrix resolution, 343, 352, 368
  matrix-squaring method, 427
  minimized iterations, 357, 413
  orthogonal vectors, use of, 357
  pivotal condensation, 356
  residual errors, 342, 355, 359
  Seidel's iterative method, 423
  square-root method, 344
  triangular equations, 337
  unsymmetrical equations, 351, 354
  See also *Relaxation method*
Algebraic (transcendental) equations, roots of—
  by "false position," 249
  by Newton-Raphson method, 250, 253
  by Wegstein method, 261
  close and multiple roots, 254, 295
  complex roots, 266
  simultaneous equations, 262
  See also *Polynomial equations*
Allen, D. N. de G., 523, 566
Alt, F. L., 41
Alternating series, 161
Amplitude and phase method, 194, 201
Anderson, R. L., 323, 583
Arc tan x, tabulation of, 162, 204
Arsham, I., 272–3
Asymptotic series, 188 *et seq.*

Babbage, W., 32
Baggott, E. A., 174, 241, 244
Bairstow, L., 274
Banachiewicz, T., 344
Bateman, E. H., 295, 296
Bernoulli, D., 277
Bernoulli-Aitken method, 277, 394
Berry, M. M., 41
Bessel's equation, 171, 186, 193, 222, 240
Bessel's interpolation formula, 111, 114, 116, 119, 123, 147, 574
Bickley, W. G., 126, 155, 166, 458, 508, 580, 582

Biharmonic equation, 514, 565
Birge, R. T., 312, 314, 323, 389, 583
Birkhoff, G. D., 507
Black, A. N., 339, 346
Blanch, Gertrude, 421
Bodewig, E., xi, 255, 256, 285, 295, 296
Boole, G., 80
Boole's rule, 80, 87, 88, 89, 219, 498
Booth, A. D., 41
Booth, K. H. V., 41
Boundary conditions—
  for ordinary differential equations, 173, 197
  for partial differential equations, 512, 563
  involving derivatives, 453
  two-point, 240, 446
Bowden, B. V., 41
Brillouin, L., 207
Brodetsky, S., 292
Bromwich, T. J. I'A., 188
Brooker, R. A., 266
Brown, S. L., 276
Brunt, D., 329
Bush, V., 43

CALCULATING machines, 32
  analogue machines, 43
  cinema-integraph, 44
  desk calculators, 33
  electronic digital computers, 42
  harmonic synthesizer, 276
  isograph, 276
  National accounting machine, 32, 41, 122
  punched card machines, 41
  relay computers, 42
  slide-rules, 32
Calculations, unit, 36
Carr III, J. W., 241
Carré, B. A., 547
Characteristics of partial differential equations, 511
Chebyshev polynomials, 120
Chevilliet, 88
"*Choleski*," 339, 344
Clemence, 16
Clenshaw, C. W., 209, 217
Cofactors, 357, 373
Collar, A. R., xi, 246, 392, 420, 432, 445, 477
Collatz, L., xi, 466, 476, 478
Complex variable, functions of, 507
Comrie, L. J., 29, 32, 41, 123, 484
Cooper, J. L. B., 458
Cosen, C. R., 31

599